Xiangfu Chen

Settlement Calculation on High-Rise Buildings

Theory and Application

With 229 figures

Science Press
Beijing

Springer

Author
Xiangfu Chen
Professor, Ph.D of Civil Engineering
China State Construction Engineering Corporation
(CSCEC), Beijing 100037, China
E-mail: chenxiangfu@sina.com

ISBN 978-7-03-024336-2
Science Press Beijing

ISBN 978-3-642-15569-7 e ISBN 978-3-642-15570-3
Springer Berlin Heidelberg New York

Library of Congress Control Number: 2010933307

Cover design: Frido Steinen-Broo, EStudio Calamar, Spain

Printed on acid-free paper

Springer is part of Springer Science+Business Media (www.springer.com)

Foreword

Estimating foundation settlement of various structures is, in general, an important area of study in the field of geotechnical engineering. With the growth of metropolitan areas around the world and with scarcity of land, high rise building construction has become a necessity. In high rise building construction, it is important to evaluate the allowable bearing capacity and settlement of foundations for proper design and performance in the post-construction stage. Considering the nonhomogeneous, and anisotropic nature of subsoil, settlement calculation is truly a challenge for geotechnical engineering.

This text by Professor Xiangfu Chen is a welcome addition to scholars and practitioners in geotechnical engineering. It provides the state-of-the-art of settlement calculation procedures of deep foundations available in literature at this time for super high rise buildings that are built on raft foundations, raft foundations on floating piles, and raft foundations on end bearing piles as well as several case studies.

The book summarizes very well theories and application of the Winkler foundation model, elastic half space model, layered foundation model, double parameter elastic foundations models, cross-isotropic model, and nonlinear elastic model, along with the procedures to estimate sub-grade Poisson's ratio and elastic modulus which are essential parameters for estimating elastic settlement. It also has an excellent chapter on consolidation settlement.

I congratulate Professor Chen for the excellent work he has done in explaining the theoretical models and the field observations on settlement of foundations of structures. I sincerely trust that this will be a useful book for researchers and practicing engineers.

California State University Sacramento *Prof. Braja M. Das*

September 2009

Preface

Settlement calculation is one of the three major issues in foundation engineering and it has not yet been resolved completely. Especially settlement calculation of super high-rise buildings still remains the most difficult problem for engineers. Due to lack of practical settlement data, there is few systematic research result and rarer monograph to investigate this special problem.

This book summarizes the author's three decades of experiences and research results on deep foundation in design and construction of high-rise buildings. It presents a full coverage of settlement calculation issues theoretically with case studies, according to the characteristics and requirements of super high-rise buildings. It also brings forward the author's several original research results, which form a series of settlement calculation theory and application on high-rise buildings.

The book contributes to the problems of the constitutive model of soft soil, analysis of ground stress and deformation, the pile group effects and the behavior of super-long piles, settlement calculation methods in China and in the world.

The book focuses on settlement calculation of deep foundation of super high-rise buildings and its case studies. Based on the new Code for Design of Building Foundation in China and practical settlement data collected from more than 20 high-rise buildings, it for the first time deals with the effects of retaining structure in deep excavation on the settlement of the three kinds of deep foundations of high-rise buildings, i.e., box (raft) foundation, box (raft) foundation on floating piles, box (raft) foundation on end bearing piles. The calculation methods for the settlement of these foundations are proposed. A new design method for space-varying rigidity pile group with equal settlement has been invented and applied to high-rise buildings, based on the author's research results on the advantages of super-long piles on settlement control and that of short pile and middle length piles on bearing capacity. The method brings a new insight in the design theory of pile foundation. Other innovative studies are also covered in this book including the layered summation method for oblique stepped strata, and the integrated coefficient method of box foundation on sandy.

In the book, settlement data from super high-rise buildings in China and other countries are collected and analyzed, and special focus are given to the data of the Building of China Bank in Qingdao (designed by China Construction Beijing Design & Research Institute). The settlement calculation of finite element and Chinese methods (semi-theoretical & semi-empirical method) shows that the theoretical results are very close to the practical settlement data. After calculations and comparisons, several important results have been obtained, for example, the empirical settlement coefficient for strongly weathered granite in the Qingdao area is about 0.2; the adjustment coefficient of settlement calculation depth is 0.4. Other conclusions are also gained through analysis of the settlement data of Shanghai Jinmao Tower, Shanghai Senmao Building in China, Shenzhen Saige Plaza in China and Guangdong International Tower in Guangzhou China. The results can be considered as useful reference for project design and construction of super high-rise buildings.

The book is technical reference including technical experiences of typical practical projects, combining theoretical research with practical application, and design with construction.

This book is composed of 10 chapters. Chapter 1 mainly introduces the development of super high-rise buildings and deep foundation, and the international progress in settlement research. Chapter 2 presents six practical computing models for subsoil and the choice of calculation parameters. Chapter 3 deals with the mechanical issues in settlement calculations, i.e., space and plane analysis, contact pressure on the bottom of foundation, stress analysis in non-homogeneous and anisotropic subgrade. Chapter 4 covers the ground deformation theory, i.e., the compression characteristics of soil, the final settlement calculation, the calculation method of elasticity, the initial and consolidation settlement, the hypo-consolidation settlement, the settlement calculation of sand, the deformation theory of saturated soft soil, and the finite element solution of foundation settlement. Chapter 5 introduces the settlement calculation method of box (raft) foundation on super high-rise building, including simplified methods for settlement calculation, the calculation methods based on the national design codes, the settlement calculation of box (raft) foundation proposed by the author for the first time, taking into account the effect of the retaining structure in deep excavation on super high-rise buildings. This chapter also covers all the settlement calculation methods successfully applied to the box foundation of Qingdao Zhongyin Tower in Qingdao China (the highest building in Mainland China solely designed by Chinese, also the highest building in the world adopting box foundation), such as finite element method, settlement formulas considering the effect of retaining structure, the settlement calculation method for box foundation with effects of integrated coefficient, the spline function method for layered subsoil, the regional experience factor in the settlement calculation, with over five years of settlement data, and the analysis of the results. Since the author takes charge of the design of the project, the data in this case are reliable. There are also measured data and analysis results from the rock subgrade of Guangdong International Tower. Chapter 6 introduces the loading behavior and settlement calculation of super-long pile, i.e., settlement calculation of single pile and pile group, the empirical formula and simplified method of settlement calculation. Chapter 7 introduces the new design method for space-varying rigidity pile group with equal settlement, which has been proposed by the author. The design principle, design process and design parameters are also presented in this chapter. Chapter 8 is about the case study of Jinmao Tower and Senmao Tower, both in Shanghai China. Analysis and research of the settlement data of the diaphragm wall + super long floating piles + raft foundation shows the settlement characteristic of the foundation (for 50 meters plus long pile-raft foundation, the settlement is 60—100 mm). Analysis is also carried out on the effect of diaphragm wall with brace structures and load-bearing diaphragm walls in the settlement calculation. At the same time, the structure–foundation– subsoil interaction, the subsoil–pile interaction and the pile–subsoil–pile interaction is analyzed with the sub-domain method of spline function. Chapter 9 focuses on settlement of rock subgrade based on the data from Saige Plaza in Shenzhen China. Settlement computation of combined diaphragm wall + end pile + raft foundation in rock subgrade for super high-rise buildings is given in this chapter. In Chapter 10, the main innovative results (semi-theoretical & semi-empirical XFC method) and conclusions are summarized, and further subjects needed to be studied on settlement of super high-rise buildings are proposed.

The author sincerely gives his gratitude to the following organizations and experts. Without their support and help, this book would not have come to publication: Chinese Foundation for Excellence and Concern for the Grants, CPC Central Committee United Front Work Department and its Sixth Bureau, the State Council, the SASAC and its Group Work Department, the Ministry of of Housing & Urban-Rural Development Construction and its Science & Technology Division, China State Construction Engineering Corporation (CSCEC). The author is indebted to Tongji University, the author's Alma Mater and its leaders, to Professor Xueyuan Hou, the author's doctoral tutor, and to the colleagues at China Construction Beijing Design & Research Institute.

The author's gratitude also goes to the reviewer of the manuscript, Academician Sijing Wang, Academician Xiling Huang, Academician Jianhang Liu, Swedish Academician Ronglie Xu, Professor Guangqan He, Professor Yaozong Zhang, Professor Mingwu Yuan, Professor Longguang Tao, Professor Jin Chen, Professor Baohan Shen, Professor Min Yang, Professor Hongru Zhang, Professor Guobin Liu, Professor Wei Xu, Professor Jianhua Wang, Professor Hehua Zhu, Dr. Yongjing Tang, Dr. Shaoming Liao, Dr. Bo Liu, for their valuable opinions and suggestions to make the theory and application of settlement calculation on super high-rise buildings a more complete system.

At the same time, the author is also grateful to Professor JunYi, Professor Zhaohe Zeng, Professor Zhibing Mao, Professor Zhang Xuchang, Dr. Zhengmao Zhou, Senior engineer Bingrong Yang, Mr. Chong Chen, Mr. Xin Tang, Mr. Facheng Zhuo, Mr. Libing Tao, Senior engineer Zehui Wang, Dr. Zhongkun Zhang, Dr. Min Wang and Bentley Corp. of USA for their support.

The settlement calculation is a very complicated problem. The author believes that with the fast development of advanced technologies, and based on the evolution already accomplished, a complete solution to settlement calculation will be achieved with joint efforts of researchers across the world. Finaly, I wish to thank deeply Professor Braja M.Das for writing Foreword and making high evaluation in the book.

China State Construction Engineering Corporation(CSCEC), Beijing

Prof. Xiangfu Chen
November 2010

Contents

Chapter 1 Introduction

Nations across the world including China have entered the stage of modern urbanization, and there have been common problems such as urban population explosion, housing scarcity, land shortage, environmental pollution, traffic congestion and so on. Even though there are more or less arguments on high-rise and super high-rise buildings, the surging trend of the construction cannot yet be discouraged. This trend not only inaugurates a new epoch of construction industry, but also will necessarily brings human into overground and underground space. The evolution of super high-rise buildings remarkably promotes the research, development. and application of engineering technology of foundation & subgrade. Compared with underground foundation engineering, calculation, design, model experiment and field measurement for superstructure of super high-rise buildings are much easier. All of the above processes can be conducted by computer to completely meet the requirements of engineering. While as research and computerization of foundation, subsoil and geotechnical engineering progress relatively much slowly. Theory of settlement calculation of deep foundation is more complicated, and many questions are still left unsolved today, and might remain unsolvable in short term. It indeed requires arduous efforts of generations to get results.

1.1 Development of Super High-Rise Buildings and Strategy for Projects with Deep Foundation

With the spreading of urbanization, the promotion of productivity, the advancement of science & technology and the upgrading of life standard, high-rise buildings are blooming in metropolises around the world. They not only alleviate the issues mentioned above, but also create a brand-new epoch of the whole construction industry. It's necessary that modern cities are entering the stage of high-rise buildings along with the exploration of more and more scarce overground and underground space.

Nowadays high-rise buildings keep expanding around the world despite there still remain unsolved problems with design theory, architectural style, economic efficiency, environmental influence and usage functions. In Singapore, construction of high-rise buildings has accounted for over 70% of urban construction. Most high-rise buildings around the world serve as residence, hotel, commercial and office mansion and partially relief the pressure of housing requirements. It can be said that the high-rise building is a historical necessary output which accelerates the development of construction science, building materials and equipment and meanwhile changes the traditional concepts of architectural design, computation theories and construction methods. A unique academic system is being developed gradually, particularly including deep foundation engineering.

1.1.1 Development and Enlightenment of Overseas Super High-Rise Buildings

It is well known that modern high-rise buildings originated in 1880s. The Home Insurance Company Building, which was put up in Chicago in 1885 and was with only 10 storeys, 55 meters high, was regarded as the first high-rise building in the world. Henceforth, with development of economy, science, technology and human needs for material and non-material, great improvements were made in many aspects of high-rise buildings, namely height, style, architectural function, structural system, anti-seismic, disaster prevention capability and landscape art. Therefore,the number of various high-rise buildings are growing rapidly in metropolises around the world especially after 1950s because great achievements in construction economy and science & technology dramatically spurred the development of high-rise buildings.

In order to get further understanding of super-high-rise buildings in the world, basic information of the highest buildings of some major nations and regions is to be introduced briefly.

1) Jinmao Tower, with 88 storeys and 420.5 meters high, located in Shanghai, is the highest building in mainland of China. Its foundation is pile-box type and the length of piles is over 80 meters. Shanghai World Financial Center that is under construction at present is 492 meters high (not including the antenna) and will be the tiptop building worldwide.

2) Liang Ceremony Ignatiev buiding is the tallest building in Russia, being 210-meter-high with 42 storeys. And a building above 400 meters is under planning in Russia.

3) Ryugyong Hotel is the highest steel-concrete construction in the world. It lies in Pyongyong of North Korea, and is 101 storeys and 334 meter high.

4) The highest building in South Korea is Koreains Company Building, which was built in 1986 and is of 63 storeys and 223 meter high.

5) In 1968, Overseas Union Bank building was completed in Singapore with 63 storeys and 208 meter height.

6) Tower of China Bank, which was built in 1988, used to be the tiptop building in Hong Kong with 368 meters height, 72 storeys and pile-box foundation. Hong Kong Central Plaza of 374.3 meters is now the tallest building in Hongkong.

7) In Taiwan of China, Bank of Kaohsiung was built in Kaohsiung City in 1998, with 85 storeys, 370 meter height, and rectangular plate foundation. Afterwards, TAIPEI 101 was completed in 2003 and its height reaches 508 meters including the length of antenna. This building is the highest one in the world (shown in Fig. 1-1).

Fig.1-1 101 Tower in TaiPei of China

8) The highest building in Japan is Tokyo Government Tower of 243 meters height.

9) The Petronas Twin Towers is the tallest building in Malaysia and also is the second highest building in the world. It was built in 1996 with 95 storeys and 453 meters height

(including a 73 meters mast). Pile-raft foundation was adopted and the longest pile was over 100 meters (shown in Fig. 1-2).

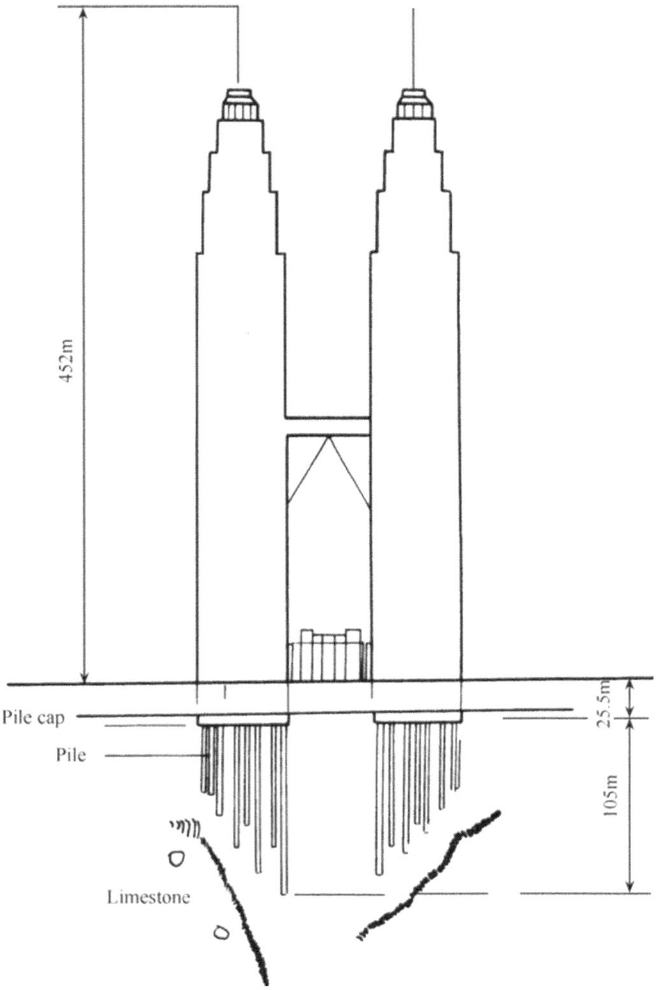

Fig.1-2 Sketch of foundation

10) Palac Kultury Inauki Mansion, which is located in Warsaw with 42 storeys and 241 meters height, is the tiptop building in Poland. It was constructed in 1955 and had been regarded as the highest one in Europe for 35 years until 1990.

11) The tallest building in German is Messe Turm Mansion which lies in Frankfurt with 60 storeys and 256 meters height. This building was completed in 1990 and compensated pile-raft foundation was used here, which means that inside piles in the subgrade are longer than outside ones.

12) Maine Montpamasse with 64 storeys and 229 meters height is the highest building in France. It was built in 1973.

13) National Bank of London is the tallest building in British with 60 storeys and 189 meter height.

14) The tiptop building in Africa goes to Carlton Center Mansion which is in Johannesburg of South Africa and has 50 storeys and a height of 189 meters.

15) Rialto Center Mansion with 70 storeys and 243 meters height was built in Melbourne in 1986. It is the tallest building in Australia.

16) Petrolaos Maxicanos Building with 52 storeys and 214 meters height was built in Mexico in 1984. It is the highest building in Central America.

17) Mazzella building, located in Bogota, with 70 storeys and 248 meters height, is the highest building not only in Colombia but also in South America.

18) The tallest building in Canada is First Bank which is located in Toronto. It was built in 1975 and has 72 floors and a height of 285 meters.

19) The tiptop building in Venezuela is Capital Official Building which was completed in 1985 with 60 storeys and 237 meters height.

20) In U.S.A, Sears Tower located in Chicago with 110 storeys and 443 meters height is taken for the highest construction in the world. The length of the mast is not included in the total height.

Besides continuous innovation and improvement in architectural functions, appearances and structural system, some essential characteristics of the development of overseas super high-rise buildings are continuous growth of height and emphasis on deep foundation engineering. The height of super high-rise buildings and the depth of deep foundation engineering can actually reflect, in a certain sense, the comprehensive national strength and the general level of science and technology, particularly of construction science and technology. Furthermore, famous super high-rise buildings are the historical portrayal and era milestones. Since the first modern high-rise building emerged in 1885, it took 13 years (until 1898) for the height of buildings to exceed 100 meters. After 11 years(in 1909) and 21 years(in 1930), the height was beyond 200 and 300 meters respectively and the era of super high-rise buildings begun. In 1931, Empire State Building was established in New York of U.S.A with 102 storeys and 381 meter height, and after 41 years (in 1972), World Trade Center Towers were over 400 meters with 110 storeys, 417 meters height and 7 levels for basement. Accordingly, experts predicted that super high-rise buildings were able to exceed 500 meters at the beginning of 21st century and further surmount 1000 meters in 2050s (the designs are shown in Fig.1-4 and Fig.1-5). This prediction can also be matched by the following curves which represent the height growth of high-rise buildings worldwide (shown in Fig.1-3).

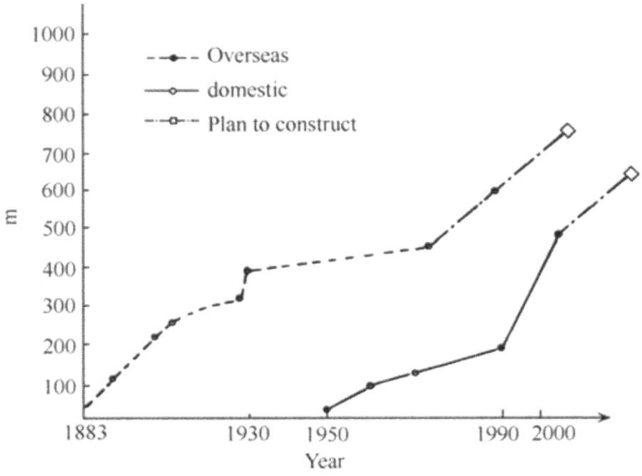

Fig.1-3 Curves of height development of domestic and overseas high-rise buildings

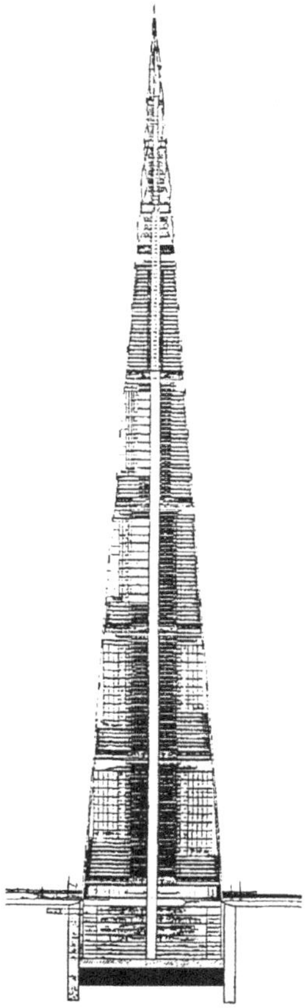

Fig.1-4 Blue print of Millennium Tower in Tokyo of Japan (800 meter height and 600 meter bottom perimeter)

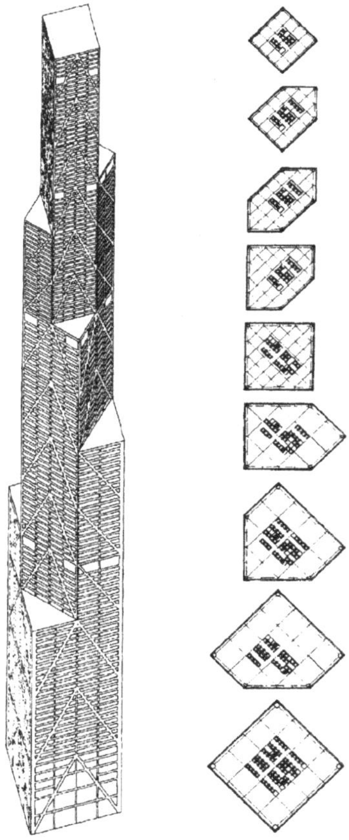

Fig.1-5 Blue print of Vierck Tower in Chicago equiaxial graph and plane graphs for all standard floors

There are some enlightenments from the characteristics of the development of overseas high-rise buildings:

1) The major structure form taken for super high-rise buildings exceeding 40 storeys is usually steel structure. Analysis of 100 high-rise buildings indicates that steel structure accounts for 66%, steel reinforced concrete (SRC) structure accounts for 18%, and reinforced concrete structure only takes 16%. The maximum storey numbers of super high-rise buildings with different types of steel structure are illuminated in Fig.1-6. Moreover, box or raft foundations are widely used in the construction of super high-rise buildings.

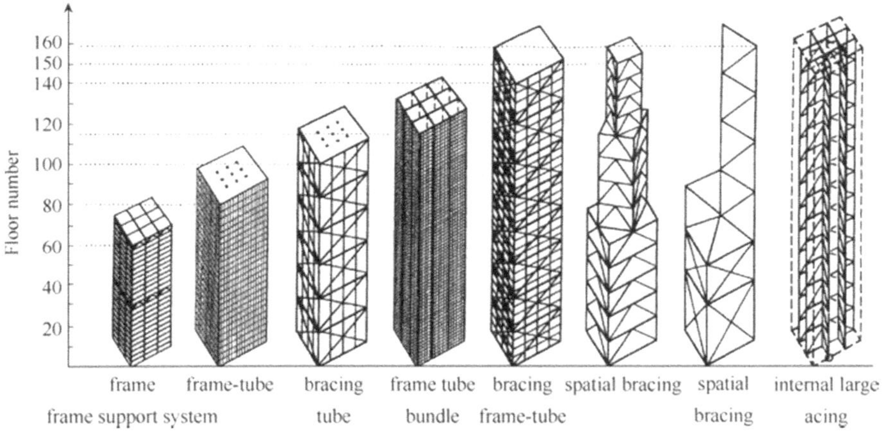

Fig.1-6 The maximum floor numbers of super high-rise buildings with different types of steel structure

2) The strength grade of concrete is increasing, for example, it has reached 45.7 MPa for columns in a high-rise building constructed in San Francisco in 1983. Meanwhile, highstrength reinforced bar is also widely used in this kind of projects.

3) Structural form of plate-column is usually applied to high-rise buildings with cast-in-place reinforced concrete structure, by with construction technology of girder and plate is simplified. Pile foundations and box foundations are adopted for subgrade conditions of soft soil and rock respectively. Given the heavy weight, there is much limitation for structural form, storeys number and deep foundation style (shown in Table1-1 and Table1-2).

Table 1-1 The maximum height and foundation depth of high-rise steel structures

Fortified intensity / Structure forms	Non-fortified	Seismic fortified intensities		
		VI and VII	VIII	IX
	Foundation depth	Foundation depth	Foundation depth	Foundation depth
Frame-bracing (shear walls)	240	200	180	—
	12	10	9	—
all kinds of tubes	400	350	300	250
	20	17.5	15	12.5

continued

Structure forms \ Fortified intensity	Non-fortified	Seismic fortified intensities		
		VI and VII	VIII	IX
	Foundation depth	Foundation depth	Foundation depth	Foundation depth
Steel frame-concrete shear wall	220	180	—	—
Steel frame-concrete tube	11	9		
Steel frame tube concrete core tube	220	220	150	—
	11	11	7.5	
Frame-shear wall	180	150	—	—
	9	7.5		
All kinds of tubes	200	180	150	—
	10	9	7.5	

Notes: 1) Refer to "Specifications of design and construction of high-rise steel structures" and "Code for box foundation"

2) It is not suitable for depth of box or raft foundation to be shorter than 1/15 of the height of buildings, and for pile-box foundation regardless of the length of piles, the depth of foundation ranges from 1/18 to 1/20. In this table, 1/20 of the height of building is taken.

3) The depth of pile-box foundation of super high-rise building is 25 m on the condition that building height is 500 m, and is 40 m and 50 m for building height of 800 m and 1000 m respectively Thus, the study on deep foundation is more important than that on ground structure form.

Table 1-2 The maximum height and foundation depth of high-rise reinforced concrete structures

Structure form		Non-fortified	Seismic fortified intensities			
			VI	VII	VIII	IX
Frame	cast-in-place	60	60	55	45	25
	general assembly	50	50	35	25	—
Frame-shear wall Frame tube	cast-in-place	130	130	120	100	50
	general assembly	—	100	90	70	—
Cast-in-place shear wall	all shear wall	100	140	120	100	60
	bottom partial frame at bottom	120	120	100	80	—
tube-in-tube or frame-tube bundle		180	180	150	120	70

Notes: 1) the depth of deep foundation is 1/15 of the height of buildings and is 1/18 to 1/20 for pile foundation.

2) There is no specific requirement of depth of foundation for buildings less than 200 m high. If the building is 200 m high, the depth of box foundation and pile foundation is respectively 14 m and 11–10 m. If the height is 300 m, the related depth is 20 m and 17–15 m, and is 26.6 m and 22–20 m for 400 m height. Until now, there is no foundation of super high-rise building in China whose depth is over 30 m and meanwhile it reflects the difficulties in deep foundation engineering.

4) The treatment techniques of subgrade and foundation are very sophisticated and deep foundation is usually the major foundation form for buildings with no less than 3 levels in

basement. For instance, there are 7 levels in the basement of World Trade Center Towers, 4 levels of which are used for garage with capacity of holding 2,000 cars, and other levels serve as stores and underground stations.

5) Wider attention from architects, structural engineers and concerned experts is paid to the study on intelligent building, ecological and high-rise effects. Meanwhile, more emphasis is laid on the relationship among building, environment and men, including the environment of geotechnical engineering.

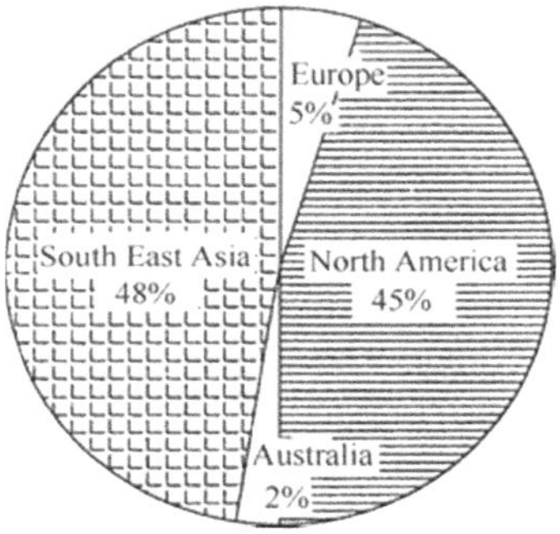

Fig.1-7 Worldwide distribution of high-rise buildings

6) Not only planning of ground space and harmony of ground space with city have got fully concern, but also planning and exploitation of underground space have been put into important position. Laws have been legislated to announce that underground space is among precious resources.

7) Even soft soil subground or earthquake zone is rare and subgrade is mainly rock for deep foundation of foreign super high-rise buildings, research and study on deep foundation is still paid enough attention to and much important data has been accumulated.

From the development of foreign high-rise buildings over the past more than 100 years, it can be concluded that most high-rise buildings are distributed in North America and Asia, and all the characteristics and enlightenments mentioned above are worth study and reference for us. In China, large population and scarce land resource result in great intense in land use, especially in big and middle-sized cities. Since the nation's reform and opening up policy was introduced, the process of urbanization in China is getting faster. As a result, land use, housing, and transportation have become the most prominent issues in big and middle-sized cities. What is the way to solve the urban inhabitation problem? It seems that building more and better high-rise apartments with Chinese characteristics is the only way, which definitely creates more opportunities for development of deep foundation engineering.

1.1.2 Development and Strategy of Domestic High-Rise Buildings

As the real cradle of high-rise constructions, China is well known for world famous ancient towers, which have glorious and long history. For example, Songyue Temple Tower built in Henan province in 524 A.D. is a single tube construction with 15 storeys and 50 meter height; Liaodi Tower in Dingxian of Hebei province was built as a tube structure with 11 storeys and 82 meter height in 1055 A.D., which had reached the technical level of that of the end of the 20th century in USA; Yingxian Wooden Tower in Shanxi province was put up in 1056 with 9 storeys and 60-meter height and has been regarded as a wonder of wooden structure around the world. These ancient towers show high-level not only in art, but also in structural system, foundation treatment, wood pile foundation and construction technology, and have successfully survived several big earthquakes. From the beginning of the 20th century to the establishment of the people's Republic of China, there were only a few newly-built high-rise buildings, most of which were designed by foreigners, such as HuaYu apartment built in shanghai in 1925 with 13 storeys and 57-meter height, Broadway Mansion built in shanghai in 1934 with 21 storeys and 76-meter height, Shanghai International Hotel with 24 floors and 85-meter height, Aiqun Mansion in Guangzhou, and so on.

1. Briefing of development of domestic high-rise buildings

High-Rise buildings designed and constructed by Chinese originated in 1950s. In Beijing, Peace Hotel with 8 storeys was built just after the liberation. From 1958 to 1959, the development of high-rise buildings was greatly fastened by the coustruction of Top Ten Great Buildings in Beijing.

In 1960s, high-rise buildings got further development, such as Guangzhou Hotel built in 1968 as the tallest building in 1960s with 88 meters in height. At the same time, prefabricated pile foundation was applied in construction.

In 1970s, high-rise buildings progressed faster. For example, Baiyun Hotel built in Guangzhou in 1977 with 33 storeys and 112.4 meter height became the highest building in China during 1970s.

The development of high-rise buildings got even faster after 1980 and the characteristics of this phase were larger amount of constructions, increasing floor numbers, complication of structural form, wide distribution areas and continuous application of new structural systems and deep foundation. The total floor area of high-rise buildings in Beijing has accounted for more than 52% of floor area of all kinds of buildings (shown in Fig.1-4). Beijing Central Color TV Center became the tiptop building in the area of VIII seismic intensity (fortified as IX intensity) with 27 storeys and 112.7-meter height. The first five-star hotel in China—Hilton

Hotel in Jing'an district of Shanghai, was 143.62 m high and had 43 storeys. Shanghai Exhibition Center Mansion with 164.8 meter height was a first-rank hotel in the world. During this time, bored filling pile foundation was widely used.

Coming to 1990s, there were many famous super high-rise buildings that were completed in some metropolises such as Beijing, Shanghai, Guangzhou, Shenzhen, Wuhan, Xiamen, Chongqing, Chengdu, Xi'an, Shenyang, Dalian and Haerbin. The entire construction level of domestic super high-rise buildings was dramatically improved. The disparity with foreign countries was getting smaller and smaller, and Chinese are even in the leading position in some fields.

2. Basic Strategies

It is certainy that high-rise buildings will be widely constructed and will get sustainable development in our country in the future. However, it has to be fully considered to integrate Chinese local conditions and to be adaptable to the national development of economy, science and technology. More attention should be paid to the study on deep foundation and to the accumulation of project experiences along with the research of new form of super-structure. Therefore, strategies of sustainable development of domestic high-rise buildings and deep foundation engineering can be concluded as follows:

1) Deep foundation on one hand limits the height of buildings, on the other hand takes the first place in engineering quality and security. Meanwhile, investment associated with deep foundation is also higher, almost accounting for 1/4~1/3 of the whole structure. Moreover, underground diaphragm wall, pile foundation and pit retaining structure of deep foundation need to be further examined.

2) While new structural forms are being improved and developed (such as mega-structure, tube-bundle structure, stressed-skin structure, suspended structure, structur with transfer storey and rigid horizontal element, vibration controlled damping structure and seismic structure), it is necessary to expand investment into the research on deep foundation and to organize experts in the related fields to earnestly study, actually measure, roundly statistic and analyze with reference of pratical engineering projects in order to make achievements combining theory and practice.

3) Areas of high-rise structure of steel, steel reinforced concrete, steel-concrete composite, steel tube-concrete composite, need to be actively studied, while high-rise buildings with reinforced-concreate structure are extensive developed.

4) The research on nonlinear and nondeterministic problems in structure and deep foundation of high-rise buildings should be strengthened and dynamic analysis and modeling experiments should be conducted to insure the stability, reliability and security of building structures.

5) It is essential to enhance the theoretical study and practical application of optimized design of high-rise building and deep foundation. The topological optimization of one particular structure and deep foundation also needs to be studied step by step on the basis of optimization of dimensions of structural sections. During this study, the key part is to develop practical software to realize the economic benefits.

6) For more rational and scientific investment decisions, feasibility analysis, plan selection, and structural design of high-rise buildings, it is significant to expand research onto expert systems and artificial intelligence of geotechnical engineering and high-rise building to develop CAD systems and establish database and knowledge base for all domestic and foreign high-rise buildings (including deep foundations) based on experts' experiences. Most studies are still in theorietical stage at present and need to be used in construction engineering, and application softuare needs to be developed, to exert its function.

7) Numerical methods, such as finite element method, finite strip method, weighted residential method, spline function method, boundary element method and some semi-analytic and semi-discrete methods, need to be placed more emphases on for building finer mathematical-mechanical models and high-precision elements to improve calculation accuracy.

8) Three are still a lot of incompletely solved questions in deep foundation engineering, for instance, constitutive relation of rocks, physical-mechanical characteristics of super-deep subgrade, foundation stress, foundation settlement and stability, top-down method for deep foundation and super-deep basement, interaction among subgrade, foundation and superstructure, seismic dynamic and nondeterministic analysis, numerical calculation, underground space utilization, simulation of foundation engineering, CAD and expert systems, etc. Thus, more researchers, physical and financial resources should be put into the research on rock and soil mechanics, geotechnical engineering and deep foundation to ensue great economic benefits. There is still a long way to go before the issue of settlement calculation of deep foundation of super high-rise building be completely solved, and the two key points are to research the interaction and coordination among subgrade, foundation and superstructure, and to strengthen the test of real settlement data and calculation parameters.

1.2 Foundation Settlement Calculation — One of the Three Major Difficulties in Subsoil and Foundation Engineering

Foundation settlement calculation has always been one of the three major difficulties in subsoil and foundation engineering. During the past one hundred years, even hundreds of years, many experts and scholars made great contributions in this field but there are still lots of problems unsolved. An old saying goes that *skyscraper rises from the earth*, and another goes that *going down to the earth is even more tough than flying up to the sky*. It is true that underground engineering is more difficult than abve ground engineering because of so many unclarified problems, unknown and nondeterministic factors in deep foundation. Similarly, settlement calculation of deep foundation of high-rise building is far from complete solution. Ways to treat with the problem now are as follow:

1. Analytical Method

Based on the elastic theory which assumes that subgrade is a linear-elastic continuum, the calculation formula of subsoil stress (as in Chapter 3) and the analytical solution of subsoil deformation (as in chapter 4) can be got on the condition of all kinds of loads on the surface or inside the semi-infinite body. Because of the limitation of initial boundary conditions in elastic mechanics, the precise solution can be obtained in very few conditions. On the other hand, the physical–mathematical properties of subsoil and the constitutive relation are too complicated to meet the requirement of elastic mechanics. That is why great difference exists between foundation settlement value drawn from analytical solution and the value from actual measurement in construction projects, sometimes the gap can be as large as a few times of the smaller one.

2. Numerical Method

Numerical method gets fast improvement by taking finite element as representative on account of the development of computer technology. The particularities of this method include simulating nonlinear, discontinuous and inelastic properties of subsoil, dealing with various boundary conditions, and quickly calculating of stress field and displacement field under different kinds of loads and boundary conditions by reliable software. However, the value of foundation settlement calculation, which has considerable difference with actual measurement value on site, is still unsatisfactory, because the fundamental of numerical method is still elastic theory.

3. Semi-analytical & Semi-numerical Method

With the further development of finite element method, other mthods including finite strip method, infinite element method, boundary element method, weighted residential method and spline function method emerged gradually. There is a brilliant prospect of combination of boundary element method and finite element method for semi-infinite foundation settlement calculation. Lately, it is popular to combine finite element method and boundary element method with infinite element method to conduct mixed analytic & numerical analysis, so as to simulate semi-infinite foundation settlement, taking into account nonlinear, discontinuous, inelastic properties of subsoil and various boundary conditions. After high-precise elements were created, the plane problem, even more complicated spatial problem, can be analyzed by coupling infinite element with finite element. Satisfactory solutions can sometimes be got by these methods which are definitely good, but unfortunately limited by calculation parameters.

4. Semi-theoretical & Semi-empirical Method

The key of semi-theoretical & semi-empirical method for foundation settlement calculation (also called experience method or simplified method) is based on analytic method. The empirical coefficients or formula are obtained from statistic analysis on real measured settlement data from engineering projects. It is obvious that the results of this method are closer to real settlement. For this reason, this method is mostly used in the domestic and foreign codes, particularly in "*Code for Design of Building Foundations*" of China.

It can be concluded from the above discussions that the calculation of deformation or settlement of foundations involves certain disciplines and has close relation with geological situations, physical-mechanical properties of subsoil and real engineering projects. So far there is still no perfect approach to make theoretical results consistent or very close to real measurements of settlement. The third and forth methods mentioned above, hereby, are clearly important and effective methods and commonly used in practical projects at present.

1.3 Progress and Problems in Research on Settlement of Deep Foundations of Super High-Rise Buildings

The subsoil deformation of general buildings includes: ① initial settlement, a kind of settlement which is caused by the lateral deformation resulting from shear strain of subsoil under loads, presuming that subsoil is saturated clay without drainage and with constant volume. ② consolidation settlement, which is brought by the compression deformation and shear strain of subsoil on the condition of gradual dissipation of excess hydrostatic pressure (from non-drainage stage to drainage stage) in saturated cohesive subsoil. ③ secondary compression settlement (or secondary consolidation settlement), which results from subsoil creep deformation occurring in saturated clay subsoil under constant effective stress. This kind of settlement always happens in soft-soil areas like Shanghai and Tianjin. For saturated non-cohesive sandy subsoil, its settlement is mainly initial settlement and soil compression finishes in a short time because no excess hydrostatic pressure (excess pore water pressure) is created during the construction due to the super permeability. In general, the settlement ratio of buildings on this kind of subsoil is over 80% just after the completion and the settlement tends to be stable in about one year. The subsoil deformation is of this kind in strong weathered granite areas like Qingdao and Shenzhen. In addition, other factors such as earthquakes, dynamic loads, changes in groundwater level and in water content of subsoil, physical-chemical reactions in soil (as organic decomposition etc.), influence from adjacent undergoing engineering etc, are likely to induce new settlement of subsoil. General studies focu on vertical deformation and displacement of subsoil caused by building loads (geostatic stress and additional stress) and the main target of the research in this book is the settlement of deep foundations of super high-rise buildings.

1.3.1 Progress of Domestic and Foreign Research on Subsoil Settlement Calculation

For the recent decades, domestic and overseas experts have been paying more attention to and showing special interest in subsoil settlement calculation due to its importance and incomplete solution. The calculated results got by proposed approaches are still not very close to the real situations. These approaches can be summed up briefly as follows:

1. Semi-theoretical & Semi-empirical method (modified layer-wise summation method)

The prominent characteristic of this method is to identify the empirical factor between theoretical and actual values statistically and analytically by accumulating actual settlement data in projects. Because of the comprehensive, reliable, applicable, and regional characteristics of the empirical factor, this method is apt to tally with the reality of different areas and solve problems in project design. In view of this fact, the settlement calculation method in Chinese national code is based on this approach mentioned above.

2. Stress history method

There are already previous consolidation pressures in natural subsoil during the geological history. Casagrande measured this pressure by a laboratory test in 1936 and compared it with the site effective pressure to categorize cohesive soil into normally consolidated soil, over-consolidated soil and secondary consolidated soil. Aiming at these three types of subsoil, different methods should be taken for settlement calculation.

3. Stress path method

Prof. Huang Wenxi proposed an approach called three-dimensional stress settlement calculation method, in which the results from one-dimensional calculation are multiplied by a coefficient bigger than one. In 1957, Skempton and Bjerrum gave an opinion of multiplying the results from one-dimensional calculation under the circumstances of under-consolidated subsoil by a coefficient smaller than one. Lambe brought up stress path method in 1967. The procedure of it is as follows:

1) Counting vertical and lateral stress caused by additional pressure on the basis of the geostatic stress of certain point by principles of elastic mechanics.

2) Firstly carrying tri-axial test to make soil consolidated under geostatic stress and then put on additional stress.

3) Measuring the vertical strains before and after consolidation under additional stress.

4) Calculating initial settlement and consolidated settlement of subsoil respectively with these two strains got in the previous step.

4. Deformation properties method

Initial settlement, consolidation settlement, and secondary consolidation settlements will occur in subsoil under loads. The elastic mechanic method is often used in counting initial settlement, and calculation parameters are chosen as initial tangent elastic modulus and poisson ratio in non-drainage situation. Considering the plastic deformation of subsoil, it is suggested to divide initial settlement by a coefficient bigger than one. When it comes to consolidated settlement, there are many methods and the differences of results from these methods are not so big. Because secondary consolidated settlement happens along with primary consolidated settlement and is combined with shear creep deformation and compressed deformation at the same time, it is hard to separate these two kinds of consolidated settlement completely.

5. Finite element method

Because there is big error in analytical method of subsoil settlement calculation, and it is difficult to handle complicated boundary and initial conditions, and it's difficult or even impossible to consider the nonlinear, discontinuous and nondeterministic properties of subsoil, Finite Element method or Finite Difference method is more likely to count subsoil settlement under complicated circumstances. For examples, the elastic-plastic and visco-plastic problems could be calculated, the consolidated settlement and final settlement in any time could be further obtained by simulating the process of loading by stages (construction process simulation).With the development of finite element method, nowadays many kinds of applied elements and high-precise elements have been developed (refer to books written by Long Yuqiu for details). All of these bring great breakthrough in subsoil settlement calculations. Meanwhile, integration of boundary element method and finite element methods and the improvements of other numerical methods (such as semi-numerical & semi-analytic method, Weighted Residential method, Infinite Element method, Spline Function method, Finite Strip method, etc.) also facilitate subsoil settlement calculations. However, there is a common difficulty in all these methods, that is, how to identify the calculation parameters. There are often very big or very small settlement in the calculation results due to inappropriately chosen parameters. We got a settlement of 3~5 mm when counting the settlement of China Bank Tower in Qingdao by the finite element method, and the real settlement is ten times bigger than that of the calculated result. Moreover, there are still problems in analysis and judgment of results of settlement calculations.

6. Comprehensive method

Recently the studies on subsoil stress-strain model, determination method, and calculation method for calculation parameters develop very fast. Meanwhile, more and more real settlement data and experiences have been accumulated. Many scholars and engineers have started the research and application of comprehensive methods. It presents important enlightenment that subsoil settlement can be assessed for structural engineers by comprehensively comparing and analyzing several results from many methods with the real measured settlement data. This kind of calculation method is called comprehensive method, which has been proved to have wonderful prospect in practice especially when computers are widely used.

7. Research on testing techniques of calculation parameters of subsoil settlement

So far foundation settlement calculation is far from complete solution, and one of the difficulties is testing of calculation parameters. Now more emphasis is placed on the research on in-situ testing method and testing equipment.

1.3.2 Progress of Research on Settlement Calculation of Box Foundations of Super High-Rise Buildings

Box foundations are widely applied due to great stiffness, strong capacity of coordinating uneven settlement and excellent seismic capacity. The items in the research on box foundation settlement include not only geostatic stress deformation, resilience-recompression deformation, and constant-load deformation, but also interactions among superstructure, foundation and subsoil and testing equipments & methods. Meanwhile, the research on calculation model and subsoil parameters is being conducted. There are many application cases overseas of box foundation engineering of super high-rise buildings, only a few cases in China. There are only a bit more than ten buildings over 100 meters which have box foundation, and only two of them are above 200 meters (China Bank Tower in Qingdao and International Mansion in Guangzhou). Instead of adopting pile foundations, box (or raft) foundations are used as far as possible for buildings exceeding 200 meters abroad. Accordingly, the progress of research on settlement calculation of box foundations in China is mainly aiming at high-rise buildings and multy-storey buildings, and it is introduced by taking two sets of national codes as master line. As for the research progress overseas, more emphasis is placed on settlement calculation methods.

1. Progress of research on settlement of box foundations in China

In 1970s, a lot of achievements were obtained in the study on settlement of box and raft foundations of 8~12-storey buildings (within 60 meters in height), such as compressed depth analysis and calculation method of box foundations (the compressed depth of soft soil subgrade is about 1.5 times of the width of box foundation, and is about 1 time and 0.6~0.8 times for quaternary period clay and sandy soil respectively). In particular, a lot of tests on box foundations were organized in 1974 by China Academy of Building Research and some institutes, namely Tongji Univertity, Commerce Ministry Design Institute, Civil Building Design Institute of Shanghai, Beijing Investigation Institute and so on, and *Code for Box Foundation (JGJ6-80)* was compiled. Then, some calculation methods of subsoil deformation as layer-wise summation method and so on (elastic mechanic method, numerical method, and empirical method) were further proposed with consideration of compensability of box foundations, resilience-compressibility of subsoil, and stress redistribution after excavation of foundation pit. When calculating box foundation settlement, more concentration was laid on research on resilience-compression of pit bottom and it was written into *Code for Box and Raft Foundations of High-Rise Buildings (JGJ6-99)*. Several useful conclusions have been drawn from plenty of real measurements of box founbation settlement and integrated analysis Thus, these tow codes can basically reflect the research progress of settlement calculations of box foundation. It was much earlier for foreigner experts to research box and raft foundations and super high-rise buildings. In 1971, for example, Shell Plaza Mansion in Huston, U.S.A was completed with 52 floors above ground and 218 meters height. Its basement had 4 levels and the depth of raft foundation was 18.3 meters. The thickness of the raft plate was 2.52 meters. The real measured resilience in the foundation pit center ranged from 10.2 to 15.2 cm, and that on the sides of the foundation pit was from 2.5 to 5.0 cm. The average settlement of the raft foundation was 12.45 cm and the settlement difference between center and sides was very small. In China settlement tests of box foundation are also taken into account. For instance, China Bank Tower in Qingdao was completed in 1996 with 54 floors above ground and 245.8 meters height. This mansion had a 4-level basement and the depth of the box foundation and the thickness of foundation bottom plate were 19.3 m and 2.5 m respectively. The biggest settlement was 7.4 cm and the difference was only a little more than 2 cm. In recent years, many researchers, including Huang Xiling in China Academy of Building Science, Zhang Zaiming in Beijing Investigation Institute, Huang Shaoming in Shanghai Civil Building Design Institute, and Yang Mi, Dong Jianguo, Ma Zhongzheng, Liu Xiqian, Zhao Xihong in Tongji University, etc., have done much work on interaction among structure above ground, box foundation and subsoil and on settlement calculation, and have got several pieces of instructive achievements. For example, for settlement of box foundation in silty-sand soil in Shanghai, there is no big difference between calculated value and measured value when applying B Method and M Method. By non-linear foundation model, calculation result closer to the measured real foundation settlement can be obtained and calculation and control of this settlement difference can also be realized for high-rise buildings with podiums. Since 1985, Hou Xueyuan from Tongji University has kept concentrating on the research on soft-soil subgrade properties and compensated foundations, meanwhile he has been researching calculation method of residual stress of soft-soil subgrade upheaval deformation with Liu Xuebin, and settlement pre-evaluation method of shield tunnels with Liao Shaoming. All these research achievements are reflected both in *Code for Box and Raft Foundations (*JGJ6-99*)* and *National Code for Building Foundation Design* (GB57-2002).

2. Overseas progress of research on settlement of box foundations

The general subsoil settlement calculation originated from the proposal of one-dimension consolidation theory by Terzaghi in 1925. In this theory, elastic mechanics method is applied to counting subsoil settlement. In 1943, Terzaghi published his book named *Theoretical Soil Mechanics*, Frohlick proposed foundation settlement calculation in 1934 and some former USSR researchers proposed beam-plate calculation method of elastic subsoil. In 1936, Rendulic expanded one-dimension consolidation problem to three-dimension situation under the assumption that total stress keeps constant. Biot came up with a rigorous consolidation theory in 1941 and further expanded to dynamic fields in 1956. Then Trusdell stated mixture theory (taking solid particles and void fluids in subsoil as separate targets and later integrating them into subsoil) which actually did not have much difference with Biot's consolidation theory and had little application significance. At the same time lots of subsoil settlement calculation methods were brought up. In terms of the settlement of cohesive subsoil, it can be divided into initial settlement, consolidation settlement and secondary consolidation settlement. On the contrary, the former two kinds of settlements in sandy subsoil can not be clearly separated, and elastic modulus of sandy subsoil may get bigger along with the increasing depth. For this reason, it is obvious that error may result from calculating settlement with elastic theory. So it is wise to evaluate the influence of the history of subsoil pressure on subsoil settlement by e-lg$P$ compression curve, and to calculate settlement based on previous consolidation pressure (counting as ordinary consolidated subsoil, over-consolidated subsoil and secondary consolidated cohesive subsoil respectively). When the thickness of cohesive subsoil is greater than the width of foundation, the lateral deformation of subsoil would have great influence on consolidation settlement. So it is necessary to take into account a correction factor of lateral influence to make the result of one-dimension compression more compatible with the reality.

After counting the settlement by elastic method, the result could be modified by finite element method considering the effect of plastic expansion areas (Appolonia, 1971). In 1948, Terzaghi proposed the calculation method for sandy subsoil settlement, and thereafter, some scholars conducted some studies and presented some methods which had all been proven unreliable. In 1970, Sckmertmann brought up a semi-empirical calculation formula for sandy subsoil settlement which had turned out to be consistent with practice after tests in real projects. Layer-Summation method can be used for layered subsoil.

All these methods mentioned above can be summed up with stress path which shows the change of internal stress and strain in subsoil during the stages of pre-construction, undergoing construction and past-construction, but the stress increment in subsoil sill has to be calculated for elastic mechanics method.

As far as box foundation settlement calculation is concerned, because of the deep burial depth, the complicated interaction, and the lateral restriction effect of shoring structures, the settlement calculation method differs from ordinary subsoil deformation calculation methods. It is more complicated and even involves many incompletely solved problems such as subsoil compensative use, groundwater buoyancy, subgrade resilience and recompression after pit excavation and unloading, effects of shoring structures, stress and strain in subgrade after pit excavation and the integrated interaction among superstructure, box foundation and subgrade. The major part of box foundation settlement is the final settlement just like other ordinary foundations. The calculation methods can be categorized into four types: elastic theory method, indirect calculation method, semi-theoretical and semi-empirical method and numerical method. The elastic theory method is mainly used to count initial settlement, and the results got from this method differ greatly from the real measured settlements. The indirect method can be sub-divided into compressionmeter method (Terzaghi, 1925), Skemptore-Bjerrum method (1957), stress path method (Lanbe, 1963), status boundary surface method (Burland, 1969), and so on. All these widely applied methods are based on elastic theory to count additional subgrade stress, and while based on test results to evaluate the relationship between stress and strain in subgrade. The results from these methods include initial settlement and consolidation settlement. The semi-theoretical and semi-empirical methods involve various modified elastic theory methods, modified layer-summation methods, and evaluation methods based on in-place tests. The numerical methods include finite element method which is apt for all kinds of boundary and initial conditions, Boundary Element method, Spline Function method, Finite Difference method and Weighted Residuals method. Except finite element method, other numerical methods always have some limitations in real application. Moreover, all numerical methods are based on elastic theory and can be used to handle discontinuous, heterogeneous and nonlinear issues. When it comes to cohesive subgrade, it is usual to use elastic theory method, layer-summation method and specification method to count box foundation settlements. On the other hand, for sandy subgrade, inevitably there are some differences in settlement calculation only applying elastic theory method, because compression deformation and shear deformation always take place simultaneously and finish quickly, so they cannot be completely separately, and for other things, the elastic modulus of sandy subgrade would increase along with the depth of subsoil. So far there haven't been satisfactory calculation method for sandy subgrade deformation yet. In U.S.A, an empirical formula (got from load test) recommended by Terzaghi and Peck is often used in practice, but the errors are big. In 1970, Sckmertmann proposed a semi-empirical formula with a little error. Because super high-rise buildings with box foundations are generally built on subgrade with good soil conditions, usually as sandy subgrade and strong weathered granite subgrade, and these subgrade conditions are also even, the result from modified layer-summation method would be much closer to the real measured settlement. Of course it can also be counted by empirical formula and in chapter 5, Xiangfu Chen suggestes to adopt the elastic mechanics solution with general modified factors which include depth correction of elastic modulus, correction of subgrade lateral deformation, correction of subgrade resilience and recompression, correction of lateral restriction effect of retaining structures and so on. The specific empirical formula has been described in national codes of China, and the modified factor method will be particularly discussed later. As there have been many papers focusing on finite element method for box foundation settlement, further illuminations wouldn't be presented here.

1.3.3 Progress of Research on Settlement Calculation of Pile Box/Raft Foundations of Super High-Rise Buildings

The research on settlements of pile-box or pile-raft foundation of super high-rise buildings involves single-pile settlement, piles-group settlement, and the interaction among superstructure, foundation and subgrade. Single-pile settlement calculation is the basis of all settlement calculations. Under vertical loads, the single-pile settlements can be divided into the elastic compression deformation of the pile, the deformation of the pile tip and the deformation of soil below the pile tip. The main calculation methods for single-pile settlements are as follows: load transmission analysis method, layer-summation method, elastic theory method, shear deformation transmission calculation method, and simplified empirical method. There are always errors in these methods. Thus it is necessary to take pile test (generally at least 3 piles) in normal project design to obtain the *Q-s* curve which could be considered as very reliable data. Athough there have been many scholars who devoted themselves to the studies on the relationship between single-pile settlement and pile-group settlement, it is hard to find uniform relation due to the complexity, variability and regionality of subgrade. So it is suggested to use regional empirical factor method (the factor reflects relation between single-pile settlement and pile-group settlement) under the condition of the same pile sinking technology. There are two characteristics here of pile group settlement: ① the calculation result of pile-group settlement accounts for 0.2~0.9 of the total calculation settlement; ② the settlement of pile-group is several times or even several dozen times larger than that of single-pile. Therefore, the actual measurements and model tests of pile-group settlement are put into the first place by domestic and foreign experts.

1. pile-group settlement measurement and model test

1) In 1973, Blanchet,Tavenas and Garneaa carried the test with four friction piles under piers and concluded that:

a. the elastic compression of pile body of 16 meters is 3 mm;

b. the lateral friction resistance is negative in the depth of 3/4 of pile length, which means the settlement within this range (30 mm in 4.2 meter depth) is larger than that at pile tip (22mm).

c. the sinking distance of pile tip is 20 mm, but subgrade settlement below the pile tip is only 10 mm, which indicates that stab deformation occurs at the pile tip (300 days after settlement).

d. the long term observed settlement (after 1600 days) of the tip of pile group is 18 mm, the lateral friction resistance is positive, there is stab deformation at pile tip and shear deformation in inter-pile subgrade, and the compression of subgrade below the pile tip is very small (only 3 mm).

Two important conclusions were drawn from these actual measured results: ① the consolidation settlement of cohesive subgrade below friction tips of pile-group is very small; ② the final settlement of pile-group consists of the stab deformation of pile tips and the shear deformation among piles. These two conclusions contradict with the traditional settlement calculation methods.

2) In 1984, Butterfield took a pile-group test and achieved a significant result, that is, the settlement ratio (settlement of pile-group divided by settlement of single-pile) is basically consistent with the calculation of elastic mechanics and this ratio goes stable gradually when the ratio of pile length to pile diameter is over 30 (but the ratio is 3.8 or 4.2 when the ratio of pile interval to pile diameter is 2.5 or 5.0, and can be taken as 4).

2. Semi-theoretical and semi-empirical method for pile-group settlement calculation

The settlement of pile-group is composed of elastic compression of pile body, compression deformation and shear deformation of inter-pile subgrade, sinking distance of pile tips (stab deformation), and compression deformation of subgrades below pile tips. Not considering interaction, the main settlement calculation methods for pile-group include semi-theoretical and semi-empirical method, elastic mechanics method, equivalent effect layer-summation method, simplified method, etc. Terzaghi and Peck proposed an assumed entity deep foundation method in 1967. In 1994, Tomlinson thought pile-group settlement in cohesive subgrade was made up of initial settlement and consolidation settlement, and the former could be counted in elastic mechanics method and the latter could be got by multiplying the additional stress in the middle of recompression subgrade depth with the compression subgrade depth and some factors namely *geological effect factor*, *depth effect factor* and *subgrade volume compression factor* obtained from laboratory tests. Huang Shaoming etc. presented a method to count pile-group settlement in 1982. In this method, firstly settlement of subgrade below pile tips is calculated by taking pile-group effect into account, together with effect map based on Mindlin stress solution of single-pile; and then the additional vertical stress of subgrade below pile group is accumulatively counted; finally settlement is got by layer-summation method. Thus final settlement can be obtained by adding the compression of pile body to the calculated settlement of subgrade below pile tips. In 1994, equivalent effect layer-summation method was introduced in the issued *Code for Pile Foundations of Buildings (JGJ94-94)*. In 1999, non-diffusion angle entity deep foundation method was illuminated in *Shanghai Codes for Design of Subsoil & Foundation (DBJ08-11-89)*, in which pile group settlement was counted by applying an empirical coefficient for Shanghai region to entity deep foundation settlement that is calculated by layer-summation method based on compression modules of subgrade under geostatic pressure and additional pressure. There are also lots of other methods; some of them are general, the others are local. To sum up, the settlement calculation methods in Shanghai region are more practical.

3. Poulos' elastic theory method for pile-group settlement calculation

Poulos from Australia gave a lecture titled with *Analysis and Design of Pile Foundation* in Hongkong University in 1997. In this lecture, he summarized settlement calculation methods and introduced his own research results.

Poulos categorized pile settlement calculation methods into three categories: ① empirical methods; ② easy-hand-calculation methods based on simplified theories and subgrade mechanics principles, which can be further divided into two types: methods based on linear theory and rigid-plastic theory, and methods based on non-linear theory and elastic-plastic theory. ③ methods based on all kinds of strength theories and subgrade mechanics principles, which can also be classified as linear or rigid-plastic theory method, simple non-linear model method and various non-linear constitutive model method. Charts and graphics used in methods of category two (②can often be got in methods of category three ③).

The common settlement analysis methods particularly include: load transfer method (2-2), simplified analytic method, Boundary Element method and Finite Element method.

From the point view of Poulos, the results from these methods for certain subgrade data are basically consistent. Therefore, he took Boundary Element method, which is still based on elastic theory, and drew some significant conclusions: ① the instant settlement of piles is the main part of total settlement, usually accounting for more than 80% of total; ② the compressibility of slim piles has great effect on settlement; ③ the bearing stratum under pile tips doesn't noticeably affect settlement of slim piles; ④ the load—settlement relationship of piles under normal loads is nearly linear and can be evaluated by elastic theory; ⑤ the non-linear properties of subgrade have important effect on the bearing capacity of tip resistance piles such as piles in sandy subgrade, pedestal piles, large diameter bored piles, and so on.

Methods for determining calculation parameters include: laboratory test, on-site load experiment, laboratory or on-site data and empirical formula calculation.

Poulos believed that computation should be taken into account when the following issues were encountered: ① the result is out of valid range of parameter ; ② the distribution of load transmission of piles needs to be determined; ③ there are enough data of subgrade which can be layered; ④ the cross section of pile is not even; ⑤ the settlement of pile group and the distribution of loads need to be obtained; ⑥ deformation mechanism needs to be determined; ⑦ the complete load—settlement curve till damage situation needs to be drawn.

The common pile-group settlement calculation methods overseas include: interaction factor method, settlement ratio method, equivalent raft or equivalent frusta method. In interaction factor method, the interaction factor α between two piles is introduced as:

$$\alpha = \frac{\text{additonal settlement caused by nearby piles}}{\text{settlement caused by loads on piles}}$$

When the factor mentioned above is counted by various methods, the finial settlement is:

$$S = \rho \sum_j P_j \alpha_{ji}$$

where: P_j— load on the j pile ;

$\rho = E_s / E_s$—E_s elastic module of soil in the middle part of the pile;

E_s— elastic module of soil undet the pile tip;

ρ— uneven coefficient of soil.

In settlement ratio method, settlement ratio is represented as:

$$R_s = \frac{\text{average settlement of pile group}}{\text{settlement of single-pile under average load}}$$

pile group shrink factor is:

$$R_G = \frac{\text{average settlement of pile group}}{\text{settlement of single-pile under total load}} = \frac{\text{rigid of pile group}}{\text{n} \times \text{ rigid of single-pile}}$$

Then

where: n — pile number.

The final settlement of pile group is:

$$S_G = R_s P_{av} S_1$$

where: S_1 — the settlement of single-pile under unit load;

P_{av} — average load of pile;

R_s —can be calculated as the following equation (Randolph, 1979):

$$R_s = n^{\omega}$$

where: the theoretical value of ω is between 0.4 and 0.6. In practical application, $\omega = 0.5$ for the friction pile group in clay subgrade and $\omega = 0.33$ for the friction pile group in sandy subgrade.

4. Simplified methods for settlement calculation of pile group

In 1953, Skempton came up with a formula involving settlement ratio and plane width of pile group on the basis of some in-place real measured data:

$$R_s = S_G / S_t = (4B+9)^2 / (B+12)^2$$

In 1959, Meyerhof suggested a relation formula of settlement ratio, pile number, pile interval, and ratio of pile lengthen to diameter when he hit a square pile into sandy subgrade; Vesic suggested a settlement ratio based on sandy subgrade model test in 1967:

$$R_s = \sqrt{\frac{B'}{d}}$$

where: B' — the distance of the centers of piles in the both sides of pile group;

d — pile diameter.

In 1961, Soviet Russia scholars suggested that:

$$R_s = B/b$$

where: B, b — side lengths of pile bottom after both-side expansion of pile group or single-pile.

In 1978, Sckmertman proposed a simplified calculation formula of pile-group settlement in sandy subgrade.

1.3.4 Yang Min's Settlement Control Design Method for Pile Foundations

Yang Min and other scholars proposed a simplified practical settlement calculation formula with consideration of interaction among pile, subgrade and bearing platform based on lots of calculation results of raft-pile-subgrade interaction and practical experiences of engineering projects. With this formula, not only the average settlement, difference settlement of pile-raft foundations and internal moment of raft plate, can be counted easily and rationally but also the settlements of reducing-settlement pile foundations (settlement control compound pile foundations) and flexible pile foundations (cement injection piles, cement-soil mixing piles, etc.) can be counted. Meanwhile, a method based on Geddes additional stress coefficient formula and "Cut-Off" of loads was developed for analyzing interaction among pile, subgrade and raft plate (bearing platform). The possible ultimate capacity of piles and the partial subgrade surface under bearing platform is taken into account in this method to simulate the ideal elastic-plastic property of subgrade of pile-raft foundations.

In recent years, for foundation on soft soil subgrade just as the case in Shanghai region, settlement control has become a major content of design. Shanghai Civil Construction Committee has issued a special document to enforce that settlement calculation be conducted in foundation design of almost all buildings, and software for settlement calculation should of pile foundation has been developed. There are also some other scholars in China who have done much in this field, such as Huang Shaoming and Guan Zili.

Overseas, Zeevaert initially proposed the concept of reducing-settlement pile in 1973; Barland with other scholars clearly explained reducing-settlement pile in 1977; and in 1979 Hooper and others concluded on the basis of finite element calculation results that it was not necessary to have lots of piles in some larger pile-group foundations (the number of piles can be reduced according to current design code), and there was no marked influence on the maximum settlement and settlement difference from increasing or decreasing the numbers of piles; Cook obtained the settlement-pile number relation by model test in 1986. Thereafter, Mandolini, VIggian, Poulos, Horikoshi and so on have all contributed to settlement control design.

1.3.5 Progress of Settlement Research on Interaction Among Subgrade, Foundation and Superstructure of Super High-Rise Buildings

The interaction among superstructure, subgrade and foundation of super high-rise buildings is more important than ordinary buildings. Given the fast development of numerical method and computational technology, the research on the interaction is generally stepping from theoretical and qualitative research to practical, quantitative and digitalized research. In 1953, G. G. Meyerhof proposed the calculation formula of equivalent stiffness of frame structures to consider this interaction; in 1965, S.Chamechi and H.Grosshof put forward a method to count foundation settlement with the consideration of superstructure stiffness; in 1965, O.C.Zeinkeiwicz from British and Y.K.Cheung from Hongkong started applying Finite Element method and Finite Strip method to study the interaction on the basis of the development of numerical methods (Finite Element method, Finite Strip method, Boundary Element method, etc.); in 1968, J.S.Przemieniecki initially came up with an effective analysis method for sub-structure, and in 1971, M.J.Haddadin firstly applied this method to study the interaction among superstructure, subgrade and foundation; In 1972, J.T. Christian illuminated the issue of the interaction at High-Rise Building Planning and Design Conference; After that, lots of mechanics, structural engineers and geotechnical experts such as I.K.Lee, H.B. Harrison, S.J.Hain, W.J.Lamach, L.A.Wood, J.A.Hooper, G.J.W.King, V.S.Chandresekam, L.J.Wardle, R.A.Frazer, et al., started focusing on research of the interaction. In 1977, the 1st International Conference on Interaction between Subgrade and Structures was held in India and the papers in the proceeding of this conference reflected the high level of research on the interaction. There were also topics about "interaction between subgrades and constructions" on the 10th and 11th International Conference on Subgrade Mechanics and Foundation Engineering (1981,1985) and the 3rd, 4th and 5th International Conference on Subgrade Mechanics and Nnumerical Methods (1979,1982,1985). In 1980, H.G.Poulos proposed an elastic theory method for the interaction between piles and subgrade on the basis of R.D.Mindlin's solution and promoted further research on the interaction among pile, superstructure and foundation. In 1981, H.G.Poulos issued a key report about the interaction between subgrade and construction at the 10th International Conference on Subgrade Mechanics and Foundation Engineering and discussed the development prospect of studies on the interaction between subgrade and structure. In 1986, G.Price and others designed a high-rise building with 11 storeys and pile-raft foundation based on the interaction theory.

In China, starting from 1974, on-site tests have been done on the interaction between subgrade and box foundation of 10 high-rise buildings in Beijing and Shanghai regions. Meanwhile, theoretical exploration was also carried out and precious data were accumulated. All these work provided the basis for compiling *Codes for Design and Construction of Box Foundation of High-Rise Building (JGJ6-80)*. In 1981, Academic Conference on Interaction among High-Rise Building, Foundation and Subgrade was held at Tongji Universtiy in Shanghai, at the conference Zhang Wenqing from Tongji University put forward an expansion sub-structure method to count the stiffness of high-rise buildings; Zhang Guoxia from Beijing Exploitation Institute, He Yihua from China Academic Institute of Building, Qin Rong from Guangxi University, Ye Yuzheng from Beijing University of Technology, etc. successively introduced the theoretical studies and practices of the interaction among subgrade, foundation and high-rise buildings.

At the 1st, 2nd and 3rd Geotechnical Mechanics Analytic and Numerical Method Conferences during 1982 to 1990 and the 4th, 5th, and 6th Mechanics and Foundation Engineering Conferences during 1983 to 1991, the topic of interaction was put on the agenda as an important one. Particularly, great advancement of the interaction research on geotechnical engineering was made at the 1st Conference on Interaction between Structures and Mediums in 1993. In 1985, Dong Jianguo and Lu Jia initially applied the interaction theory to foundation of high-rise buildings. Zhao Xihong put forward *"design theory for pile-raft and pile-box foundations of high-rise buildings in Shanghai"* in 1985; Dong Jianguo came up with some suggestions in 1992 about applications of the interaction theory to foundation design; Yang Mi made further theoretical and empirical studies on the interaction between superstructure and pile-raft foundation; In 1991, Huang Shaoming and Pei Jie discussed the reducing-settlement pile and its application to multi-story buildings. In *Technical Codes for Building's Pile Foundations* compiled in 1991, the interaction among bearing platforms, pile group and subgrades is taken into account.

Even there are great difficulties in the analysis of the interaction, some qualitative conclusions have already been drawn so far which can be used for conceptive design of buildings, and more importantly for promoting fundamental studies and applications to calculation to get quantitative analysis of the interaction so as to better serve projects.

In the existing studies on the interaction, a vital yet neglected problem in project that badly needs to be solved is the interaction between a high-rise building and a low building, between a super high-rise building and its annex, and between two high-rise buildings. In particular, the analysis of difference settlements is very important and exigent for constructions, even though it is very complicated and difficult. Huang Xiling, academician of China Academy of Building Science and Research, and others have done plenty of creative work and got great achievements, the important conclusions of which have been written into *National Codes for Building's Foundation & Subsoil Design (GB500007-2002).*

Until now, the latest research achievements of the interaction between subgrade and box/raft foundations of high-rise buildings are as follows: ① the effect of the stiffness of superstructures on foundation is limited, especially for super high-rise buildings with box or raft foundations which have multiple-level basement, this effect is more limited for large stiffness basement and thick bottom plate; ② how to determine appropriate calculation parameters and subgrade constitutive models is a critical problem for foundation settlement calculations, and the calculation results are likely to be anamorphic if wrong selection is made; ③ there obviously exists resilience and recompression settlement in the total settlement of box/raft foundations of super high-rise buildings; ④ initial settlement account for a large proportion, about over 80%, of the total settlement of box/raft foundations of super high-rise buildings, which are usually built on subgrade of sandy and cobble soil, or strong weathered granite; ⑤ it is technologically and economically significant to analyze the difference of settlement between the super high-rise building and its annex, or underground parking garage.

Although quantitative analysis is the main part of studies on the interaction of pile-box or pile-raft foundations of super high-rise buildings, many qualitative evaluations are still very useful for preliminary design and conceptual design of pile foundations. The mechanical characteristics of single-pile and pile group, and the general rules of settlement control will be further discussed in chapter 7, and only some achievements of settlement research with consideration of interaction are to be introduced here: ① pile foundations play a key role in reducing settlement; ② long piles are apt to controlling settlements and short piles are good at bearing loads; ③ piles bear loads together with subgrade, and for foundation design, proper reduction in number of piles according to the national code doesn't have great influence on settlement; ④ settlement reduction is not remarkable when the slenderness ratio of piles (L/D) is larger than 60; ⑤ the interaction between subgrade and pile-box or pile-raft foundations of high-rise buildings has certain influence on some lower parts of superstructure, especially on corner columns and outer frame tub structure. There are certainly other conclusions and suggestions for related design; ⑥ the settlement calculation analysis of pile-box or pile-raft foundation of high-rise buildings and lower adjacent buildings, or high-rise buildings and its annex , can be used to judge whether settlement joint or post-cast joint (with larger risk) should be set. If post-cast joint would be set, it is necessary to ascertain the timing of casting it.

1.3.6 Progress of Numerical Method Research on Settlement Calculation of Deep Foundations of Super High-Rise Buildings

The numerical methods for settlement analysis of deep foundations of super high-rise buildings mainly include Finite Element method and Boundary Element method. Integration of these two methods can solve problems of deep foundation settlement under any initial and boundary conditions. Finite Element method is many more applied to count single-pile settlement, and less to pile-group settlement. And there are not much achievements of analyzing the interaction among superstructure, pile-box/raft foundation and subgrade. In 1975, Ottavani initially made analysis of three-dimensional pile group with Finite Element method; Banerjee and others applied Finite Element and Boundary Element methods to pile group analysis after 1977; Zeinkeiwicz, Cheung and cooperators (Yang Min, etc.) used Finite Element and Finite Strip method to analyze subgrade and foundation topics, including settlement issues; the invention of finite element sub-structure method facilitated the research on subgrade & foundations. On the other hand, the application of Finite Element and Boundary Element methods encountered three big difficulties, namely spatial or three-dimensional characteristic, infinite field, and different structural systems in settlement research. Therefore, various semi-analytic and semi-numerical methods (Prof. Cao Zhiyuan categorized theses methods into 7 categories, 30 types) are developing faster. Prof. Cao Zhiyuan analyzed pile-subgrade interaction problems of pile group with semi-analytic methods. At present, the popular semi-analytic methods include semi-analytic combination unit method, semi-analytic boundary element method, infinite element and infinite boundary methods, and coupled region method. These semi-analytic methods have contributed to the solution of the three major difficulties to some extent. In addition, all numerical methods can be facilitated by computer technology to simulate the discontinuous, uneven, and non-linear properties of subgrade, to analyze creep deformation and consolidation of subgrade, and also to simulate the process of construction and consecutive loading. However, the theoretical basis of all these methods is still elastic mechanics, and for this reason, the correction and errors cannot be asserted as it is hard to determine subgrade models, calculation parameters, boundary conditions and geological conditions. Thus, there is still a long way before developing practical software for settlement calculation of pile-box/raft foundations of super high-rise buildings.

To sum up, among all these methods for settlement calculation of pile-box or pile-raft foundations of super high-rise buildings, the modified layer-summation method is recommended with priority.

1.3.7 Major Problems and Prospects of Settlement Calculation of Deep Foundations of Super High-Rise Buildings

The problems in foundation settlement calculation can be summarized as: there is a difference between theoretical calculation result and actually measured value from projects, and sometimes the difference can be very big. Theoretical calculation result should be a little smaller than actually measured value due to great compressibility of subgrade, and the result should be a little bigger under the opposite condition. Therefore, the foundation settlement calculation hasn't been completely solved and the major problems are as follow:

1) While the additional stress of foundation bottom of deep pit is counted, it no longer

accords with the equation $P_0 = p - \gamma_p D$ due to the resilience of pit bottom, and the resilience recompression coefficient ranging from 0 to 1 is hard to determine. That is why the additional stress cannot be accurately counted.

2) Certain calculation parameters of associated physical and mechanical properties of subgrade cannot be ascertained correctly and accurately. For example, there are elastic modulus, deformation modulus, compression modulus and Poisson ratio for subgrade.

3) For all settlement calculation methods, the considered depth of settlement calculation is simplified to a certain extent (limited depth), which causes errors inevitably.

4) Several major methods for calculation of final subgrade settlement are based on elastic mechanics and take the assumption that subgrade is a non-lateral limited and continuous linear elastic body without considering the lateral limitation effect of shoring structures on deep pits and the resilience effect of pit bottom. Unfortunately, subgrade usually has discontinuous, uneven and non-linear properties, and it is hard to analyze without taking numerical methods. Moreover, we obtain the analytic solution on the assumptions of semi-infinite plane and spatial body subgrade, but actually the compression layer of real subgrade is counted according to very limited depth. So the calculated result is definitely bigger.

5) The three phases of clay subgrade settlement (initial settlement, consolidation settlement, and secondary consolidation settlement) can be clearly separated. On the contrary, the former two phases of sandy subgrade settlement can hardly be divided yet and they account for a major part of total settlement. The secondary consolidation settlement is relatively small and hard to count.

6) When numerical methods are applied to the settlement calculation of deep foundations of super high-rise buildings, the major problem is how to select constitutive subgrade model and calculation parameters and how to take three-dimensional analysis of overall structures (including pile-box/raft foundation, subgrade and superstructure).

7) There are very little actually measured data on foundation settlement, and much less data on foundation settlement of high-rise and super high-rise buildings. Therefore, it is hard to establish a database and expert system for settlement research.

8) There are still some problems in calculation parameter tests and equipments.

In summary, it is impossible to solve all these problems in a short term, and it might take several decades to solve one or some problems with preliminary estimation. On the other hand, with more and more real measured settlement data, the regional empirical factor would get more accurate so that error of theoretical calculation value could be minimized to acceptable range. Meanwhile, with the continuous development of numerical methods and computer technologies and the improvement of test technologies, there is a brilliant prospect for solving the above problems by computer technologies. It will bring great technological and economic benefits by combing optimization theory and optimization technologies with settlement calculations.

1.4 Brief Introduction of Research in This Book

At present, how to calculate deep foundation settlement of super high-rise buildings is an urgent and important problem, but it is still incompletely solved. There are more than one hundred high-rise buildings exceeding 200 meters in height, most of which are distributed in U.S.A and Asia (Fig. 1-7), and others lie around the world dispersedly. In China, there are only 20 buildings exceeding 200 meters, which are located in Beijing, Shanghai, Guangzhou, Shenzhen, Qingdao, Wuhan, Nanjing, Dalian and other metropolises (referred to Chapter 1). Consequently there are a few theoretical studies and real measured data on settlement. According to the geological conditions and structural systems in China, the applied deep foundations at present can be divided into three types: box/raft foundations, friction pile box/raft foundations, and end-bearing pile box/raft foundations. There is apparently a significant difference between high-rising buildings and multi-story buildings, which can be summarized as: ① by using box or raft foundations, subgrade bearing capacity f_k is at least 1000kPa, and the subgrade quality is much better, as sandy cobble soil and weathered granite, etc.; ② the length of piles for super-long pile box/raft foundations are all over 50 meters; ③ large diameter & end bearing pile which is cast by digging is apt for rock ground with limited compression layers; ④ the shoring structures and the exterior walls of basements can be integrated or separated; ⑤ the basement has at least 3 levels and is constructed by top-down or semi-top-down methods; ⑥ the settlement difference and the tilting value have to be much smaller to ensure better vertical movement of elevators. In view of the above situation, this book focuses on studies on settlement theory and real measured data in projects. In the case study of real measured data of five super high-rise buildings, the main problems with foundation settlement are discussed intensively and some important conclusions and inovations are made in each chapter of the book, which is significant for project design and further research. Brief introduction of this book is given chapter by chapter :

1) After discussing the subgrade constitutive relation, the linear-elastic constitutive model is recommended for the analytic method or semi-empirical and semi-theoretical method when it comes to settlement calculation of deep foundation of super high-rise buildings. In the analysis, other subgrade constitutive models which are consistent with geological and project conditions,

like elastic-plastic model, non-linear model, etc. are applied to numerical methods, together with computer technologies.

2) In this book, a formula is proposed for calculation of subgrade stress under various loading and boundary conditions. For putting is formula into practice, there are some suggestions: ① stress should be counted with elastic mechanics formula, for example, additional vertical stress should be counted with Mindlin or Boussinesq formula; ② analysis of spatial subgrade stress should be considered in numerical stress calculation; ③ settlement calculation of deep foundations of super high-rise buildings should be integrated into the overall structural analysis of superstructure, foundation, and subgrade by overcoming the problems of block calculation and integral coordination.

3) All the methods for subgrade deformation analysis, including analytic or semi-empirical and semi-theoretical methods for settlement calculation, are based on elastic mechanics. However, the stress-strain relationship of subgrade doesn't conform to the characteristics of elastic body and the deformation of subgrade differs greatly from that of ideal elastic body due to the three-phase structure of subgrade. Therefore, it is impossible to get any results that accord with real measured settlement by all these methods. In this book, various settlement calculation methods and their application scopes are explained, and comprehensive coefficient method for settlement calculation of box foundations in sandy subgrade is described. Meanwhile, a proposal is raised about government's legislative requirement: settlement observation of all super high-rise buildings should be conducted from the beginning to the end (at least across 20 years) in order to establish and issue regular settlement database to provide reliable data referrence for semi-empirical and semi-theoretical method for settlement calculation. Moreover, it is necessary to continally summarize regional experiences and propose regional calculation methods for subgrade deformation.

4) Super-long piles are more and more applied in China, but related research and experimental data are scarce. The experimental data of more than 40 large-diameter piles with over 50 meters in length and post-perfuse piles from Shen Baohan and others are collected in this book. Analysis shows that there are differences in mechanical behavior between super-long piles and short piles. One of the biggest differences is that super-long piles have great capacity of controlling settlement. Thus, we suggest that post-grouting technology be applied to bored piles to solve the problems of pile bottom sediments and borehole wall relaxation. In addition, some major methods for settlement calculations of single-pile or pile group are introduced in this book, especially the method recommended in the new codes.

5) In terms of settlement calculation of box foundations of super high-rise buildings, various calculation methods and the method in the code are illuminated, and a settlement

calculation method with consideration of the effect of shoring structures in deep pits is initially proposed, meanwhile three calculation sketches, models and corresponding calculation plans are listed according to the relationship between shoring structures and outer walls of basements.

6) The completely measured settlement data of the box foundation of China Bank Tower in Qingdao are detailed and analyzed, and are compared with the calculation results from several settlement calculation methods such as finite element method. After plenty of trial calculation, the empirical coefficient of strong weathered granite settlement in Qingdao region ψ_s is 0.2, depth adjustment coefficient β is 0.4. Because this building is the highest building with box foundation in China, the settlement data are completely accumulated and the observation time period is over 5 years. Some conclusions have been drawn from the research on the data:

a. Calculation results from Finite Element method are basically consistent with the ones from elastic theory and the calculation error deviation is only a little more than 20 mm.

b. The main deformations of subgrade are initial settlement and consolidation settlement for strong weathered granite areas. They are hard to be separated in Qingdao area. The secondary consolidation is not noticeable.

c. There is remarked resilience and recompression in deep pit, whose value is only half of its gravity stress because of the restriction effect of shoring structures.

d. The total settlement is 74 mm and the settlement difference is more than 20 mm. The tilting value of this building meets the demands of the code.

e. Settlement had reached 80%–90% of the total up till the completion of the building, and after about 400 days, the total settlement was completely stable.

7) In 1997, Xiangfu Chen firstly put forward thinkings on settlement design and a concrete plan of spatial variable stiffness of pile group, and tried further research in his doctoral dissertation, unfortunately it didn't realize due to shortage of real measured data. These design thinkings and concrete plan are discussed in this book, by illuminating subgrade stress-strain rule, single-pile mechanical rule, pile-group effect and characteristics of long piles and short piles. In this method, long piles are mainly for controlling settlement, and short piles are for bearing loads. This kind of optimized combination of long and short piles can realize comprehensive economic and technological benefit of "larger bearing capacity, less settlement, lower cost and shorter construction period".

8) It is of great advantage to calculate interaction among structure, subgrade and foundation by Spline Function method.

9) Calculation of comprehensive modulus of pile and subgrade shows that settlement calculation can be simplified so as to be computerized more easily.

10) Research on deep foundation settlement will be further promoted by studies on super-deep subgrade mechanics.

11) In this book, main settlement data of Jingmao Tower and Senmao Tower in Shanghai are collected and compared with those of several other super high-rise buildings, and finally two important conclusions are drawn: ① The settlement of pile-box and pile-raft foundations of super high-rise buildings with super-long piles is usually only 60—100 mm, and it is even and with little difference. All the super-long piles are over 50 m in length; ② Result obtained with the method specified in the code is far bigger than real measured value. However, the calculated settlement of Jingmao Tower is 85.2 mm and the real measured settlement is 82 mm, which challenges and fluctuates traditional method for settlement calculation of entity deep foundations. It is indispensable to consider the effect of subgrade walls and shoring structures, which benefits settlement control.

12) Settlement data of Saige Mansion in Shenzhen and International Mansion in Guangdong are also collected in this book to prove that major settlement of end-bearing pile box or raft foundations of super high-rise buildings results from the elastic compression of pile itself, and the compression deformation of rock grounds under end bearing piles is very small (as is the case for Saige Mansion). As for a super high-rise building whose foundation is laid directly on rock (as is the case of International Mansion), its main settlement is the compression deformation of rock ground.

13) The direction, path and topics of research on deep foundation settlement of super high-rise buildings are: to determine the relation between pile group and data of pressing experiments of single-pile (Q-s) in different areas; to establish real measured database and expert system for deep foundatio of super high-rise buildings; to identify empirical coefficient and settlement calculation formula on a regional basis; to develop CAD system and a system for finite element analysis and related optimization; to build a precise test and observation system.

All the achievements mentioned above are breakthrough based on combination of theory and project practice, which could be innovative enough to present guidance for project design and construction.

References

Banerjee P. K., Davis T.G. 1977. Analysis of Pile Groups Embedded in Gibson Soil. Proc., 9th Int. Conf., Soil Mech. Fdn. Engng., Tokyo.

Das B.M. 2006. Principles of Geotechnical Engineering, 6th Edition, USA: Brooks/Code

Chen X.F., Liao S.M., Kong X.P. 2003. Modern Geotechnical Engineering, Shanghai: Tongji University Press.

Chen X.F., Yuan W.B. 1990. Progress of Geotechnical Mechanics, Beijing: China Prospect Press.

Chen X.F. 2000. Theory and Engineering Cases of Settlement Calculation on Super High-Rise Buildings, Shanghai: Doctoral Dissertation of Tongji University.

Chen X.F. 2004. Methods and Research Progress of Deep Foundation Settlement Calculation, Journal of Civil Engineering.

Cui J.Z., Chen X.F. 2000. Proceedings of the Symposium of Civil Engineering in the 21st Century. ICETS2000 Section 5, Beijing: Science Press.

Dunean J. M., Chang C. Y. 1970. Nonlinear Analysis of Stress and Strain in Soils, J. Soil Mech. Found. Div., ASCE, Vol.9

Dong J.G., Zhao X.H. 1997. High-rise Building Foundation, Shanghai: Tongji University Press.

Gao D.H. 1992. Theory and Practice of Soft Soil in Shanghai, Beijing: China Building Industry Press.

Hou X.Y., Yang Min. 1996. Theory and Engineering Practice of Soft Subgrade Deformation Control Design, Shanghai: Tongji University Press.

Huang Qiang. 1996. A Number of Hot Issues of Pile Foundation Technology, Beijing: China Building Materials Industry Press.

Huang X.L. 1990. Planning and Design Principles of Foundation, Beijing: China Building Industry Press.

Huang X.L. Design Specifications of Building Foundation, GB5007-2002.

Liu J.L. 1990. Design and Calculation of Pile Foundation, Beijing: China Building Industry Press.

Liu J.H., Hou X.Y. 1997. Handbook of Foundation Engineering, Beijing: China Building Industry Press.

Mitchell J. K., Katti R. K. 1981. Soil Improvement, State of the Art Report. Proc. 10th ICSMFE, Stoctholm.

Meyerhof H. G. 1953. Some Resent Foundation Research and Its Application to Design, The Structural Engineer, Vol.31.

Poulos H. G., Davis, E.H. 1980. Pile Foundation Analysis and Design, New York: Krieger Pub. Co.

Qin Rong. 2005. Calculation Structural Mechanics, Beijing: Science Press

Sun Jun, Hou X.Y. 1987. Underground Structure (Volumes), Beijing: Science Press.

Tergzghi K. 1943. Theoretical Soil Mechanism, New York: John Wiley & Sons.

Teng Y.J. 2004. Development and Application of Foundation Technology, Beijing: Intellectual Property Press.

Xu Wei, et al. 1999. Calculation Method and Design Handbook of Construction Structure, Beijing: China Building Industry Press.

Xu R.L., Chen Xiangfu, et al. 1991. Pile and Deep Foundation Theory and Practice in China (English), Beijing: China Building Industry Press.

Xu R.L. 2000. Guidebook of China Civil Engineering (2nd Edition), Beijing: Science Press.

Yang Min, Ai Z.Y. 1998. Theory and Practice of Pile Foundation Design on the Basis of Settlement Control, Memoir of Civil and Structure Engineering Exchange and Symposium Among Colleges and Universities from Hong Kong and Across the Taiwan Strait, Shanghai.

Zhao X.H., et al., 1999. Design Theory and Practice of the Subgrade-Foundation Interaction for High-Rise Building with Podium, Shanghai: Tongji University Press.

Zheng Y.R., Gong X.N. 1989. Geotechnical Plastic Mechanics Foundation, Beijing: China Building Industry Press.

Zhu B.F. 1979. Principle and Application of Finite Element Method, Beijing: Water Conservancy and Electric Power Press.

Zhang Z.K., Hou X.Y., Liu G.B., Yin Z.Z., Cao Z.K. 1998. Calculation Method Discussion of Composite Foundation Settlement Development Under Embankment, Highways, No.10.

Zienkiewicz O.C. 1971. The Finite Element Method in Engineering Science, New York: MeGraw-Hill.

Chapter 2 Practical Models and Parameters for Settlement Calculation of Deep Foundation of Super High-Rise Buildings on Soft Subgrade

In 1867, Winkler put forward the most simple linear-elastic ideal model, which assumed that pressure of each point on the medium surface of subgrade is in direct ratio with the vertical displacement of this point, and is completely irrelevant with pressure of other points on the interface between subgrade and foundation. Although this assumption has some disadvantages, it is still applied now. Another ideal model describes subgrade medium by elastic half-space continuum, i.e. the elastic half-space foundation model, which takes into account the continuity feature of subgrade, and integral equation calculation is needed accordingly for the analyzing process of the interaction between subgrade and foundation. So this model has more complex calculation process, and the result of internal force of foundation is larger than real. Afterwards, Filonelko-Borodich (1940), Hetenyi (1946), etc, put forward a kind of intermediate double-parameter subsoil models, which was a intervenient one between Winkler foundation model and elastic half-space foundation model. One of such models introduces the mutual mechanics action between springs to make the result more sensible by breaking the limit that the displacement of subgrade medium surface is within the area of load, based on Winkler subsoil model. Cross isotropic model is a linear-elastic model, which considers the stratum feature of subgrade medium. Recently, application of the layered model is more popular in the field of subgrade-structure interaction analysis, the result is between Winkler subsoil model and elastic half-space subsoil model, and is more reasonable. For the complexity of properties of soft subgrade, new models are still to be researched to consider the factors of non-linear feature, elastoplastic feature, and time-dependent feature of subgrade.

Many practical calculation and testing results show that precision of the result mostly depends on the subgrade parameters selected, among which, the Winkler subgrade reaction coefficient k, the subgrade Poisson ratio μ_0, the soil modulus of deformation E_0 are the major ones and their calculations are very important.

2.1 Winkler Subsoil Model

Winkler presupposes that the pressure value of any point on subgrade surface is in direct ratio with this point's settlement. The formula is as:

$$p = ks \tag{2-1}$$

where: p —unit area pressure of the point on subgrade surface (kN/m^2);

k —coefficient of subgrade reaction (kN/m^3);

s —relative vertical displacement (m).

This presupposition essentially treat the subsoil as lots of unrelated springs, and spring's stiffness is just the subgrade reaction coefficient k. Fig. 2-1 describes the deformation situation of Winkler subsoil under different kinds of load and foundation stiffness. It is obvious that the calculation method under the presumption that bearing pressure distribution is linear is just the perfectly rigid foundation situation of Winkler subsoil.

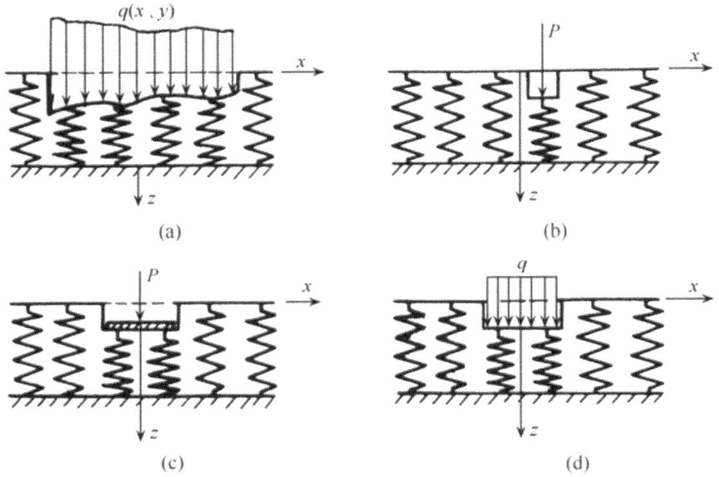

Fig. 2-1 Winkler foundation model

(a) Nonuniformly distributed load; (b) Concentrated load;
(c) Rigid load; (d) Uniformly distributed flexible load

The shortage of this presupposition is gradually discovered after further detailed research. Firstly, the shear force of subsoil is neglected, and subsoil deformation is limited to the range of the load area accordingly without consideration of stress diffusion. This is apparently incompatiable with reality. Secondly, the laboratory test reveals that the subgrade reaction coefficient k is not a constant, rather, it is a variable not only relevant to the subsoil property, subsoil category, but also associated with the area and the shape of foundation base, and the embedded depth of foundation, etc.

Because the calculation process based on Winkler model is relatively simple, this model is still very popular in practice. Generally Winkler model is suitable for the situations of soft subgrade (such as sludge and soft clay subgrade), or of relatively thin compressible stratum in foundation compared with the maximum horizontal dimension of foundation.

2.2 Elastic Half-Space Foundation Model

In order to improve the Winkler subsoil model and overcome its shortage, the elastic half-space subsoil model is put forward, which treats the subsoil as homogeneous isotropic semi-infinite elastic solid, and the relationship between pressure and deformation is analyzed theoretically.

According to the elastic theory, for the problems of plane stress, putting concentrated load P [Fig. 2-2(a)] under the surface of the semi-plane body, if take point M as benchmark, Flaiment came to that any point i 's vertical relative displacement to M point can be expressed as:

$$y = \frac{2p}{\pi E}\ln\frac{D}{r} \tag{2-2}$$

where: p —concentrated load;

E —elastic modulus;

D —the distance between the point p and the benchmark M;

r —the distance between the point p and the calculated point i.

If unit load is uniformly distributed within the distance from c to the boundary of semi-plane solid [Fig. 2-2(b)], and the load intensity is expressed as $P_0 = \frac{1}{c}$, the relative vertical displacement of the point i, whose distance to the center point j of the distributed load is x, is got by applying Eq.(2-2) and integral calculation.

If the point i is outside the distribution length of load, the expression is as follows:

$$\begin{aligned} Y_{ij} &= \frac{2}{\pi Ec}\int_{x-\frac{c}{2}}^{x+\frac{c}{2}} \ln\frac{D}{r}\mathrm{d}r \\ &= \frac{1}{\pi E}\left\{-2\frac{x}{c}\ln\left[\frac{2\frac{x}{c}+1}{2\frac{x}{c}-1}\right] - \ln\left[\left(2\frac{x}{c}+1\right)\left(2\frac{x}{c}-1\right)\right] + 2\ln\frac{D}{c} + 2 + 2\ln 2\right\} \end{aligned}$$

Let

$$F_{ij} = -2\frac{x}{c}\ln\left[\frac{2\frac{x}{c}+1}{2\frac{x}{c}-1}\right] - \ln\left[\left(2\frac{x}{c}+1\right)\left(2\frac{x}{c}-1\right)\right] \tag{2-3}$$

$$G = 2\ln\frac{D}{c} + 2 + 2\ln 2$$

Then it can be derived as:

$$y_{ij} = \frac{1}{\pi E}\left(F_{ij} + G\right) \tag{2-4}$$

If point i is in the central point of distributed load, i.e. $x = 0$, then

$$y_{ij} = \frac{2}{\pi E}\int_0^{\frac{c}{2}} \frac{2}{c}\ln\frac{D}{r}\,\mathrm{d}r \tag{2-5}$$

Eq.(2-5) can still be obtained by integral result, it is just that $F_{ij} = 0$.

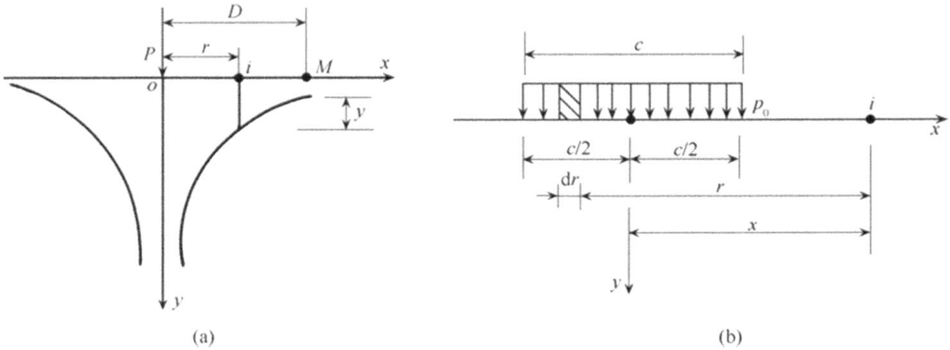

Fig. 2-2 The concentrated load and distributed load on the semi-plane solid boundary

For the plane strain problems, the calculation formula should be $\frac{E}{1-\mu^2}$ instead of E (μ is the Poisson ratio of the geo-material).

When the action on elastic half-space solid comes from concentrated load P(Fig.2-3), the vertical displacement (settlement) of any point on the surface of this elastic half-space solid could be derived by the Boussinesq solution as

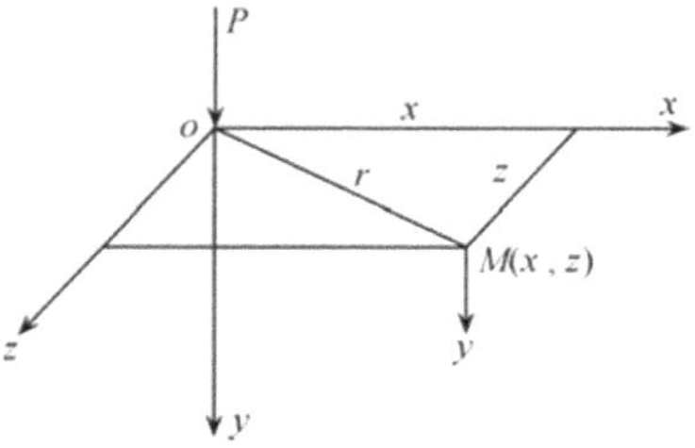

Fig. 2-3 Concentrated load on the surface of elastic half-space

$$y = \frac{P(1-\mu^2)}{\pi E r} \tag{2-6}$$

where: μ —the Poisson ratio of the elastic material;

E —the elastic modulus of the elastic material;

r —the distance between the concentrated load and calculated point.

When the action on the elastic half-space solid is arbitrary distributed load $P(\varepsilon,\eta)$ (Fig. 2-4), the vertical displacement of any point on the subsoil surface can be obtained by the integral of equation (2-6), the expression is

$$y(x,z)=\frac{1-\mu^2}{\pi E}\iint\frac{P(\varepsilon,\eta)\mathrm{d}\varepsilon\mathrm{d}\eta}{\sqrt{(\varepsilon-x)^2+(\eta-z)^2}} \tag{2-7}$$

Let the uniformly distributed load p act on the rectangular load area $b\times c$ (Fig. 2-5), and the origin of the coordinates system be the center point j of the rectangle, then the vertical displacement of the i point on the x axis could be derived through the integral of Eq.(2-6) on this rectangle.

$$y_{ij}=2p\int_{\xi=x-\frac{c}{2}}^{\xi=x+\frac{c}{2}}\int_{n=0}^{n=\frac{c}{2}}\frac{(1-\mu^2)}{\pi E}\cdot\frac{\mathrm{d}\zeta\mathrm{d}\eta}{\sqrt{\zeta^2+\eta^2}}=\frac{1-\mu^2}{\pi E}\cdot\rho bF_{ij} \tag{2-8}$$

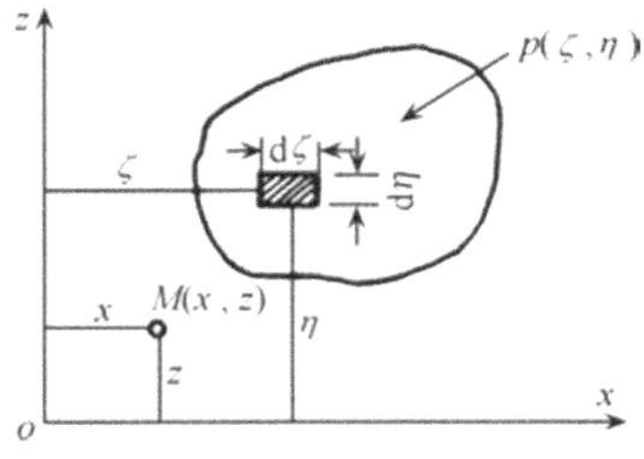

Fig. 2-4 The displacement calculation of arbitrary distributed load on elastic half-space solid boundary

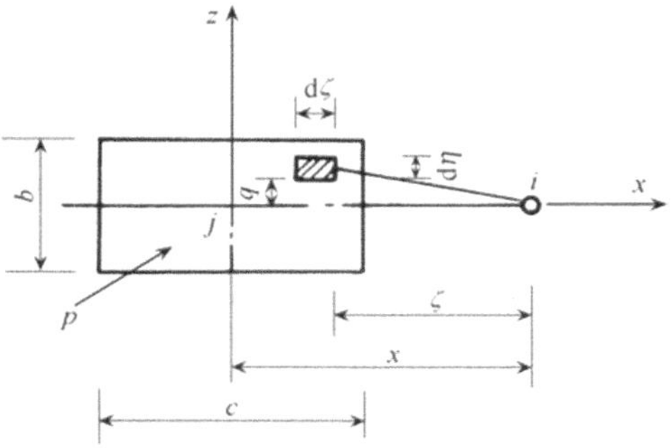

Fig. 2-5 The displacement calculation of rectangular distributed load on elastic half-space solid boundary

where: p —the uniformly distributed load;

b —the width of the rectangle;

F_{ij} —coefficient, whose expression is.

$$F_{ij}=\frac{c}{b}\left\{2\ln\frac{b}{c}-\ln\left[\left(2\frac{x}{c}\right)^2-1\right]-2\frac{x}{c}\ln\frac{2\frac{x}{c}+1}{2\frac{x}{c}-1}\right.$$

$$\left.+\frac{b}{c}\ln\frac{\left(2\frac{x}{b}+\frac{c}{b}\right)+\sqrt{\left(2\frac{x}{b}+\frac{c}{b}\right)^2+1}}{\left(2\frac{x}{b}-\frac{c}{b}\right)+\sqrt{\left(2\frac{x}{b}-\frac{c}{b}\right)^2+1}}\right.$$

$$+2\frac{x}{c}\ln\frac{1+\sqrt{\left(2\frac{x}{b}+\frac{c}{b}\right)^2+1}}{1+\sqrt{\left(2\frac{x}{b}-\frac{c}{b}\right)^2+1}}$$

$$\left.+\ln\left[1+\sqrt{\left(2\frac{x}{b}+\frac{c}{b}\right)^2+1}\right]\left[1+\sqrt{\left(2\frac{x}{b}-\frac{c}{b}\right)^2+1}\right]\right\}$$

When point i is the center point j of the rectangular load area, the vertical displacement is

$$y_{ii}=4p\int_{\xi=0}^{\xi=\frac{c}{2}}\int_{\eta=0}^{\eta=\frac{b}{2}}\frac{1-\mu^2}{\pi E}\cdot\frac{\mathrm{d}\zeta\,\mathrm{d}\eta}{\sqrt{\zeta^2+\eta^2}} \tag{2-9}$$

The integral result can be expressed as Eq.(2-8), i.e.

$$y_{ii}=\frac{1-\mu^2}{\pi E}pbF_{ii} \tag{2-10}$$

Where the expression of the coefficient F_{ii} is

$$F_{ii}=2\frac{c}{b}\left\{\ln\left(\frac{b}{c}\right)+\frac{b}{c}\ln\left[\frac{c}{b}+\sqrt{\left(\frac{c}{b}\right)^2+1}\right]+\ln\left[1+\sqrt{\left(\frac{c}{b}\right)^2+1}\right]\right\} \tag{2-11}$$

From Eq.(2-9), the relation between F_{ij}, $\frac{x}{c}$, and $\frac{b}{c}$ can be shown in Table 2-1.

Table 2-1 F_{ij} table

$\frac{x}{c}$	$\frac{c}{x}$	F_{ij}					
		$\frac{b}{c}=\frac{2}{3}$	$\frac{b}{c}=1$	$\frac{b}{c}=2$	$\frac{b}{c}=3$	$\frac{b}{c}=4$	$\frac{b}{c}=5$
0	∞	4.265	3.525	2.406	1.867	1.543	1.322
1	1	1.069	1.038	0.929	0.829	0.746	0.678
2	0.5	0.508	0.505	0.490	0.469	0.446	0.424
3	0.333	0.336	0.335	0.330	0.323	0.315	0.305
4	0.250	0.251	0.251	0.249	0.246	0.242	0.237
5	0.200	0.200	0.200	0.199	0.197	0.196	0.193
6	0.167	0.167	0.167	0.166	0.165	0.164	0.163
7	0.143	0.143	0.143	0.143	0.142	0.141	0.140
8	0.125	0.125	0.125	0.125	0.124	0.124	0.123
9	0.111	0.111	0.111	0.111	0.111	0.111	0.100
10	0.100	0.100	0.100	0.100	0.100	0.100	0.099

For foundation on elastic half-space subsoil, in order to solve the relationship between foundation base reaction and settlement, the foundation base is divided into n grids. Each grid's planar size is $b\times c$, and the concentrated reaction of each grid is P_1, P_2,$\cdots$, P_n respectively, then each grid's distributed action is $P=\frac{p}{bc}$, which is uniform approximately. If f_{ij} is grid i's settlement under grid j's unit concentrated load P_j=1 at the center point, grid i's total settlement S_i at the center point is the sum of this point's settlement under each grid's foundation base pressure, according to the superposition principle, i.e.

$$\begin{aligned} S_i &= f_{i1}P_1 + f_{i2}P_2 + \cdots + f_{in}P_n \\ &= \sum_{j=1}^{n} f_{ij}P_j \end{aligned} \tag{2-12}$$

For the whole foundation, the concentrated reaction and settlement of each grid of foundation base can be shown as:

$$\begin{Bmatrix} S_1 \\ S_2 \\ \vdots \\ S_i \\ \vdots \\ S_n \end{Bmatrix} = \begin{bmatrix} f_{11} & f_{12} & \cdots & f_{1n} \\ f_{21} & f_{22} & \cdots & f_{2n} \\ \vdots & \vdots & & \vdots \\ f_{i1} & f_{i2} & \cdots & f_{in} \\ \vdots & \vdots & & \vdots \\ f_{n1} & f_{n2} & \cdots & f_{nn} \end{bmatrix} \begin{Bmatrix} P_1 \\ P_2 \\ \vdots \\ P_i \\ \vdots \\ P_n \end{Bmatrix} \tag{2-13}$$

or

$$\{s\} = [f]\{p\} \tag{2-14}$$

where: $\{S\}$ —the settlement column vector of the center point of the grids of foundation base;

$[f]$—the flexibility matrix of subsoil;

$\{P\}$—the concentrated action column vector of the grids of foundation base.

For each item f_{ij} in the subsoil flexibility matrix $[f]$, if $i \neq j$, calculation Eq.(2-6) can be adopted approximately; if i=j, calculation Eq. (2-10) should be adopted to calculate the grid's settlement on condition of concentrated load.

The elastic half-space subsoil model makes progress compared with Winkler subsoil model, for the reason that each point's settlement on the foundation base is relevant to the pressure of not only itself, but also other points. But subsoil is not ideally homogeneous isotropic elastic solid, and the thickness of the subsoil's stratum of compressibility is finite, which causes that the stress diffusion ability of this subsoil model usually goes beyond the reality. Practice reveals that the calculated results based on the elastic half-space subsoil model are larger than real for both foundation settlements and foundation internal forces.

2.3 Layered Subsoil Model

In recent decades, the layered subsoil model, i.e. finite compression subsoil model is popularly adopted in the analysis of the interaction between subgrade and foundation, because this model further considers the stratum feature of subgrade, compressibility of subgrade and the finite compressing depth of foundation. This model adopts elastic theory to calculate the stress of subsoil, and layerwise summation method of subgrade mechanics to calculate the subsoil deformation in the analysis process, so the result is more practical.

According to the fundamental theory of subgrade mechanics, the general expression of foundation settlement calculation by the layerwise summation method is

$$S=\sum_{i=1}^{n}\frac{\bar{\sigma}_{zi}\Delta H_i}{E_{si}} \tag{2-15}$$

where: $\bar{\sigma}_{zi}$ —the ith subgrade layer's average induced stress (kN/m^2);

ΔH_i —the ith subgrade layer's thickness (m);

E_{si} —the ith subgrade layer's modulus of compressibility (kN/m^2);

m—the subgrade layers number within compressibility depth.

In the layered subsoil model analyzing process, firstly, the interface of subgrade and foundation is divided into n units (Fig. 2-6). Let the concentrated induced pressure P_j=1 act on unit j of the foundation base, then the induced stress $\sigma_{k_{ij}}$ at the center point of the kth subgrade layer under unit i can be solved by the elastic theory's Boussinesq formula. From Eq.(2-15), settlement at the center point of unit i can be expressed by the equation as below.

$$f_{ij}=\sum_{i=1}^{m}\frac{\sigma_{kij}\cdot\Delta H_{ki}}{E_{ski}} \tag{2-16}$$

where: ΔH_{ki} —the thickness of the kth subgrade layer under unit i (m);

E_{ski} —the modulus of compressibility of the kth soil layer under unit i (kN/m^2);

m—the subgrade layers number under unit i.

When j=i, action P_j=1 is uniformly distributed on unit i, $\sigma_{k_{ij}}$ and f_{ij} could be calculated.

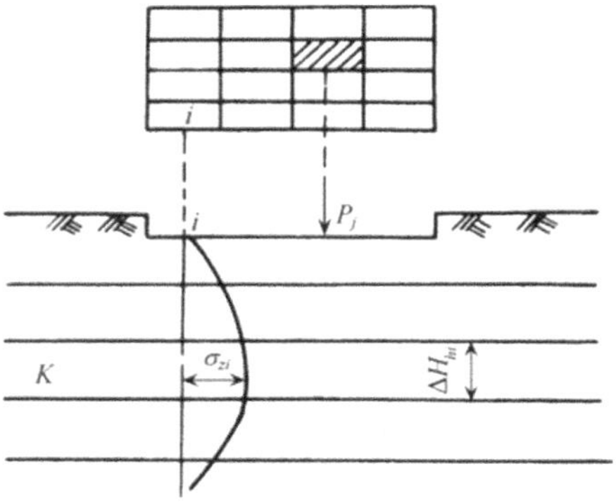

Fig. 2-6 The calculation of layered subsoil model

According to superposition principle, settlement at the center point of unit i, S_i should be the sum of this unit's settlement under pressure from each unit of foundation base. Its calculation equation is the same as Eq.(2-12), i.e.

$$S_i = \sum_{i=1}^{n} f_{ij} P_j$$

All the foundation units' function between foundation base pressure and settlement is as equation (2-14), except that elements f_{ij} of the flexibility matrix [f] are calculated by Eq.(2-16).

Research shows that the layered subsoil model, which is somewhere between Winkler subsoil model and elastic half-space subsoil model, is closer to reality, so it is popularly applied in engineering.

2.4 Double Parameters Elastic Subsoil Model

Winkler model simplifies subsoil and assumes it to be composed of lots of individual springs, so in this model subgrade does not have the property of continuity. In order to compensate for it, the double parameters subsoil mode is developed as an improvement of the Winkler subsoil model, and it adopts two separated parameters to determine the feature of subsoil.

2.4.1 Filonenko-Borodich Double Parameters Model

This model covers an elastic membrane with tension force T on the surface of the springs of the Winkler foundation [Fig. 2-7(a)]. So the deformation of subgrade has the continuity under load actions [Fig. 2-7(b)—(d)].

When the load is uniformly distributed, let it be q, then the deflection equation is as below, for three-dimensional problems (such as rectangle or round foundation).

$$q(x,y) = kw(x,y) - T\nabla^2 w(x,y) \tag{2-17}$$

where: $\nabla^2 = \dfrac{\partial^2}{\partial x^2} + \dfrac{\partial^2}{\partial y^2}$ —Laplacian of orthogonal Cartesian system of coordinates;

k—subgrade reaction coefficient;

$w(x,y)$—vertical displacement of the subgrade surface.

For two-dimensional problems, Eq.(2-17) can be simplified as

$$q(x) = kw(x) - T\frac{d^2 w(x)}{dx^2} \tag{2-18}$$

In this expression, the signs are the same as above.

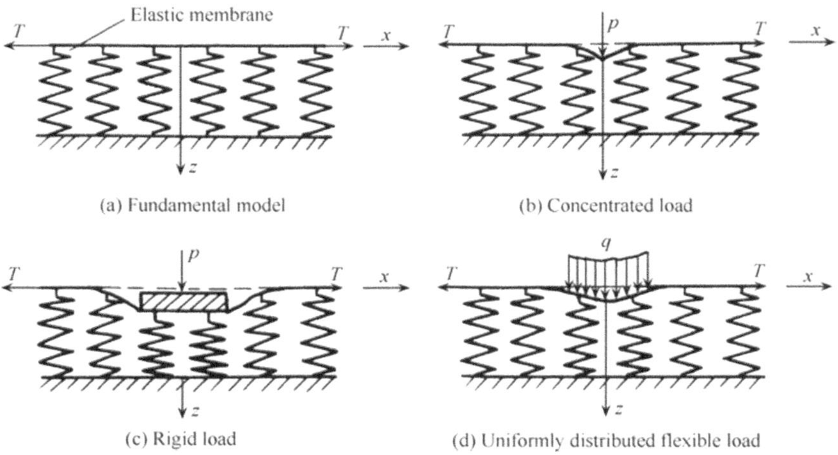

Fig. 2-7 The surface displacement of Filonenko-Borodich model

2.4.2 Hetenyi Double Parameters Model

This model covers an elastic slab or beam on the separated springs to introduce the interaction of springs. The flexural equation is as below:

For three-dimensional problems:

$$-q(x,y) = kw(x,y) - D\nabla^4 w(x,y) \tag{2-19}$$

For two-dimensional problems:

$$q(x) = kw(x) - D\frac{\mathrm{d}^4 w(x)}{\mathrm{d}x^4} \tag{2-20}$$

where: $D = Eh^3/12(1-\mu^2)$—the flexural stiffness of slab, in which: h—the thickness of slab; μ—the Poisson ratio of material of slab.

2.4.3 Pasternak Double Parameters Elastic Model

In this model, a shear layer is assumed to be on the spring unit (Fig. 2-8). This shear layer can only produce shear deformation but not compressible, so the mutual shear actions of spring units are induced.

Let the shear layer be homogeneous in the x, y plane, and its shear modulus be G_x=G_y=G_p, then

$$\left.\begin{aligned} \tau_{xz} &= G_p\gamma_{xz} = G_p\frac{\partial w}{\partial x} \\ \tau_{yz} &= G_p\gamma_{yz} = G_p\frac{\partial w}{\partial y} \end{aligned}\right\} \tag{2-21}$$

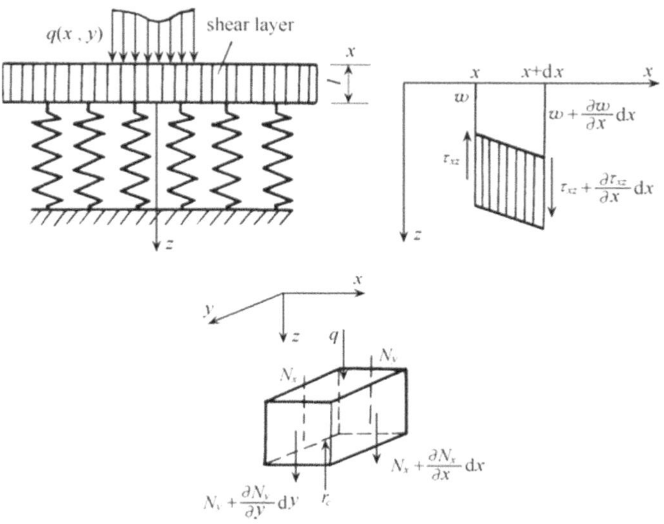

Fig. 2-8 The Pasternak model

The total shear force of the shear layer's unit length is

$$\left.\begin{aligned} N_x &= \int_0^1 \tau_{xz}\mathrm{d}z = G_p\frac{\partial w}{\partial x} \\ N_y &= \int_0^1 \tau_{yz}\mathrm{d}z = G_p\frac{\partial w}{\partial y} \end{aligned}\right\} \tag{2-22}$$

From the force's equilibrium condition in the z direction

$$\frac{\partial N_x}{\partial x} + \frac{\partial N_y}{\partial y} + q - r_0 = 0 \tag{2-23}$$

where: $r_0=kw$.

It can be derived as below by put Eq.(2-22) into the foregoing equation.

$$q(x,y) = kw(x,y) - G_p\nabla^2 w(x,y) \tag{2-24}$$

Comparing Eq.(2-17) with Eq.(2-24), it can be revealed that the two equations are completely the same if $G_p=T$.

Winkler model is an extreme situation, when T, D, and G_p are on the verge of zero in the three double-parameters elastic models.

2.5 Cross Isotropic Model

Every point in the cross isotropic solid has one plane whose elastic feature is equal. In Fig. 2-9, it is isotropic in the *xoz* plane, and this is a special example of the general orthogonal anisotropic elastic material. This model considers the layered characteristic of subgrade in the forming process, and modifies the isotropic elastic half-space model. For the situation shown in Fig. 2-9, the stress-strain expression is:

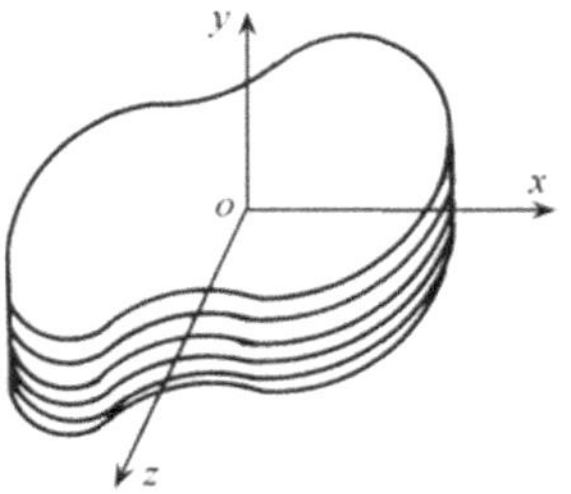

Fig. 2-9 The cross isotropic model

$$\left.\begin{aligned}
\varepsilon_x &= \frac{\sigma_x}{E_1} - \mu^2\frac{\sigma_y}{E_2} - \mu_1\frac{\sigma_z}{E_1}\\
\varepsilon_y &= \frac{\sigma_y}{E_2} - n\mu_2\frac{\sigma_z}{E_1} - n\mu_2\frac{\sigma_z}{E_1}\\
\varepsilon_z &= \frac{\sigma_z}{E_1} - \mu_1\frac{\sigma_z}{E_1} - \mu_2\frac{\sigma_y}{E_2}\\
\gamma_{xy} &= \frac{\tau_{xy}}{G_2}\\
\gamma_{yz} &= \frac{\tau_{yz}}{G_2}\\
\gamma_{zx} &= \frac{\tau_{zx}}{G_1}
\end{aligned}\right\} \tag{2-25}$$

where: E_1—the elastic modulus in the isotropic plane;

μ_1—the Poisson ratio in the isotropic plane;

E_2—the elastic modulus in the plane which is perpendicular to the isotropic plane;

μ_2—the Poisson ratio, indicating the strain in the isotropic plane induced by the unit strain in the plane which is perpendicular to the isotropic plane;

G_2 —the shear modulus of the plane which is perpendicular to the isotropic plane;

$n = \dfrac{E_1}{E_2}$

G_1 —the shear modulus of the isotropic plane.

For the planar strain problems, foregoing stress-strain expression can be expressed as

$$\begin{Bmatrix}\sigma_x\\ \sigma_y\\ \tau_{xy}\end{Bmatrix} = \frac{E_2}{(1+\mu_1)(1-\mu_1-2n\mu_2^2)} \times \begin{bmatrix} n(1-n\mu_2^2) & n\mu_2(1+\mu_1) & 0\\ n\mu_2(1+\mu_1) & 1-\mu_1^2 & 0\\ 0 & 0 & m(1+\mu_1)(1-\mu_1-2n\mu_2^2)\end{bmatrix}\begin{Bmatrix}\varepsilon_x\\ \varepsilon_y\\ \gamma_{xy}\end{Bmatrix} \tag{2-26}$$

where: $m = G_2 / E_2$ (2-25), it can be abbreviated as

$$\{\sigma\} = [D]\{\varepsilon\} \tag{2-27}$$

where: $\{\sigma\}$ —the stress column vector;

$[D]$ —the elasticity matrix;

$\{\varepsilon\}$ —the strain column vector.

This model has been applied to analyze the interaction between subgrade and structure, and the result is satisfactory.

2.6 Non-linear Elastic Model

The diagram of stress-strain relation is shown in Fig. 2-10(a). The essential difference from linear elastic model is that the subgrade elastic modulus and Poisson ratio are all related with stress.

The most popularly applied non-linear elastic model is Duncan-Cheung model. According to Kondner's suggestion, its stress-strain relationship can be expressed as a curvilinear function when σ_3 is invariable, in the tri-axial compression test [Fig. 2-10(b)], i.e.

$$\sigma_1 - \sigma_3 = \frac{\varepsilon_1}{a + b\varepsilon_1} \tag{2-28}$$

where: $\sigma_1 - \sigma_3$—principal stress difference;

ε_1—axial strain;

a—the reciprocal of initial tangent modulus E_i;

b—the reciprocal of principal stress difference $(\sigma_1 - \sigma_3)_{ult}$.

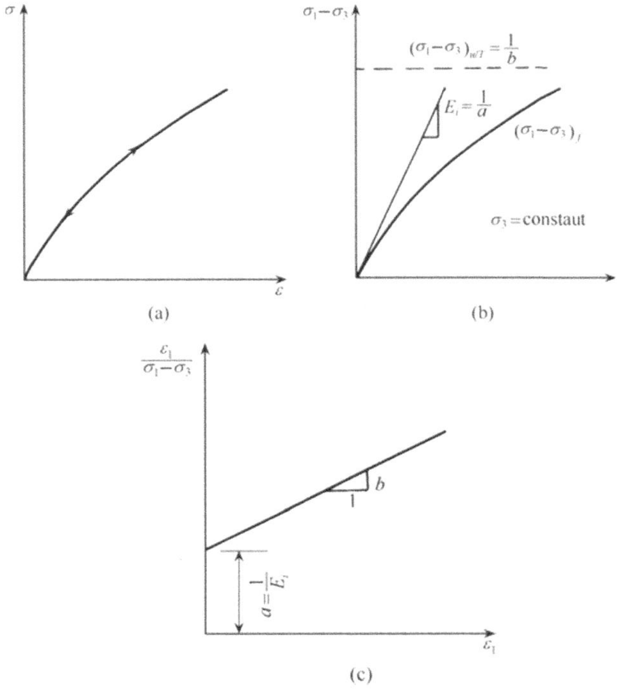

Fig. 2-10 The stress-strain relation diagram of non-linear elastic model

If change the ordinate in Fig. 2-10(b) to $\varepsilon_1 / \sigma_1 - \sigma_3$, then the hyperbola becomes a straight line, which is shown in Fig. 2-10(c), the equation of this line is:

$$\frac{\varepsilon_1}{(\sigma_1-\sigma_3)}=a+b\varepsilon_1 \tag{2-29}$$

It is obvious that it is easier to solve a and b through the beeline in Fig. 2-10(c), then E_i and $(\sigma_1-\sigma_3)_{ult}$ under the action of σ_3 can be derived accordingly.

From Fig. 2-10(b), it can be seen that hyperbola is lower than the asymptote, so the principal stress difference $(\sigma_1-\sigma_3)_f$ is less than $(\sigma_1-\sigma_3)_{ult}$. The ratio of the former to the latter is termed as failure ratio R_f, i.e.

$$R_f=\frac{(\sigma_1-\sigma_3)_f}{(\sigma_1-\sigma_3)_{ult}} \tag{2-30}$$

For different kinds of subgrade, R_f ranges from 0.75 to 1.0, and this value is irrelevant to lateral pressure. Eq.(2-28) can also be expressed as

$$\sigma_1-\sigma_3=\frac{\varepsilon_1}{\dfrac{1}{E_i}+\dfrac{\varepsilon_1 R_f}{(\sigma_1-\sigma_3)_f}} \tag{2-31}$$

Derivative for Eq.(2-31), the tangent modulus of any point on the stress-strain curve is derived as

$$E_t=\frac{d(\sigma_1-\sigma_3)}{d\varepsilon_1}=\frac{\dfrac{1}{E_i}}{\left[\dfrac{1}{E_i}+\dfrac{R_f\varepsilon_1}{(\sigma_1-\sigma_3)_f}\right]^2} \tag{2-32}$$

In this expression, the tangent modulus E_t is related to both the principal stress difference and the axial strain. In order to remove axial strain ε_1 from the Eq.(2-32), alter Eq.(2-31) in ε_1 's expression, then put it into Eq.(2-32) to derive the new expression of E_t, i.e.

$$E_t=\left[1-\frac{R_f(\sigma_1-\sigma_3)}{(\sigma_1-\sigma_3)_f}\right]^2\cdot E_i \tag{2-33}$$

According to Janbu's test research, the relationship between initial tangent modulus E_i and consolidation pressure σ_3 can be expressed as:

$$E_i=kP_a\left(\frac{\sigma_3}{P_a}\right)^n \tag{2-34}$$

where: k, n—the test determined parameters, according to the $\log E_i$-$\log\sigma_3$ relation line, see Fig.2-11;

P_a—atmospheric pressure, its unit is the same as E_i to make k be dimensionless.

According to Mohr-Coulomb failure criterion, the expression is

$$(\sigma_1-\sigma_3)_f=\frac{2c\cos\varphi+2\sigma_3\sin\varphi}{1-\sin\varphi} \tag{2-35}$$

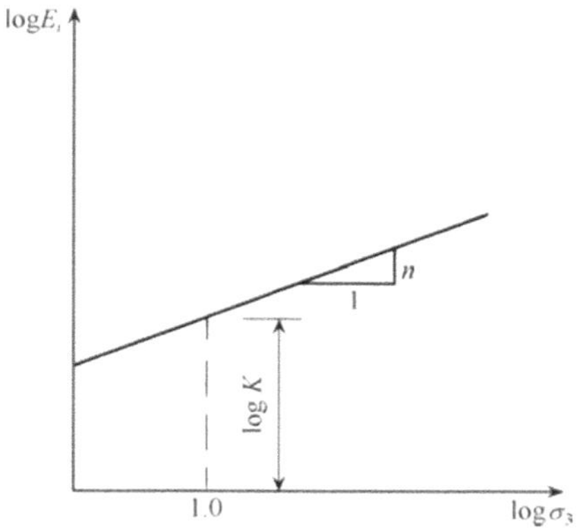

Fig. 2-11 The Q-s curve of load test

Put Eq.(2-34) and Eq.(2-35) into Eq.(2-33), the tangent modulus expression is derived as

$$E_t = \left[1 - \frac{R_f(1-\sin\varphi)(\sigma_1 - \sigma_3)}{2\cos\varphi + 2\sigma_3\sin\varphi}\right]^2 kP_a\left(\frac{\sigma_3}{P_a}\right)^n \tag{2-36}$$

where: c— the subgrade cohesion;

φ— the subgrade angle of internal friction, the five parameters, R_f, c, φ, k, and n are all determined by tri-axial compression test.

2.7 Calculation Methods of Subgrade Reaction Coefficient

According to Winkler presumption, subgrade reaction coefficient k is defined as the load that is needed for unit settlement in unit area on the surface of subgrade. The value is related to not only the type of subgrade, but also the area and the shape of foundation base. Test shows that k decreases with the increase of foundation width under the same pressure; k of rectangular foundation is lower than that of square one, while k of circular foundation is higher than that of square one, for the same pressure and area of foundation base. Concerning the same foundation, the subgrade k increases with the increase of imbedded depth. Test also indicates that k of clayey subgrade decreases with the increase of duration of load. Therefore, the value of k is not a constant, and determining it is a complex problem. Some common methods are elaborated as below.

2.7.1 The Calculation Method Based on Static Load Test

The static load test is a kind of in-place test, which is conducted to determine the deformation modulus of subgrade, bearing capacity of foundation, etc. In this test, jacks or other kinds of heavy objects are used to add graded load to the board, then the stabilized settlements of the load board for each load grade are measured, and the load-settlement curve (Q-s curve) is drawn accordingly, which is shown in Fig. 2-12.

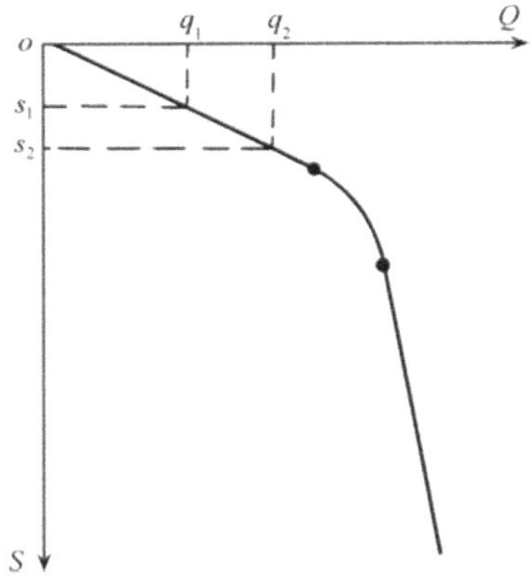

Fig. 2-12 The Q-s curve of load test

Select q_1 and q_2 in the straight portion of this curve, and get the corresponding settlement s_1 and s_2, then calculate k according to the equation as below:

$$k = q_2 - q_1 / s_2 - s_1 \tag{2-37}$$

where: q_2, q_1— contacting pressure and geostatic pressure (kN/m^2);

s_2, s_1— the stabilized settlement of q_2, q_1 respectively (m).

When applying this value of k got from the static load test to practical engineering, there is a problem, that is, the base area of the load board is generally small, which is normally 0.25 m^2 or 0.5 m^2, but the real base area of foundation is much bigger than the load board area. Therefore, the value of k should be discounted considering the factor of base area.

Terzaghi reveals that the value of k decreases with the foundation width b and gives the modifying equation as below, after in-depth research on the subgrade coefficient.

For sand subgrade:

$$k = k_1 \left(\frac{b + 0.305}{2b} \right)^2 \tag{2-38}$$

For clayey subgrade:

$$k = k_1 \frac{0.305}{b} \tag{2-39}$$

where: k_1— the subgrade reaction coefficient of rectangular or square board with 0.305 m in width or side respectively;

b— the width of foundation.

Terzaghi points out that Eq.(2-39) is valid when the contacting pressure is less than half of ultimate bearing capability.

For rectangular foundation, when the ratio of foundation length l to width b is m, there is:

$$k = k_1 \frac{m + 0.5}{1.5m} \tag{2-40}$$

where: $m=l/b$, k_1 is the subgrade reaction coefficient of square subgrade.

For strip foundation:

$$k = 0.67k_1 \tag{2-41}$$

2.7.2 Calculation Method Based on Subgrade Deformation Modulus and Poisson Ratio

For many years, lots of scholars domestic and overseas have researched the relationship among subgrade reaction coefficient k, deformation modulus E_0 and Poisson ratio μ_0, and lots of related equations are derived accordingly. Several main methods are introduced as below.

Vesic (1963) put forward a calculation formula considering the stiffness of foundation as:

$$k = \frac{0.65E_0}{b(1-\mu_0^2)}\left[\frac{E_0 b^4}{EI}\right]^{\frac{1}{12}} \tag{2-42}$$

where: E and I are the elastic modulus of foundation material and the sectional moment of inertia of foundation. Other terms' properties are as the foregoing.

The $0.65\left[\frac{E_0 b^4}{EI}\right]^{\frac{1}{12}}$ of Eq. (2-42)'s value is between 0.9 and 1.5, whose mean value can use 1.2, then Eq.(2-42) is simplified as

$$k = 1.2\frac{E_0}{(1-\mu_0^2)b} \tag{2-43}$$

Vesic formula is applied more in west European countries. Bolues (1977) thinks that this formula can get satisfactory result, as long as the subgrade parameters of E_0 and μ_0 are set appropriately.

For the situation of concentrated load on the beam with infinite length, Biot (1937) compares the beam's maximum bending moments based on Winkler foundation model with that based on Elastic half-space foundation model to get the formula as below:

$$k = \frac{1.23E_0}{(1-\mu_0^2)b}\left[\frac{E_0 b^4}{16c(1-\mu_0^2)EI}\right]^{0.11} \tag{2-44}$$

where: c— a coefficient. When the pressure is uniformly distributed along wide dimension of beam, c=1; and when the deflection is uniformly distributed along wide dimension of beam, c=1 – 1.13. Other terms' properties are the same as the foregoing.

In China, the elastic formula for subsoil settlement calculation was transformed to be the subgrade coefficient expression as below:

$$k = \frac{E_0}{(1-\mu_0^2)\omega\sqrt{A}} \tag{2-45}$$

where: A— the base area of foundation (m^2);

ω— the influencing coefficient of settlement, whose values are listed in Table 2-2.

Table 2-2 ω values

l:b	1	1.5	2	3	4	5	10	round
ω	0.88	1.08	1.22	1.44	1.61	1.72	2.10	0.79

Note: l represents the longer side of foundation base, and b the shorter side.

2.7.3 Calculation Method Based on Compression Test

Yong (1960) suggests that the value of k can be calculated based on compression test result by the equation

$$k = \frac{1}{m_v H} \tag{2-46}$$

where: m_v—the volume compression coefficient of subgrade (kPa^{-1});

H—the thickness of subgrade, its value is $(0.5 - 1)b$, where b is the foundation width (m).

The volume compression coefficient of subgrade can be got by the equation as below:

$$m_v = \frac{a}{1+e_1} = \frac{1}{E_s} \tag{2-47}$$

where: a—the compression coefficient of subgrade (kPa^{-1});

e_1—the natural void ratio of subgrade;

E_s—the compression modulus of subgrade (kPa).

2.7.4 Empirical Calculation

As for the determination of subgrade reaction coefficient, scholars and engineers at home and abroad have collected much experience, which is listed in Table 2-3 and Table 2-4.

Table 2-3 Empirical value of subgrade coefficient k

Subgrade category	Subgrade coefficient k($\times 10^4 kN/m^3$)
Sullage or organic subgrade	0.5—1.0

continued

Subgrade category	Subgrade coefficient $k(\times 10^4 kN/m^3)$
Cohesive subgrade	
In weak state	1.0—2.0
In plastic state	2.0—4.0
In hard plastic state	4.0—10.0
Sand subgrade	
In loose state	1.0—1.5
In medium dense state	1.5—2.5
In dense state	2.5—4.0
Medium dense gravelly subgrade	2.5—4.0
Loess and loessial silty clay	4.0—5.0

Note: This table is suitable for buildings with area more than 10 m^2.

Table 2-4 value of *k* given by Bowles

Subgrade category	k(kgf)	$k(kN/m^3)$
Loose sand	30—100	4800—16000
Medium dense sand	60—500	9600—8000
Dense sand	400—800	64000—12800
Medium dense clayey sand	200—500	32000—80000
Medium dense silty sand	150—300	24000—48000
Clayey subgrade		
$q_u \leqslant 200$kPa(4kgf)	75—150	12000—24000
$200 < q_u \leqslant 400$kPa	150—300	24000—48000
$q_u > 800$kPa	>300	>48000

Note: 1kgf = 9.80665N.

2.8 Determination of Subgrade Poisson Ratio and Deformation Modulus

2.8.1 Determination of Subgrade Poisson Ratio

Subgrade Poisson ratio μ_0 is defined to be the ratio of subgrade lateral strain ε_x to vertical strain ε_Z, i.e.

$$\mu_0 = \frac{\varepsilon_x}{\varepsilon_z} \tag{2-48}$$

Subgrade Poisson ratio can be determined by tri-axial compression test. The result of Poisson ratio got by tri-axial compression test changes along with the value and area of stress, and is also affected by the test method. Therefore it is difficult to calculate Poisson ratio accurately. The method below can be adopted practically. Let the vertical effective stress for the subgrade sample be σ_z, and the produced lateral effective stress be $\sigma_x = \sigma_y$, then the lateral strain is

$$\varepsilon_x = \varepsilon_y = \frac{\sigma_x}{E_0} - \mu_0 \frac{\sigma_y}{E_0} - \mu_0 \frac{\sigma_z}{E_0} \tag{2-49}$$

Static coefficient of subgrade lateral pressure K_0 represents the ratio of lateral effective stress to vertical effective stress under the condition that the subgrade doesn't have lateral deformation ($\varepsilon_x = \varepsilon_y = 0$), e.g.

$$K_0 = \frac{\sigma_x}{\sigma_z} \tag{2-50}$$

Put the expression above in to Eq.(2-49), it can be obtained as below:

$$\frac{\sigma_z}{E_0}(K_0 - \mu_0 K_0 - \mu_0) = 0 \tag{2-51}$$

Then the expression of μ_0 can be got as:

$$\mu_0 = \frac{K_0}{1 + K_0} \tag{2-52}$$

where the static coefficient of subgrade lateral pressure K_0 can be determined by empirical method. Jaky (1944) suggests the following expression, based on abundant testing research.

$$K_0 = 1 - \sin\varphi \tag{2-53}$$

where: φ—effective friction angle of the subgrade. The expression above is suitable for sandy subgrade and normal consolidation clayey subgrade. For the typical values of subgrade Poisson ratio, see Table 2-5.

Table 2-5 Typical value of subgrade Poisson ratio μ_0

subgrade category	M_0
sand: dense sand	0.3—0.4
loose sand	0.2—0.35
fine sand(e=0.4-0.7)	0.25
coarse sand(e=0.4-0.7)	0.15
rock: basalt, granite, limestone, sandstone, gneiss ,shale	0.1-0.4 to be determined by lithology, density and break degree
clayey subgrade:	
wet clayey subgrade	0.10—0.30
sandy clayey subgrade	0.20—0.35
sludge	0.30—0.35
saturated clayey subgrade or sludge	0.45—0.50
frozen boulder clayey subgrade (wet)	0.20—0.40
loess	0.10—0.30
ice	0.36
concrete	0.15—0.35

2.8.2 Determination of Subgrade Deformation Modulus

The subgrade deformation modulus E_0 is the ratio of stress to strain when unconfined laterally, where the strain contains subgrade elastic strain and plastic strain. Hence, deformation modulus E_0 is much smaller than elastic modulus E. The deformation modulus E_0 is commonly adopted in the analysis of the interaction between subgrade and foundation. The following methods can be used to determine the deformation modulus E_0.

1. Evaluation by compressive modulus E_s

The compressive modulus E_s is the ratio of vertical stress to vertical strain when confined laterally, e.g.

$$E_0 = \frac{\sigma_z}{\varepsilon_z} \tag{2-54}$$

According to the elastic theory, the elastic solid's strain of three dimensions can be expressed by the stress of three dimensions, e.g.

$$\left.\begin{aligned}
\varepsilon_x &= \frac{1}{E_0}[\sigma_x - \mu_0(\sigma_y + \sigma_z)] \\
\varepsilon_y &= \frac{1}{E_0}[\sigma_y - \mu_0(\sigma_z + \sigma_x)] \\
\varepsilon_z &= \frac{1}{E_0}[\sigma_z - \mu_0(\sigma_x + \sigma_y)]
\end{aligned}\right\} \tag{2-55}$$

Because compression test is under the precondition of being confined, it can be got that $\varepsilon_x = \varepsilon_y = 0$ and the horizontal stresses are equal $\sigma_x = \sigma_y$. Putting the two expressions into the equation above, it can be got as:

$$\sigma_x = \sigma_y = \frac{\mu_0}{1-\mu_0}\sigma_z \tag{2-56}$$

Putting the expression above and the third expression in Eq.(2-55) into Eq.(2-54), the expression of deformation modulus E_0 can be got as:

$$E_0 = \frac{(1+\mu_0)(1-2\mu_0)}{1-\mu_0} \cdot E_s = \beta E_s \tag{2-57}$$

where

$$\beta = \frac{(1+\mu_0)(1-2\mu_0)}{1-\mu_0}$$

It is simple and practical to evaluate deformation modulus E_0 by compressive modulus E_s, because that compression test is a common geotechnical test. But the result got from Eq.(2-57) is not accurate enough, and it is smaller than the result got from on-site loading pressure test. That is because the original structure of samples for compression test might be destroyed in laboratory, and the compression test can not completely simulate on-site pressure situation of real subgrade. According to statistical data, the value of E_0 and βE_s are close to each other for soft subgrade, while E_0 is about 2—8 times of βE_s for hard subgrade, and the harder is the subgrade, the bigger is the multiple.

2. Determination by site investigation loading test

Through site investigation loading test, the unit area's relation curve of pressure *P* and corresponding settlement *S* can be obtained. Firstly get pressure *P* and corresponding settlement *S* from the straight part of the *P-s* curve, then calculate deformation modulus by the equation below.

$$E_0 = \omega(1-\mu_0^{\ 2})\sqrt{A}\frac{q}{s} \tag{2-58}$$

where: ω —a coefficient that is relevant to foundation size, shape and stiffness. For the values, see Table 2-2;

μ_0 —the subgrade Poisson ratio;

A—the area of load board.

If this test is done in a deep bored hole, this result should be further multiply by modified coefficient 0.7.

3. The empirical value of deformation modulus

The empirical value of deformation modulus E_0 is listed in Table 2-6.

Table 2-6 Reference value of deformation modulus E_0

Suboil category	E_0 (×10^2kN/m^2)	
gravel	650~450	
gravelly coarse sand (any humidity)	480(dense)	310(medium dense)
medium sand (any humidity)	420(dense)	310(medium dense)
fine sand		
little wet	360(dense)	250(medium dense)
very wet or saturated	310(dense)	190(medium dense)
silty sand		
little wet	210(dense)	175(medium dense)
very wet	175(dense)	140(medium dense)
saturated	140(dense)	90(medium dense)
silty soil		
little wet	160(dense)	125(medium dense)
very wet	125(dense)	90(medium dense)
saturated	90(dense)	50(medium dense)
silty clayey soil		
hard state	390—160	
plastic state	160—40	

continued

Suboil category	E_0 ($\times 10^2$kN/m^2)
clayey soil	
hard state	590—160
plastic state	160—40

4. Determination by static cone penetration test

Static cone penetration test is of in-situ exploration methods and test technologies. In the test, the probe is pressed into the tested soil by pressure device, and the penetration resistance is measured by resistance strain gauge. For single-bridge probe, the specific penetration resistance P_a can be measured. Comparing P_a with the deformation modulus E_0 got from site investigation loading test, the empirical formula which is suitable for a certain strict can be obtained through statistical analysis of abundant test data. For example, the Hubei Comprehensive Exploration Institute had once put forward an empirical formula which is suitable for general clayey subgrade, e.g.

$$E_0=6.37 P_a +0.88$$

Hence, this method is limited to a certain area, and needs much accumulation of tests and experiences.

5. Determination by standard penetration test

Standard penetration test is one of dynamic penetration methods. In the test, the drop hammer whose weight is 63.5 kg, and free falling distance is 760 mm, hits the penetrating device, whose outer diameter is 51 mm, inner diameter is 30 mm, and length is 500 mm, into the subgrade. When penetrating device is 300 mm in subgrade, the hitting numbers of the hammer is modified further according to pole length to get the standard penetrating hitting number N. After comparison of N and E_0, their relation expression is got, based on abundant test and statistical analysis. For example, Wuhan Exploration Company of Ministry of Metallurgical Industry got the empirical formula as below after comparison tests by 97 teams.

Normal clay ($N\leqslant 13.76$):

$$E_0=16.9 N+31$$

Old clay ($N>13.76$):

$$E_0=49.3 N-415$$

This method is also limited to a certain area, and its advantage is the convenience for application.

6. Deformation modulus of multi-layer subsoil

If the foundation's acting area has several layers of subgrade with different features, its average deformation modulus can be calculated by the expression below:

$$E_0 = \frac{\sum H_i \bar{\sigma}_{zi}}{\sum \frac{H_i \bar{\sigma}_{zi}}{E_{0i}}} \tag{2-59}$$

where: H_i —the ith stratum's thickness(m);

E_{0i} —the ith stratum's deformation modulus(kPa);

$\bar{\sigma}_{zi}$ —the ith stratum's average additional stress(kPa) .

For practical project, selection should be made among these determination methods for deformation modulus introduced above according to condition after comprehensive analysis.

2.9 Chapter Summary

This chapter mainly introduces 6 useful models for settlement calculation and the determination of their calculation parameters. These models are Winkler subsoil model, elastic half-space subsoil model, layered subsoil model, double-parameter elastic subsoil model, cross isotropic subsoil model, and Duncan-Cheung model of non-linear elastic models. Other models are not introduced here, e.g. the elastic-plastic subsoil model, the viscoelastic model, structural model (e.g. composite model, particulate model, masonry model etc.) and some models of non-linear models (e.g. Zhu-jiang Shen model).

References

Das B.M. 2008. Advanced Soil Mechanics, 3rd Edition, New York: McGrew-Hill Book Company.

Chen X.F., Liao S.M., Kong X.P. 2003. Modern Geotechnical Engineering, Shanghai: Tongji University Press.

Chen Z.G. 1990. Foundation Engineering, Beijing: China Building Industry Press.

Huang W.X., Pu J.J., Chen Y.J. 1981. Hardening Rule and Yield Function of Soil. Journal of Geotechnical Engineering, Volume 3, No. 3.

Li G.X. 1986. Solving of Duncan Hyperbolic Model Parameters by Lateral Pressure Test, Survey of Science and Technology, No. 5.

Qian J.H., Yin Z.Z. 1996. Geotechnical Principle and Calculation, Beijing: China Water Conservancy and Hydroelectricity Press.

Zheng Y.R., Gong X.N. 1989. Geotechnical Plastic Mechanics Foundation, Beijing: China Building Industry Press.

Zhu X.R. 1993. Pre-pressure Flow Characteristics Research of Soft Soil. Doctoral Dissertation of Zhejiang University.

Zhu B.L., Shen Z.J. 1990. Calculation Soil Mechanics, Shanghai: Shanghai Science and Technology Press.

Chapter 3 Mechanics in the Study on Deep Foundation Settlement of Super High-Rise Buildings

The distribution of additional stress in subsoil, which is the basis of the study and computation of settlement, is vital to the research on deep foundation settlement of super high-rise buildings. The related mechanics includes: ① geostatic stress, ② additional stress caused by the load of buildings, ③ contact pressure and contact problems of foundation base, ④ the planar and spatial distribution of subsoil stress, ⑤ the distribution of heterogeneous and anisotropic subsoil stress. Also included is the interactions among superstructure, subsoil and foundation are included, and scrutinized along with foundation type and engineering.

3.1 Geostatic Stress and Additional Stress of Subsoil

3.1.1 Geostatic Stress of Subsoil

The stress in subgrade caused by the weight of subgrade is called as geostatic stress. Since the layer of subgrade covers a large area, the subgrade can be considered as a semi-infinite body, and any arbitrary perpendicular plane is symmetric, so no lateral shearing deformation exists with the action of geostatic stress. Because of that, the vertical stress σ_{0z} at the depth of z must equal to the self-weight of overlying subgrade. According to this condition, geostatic stress in homogeneous subsoil is as

$$\left.\begin{aligned}\sigma_{0z} &= \gamma z \\ \sigma_{0x} &= \sigma_{0y} = \xi\sigma_{0z} \\ \tau_{xy} &= \tau_{yz} = \tau_{zx} = 0\end{aligned}\right\} \tag{3-1}$$

where: σ_{0z} —the vertical geostatic stress at the depth of z (kPa);

γ —the unit weight of soil(kN/m^2);

z —the depth from the surface to the calculation point(m);

σ_{0x} and σ_{0y} —the horizontal compressive stresses at the depth of z (kPa);

τ_{xy} , τ_{yz} and τ_{zx} —the shear stress. at the depth of z (kPa);

μ —the Poisson's ratio(kPa);

ξ —the lateral pressure factor.

$$\xi = \frac{\sigma_{0x}}{\sigma_{0z}} = \frac{\sigma_{0\gamma}}{\sigma_{0z}} = \frac{\mu}{1-\mu}$$

If the subgrade is composed of stratified soil, suppose that h_i and Y_i are the depth and unit weight of the i-th stratified soil, respectively, then the geostatic stress σ_{cz} occurs at the depth of $z=\sum_{1}^{n} h_i$ can be expressed as

$$\sigma_{0z}=\gamma_1 h_1+\gamma_2 h_2+\gamma_3 h_3+\cdots+\gamma_n h_n=\sum_{1}^{n}\gamma_i h_i \tag{3-2}$$

As to the unit weight of the subgrade layer beneath the groundwater level, it must be replaced by the buoyant unit weight. If impermeable layers (e.g. rock stratum) lie below, the geostatic stress subjected by this layer equals to the gross weight of overlying water and subgrade.

Generally speaking, the geostatic stress will not induce any subsoil deformation since the compression deformation of regular consolidated subgrade has already finished earlier. But for recent fill, rinse fill, et al, deformation may be caused by self-weight.

3.1.2 Additional Stress

The stress in subgrade caused by loads of buildings is called as additional stress. Its distribution rule is different from that of geostatic stress. Because of the limited foundation area and the local load, stress dispersion will appear with the stress transfer to deep soil. through subsoil subjected to load The load distribution area increases with the enlarge of depth. Hence, the stress per unit area decreases accordingly.

Ther characteristic additional stress is that it can cause new subsoil deformation, which will bring about the building's settlement. So, the analysis of additional stress becomes crucial.

3.2 Contact Pressure and Contact Problems of Foundation Base

3.2.1 The Distribution of Contact Pressure

Contact pressure is the pressure per unit area between the foundation base and subgrade, i.e. the pressure transferred from the foundation to the subsoil. If the foundation embedded depth is vanished, the contact pressure is the additional stress at the bottom of base. If the foundation is embedded beneath the ground surface, the additional stress is equal to the difference of contact pressure and self-weight of subgrade above the foundation base.

The distribution of contact pressure depends on the foundation rigidity, the subgrade property, the foundation embedded depth, as well as the magnitude and distribution of loads.

1) Since the rigidity of flexible (or elastic) foundation is very small, it almost has no bending resistance under the action of vertical loads, and deforms with the subsoil. In view of this, the distribution of contact pressure is identical with that of load.

2) On the other side, the rigidity of rigid foundation is rather lager and commonly supposed that $EI \to \infty$. Under the action of central load, the settlements of each point of the foundation base are equivalent, namely the foundation base keeps being a plane before and after the deformation, thus making the distribution of contact pressure on the foundation base uneven. It has been proved in practice that under central line load the contact pressure below rigid foundation distributes in the shape of saddle. When the load is rather large, plastic deformation zone comes into being in the subsoil around the edge of the foundation. Edge stress stops increasing, while stress in the central part continues to increase. And the distribution of contact pressure transits from saddle shape to parabolic shape. When the load grows to the extent close to the failing load of subsoil, the distribution of contact pressure changes further from parabolic shape into wedge shape with a convex center (see Fig. 3-1).

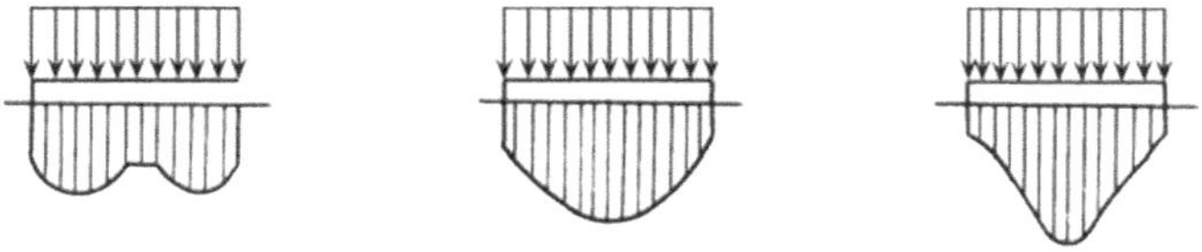

Fig. 3-1 The distribution of contact pressure of base of rigid foundation subjected to central-line load

The degree of transition of stress distribution figures as mentioned above depends on the subgrade property and foundation embedment depth. For shallow-embedded foundation with soft foundation, wedge-shaped distribution of contact pressure could occur under just small load.

3) As for limited rigidity foundation, i.e. with bend rigidity lying between those of the foundations mentioned above, in order to determine the distribution of contact pressure of this type of foundation bose, subsoil is assumed to be homogenous elastic body, and resolution is conducted by methods associated with elastic subsoil.

3.2.2 Simplified Calculation of Contact Pressure

1. When subjected to central load

$$p = \frac{N+G}{F} \tag{3-3}$$

where: N —the vertical load on the top of the foundation transferred from the superstructure (kN);

G —the self-weight of the foundation and subgrade gravity above it (kN);

F —the area of the foundation base (m^2).

2. When subjected to eccentric load (Fig. 3-2)

$$p_{max} = \frac{N+G}{F} + \frac{M}{W} \tag{3-4}$$

$$p_{min} = \frac{N+G}{F} - \frac{M}{W} \tag{3-5}$$

which: M —the moment acting on the foundation base ($kN \cdot m$), $M = (N+G)_g$;

e —eccentricity (m), $e = M / F + G$;

W —the resistance moment of the foundation base (m^3) , for rectangular foundation, $W = \frac{AB^2}{6}$, while A and B are the width and length of the foundation base, respectively (m);

p_{max} and p_{min} —the maximum and minimum pressure acting on the boundary of the foundation base (kPa).

When $e > \frac{B^2}{6}$, p_{min} —zero or negative (see Fig.3-2), while p_{max} should be calculated as follows

$$P_{max} = \frac{2(N+G)}{3Ak} \tag{3-6}$$

where: k —the distance between action point of resultant force and the boundary of the foundation lase with the maximum pressure (m).

3. Contact pressure of circular rigid foundation subjected to central load

According to the condition that the settlement of each point of rigid foundation base is the same under central load, the pressure at any point $M(x,y)$ of the circular rigid foundation base can be resolved by applying elastic theory, which is

$$P_{(M)} = \frac{P_m}{2\sqrt{1-\left(\frac{\rho}{r}\right)^2}} \tag{3-7}$$

where: $p_{(M)}$ —the pressure at any point $M(x,y)$ of the foundation base (kPa), while p_m is the average pressure acting on the circular foundation base.

It could be seen from Eq.(3-7), that $p_{(M)} = 0.5p_m$ at $\rho = 0$, $p_{(M)} = 0.58p_m$ at $\rho = \frac{r}{2}$, and $p_{(M)} = \infty$ at $\rho = r$. Profile for contact pressure of foundation base is illustrated as Fig. 3-3. The theoretical value at the boundary of the foundation is ∞, but practically due to the effect of plastic deformation and stress redistribution, the pressure pattern is saddle-shaped as is displayed by the solid line in the figure.

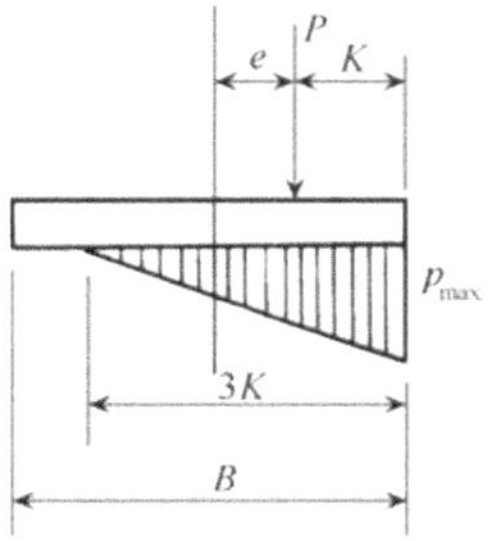

Fig.3-2 Pressure calculation of foundation base when $e > \frac{B}{6}$

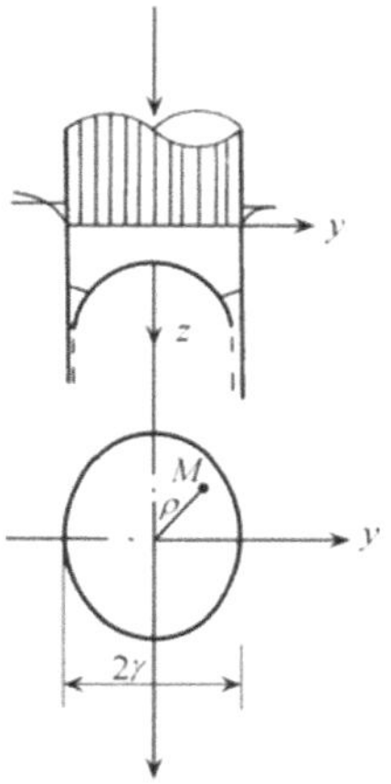

Fig.3-3 Profile for contact pressure of circular rigid foundation base (dashed line for theoretical curve, and solid line for practical curve)

3.2.3 Contact Between Elastic Subsoil and Rigid Foundation

Supposing that subsoil is homogenous and elastic, while deep foundation of a super high-rise building (i.e. box foundation) is rigid, it is convenient for solving contact problems under all kinds of loads and boundary conditions, by applying methods of elastic mechanics.

1. Contact between semi-infinite elastic subsoil and rigid foundation

1) Contact plane is initially a narrow strip, while the load is uniformly distributed vertical pressure p (Fig. 3-4).

When contact plane is smooth, the contact stress on it reads as

$$\sigma_z = \frac{2p}{\pi\sqrt{1-\left(\frac{x}{b}\right)^2}} \tag{3-8}$$

When contact plane is rough, the contact stress on it reads as

$$\sigma_x = \frac{2p}{\pi\sqrt{1-\left(\frac{x}{b}\right)^2}}\frac{1+\xi}{\sqrt{\xi}}\cos\left(\frac{\ln\xi}{2\pi}\ln\frac{1+\frac{x}{b}}{1-\frac{x}{b}}\right) \tag{3-9a}$$

$$\sigma_{x2} = \frac{2p}{\pi\sqrt{1-\left(\frac{x}{b}\right)^2}}\frac{1+\xi}{\sqrt{\xi}}\sin\left(\frac{\ln\xi}{2\pi}\ln\frac{1+\frac{x}{b}}{1-\frac{x}{b}}\right) \tag{3-9b}$$

where: $\xi = \dfrac{\lambda + 3G}{\lambda + G}$, λ and G —Lame' parameters, while p is average vertical pressure.

2) Contact plane is a narrow strip, while the load is moment (Fig. 3-5).

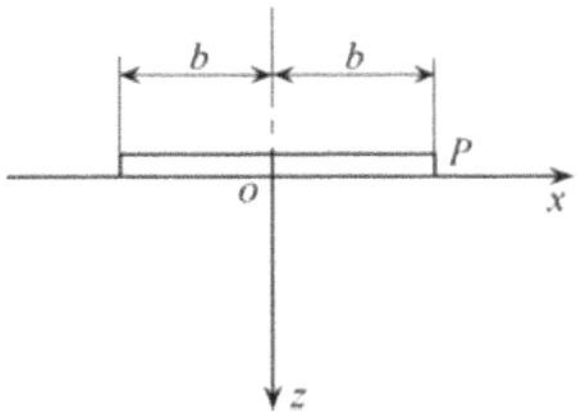

Fig. 3-4 Narrow contact strip subjected to uniformly distributed vertical pressure

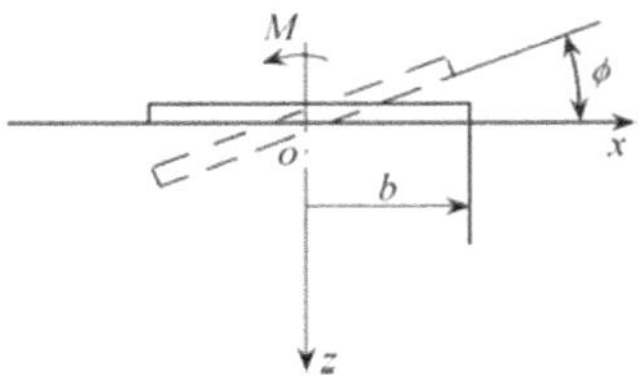

Fig. 3-5 Narrow contact strip subjected to a moment

When contact plane is smooth, the contact stress on it reads as

$$\sigma_z = -\frac{xM}{\pi b} \frac{1}{\sqrt{1-\left(\dfrac{x}{b}\right)^2}} \tag{3-10a}$$

while angle of rotation is

$$\varphi = \frac{(1+\xi)M}{4\pi G b^3} \tag{3-10b}$$

where: $\xi = \dfrac{\lambda + 3G}{\lambda + G}$;

λ and G —Lame' parameters, while M is total moment.

When contact plane is rough, angle of rotation is

$$\varphi = \frac{(1+\xi)M}{4\pi G b^3\left[1+4\left(\dfrac{\ln \xi}{2\pi}\right)^2\right]} \tag{3-11}$$

where: $\xi = \dfrac{\lambda + 3G}{\lambda + G}$;

λ and G —Lame' parameters, while M is total moment.

3) Contact plane is circular, while the load is uniformly distributed vertical pressure p (Fig. 3-6).

Contact stress on the contact plane is

$$\sigma_s = \frac{p}{2\sqrt{1-\left(\dfrac{r}{a}\right)^2}} \tag{3-12a}$$

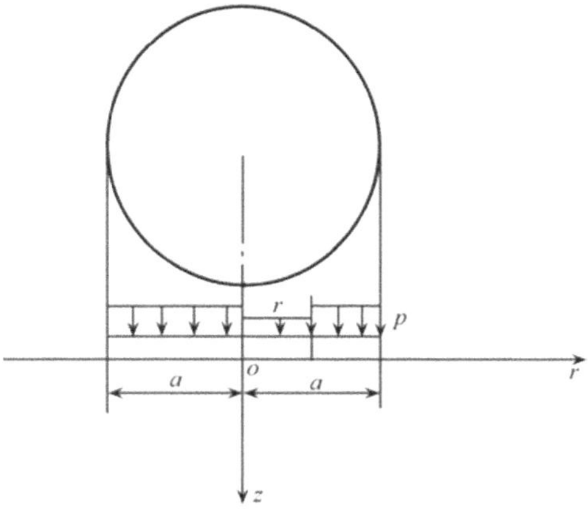

Fig. 3-6 Circular contact area subjected to uniformly distributed pressure (Maki, 1861)

while vertical displacement of each point of the contact plane it reads as

$$\upsilon = \frac{\pi a(1-\mu^2)p}{2E} \tag{3-12b}$$

where: a is the radius of circle, r is the distance between the point and the center of circle, while $p = \dfrac{P}{\pi a^2}$, in which P is total pressure.

The distribution of contact stress σ_s is exhibited by Fig. 3-7.

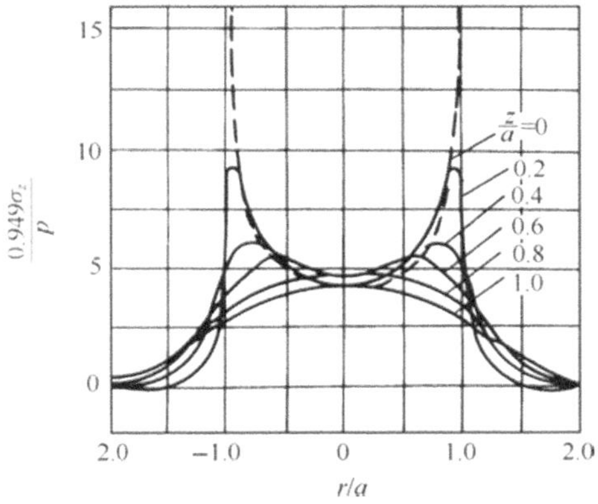

Fig. 3-7 Distribution of contact stress σ_s on circular area subjected to uniformly distributed pressure

4) Contact plane is circular, while the load is uniformly distributed horizontal force (Fig. 3-8).

Horizontal displacement in the direction of the force action for each point of contact plane is as

$$u=\frac{(7-8\mu)(1+\mu)\pi aq}{16(1-\mu)E} \tag{3-13}$$

in which q is uniformly distributed horizontal force per unit area.

5) Contact plane is circular, while the load is a moment (Fig. 3-9).

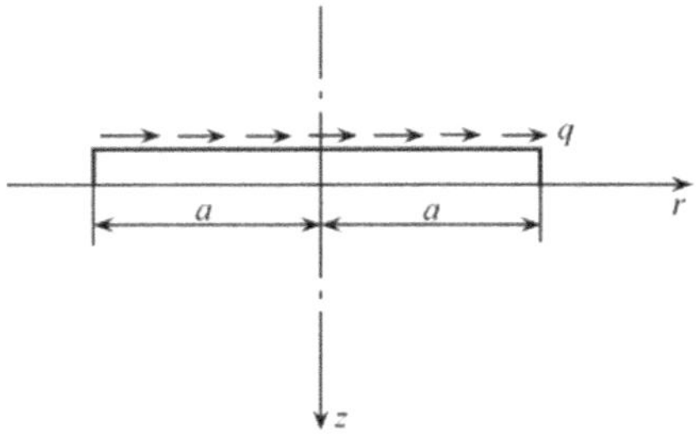

Fig. 3-8 Circular contact area subjected to horizontal uniformly distributed force

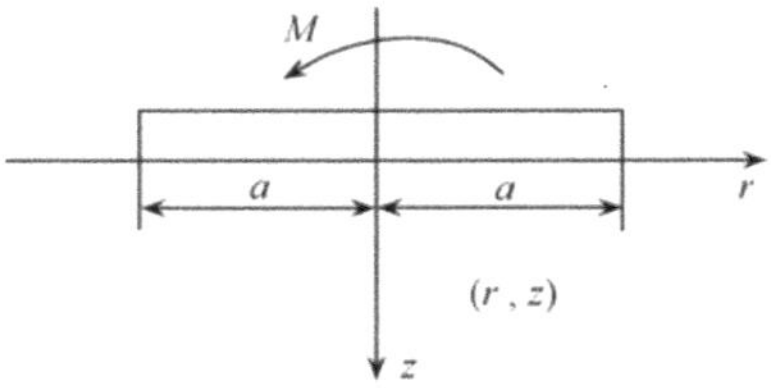

Fig. 3-9 Circular contact area subjected to a moment

Vertical stress σ_z in the semi-infinite elastic body can be expressed as

$$\sigma_z=\frac{3M}{4\pi a^3}\left\{R^{-\frac{2}{3}}\sin\left(\frac{1}{2}-\varphi\right)+\frac{z}{a}R^{-\frac{2}{3}}\left[\frac{z}{a}\sin\left(\frac{3}{2}\varphi\right)-\cos\left(\frac{3}{2}\varphi\right)\right]\right\} \tag{3-14a}$$

in which $R^2=\left[\left(\frac{r}{a}\right)^2+\left(\frac{z}{a}\right)^2-1\right]^2+4\left(\frac{z}{a}\right)^2$, $\psi=\tan^{-1}\left[\frac{2\frac{z}{a}}{\left(\frac{r}{a}\right)^2+\left(\frac{z}{a}\right)^2-1}\right]$, and M is the total moment.

Contact stress on contact plane can be expressed as

$$\sigma_z=\frac{3M}{4a^3\pi\sqrt{1-\left(\frac{r}{a}\right)^2}}\left(0\leqslant\frac{r}{a}\leqslant 1\right) \tag{3-14b}$$

while stress at the depth of z along axis z is

$$\sigma_z=\frac{3M}{4a^3\pi}\left(\frac{1+3\left(\frac{z}{a}\right)^2}{\left(1+\frac{z^2}{a^2}\right)^2}\right) \tag{3-14c}$$

and angle of rotation is given by

$$\varphi=\frac{3M(1-\mu^2)}{4Ea^3} \tag{3-15}$$

6) Contact plane is circular, while the load is twist moment (Fig. 3-10).

Angle of twist is expressed as

$$\theta = \frac{3(1+\mu)}{8Ea^3}T \tag{3-16}$$

in which T is the total twist moment.

7) Contact plane is an annulus, while the load is vertical pressure (Fig. 3-11).

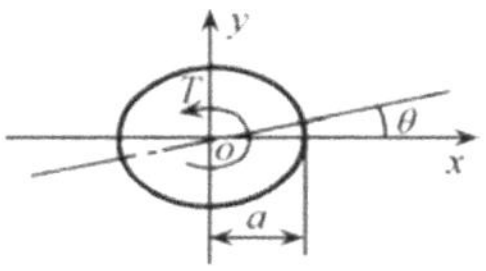

Fig. 3-10 Circular contact area subjected to twist moment

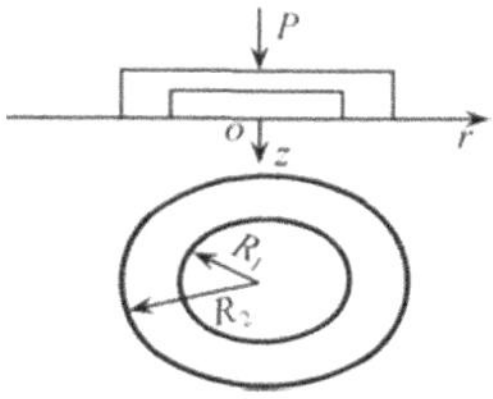

Fig. 3-11 Annulus contact area subjected to vertical pressure

Contact stress on contact plane is as

$$\sigma_x = \frac{p(1-n^2)\sqrt{\left(\frac{r}{R_2}\right)^2 - m^2}}{2E_0(K)\sqrt{(1-m^2)\left[\left(\frac{r}{R_2}\right)^2 - n^2\right]\left[1-\left(\frac{r}{R_2}\right)^2\right]}} \tag{3-17}$$

in which

$$n = \frac{R_1}{R_2}$$

$$p = \frac{P}{\pi R_2^2(1-n^2)} \ (P \text{ is total pressure})$$

$$E_0(k) = \int_0^{\pi/2}\sqrt{1-k^2\sin^2\theta}\,\mathrm{d}\theta \ (\textit{the second kind of complete elliptical integral})$$

$$k = \left(\frac{1-n^2}{1-m^2}\right)^{\frac{1}{2}}$$

$$m = 0.8n$$

if

$$0 \leqslant n \leqslant 0.9$$

obviously, when $n = 0$, the solution turns into the case of circular plane.

The distribution of contact stress corresponding to some n is exhibited by Fig. 3-12.

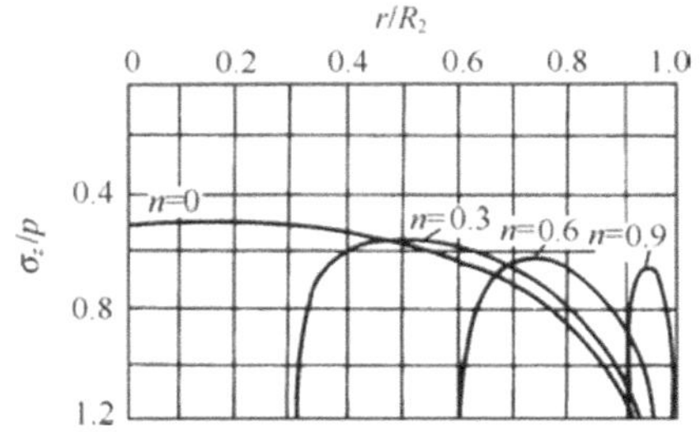

Fig. 3-12 Distribution of contact stress on annulus contact area subjected to vertical pressure

For annulus, the vertical displacement for each point can be calculated by the following equation

$$v = \frac{p(1-\mu^2)}{ER_2}\omega(n) \tag{3-18}$$

in which the values of $\omega(n)$ are recorded in Table 3-1.

Table 3-1 Values of $\omega(n)$

n	0	0.2	0.4	0.6	0.8	0.9	0.95
$\omega(n)$	0.50	0.50	0.51	0.52	0.57	0.60	0.65

8) Contact plane is a smooth rectangular area, while the load is uniformly distributed vertical pressure p (Fig. 3-13).

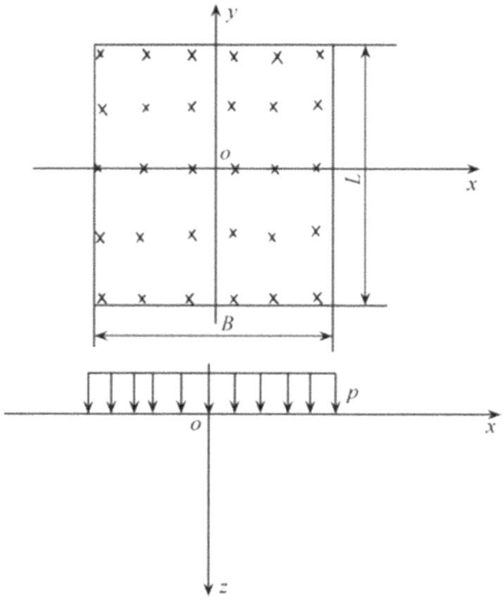

Fig. 3-13 Smooth rectangular contact area subjected to uniformly distributed pressure

Vertical displacement for each point of contact area is as

$$v = \frac{P(1-\mu^2)}{\beta_z E\sqrt{BL}} \tag{3-19}$$

where: P—total pressure;

β_z—factor dependent on $\frac{L}{B}$, which can be determined by Fig. 3-14.

9) Contact plane is rectangular, while the load is horizontal force (Fig. 3-15).

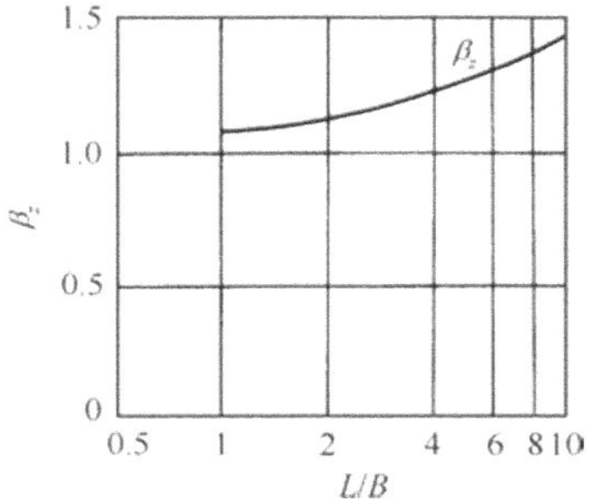

Fig. 3-14 Relation between β_z and L/B for vertical displacement for rectangular contact area subjected to uniformly distributed pressure (Whitman and Richart, 1967)

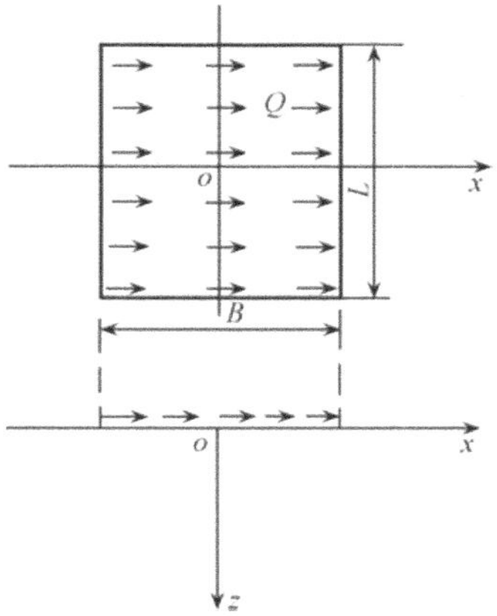

Fig. 3-15 Rectangular contact area subjected to horizontal force

Horizontal displacement for each point of contact area is as

$$u = \frac{Q(1-\mu^2)}{\beta_z E\sqrt{BL}} \tag{3-20}$$

where: Q—total pressure;

β_z—factor dependent on $\frac{L}{B}$ and μ, which can be referred to in Table 3-2.

Table 3-2 Values of β_z (Barkan, 1962)

μ	L/B						
	0.5	1	1.5	2	3	5	10
0.1	1.040	1.000	1.010	1.020	1.060	1.150	1.250
0.2	0.990	0.938	0.942	0.945	0.975	1.050	1.160
0.3	0.926	0.868	0.864	0.870	0.906	0.950	1.040
0.4	0.844	0.792	0.770	0.784	0.806	0.850	0.940
0.5	0.770	0.704	0.692	0.686	0.700	0.732	0.840

10) Contact plane is a smooth rectangular area, while the load is a moment (Fig. 3-16).

Rotation Angle of contact plane induced by the moment is as

$$\varphi=\frac{M(1-\mu^2)}{B^2LE}I_\theta \tag{3-21}$$

where: M —total moment, whose acting face is parallel to side B;

I_θ —factor dependent on $\frac{L}{B}$, which can be referred to in Table 3-3.

Table 3-3 Values of I_θ (Lee, 1963)

$\frac{L}{B}$	0.1	0.2	0.5	1	1.5	2	∞
I_θ	1.59	2.29	3.33	3.7	4.12	4.38	5.1

11) Contact plane is elliptical, while the load is uniformly distributed vertical pressure (Fig. 3-17).

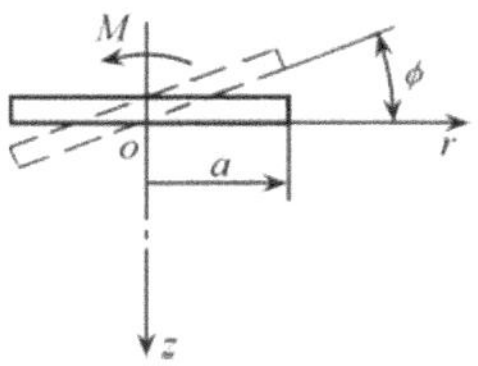

Fig. 3-16 Smooth rectangular contact area subjected to a moment

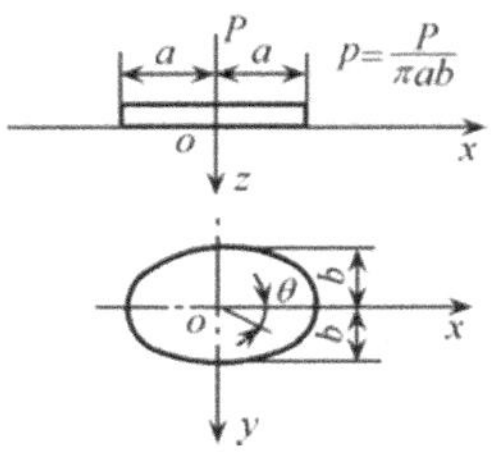

Fig. 3-17 Elliptical contact area subjected to uniformly distributed vertical pressure

Contact stress for each point of contact area is as

$$\sigma_s=\frac{p}{2}\frac{1}{\left[1-\left(\frac{x}{a}\right)^2-\left(\frac{y}{b}\right)^2\right]^{\frac{1}{2}}} \tag{3-22}$$

while the normal stress at the depth of z along axis z is as

$$\sigma_z=\frac{p}{2}\left\{\frac{(1+\zeta^2)(1+k^2\zeta^2)+\zeta^2(1+k^2\zeta^2)+k\zeta^2(1+\zeta^2)}{[(1+k^2\zeta^2)(1+\zeta^2)]^{\frac{3}{2}}}\right\} \tag{3-23a}$$

$$\sigma_x=\frac{p}{2e^2}\left\{\frac{e^2-(1-2\mu)(1+k^2\zeta^2)^2}{k(1+k^2\zeta^2)[(1+k^2\zeta^2)(1+\zeta^2)]^{\frac{1}{2}}}+(1-2\mu)\right\} \tag{3-23b}$$

$$\sigma_y = \frac{pk}{2e^2}\left\{\frac{e^2 + (1-2\mu)k^2(1+\zeta^2)^2}{k(1+\zeta^2)[(1+k^2\zeta^2)(1+\zeta^2)]^{\frac{1}{2}}} - (1-2\mu)\right\} \tag{3-23c}$$

in which

$$\zeta = \frac{z}{b}$$

$$k^2 = \left(\frac{b}{a}\right)^2$$

$$e^2 = 1 - \left(\frac{b}{a}\right)^2 = 1 - k^2$$

when $e = 0$, the ellipse transforms into a circle.

The distributions of normal stresses σ_z, σ_x and σ_y along axis z are illustrated in Fig. 3-18, Fig. 3-19 (a)~(d) and Fig. 3-20 (a)~(d), respectively.

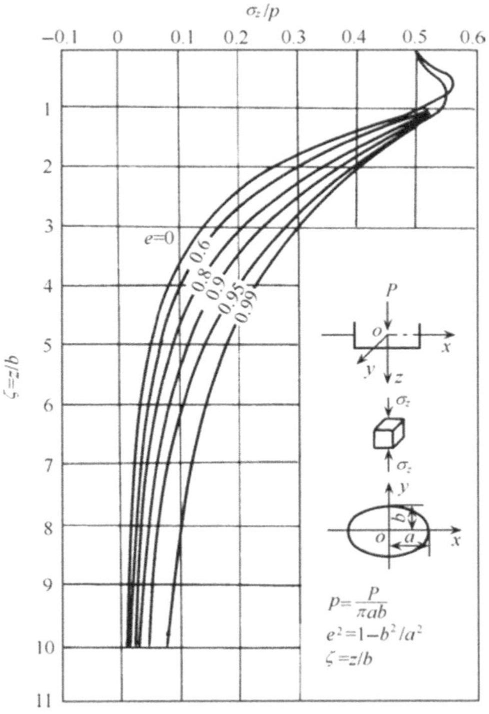

Fig. 3-18 Distribution of normal stress σ_z along axis z for elliptical contact area subjected to uniformly distributed vertical pressure (Schiffman and Aggarwala, 1961)

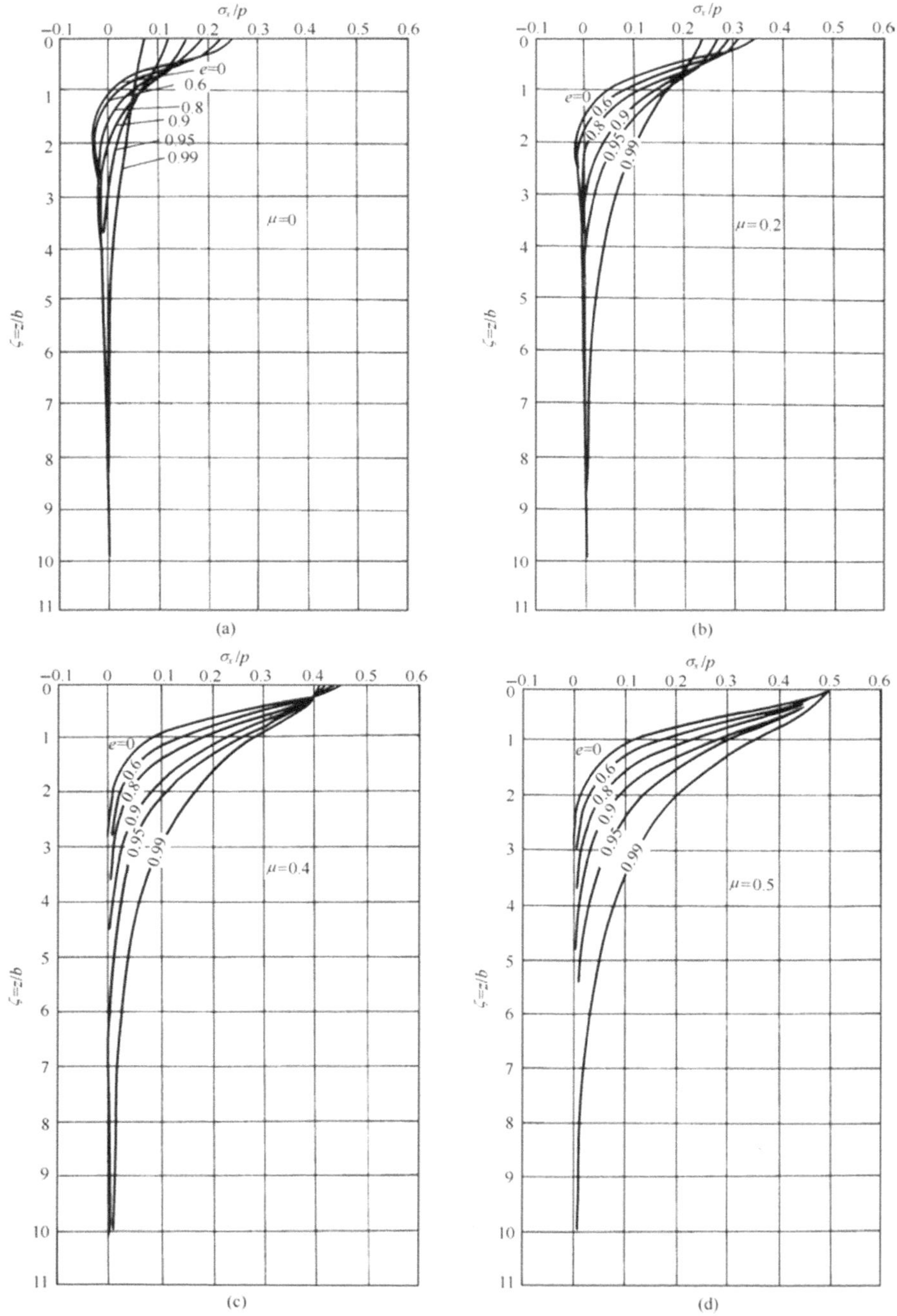

Fig. 3-19 Distribution of normal stress σ_x along axis z for elliptical contact area subjected to uniformly distributed vertical pressure (Schiffman and Aggarwala, 1961)

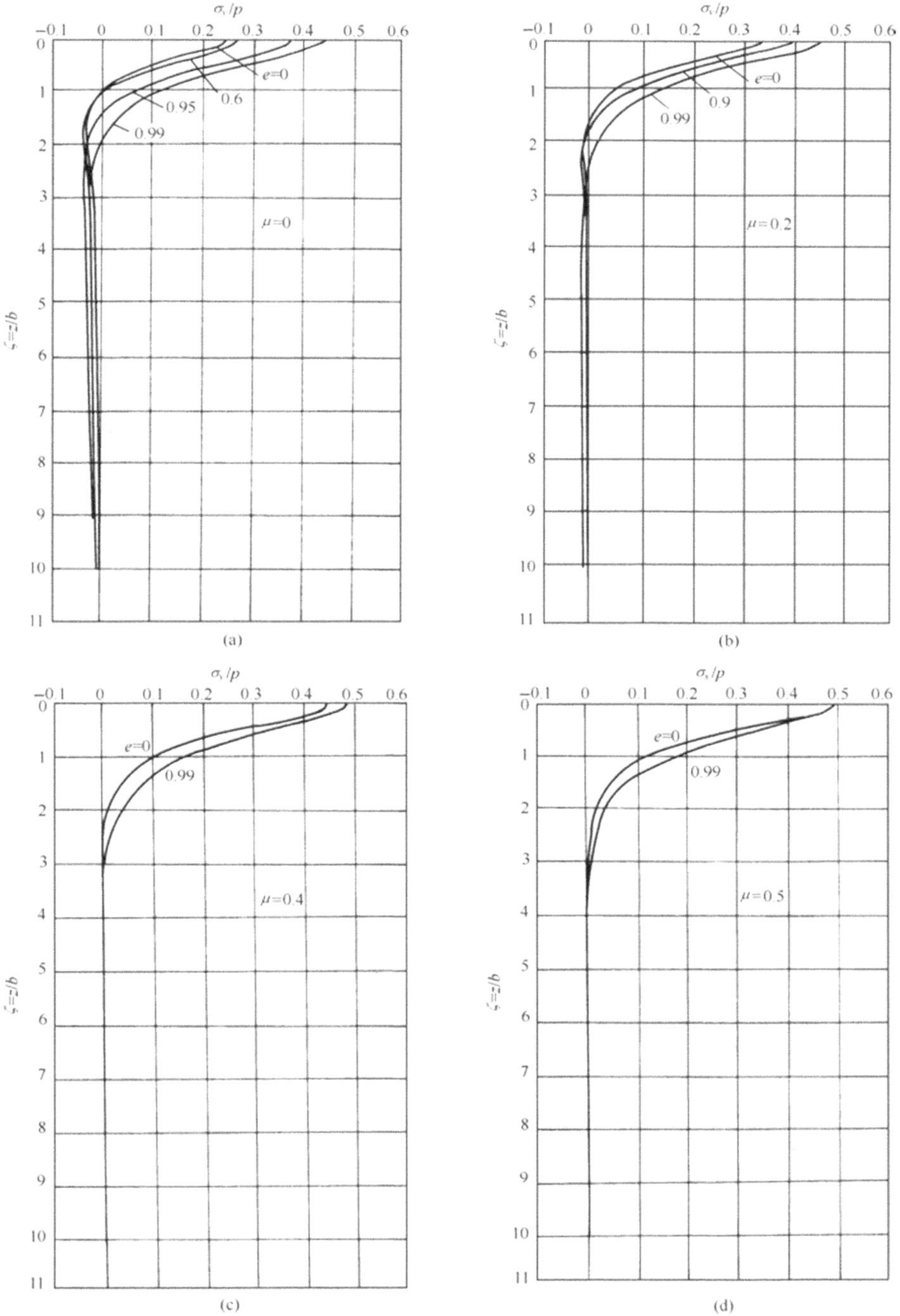

Fig. 3-20 Distribution of normal stress σ_y along axis z for elliptical contact area subjected to uniformly distributed vertical pressure (Schiffman and Aggarwala, 1961)

2. Contact between finite-layered elastic subsoil and rigid foundation

1) Contact plane is a rough infinite strip, while the load is oblique eccentric concentrated force (Fig. 3-21).

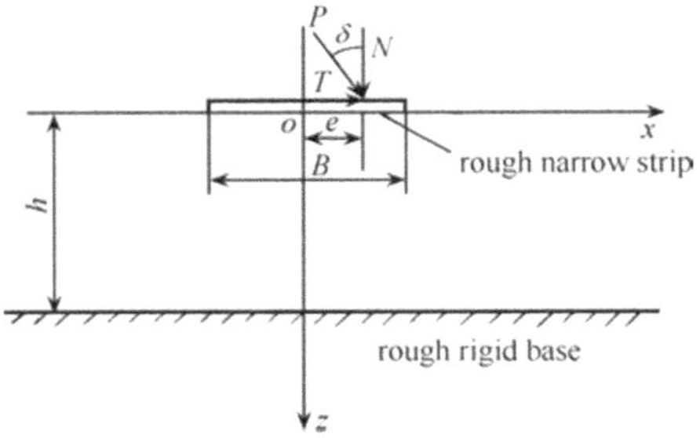

Fig. 3-21 Infinite strip subjected to eccentric concentrated force (rough contact plane with finite-layered subsoil)

Contact stress on contact plane are given by

$$\sigma_z = \frac{P}{B} K_z \tag{3-24}$$

$$\sigma_x = \frac{P}{B} K_x \tag{3-25}$$

$$\tau_{zx} = \frac{P}{B} K_{zx} \tag{3-26}$$

in which

$$K_z = K_{zN} \cos\delta + K_{zT} \sin\delta + \frac{e}{B} K_{zM} \cos\delta$$

$$K_x = K_{xN} \cos\delta + K_{xT} \sin\delta + \frac{e}{B} K_{xM} \cos\delta$$

$$K_{zx} = K_{zxN} \cos\delta + K_{zxT} \sin\delta + \frac{e}{B} K_{zxM} \cos\delta$$

where: K_{zN}, K_{xN} and K_{zxN} —stress influence factors for σ_z, σ_x and σ_{zx} respectively, which are caused by vertical component N of force P;

K_{zT}, K_{xT} and K_{zxT} —stress influence factors induced by horizontal component T of force P, while K_{zM}, K_{xM} and K_{zxM} are stress influence factors induced by moment $M = Ne$.

Stress influence factors are also related to Poisson's ratio μ and ratio $\frac{h}{B}$. For $\frac{h}{B} = 1$, values of stress influence factors are listed in Table 3-4.

Table 3-4 Stress influence factor $K\left(\frac{h}{B}=1\right)$ (Milovic, et al., 1970)

	$\frac{x}{B}$	K_z			K_x			K_{zx}		
		K_{zN}	K_{zr}	K_{zM}	K_{xN}	K_{xT}	K_{xM}	K_{xzN}	K_{xzr}	K_{xzM}
	−0.45	1.3435	−0.5272	−6.5658	0.0357	−0.4321	0.1351	−0.1841	1.2563	−0.8578
	−0.35	1.0234	−0.1788	−3.6458	0.0262	−0.1802	−0.0060	−0.0735	1.0568	−1.3841
	−0.25	0.9162	−0.0820	−2.2486	0.0172	−0.0869	−0.0168	−0.0363	0.9420	−1.5228
	−0.15	0.8682	−0.0368	−1.2488	0.0123	−0.0417	−0.0104	−0.0172	0.8847	−1.5831
μ =0.005	−0.05	0.8489	−0.0106	−0.4024	0.0101	−0.0126	−0.0027	−0.0051	0.8600	−1.6065
	0.05	0.8489	0.0106	0.4024	0.0101	0.0126	0.0027	0.0051	0.8600	−1.6065
	0.15	0.8682	0.0368	1.2488	0.0123	0.0417	0.0104	0.0172	0.8847	−1.5831
	0.25	0.9162	0.0820	2.2486	0.0172	0.0869	0.0168	0.0363	0.9420	−1.5228
	0.35	1.0234	0.1788	3.6458	0.0262	0.1802	0.0060	0.0735	1.0568	−1.3841
	0.45	1.3435	0.5272	6.5658	0.0357	0.4321	0.1351	0.1841	1.2563	−0.8578
	−0.45	1.4035	0.3529	−6.7504	0.4360	0.3914	−1.8784	0.0377	1.2349	−0.8397
	−0.35	1.0010	−0.0417	−3.4908	0.3745	−0.2194	−1.2026	0.0476	1.0600	−0.9327
	−0.25	0.9011	−0.0108	−2.1655	0.3567	−0.1113	−0.8131	0.0309	0.9459	−0.8730
	−0.15	0.8557	0.0023	−1.1983	0.3439	−0.0569	−0.4620	0.0184	0.8910	−0.8511
μ =0.303	−0.05	0.8388	0.0017	−0.3864	0.3387	−0.0175	−0.1506	0.0061	0.6873	−0.8398
	0.05	0.8388	−0.0017	0.3864	0.3387	0.0175	0.1506	−0.0061	0.8673	−0.8398
	0.15	0.8557	−0.0023	1.1983	0.3439	0.0569	0.4620	−0.0184	0.8910	−0.8511
	0.25	0.9011	0.0108	2.1655	0.3567	0.1113	0.8131	−0.0309	0.9459	−0.8730
	0.35	1.0010	0.0417	3.4908	0.3745	0.2194	1.2026	−0.0476	1.0600	−0.9327
	0.45	1.4035	0.3529	6.7504	0.4360	0.3914	1.8784	−0.0377	1.2349	−0.8397
	−0.45	1.5016	−0.2349	−7.1178	0.8455	−0.3369	−3.8359	0.2007	1.1714	−0.7384
	−0.35	0.9178	0.1995	−3.0815	0.6547	−0.3986	−1.9297	0.1527	1.0629	−0.5468
	−0.25	0.8982	0.1193	−2.1259	0.6255	−0.1705	−1.4746	0.0886	0.9556	−0.3142
	−0.15	0.8443	0.0659	−1.1185	0.6238	−0.1127	−0.7898	0.0526	0.9159	−0.2414
μ =0.450	−0.05	0.8384	0.0149	−0.3801	0.6231	−0.0295	−0.2743	0.0164	0.8948	−0.1982
	0.05	0.8384	−0.0149	0.3801	0.6231	0.0295	0.2743	−0.0164	0.8948	−0.1982
	0.15	0.8443	−0.0659	1.1135	0.6238	0.1127	0.7898	−0.0526	0.9159	−0.2414
	0.25	0.8982	−0.1193	2.1259	0.6255	0.1705	1.4746	−0.0886	0.9556	−0.3142
	0.35	0.9178	−0.1995	3.0815	0.6547	0.3986	1.9297	−0.1527	1.0629	0.5468
	0.45	1.5016	0.2349	7.1178	0.8455	0.3369	3.8359	−0.2007	1.1714	−0.7384

2) Contact plane is circular, while the load is uniformly distributed vertical pressure (Fig. 3-22).

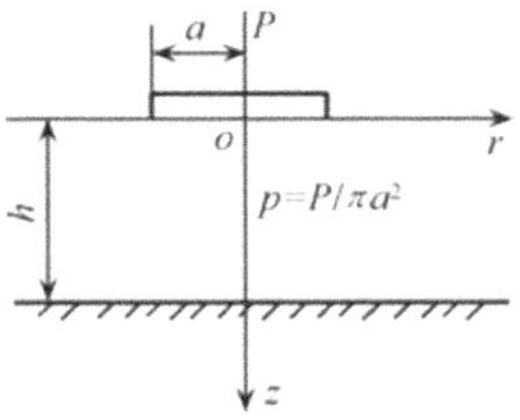

Fig. 3-22 Circular contact area subjected to uniformly distributed vertical pressure (finite-layered subsoil)

Contact stress σ_s on contact plane can be determined by Fig. 3-23. From it, It is indicated in the figure that when $\frac{r}{a}<0.8$, contact stress decreases with the increase of $\frac{h}{a}$.

Effect of Poisson's ratio μ on contact stress σ_s is illustrated in Fig. 3-24.

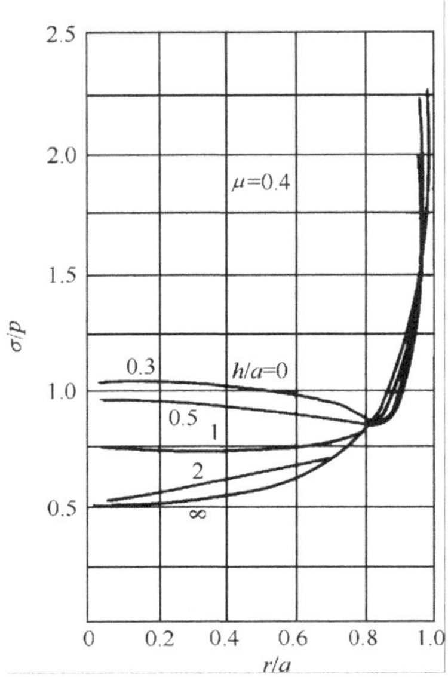

Fig. 3-23 Distribution of contact stress σ_s (Poulos, 1968a)

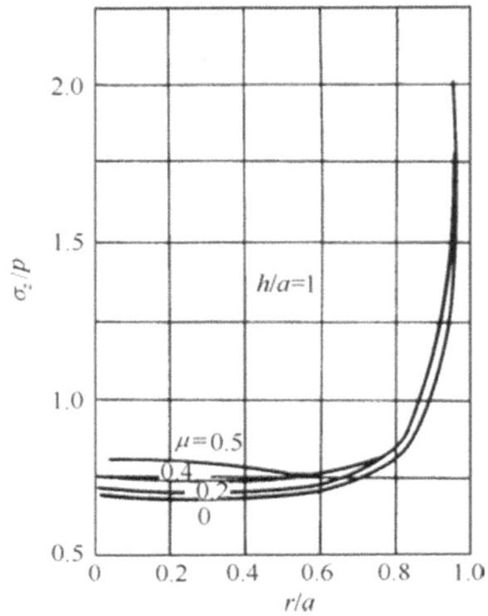

Fig. 3-24 Effect of Poisson's ratio μ on contact stress σ_s

Vertical displacement of arbitrary point on contact plane is defined by

$$v = \frac{pa}{E} I_v \tag{3-27}$$

in which I_v is influence factor, which can be determined by Fig. 3-25.

3) Contact plane is circular, while the load is a moment (Fig. 3-26).

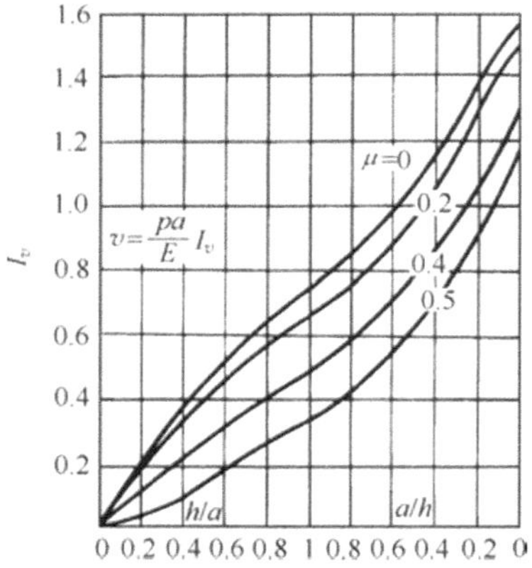

Fig. 3-25 Influence factor of vertical displacement of contact plane I_v

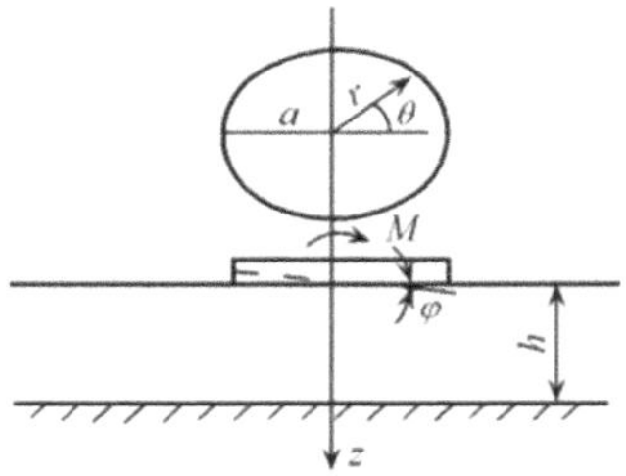

Fig. 3-26 Circular contact area subjected to moment (finite-layered subsoil)

Contact stress on contact plane is

$$\sigma_z = \frac{c_1\left(\frac{r}{a}\right)+c_3\left(\frac{r}{a}\right)^3}{B\sqrt{1-\left(\frac{r}{a}\right)^2}}\frac{M}{\pi a^3}\cos\theta \tag{3-28}$$

while rotation angle of the contact plane reads as

$$\varphi = \frac{(1-\mu^2)M}{4BEa^3} \tag{3-29}$$

in which $B=\frac{1}{3}a_1+\frac{1}{5}a_3$, $c_1=\frac{1}{2}(a_1-a_3)$, $c_3=a_3$. a_1 and a_3 can be referred to in Table 3-5.

Table 3-5 Values of a_1 and a_3 (Yegorov and Nichiporovich, 1961)

$\frac{h}{a}$	a_1	a_3
0.25	4.23	−2.33
0.5	2.14	−0.70
1.0	1.25	−0.10
1.5	1.10	−0.03
2.0	1.04	0
3.0	1.01	0
⩾5.0	1.00	0

4) Contact plane is rectangular, while the load is uniformly distributed vertical pressure (Fig. 3-27).

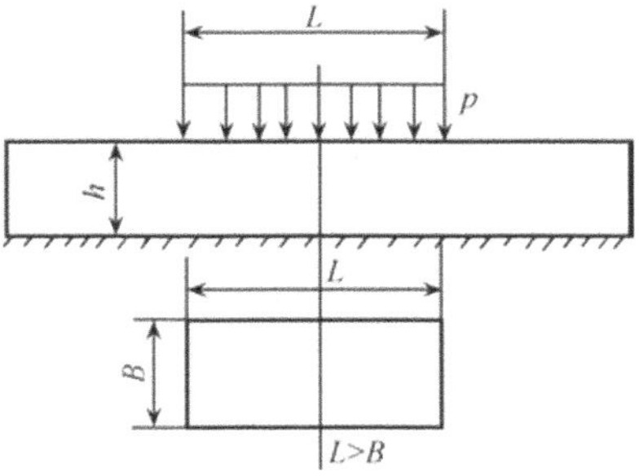

Fig. 3-27 Rectangular contact area subjected to uniformly distributed vertical pressure (Sovinc, 1969)

Vertical displacement of arbitrary point on contact plane can be obtained by

$$v = \frac{\beta pL}{E} \tag{3-30}$$

which: p —pressure per unit area;

β —displacement factor, which can be determined by Fig. 3-28.

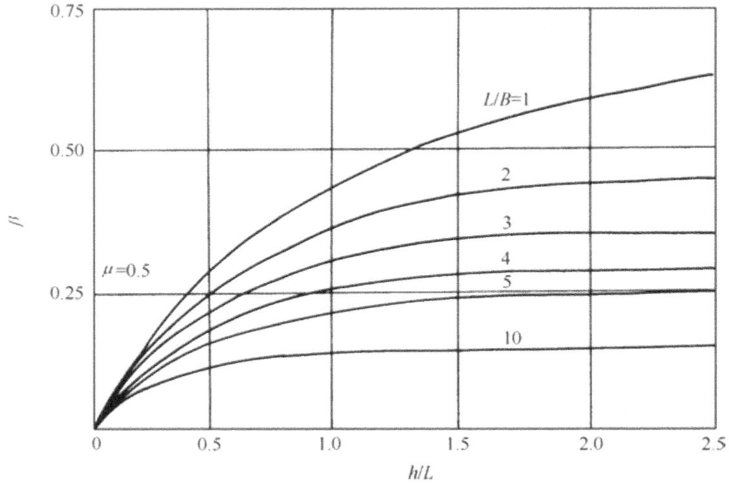

Fig. 3-28 Influence factor of vertical displacement of contact plane β (Sovinc, 1969)

5) Contact plane is rectangular, while the load is a moment (Fig. 3-29).

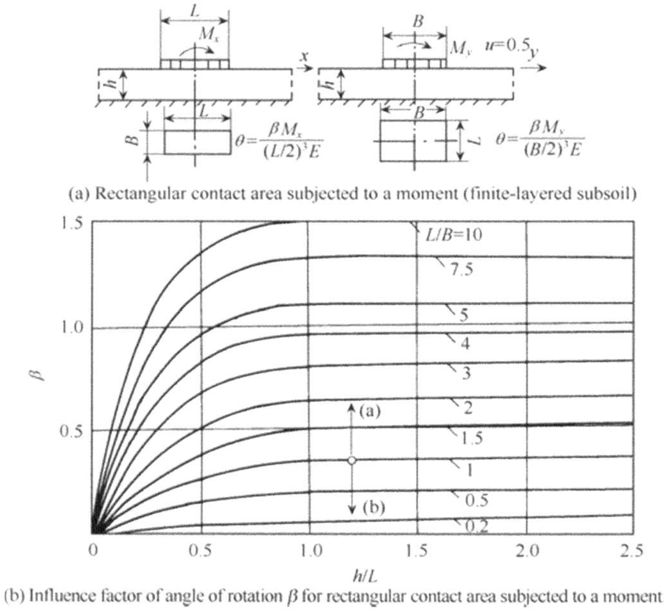

Fig. 3-29 Influence factor of rotation angle for rectangular contact area subjected to a moment (Sovinc, 1969)

Rotation angle of contact plane can be calculated as follows

$$\theta = \frac{\beta M_x}{E\left(\frac{L}{2}\right)^3} \tag{3-31a}$$

$$\theta = \frac{\beta M_y}{E\left(\frac{B}{2}\right)^3} \tag{3-31b}$$

3. Contact problem of rigid object embedded into semi-infinite elastic subsoil

1) Contact plane is circular, while the load is uniformly distributed vertical pressure (Fig. 3-30).

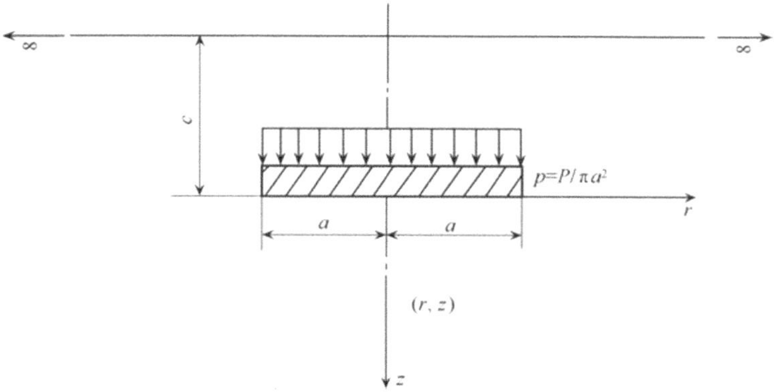

Fig. 3-30 Circular contact area subjected to uniformly distributed vertical pressure (rigid object embedded into semi-infinite elastic subsoil)

Stress σ_z at arbitrary depth under the center of circle can be determined by Fig. 3-31 (a).

Stress σ_z at arbitrary depth under the circumference of circle can be determined by Fig. 3-31 (b).

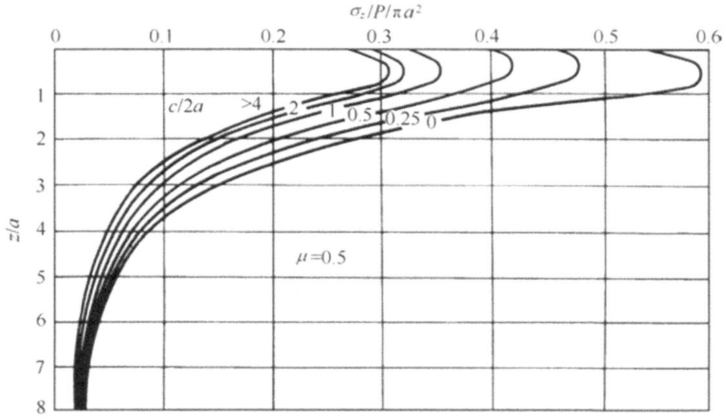

(a) distribution of stress σ_z at arbitrary depth under the center of circle

Fig. 3-31 The distributions of stresses under the center of circle and circumference (Butterfield and Bancrjee, 1971)

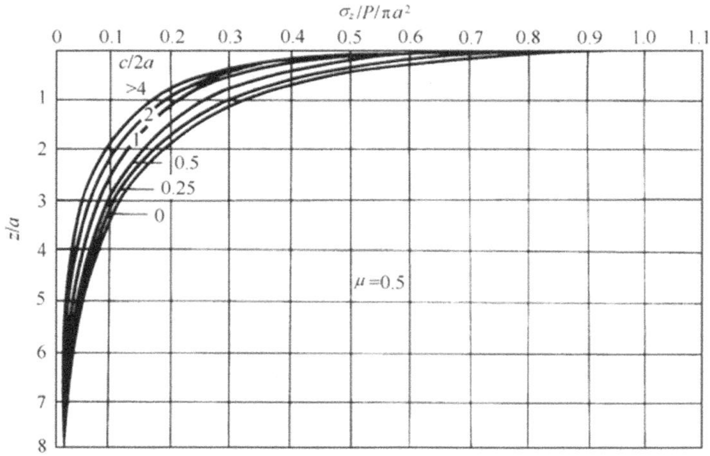

(b) distribution of stress σ_z at arbitrary depth under the circumference of circle

Fig. 3-31 The distributions of stresses under the center of circle and circumference (Butterfield and Bancrjee, 1971)(continued)

Vertical displacement v of arbitrary point on the contact plane can be determined by Fig. 3-32.

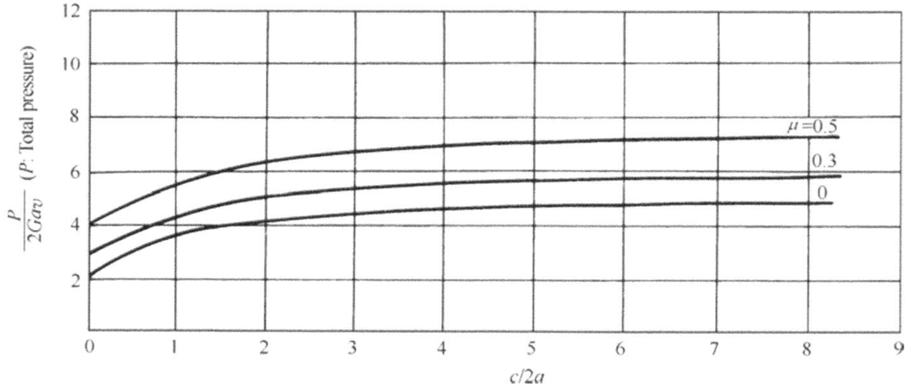

Fig. 3-32 Vertical displacement of contact plane (Butterfield and Banerjee, 1977)

Notes: The origin of coordinate is set at the center of the contact plane, so the coordinate z of any point represents the distance between the point and the contact plane. While c accounts for the distance between the contact plane and the surface of the semi-infinite elastic body.

2) Contact plane is rectangular, while the load is uniformly distributed vertical pressure (Fig. 3-33).

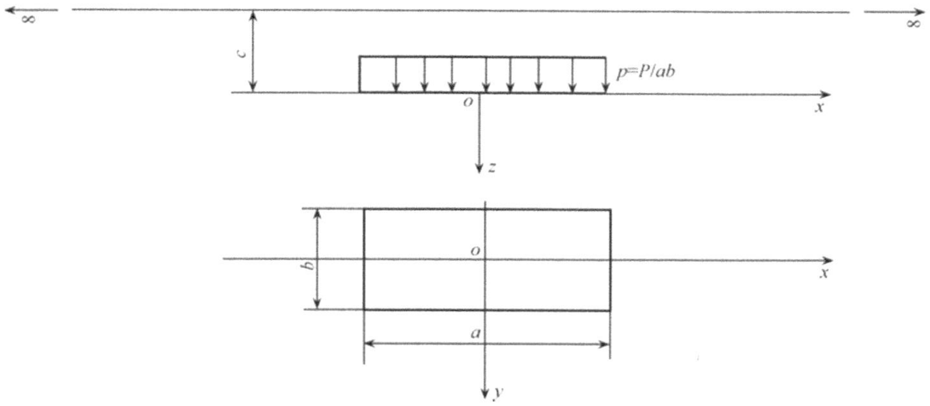

Fig. 3-33 Rectangular contact area subjected to uniformly distributed vertical pressure

Stress σ_z at arbitrary depth under the center of rectangle can be determined by Fig. 3-34.

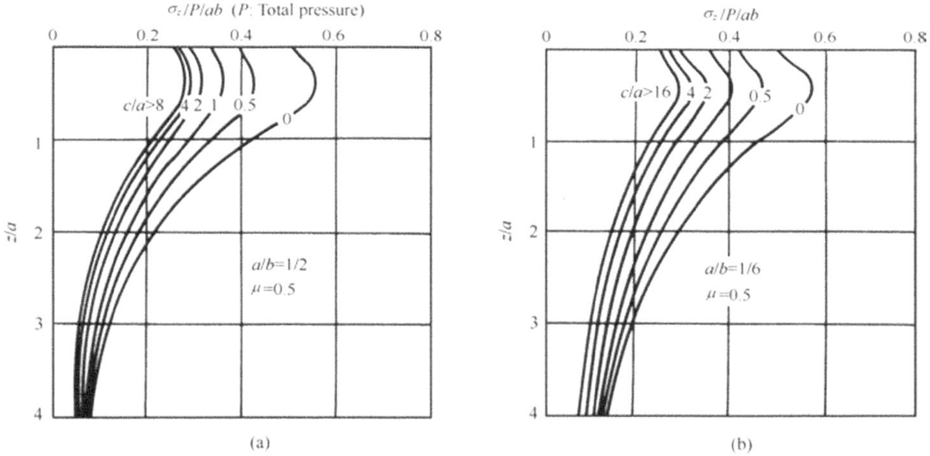

Fig. 3-34 Stress at arbitrary depth under the center of rectangle (Butterfield and Banerjee, 1977)

Stress σ_z at arbitrary depth under the angular point of rectangle can be determined by Fig. 3-35.

Vertical displacement v of arbitrary point on the contact plane can be determined by Fig. 3-36.

Notes: The origin of coordinate is at the center of contact plane, so the coordinate z of any point represents the distance between the point and contact plane. While c accounts for the distance between contact plane and the surface of semi-infinite elastic body.

3) Rigid flat plate embedded into a semi-infinite elastic body with its upper boundary subjected to horizontal force H and moment M (Fig. 3-37).

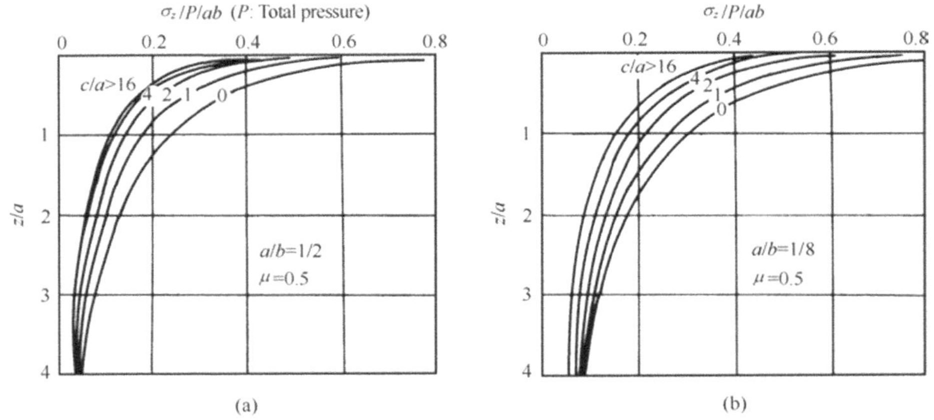

Fig. 3-35 Stress at arbitrary depth under the angular point of rectangle (Butterfield and Banerjee, 1977)

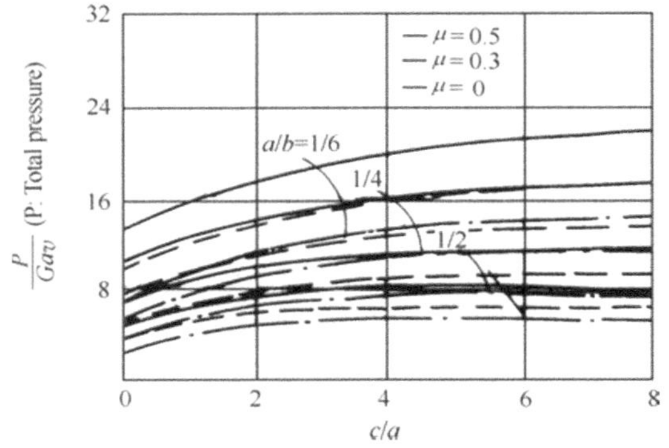

Fig. 3-36 Vertical displacement of arbitrary point on contact plane (Butterfield and Banerjee, 1977) (*P* is total pressure)

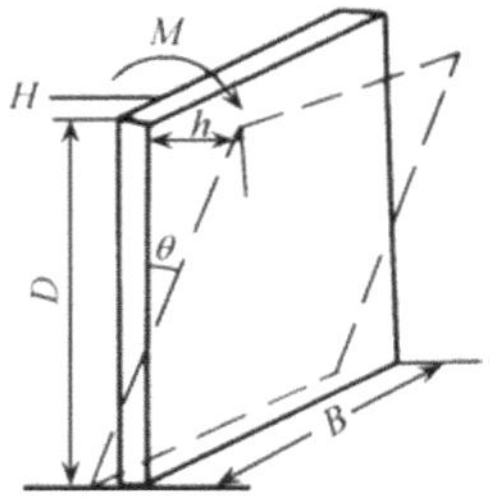

Fig. 3-37 Rigid flat plate embedded into a semi-infinite elastic body with its upper boundary subjected to a horizontal force and a moment

With the condition that the upper boundary of the rigid flat plane is parallel to the interface of the semi-infinite elastic body, the rotation angle θ of the rigid flat plate and linear displacement h of the upper boundary are as follows

$$\theta = \frac{M}{EBD^2} \cdot I_{\theta M} + \frac{H}{EBD} \cdot I_{\theta H} \tag{3-32}$$

$$h = \frac{M}{EBD} \cdot I_{hM} + \frac{H}{EB} \cdot I_{hH} \tag{3-33}$$

respectively. Where $I_{\theta M}$, $I_{\theta H}$, I_{hM} and $I_{\theta M}$ are influence factors, whose values can be determined by Fig. 3-38. The figure is applicable to materials with $\mu = 0.5$. And for materials with other values of us, it may not lead to sharp error when applying this figure in the absence of comespomding information.

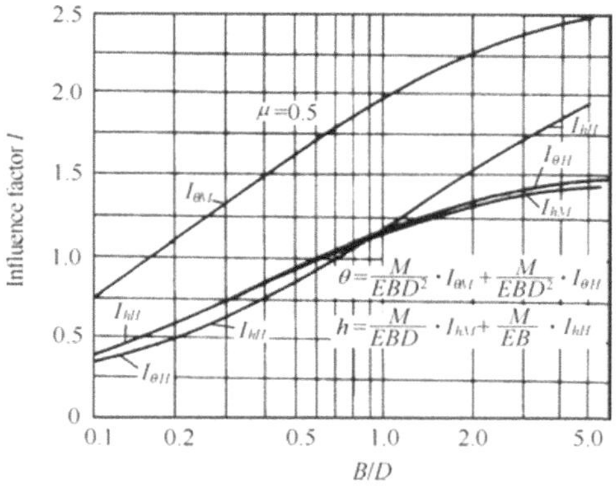

Fig. 3-38 Influence factors of rotation angle of rigid flat plate and linear displacement of upper boundary

3.3 Planar Problems of Distribution of Subsoil Stress

When the surface of a semi-infinite body is subjected to infinitely distributed strip loads, stress at arbitrary point M of the subsoil is only related to its planar coordinates (x,z) and independent of coordinate y along the direction of extension of loads. Such a case is attributable to planar strain problems. Although there is no infinitely distributed strip loads in practical engineering, dikes, dams and strip foundations with aspect ratio $l/b \geqslant 10$ are often regarded as planar strain problems.

3.3.1 Stress in Subgrade Subjected to Vertical Linear Load (Flamant Solution)

The stresse expressions in polar coordinates read as

$$\left.\begin{aligned} \sigma_r &= \frac{2\bar{p}}{\pi r}\sin\theta \\ \sigma_\theta &= 0 \\ \tau_{r\theta} &= 0 \end{aligned}\right\} \tag{3-34}$$

in which $\bar{p}$ is linear vertical load (kN/m), other symbols can be referred to Fig. 3-39.

From the above-mentioned equation, it could be seen that the stress state of subgrade is pure radial compression stress.

Stresses at arbitrary point (x,z) of the subsoil can be expressed in rectangular coordinates as follows

$$\left.\begin{aligned} \sigma_x &= \frac{2\bar{p}}{\pi}\frac{x^2 z}{(x^2+z^2)^2} \\ \sigma_z &= \frac{2\bar{p}}{\pi}\frac{z^3}{(x^2+z^2)^2} \\ \tau_{xz} &= \frac{2\bar{p}}{\pi}\frac{xz^2}{(x^2+z^2)^2} \end{aligned}\right\}$$

The values of stress are infinite at load acting point, and on horizontal plane, when $x = 0$, $\sigma_x = \tau_{xz} = 0$, while σ_z reaches the maximum and decreases with increasing distance from axis z, it also becomes smaller when the horizontal plane goes deeper. This is the phenomenon of stress diffusion in subgrade.

3.3.2 Stress in Subgrade Subjected to Uniformly Distributed Strip Load

As shown in Fig. 3-40, Stress at arbitrary point $M(x,z)$ of subgrade which is subjected to uniformly distributed strip load P can be resolved by

$$\left.\begin{aligned} \sigma_x &= a_x p \\ \sigma_z &= a_z p \\ \tau_{xz} &= a_{xz} p \end{aligned}\right\} \tag{3-35}$$

where: a_x, a_z and a_{xz} are stress factors of σ_x, σ_z and σ_{xz}, respectively, which can be referred to in Table 3-6 according to the values of $\frac{x}{b}$ and $\frac{z}{b}$.

Stress distribution of strip load can be plotted based on Eq.(3-35).

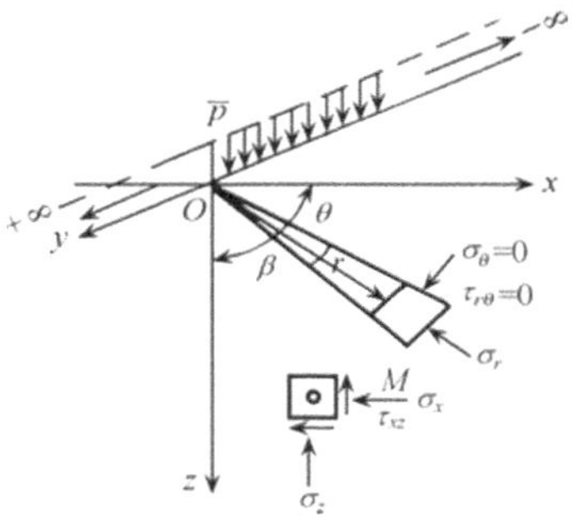

Fig. 3-39 Stress components in subsoil subjected to linear load

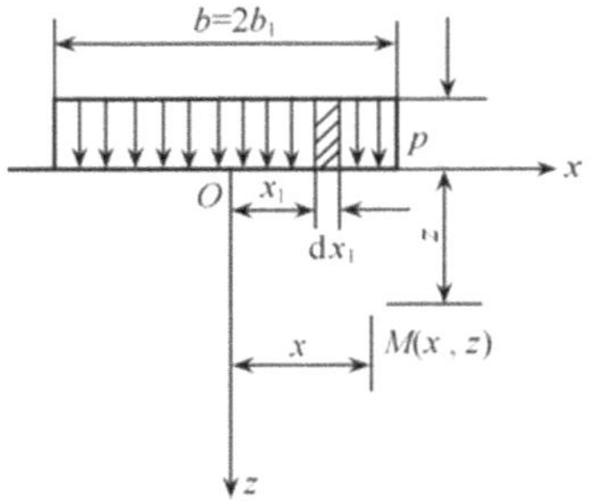

Fig. 3-40 Uniformly distributed strip load

Fig. 3-41 (a) illustrates the variation of σ_z on horizontal cross section and along depth direction when the subsoil if subjected to uniformly distributed strip load. Fig. 3-41 (b) shows the contour of σ_z, which is also called pressure bulb because of its bulb shape. Let the contour of $\sigma_z = 0.1p_0$ be the scope of major force-bearing zone of subsoil, it is shown in the figure that under strip foundation the scope of subsoil's force bearing zone is as deep as $6b_0$. The contour of σ_x is exhibited in Fig. 3-41 (c), which shows that the influence range of σ_x is smaller than that of σ_z, and its value decreases to $0.1p_0$ at the place of 1.5 times width of foundation. Thereby, the lateral dilation of subsoil occurs mainly in shallow layers, compared with the action of σ_x, it is not the major element which results in vertical deformation of subsoil. Fig. 3-41 (d) and (e) illustrate the contour of τ_{xz} and τ_{max}, respectively. The range of their distribution is not as deep as that of σ_z, which indicates that the shearing deformation of subsoil occurs mostly in shallow layers. From the viewpoint of research on building's settlement, σ_z is the principal factor bringing about settlement.

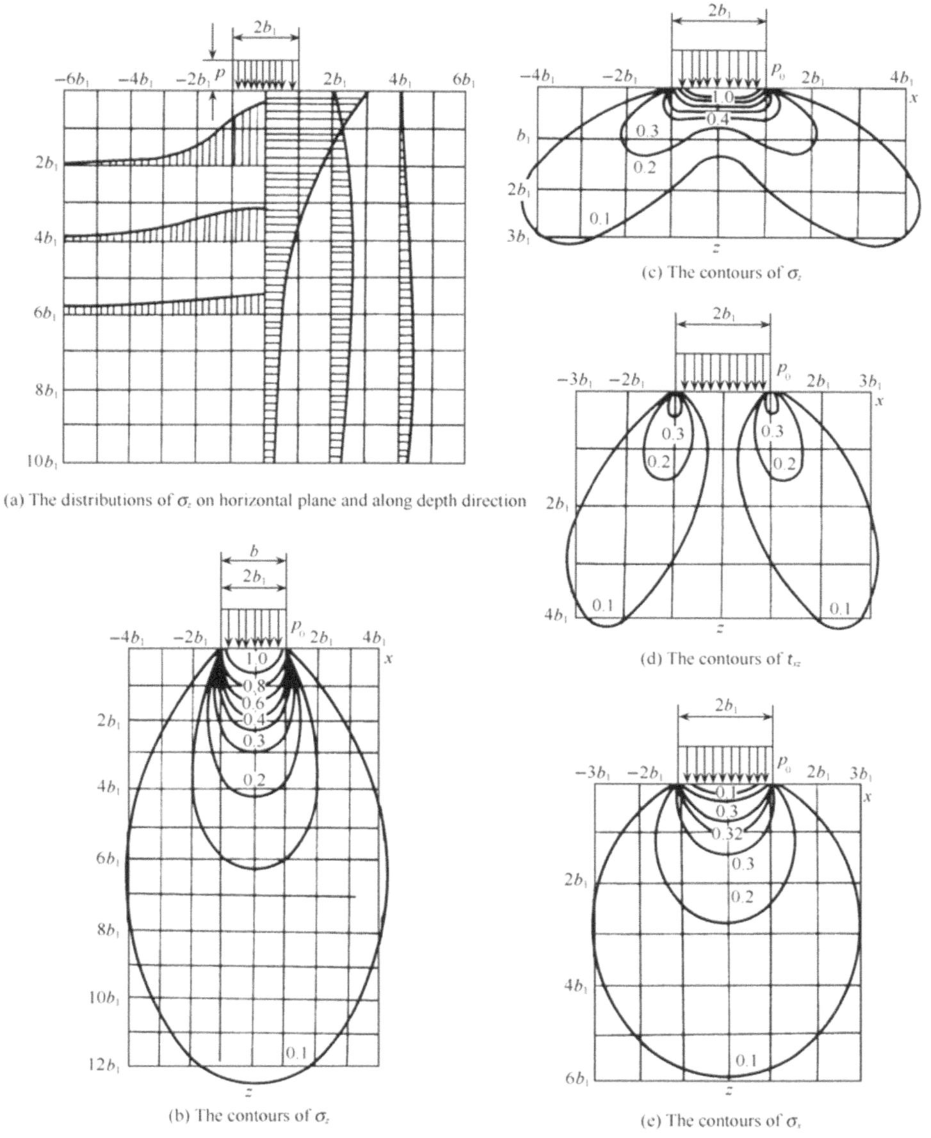

(a) The distributions of σ_z on horizontal plane and along depth direction

(b) The contours of σ_z

(c) The contours of σ_z

(d) The contours of t_{xz}

(e) The contours of σ_x

Fig. 3-41 Distributions of stresses in subsoil subjected to uniformly distributed vertical strip load (values of contour are expressed by ratios of stress to p)

The distribution of principal stress in subsoil subjected to uniformly distributed strip load is illustrated by Fig. 3-42. It can be proved that the direction of the maximum principal stress at point M is the angular bisector of look angle 2β formed by lines of sight which extend from point M to the boundary of strip load, while the direction of the minimum principal stress is perpendicular to the angular bisector (Fig. 3-43). For points on load's symmetry axis, σ_z is the maximum principal stress. The values of principal stresses at arbitrary point M can be determined by

$$\sigma_{1,3}=\frac{\sigma_x+\sigma_z}{2}\pm\sqrt{\left(\frac{\sigma_x-\sigma_z}{2}\right)^2+\tau_{xz}^2}=\frac{p_0}{\pi}(2\beta\pm\sin 2\beta) \tag{3-36}$$

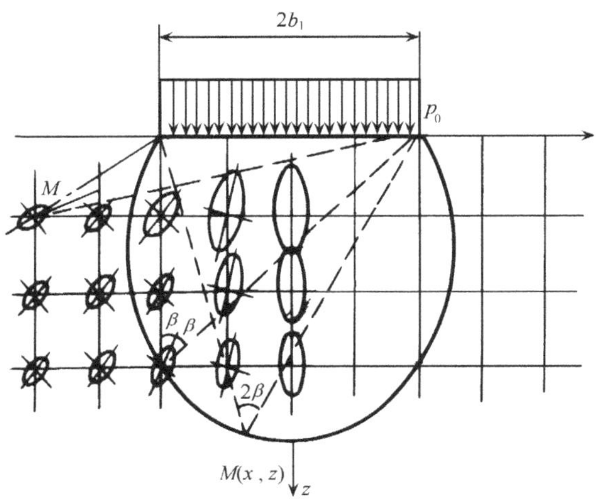

Fig. 3-42 Stress ellipse for each point of the subgrade subjected to uniformly distributed strip load

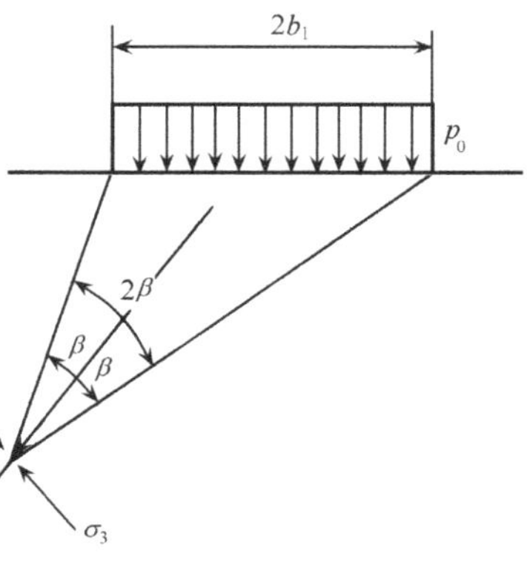

Fig. 3-43 The direction of principal stresses at point M

Table 3-6 Stress factors for uniformly distributed strip load

x/b \ z/b	0.00			0.25			0.50			1.00			1.50			2.00		
	a_x	a_z	a_{xz}	a_x	a_z	a_{xz}	a_x	a_z	a_{xz}	a_x	a_z	a_{xz}	a_x	a_z	a_{xz}	a_x	a_z	a_{xz}
0.00	1.00	1.00	0	1.00	1.00	0	0.50	0.50	0.32	0	0	0	0	0	0	0	0	0
0.25	0.96	0.15	0	0.90	0.39	0.13	0.50	0.35	0.30	0.02	0.17	0.05	0.00	0.07	0.01	0.00	0.04	0.00
0.50	0.82	0.18	0	0.74	0.19	0.16	0.48	0.23	0.26	0.08	0.21	0.10	0.02	0.12	0.34	0.00	0.07	0.02
0.75	0.67	0.08	0	0.61	0.10	0.13	0.15	0.14	0.20	0.15	0.22	0.16	0.04	0.14	0.07	0.02	0.10	0.04
1.00	0.65	0.04	0	0.51	0.05	0.10	0.01	0.09	0.16	0.12	0.15	0.16	0.07	0.14	0.10	0.03	0.13	0.05
1.25	0.46	0.02	0	0.44	0.03	0.07	0.37	0.06	0.12	0.20	0.10	0.14	0.19	0.12	0.10	0.04	0.11	0.07
1.50	0.40	0.01	0	0.38	0.02	0.06	0.33	0.04	0.10	0.21	0.08	0.13	0.11	0.10	0.10	0.06	0.10	0.07
1.75	0.35	—	0	0.34	0.01	0.04	0.30	0.03	0.08	0.21	0.06	0.11	0.13	0.06	0.10	0.07	0.09	0.08
2.00	0.31	—	0	0.31	—	0.03	0.28	0.02	0.06	0.20	0.05	0.10	0.13	0.07	0.10	0.08	0.08	0.08
3.00	0.21	—	0	0.21	—	0.02	0.20	0.01	0.03	0.17	0.02	0.06	0.14	0.03	0.07	0.10	0.04	0.07
4.00	0.16	—	0	0.16	—	0.01	0.15	—	0.02	0.14	0.10	0.03	0.12	0.02	0.05	0.10	0.03	0.05
5.00	0.13	—	0	0.13	—	—	0.12	—	—	0.12	—	—	0.11	—	—	0.09	—	—
6.00	0.11	—	0	0.10	—	—	0.10	—	—	0.10	—	—	0.10	—	—	—	—	—

That can be seen from equation: the contours of σ_1 and σ_3 are arcs passing through two boundary ends of the strip load in respect that the round angles of each point of the arc are equivalent.

3.3.3 Stress in Subsoil Subjected to Triangularly Distributed Vertical Strip Load

As shown in Fig. 3-44, vertical stress σ_z at arbitrary point $M(x,z)$ of subsoil which is subjected to triangularly distributed vertical strip load can be expressed as follows

$$\sigma_z = a_z p \tag{3-37}$$

which: p —the maximum of the triangularly distributed load (kPa) ;

α_z —stress factor of σ_z, which can be referred to in Table 3-7 according to the values of $\frac{x}{b}$ and $\frac{z}{b}$.

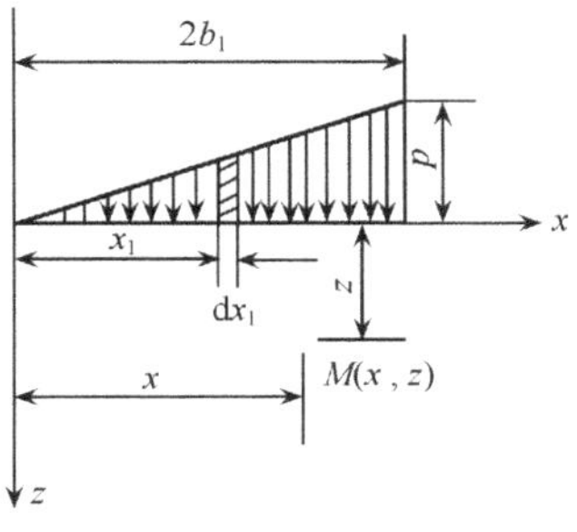

Fig. 3-44 vertical triangularly distributed vertical strip load

The shape of stress of triangular distributed vertical strip load is illustrated by Fig.3-45.

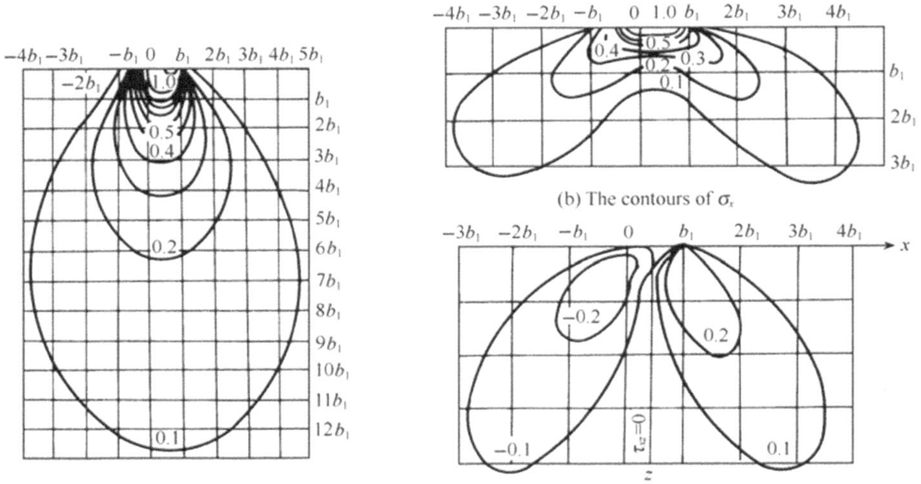

(a) The contours of σ_z (b) The contours of σ_x (c) The contours of σ_{xz}

Fig. 3-45 Stress contour for triangular distributed strip load

Table 3-7 Stress factors α_z for triangularly distributed vertical strip load

$\frac{z}{b}$ \ $\frac{x}{b}$	−1.50	−1.00	−0.50	0.00	0.25	0.50	0.75	1.00	1.50	2.00	2.50
0.00	0	0	0	0	0.250	0.500	0.750	0.500	0	0	0
0.25	0	0	0.001	0.075	0.256	0.480	0.613	0.124	0.015	0.003	0
0.50	0.002	0.003	0.023	0.127	0.263	0.410	0.477	0.352	0.056	0.017	0.003
0.75	0.006	0.016	0.042	0.159	0.248	0.335	0.361	0.293	0.108	0.024	0.009
1.00	0.014	0.025	0.061	0.159	0.223	0.275	0.279	0.241	0.129	0.045	0.013
1.50	0.020	0.048	0.096	0.145	0.178	0.200	0.202	0.185	0.124	0.062	0.041
2.00	0.033	0.061	0.092	0.127	0.146	0.155	0.162	0.153	0.108	0.069	0.050
3.00	0.050	0.064	0.080	0.096	0.103	0.104	0.108	0.104	0.090	0.071	0.050
4.00	0.051	0.060	0.067	0.075	0.78	0.085	0.082	0.075	0.073	0.060	0.049
5.00	0.047	0.052	0.057	0.059	0.062	0.063	0.062	0.065	0.061	0.051	0.047
6.00	0.041	0.041	0.050	0.051	0.052	0.053	0.053	0.053	0.050	0.050	0.015

3.4 Spacial Problems of Distribution of Subsoil Stress

3.4.1 Stress Distribution in Subgrade Subjected to Surface Load

1. Boussinesq solution for stress in subgrade subjected to concentrated vertical force

Applying concentrated vertical force P to the linear surface of a semi-infinite elastic body, which corresponds to the elevation surface of the foundation base, as shown in

Fig. 3-46 and Fig. 3-37, the induced stress and displacement at arbitrary point $M(x, y, z)$ of the semi-infinite body can be expressed as follows

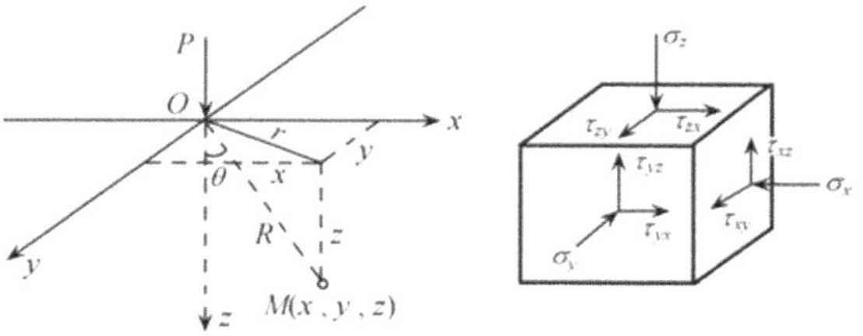

(a) Boussinesq problem (b) Stress state of point M

Fig. 3-46 Surface of subsoil subjected to concentrated force

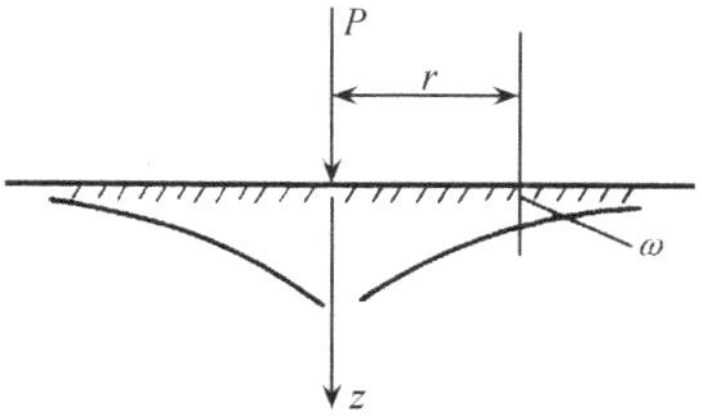

Fig. 3-47 Vertical displacement of subsoil's surface subjected to concentrated force

$$\left.\begin{aligned}
\sigma_x &= \frac{3P}{2\pi}\left\{\frac{x^2 z}{R^5} + \frac{1-2\mu}{3}\left[\frac{R^2 - Rz - z^2}{R^3(R-2)} - \frac{x^2(2R+z)}{R^3(R+z)^2}\right]\right\} \\
\sigma_y &= \frac{3P}{2\pi}\left\{\frac{y^2 z}{R^5} + \frac{1-2\mu}{3}\left[\frac{R^2 - Rz - z^2}{R^3(R+z)} - \frac{y^2(2R+z)}{R^3(R+z)^2}\right]\right\} \\
\sigma_z &= \frac{3P}{2\pi}\frac{z^3}{R^5}
\end{aligned}\right\} \tag{3-38}$$

$$\left.\begin{aligned}
\tau_{xy} &= \frac{3P}{2\pi}\left[\frac{xyz}{R^5} - \frac{1-2\mu}{3}\frac{sy(2R+z)}{R^3(R+z)^2}\right] \\
\tau_{yz} &= \frac{3P}{2\pi}\frac{yz^2}{R^5} \\
\tau_{zx} &= \frac{3P}{2\pi}\frac{xz^2}{R^5}
\end{aligned}\right\} \tag{3-39}$$

$$\left.\begin{aligned}
u &= \frac{P(1+\mu)}{2\pi E_0}\left[\frac{xz}{R^3} - (1-2\mu)\frac{x}{R(R+z)}\right] \\
v &= \frac{P(1+\mu)}{2\pi E_0}\left[\frac{yz}{R^3} - (1-2\mu)\frac{y}{R(R+z)}\right] \\
w &= \frac{P(1+\mu)}{2\pi E_0}\left[\frac{z^2}{R^3} + 2(1-\mu)\frac{1}{R}\right]
\end{aligned}\right\} \tag{3-40}$$

where: σ_x, σ_y and σ_z—normal stresses in directions of x, y and z, respectively, while τ_{xy}, τ_{yz} and τ_{zx} are shear stresses, in which the first suffix denotes the coordinate axis perpendicular to the action plane of shear stress, and the second suffix denotes the coordinate axis parauel to the action plane of shear stress; u;

v and w—displacements of point M in directions of x, y and z, respectively;

P—the concentrated force acting on the origin of coordinate and perpendicular to the ground surface;

E_0—subsoil's deformation modulus, while r Poisson's ratio;

R—the radius vector of point M, and $R=\sqrt{x^2+y^2+z^2}=\sqrt{r^2+z^2}$, At any point $(r,0)$ of the subgrade's surface $(z=0)$, vertical displacement at $r=R$ is given by

$$w=\frac{P(1-\mu^2)}{\pi E_0 r} \tag{3-41}$$

For the purpose of application, the widely-used formula for σ_z in Eq.(3-40) is often rewritten as

$$\sigma_z=\frac{3P}{2\pi}\frac{z^3}{R^5}=\alpha\frac{P}{z^2} \tag{3-42}$$

where α is stress factor, which can be referred to in Table 3-8 based on the value of $\frac{r}{z}$.

Table 3-8 Vertical stress factor α for semi-infinite body subjected to concentrated force

$\frac{r}{z}$	α	$\frac{r}{z}$	α	$\frac{r}{z}$	α	$\frac{r}{z}$	α
0	0.4775	0.65	0.1978	1.30	0.0402	1.95	0.0005
0.05	0.4745	0.70	0.1762	1.35	0.0357	2.00	0.0085
0.10	0.4657	0.75	0.1565	1.40	0.0317	2.20	0.0058
0.15	0.4516	0.80	0.1386	1.45	0.0282	2.40	0.0040
0.20	0.4329	0.85	0.1226	1.50	0.0251	2.60	0.0029
0.25	0.4103	0.90	0.1083	1.55	0.0224	2.80	0.0021
0.30	0.3849	0.95	0.0956	1.60	0.0200	3.00	0.0015
0.35	0.3577	1.00	0.0844	1.65	0.0179	3.50	0.0007
0.40	0.3294	1.05	0.7044	1.70	0.0160	4.00	0.0004
0.45	0.3011	1.10	0.0658	1.75	0.0144	4.50	0.0002
0.50	0.2773	1.15	0.0581	1.80	0.0129	5.00	0.0001
0.55	0.2446	1.20	0.0513	1.85	0.0116		
0.60	0.2214	1.25	0.0454	1.90	0.0105		

2. Stresses in subgrade with rectangular load area

(1) Stress under the angular points of rectangular plane subjected to uniformly distributed load

The vertical stress σ_z at arbitrary depth z beneath the angular points of a rectangular plane which is subjected to uniformly distributed load is given by

$$\sigma_z=\alpha P \tag{3-43}$$

where α is a stress factor for stress at angular point, which can be referred to in Table 3-9 according to the values of A/B and z/B, while A and B are the long-side and short-side lengths of the rectangle, respectively.

(2) Stress at arbitrary point of rectangular plane subjected to uniformly distributed load

Under the action of uniformly distrilbuted rectangular load, the vertical stress σ_z at arbitrary point M of the subgrade can be obtained the above method of resolving stress beneath angular points, namely by plotting several subsidiary lines across the arbitrary point M to make it the common angular point of several rectangles, then adding up stresses at angular points of each rectangle based on the principle of stress superposition, thue obtaining the stress at point M.

(3) Stress beneath mid-point of rectangular plane subjected to uniformly distributed load

The vertical stress σ_z beneath the mid-point of uniformly distributed rectangular load area(i.e., the points on axis *z* with *x*=*y*=0)is given by

$$\sigma_z = \alpha_0 P \tag{3-44}$$

where α_0 is a stress factor for stress at the mid-point, which can be referred to in Table 3-10 according to the values of A/B and z/B. The meaning of the rest symbols is the same as before.

Table 3-10 Stress factor α_0 for stress beneath the mid-point of rectangular area subjected to uniformly distributed load

A/B / z/B	1.0	1.2	1.4	1.6	1.8	2.0	2.4	2.8	3.2	3.6	4.0	5.0	>10 (strip)
0.0	1.000	1.000	1.000	1.000	1.000	1.000	1.000	1.000	1.000	1.000	1.000	1.000	1.000
0.1	0.994	0.996	0.996	0.996	0.996	0.996	0.997	0.997	0.997	0.997	0.997	0.997	0.997
0.2	0.960	0.968	0.972	0.974	0.975	0.976	0.976	0.977	0.977	0.977	0.977	0.977	0.977
0.3	0.892	0.910	0.920	0.926	0.980	0.932	0.934	0.935	0.936	0.936	0.936	0.937	0.937
0.4	0.800	0.830	0.848	0.859	0.866	0.870	0.875	0.878	0.879	0.880	0.880	0.881	0.881
0.5	0.701	0.740	0.764	0.782	0.792	0.800	0.808	0.812	0.815	0.816	0.817	0.818	0.818
0.6	0.606	0.650	0.682	0.703	0.717	0.727	0.740	0.746	0.749	0.751	0.753	0.754	0.755
0.7	0.523	0.569	0.603	0.628	0.645	0.658	0.674	0.682	0.687	0.690	0.692	0.694	0.696
0.8	0.449	0.496	0.532	0.558	0.578	0.593	0.612	0.623	0.630	0.634	0.636	0.639	0.642
0.9	0.388	0.433	0.469	0.496	0.518	0.534	0.556	0.569	0.577	0.582	0.585	0.590	0.593
1.0	0.336	0.379	0.414	0.441	0.463	0.481	0.505	0.520	0.530	0.536	0.540	0.545	0.550
1.1	0.293	0.333	0.367	0.394	0.416	0.434	0.460	0.476	0.487	0.494	0.409	0.506	0.511
1.2	0.257	0.294	0.325	0.352	0.374	0.392	0.419	0.437	0.449	0.457	0.462	0.470	0.477
1.3	0.226	0.260	0.290	0.315	0.337	0.355	0.382	0.401	0.414	0.423	0.429	0.438	0.446
1.4	0.201	0.232	0.260	0.284	0.304	0.322	0.350	0.369	0.383	0.393	0.400	0.410	0.419
1.5	0.179	0.208	0.233	0.256	0.276	0.293	0.320	0.340	0.355	0.365	0.372	0.384	0.395
1.6	0.160	0.187	0.210	0.232	0.251	0.267	0.294	0.314	0.329	0.340	0.348	0.360	0.373
1.7	0.144	0.168	0.191	0.211	0.228	0.244	0.271	0.291	0.300	0.317	0.326	0.339	0.353
1.8	0.130	0.153	0.173	0.192	0.209	0.224	0.250	0.270	0.285	0.296	0.305	0.320	0.335
1.9	0.118	0.139	0.158	0.176	0.192	0.206	0.231	0.250	0.266	0.278	0.287	0.301	0.318
2.0	0.108	0.127	0.145	0.161	0.176	0.190	0.214	0.235	0.248	0.260	0.270	0.285	0.303
2.1	0.099	0.116	0.133	0.148	0.163	0.176	0.198	0.217	0.232	0.244	0.254	0.270	0.290
2.2	0.091	0.107	0.122	0.137	0.150	0.163	0.185	0.203	0.218	0.230	0.239	0.256	0.277

continued

A/B z/B	1.0	1.2	1.4	1.6	1.8	2.0	2.4	2.8	3.2	3.6	4.0	5.0	>10 (strip)
2.3	0.084	0.099	0.113	0.127	0.139	0.151	0.172	0.190	0.204	0.216	0.226	0.242	0.265
2.4	0.077	0.092	0.105	0.118	0.130	0.141	0.161	0.178	0.192	0.204	0.213	0.230	0.264
2.5	0.072	0.085	0.097	0.110	0.121	0.131	0.150	0.167	0.180	0.192	0.202	0.219	0.214
2.6	0.068	0.080	0.092	0.103	0.114	0.124	0.112	0.158	0.171	0.183	0.193	0.210	0.236
2.7	0.064	0.075	0.086	0.097	0.107	0.117	0.134	0.149	0.162	0.174	0.183	0.200	0.227
2.8	0.059	0.070	0.081	0.091	0.100	0.110	0.126	0.141	0.154	0.164	0.174	0.191	0.219
2.9	0.055	0.065	0.075	0.085	0.094	0.102	0.118	0.132	0.145	0.155	0.164	0.181	0.210
3.0	0.051	0.060	0.070	0.078	0.087	0.095	0.110	0.124	0.136	0.146	0.155	0.172	0.202
3.1	0.048	0.057	0.066	0.075	0.083	0.091	0.105	0.118	0.130	0.140	0.148	0.165	0.196
3.2	0.046	0.054	0.063	0.071	0.079	0.086	0.100	0.112	0.124	0.133	0.142	0.158	0.190
3.3	0.043	0.051	0.059	0.067	0.074	0.081	0.095	0.106	0.117	0.127	0.135	0.152	0.183
3.4	0.041	0.048	0.056	0.063	0.070	0.077	0.089	0.100	0.111	0.120	0.129	0.145	0.177
3.5	0.038	0.045	0.052	0.059	0.066	0.072	0.084	0.095	0.105	0.144	0.122	0.138	0.171
3.6	0.036	0.043	0.050	0.056	0.063	0.069	0.080	0.090	0.101	0.109	0.117	0.133	0.166
3.7	0.034	0.041	0.047	0.054	0.060	0.066	0.077	0.087	0.097	0.105	0.112	0.128	0.161
.3.8	0.033	0.039	0.045	0.051	0.057	0.062	0.073	0.083	0.092	0.100	0.108	0.123	0.157
.3.9	0.031	0.037	0.043	0.048	0.051	0.059	0.070	0.079	0.088	0.096	0.103	0.118	0.152
4.0	0.029	0.035	0.040	0.046	0.051	0.056	0.066	0.075	0.084	0.091	0.098	0.113	0.147
4.1	0.028	0.033	0.039	0.044	0.049	0.054	0.063	0.072	0.081	0.088	0.095	0.109	0.143
4.2	0.027	0.032	0.037	0.042	0.047	0.052	0.061	0.069	0.078	0.084	0.091	0.105	0.139
4.3	0.025	0.030	0.035	0.040	0.045	0.049	0.058	0.067	0.074	0.081	0.088	0.102	0.0136
4.4	0.024	0.029	0.034	0.038	0.043	0.047	0.055	0.064	0.071	0.077	0.084	0.098	0.130
4.5	0.023	0.028	0.032	0.036	0.041	0.045	0.053	0.061	0.068	0.074	0.081	0.094	0.128
4.6	0.022	0.027	0.031	0.035	0.039	0.043	0.051	0.058	0.066	0.072	0.078	0.091	0.125
4.7	0.021	0.026	0.030	0.034	0.038	0.042	0.049	0.056	0.063	0.069	0.075	0.088	0.122
4.8	0.021	0.024	0.028	0.032	0.036	0.040	0.047	0.054	0.061	0.067	0.073	0.085	0.118
4.9	0.020	0.023	0.027	0.031	0.035	0.038	0.045	0.052	0.058	0.064	0.070	0.082	0.115
5.0	0.019	0.022	0.026	0.030	0.033	0.037	0.044	0.050	0.056	0.062	0.067	0.079	0.112

The vertical stress σ_z beneath the mid-point of rectangular plane subjected to uniformly distributed load can also be obtained by the method of solving the stress at angular points, i.e. by dividing the rectangular area into four identical small ones through the mid point, then solving the stress at angular point of any small rectangle, and multiplying the result by 4, thus obtaining the stress beneath the mid-point of the big rectangle.

(4) Stress for rectangular area subjected to triangularly distributed load

As shown in Fig. 3-48, when the origin of the coordinate is placed at the tip of the triangle, the vertical stress σ_z at arbitrary point $M(x, y, z)$ of the subgrade can be expressed as

$$\sigma_z = \frac{3pz^3}{2\pi B}\int_v^A\int_v^R \frac{x_1 \mathrm{d}x_1 \mathrm{d}y_1}{[(x-x_1)^2+(y-y_1)^2+z^2]^{5/2}} \tag{3-45}$$

The vertical stress σ_z at angular point $(0,0,z)$ is expressed as follows

$$\sigma_z = \alpha_r p \tag{3-46}$$

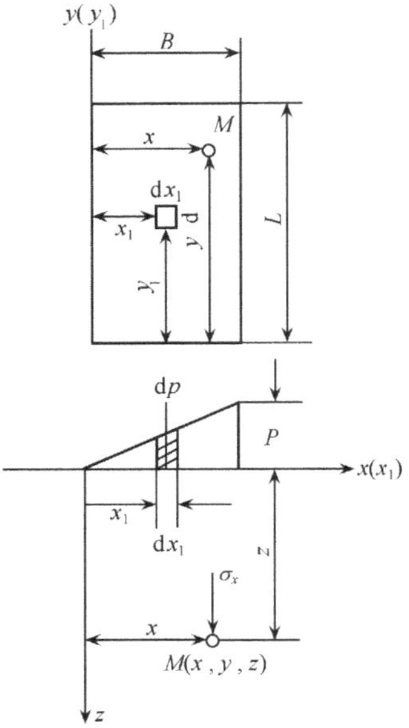

Fig. 3-48 Triangularly distributed load on rectangular foundation

where: p —the maximum of triangularly distributed load (kPa) ;

α_r —stress factor for σ_z at angular point, which can be referred to in Table 3-11 according to the values of A/B and z/B, while A and B are the long-side and short-side lengths of the rectangle, respectively (m) .

Table 3-11 Stress factor α_r of angular point $(x=0, y=0)$ of rectangular area subjected to triangularly distributed load

z/β	A/B														
	0.2	0.4	0.6	0.8	1.0	1.2	1.4	1.6	1.8	2.0	3.0	4.0	6.0	8.0	10.0
0.0	0.0000	0.0000	0.0000	0.0000	0.0000	0.0000	0.0000	0.0000	0.0000	0.0000	0.0000	0.0000	0.0000	0.0000	0.0000
0.2	0.0223	0.0280	0.0296	0.0301	0.0304	0.0305	0.0305	0.0306	0.0306	0.0306	0.0306	0.0306	0.0306	0.0306	0.0306
0.4	0.0269	0.0420	0.0487	0.0517	0.0531	0.0539	0.0543	0.0545	0.0546	0.0547	0.0548	0.0549	0.0549	0.0549	0.0549
0.6	0.0259	0.0448	0.0560	0.0621	0.0654	0.0673	0.0684	0.0690	0.0694	0.0696	0.0701	0.0702	0.0702	0.0702	0.0702
0.8	0.0232	0.0421	0.0553	0.0637	0.0688	0.0720	0.0739	0.0751	0.0759	0.0764	0.0773	0.0776	0.0776	0.0776	0.0776
1.0	0.0201	0.0375	0.0508	0.0602	0.0666	0.0708	0.0735	0.0753	0.0766	0.0774	0.0790	0.0794	0.0795	0.0796	0.0796
1.2	0.0171	0.0324	0.0450	0.0546	0.0615	0.0664	0.0698	0.0721	0.0738	0.0749	0.0774	0.0779	0.0782	0.0783	0.0783
1.4	0.0145	0.0278	0.0392	0.0483	0.0554	0.0606	0.0644	0.0672	0.0692	0.0707	0.0739	0.0748	0.0752	0.0752	0.0753
1.6	0.0123	0.0238	0.0339	0.0424	0.0492	0.0545	0.0586	0.0616	0.9639	0.0656	0.0697	0.0708	0.0714	0.0715	0.0715
1.8	0.0105	0.0204	0.0294	0.0371	0.0435	0.0487	0.0528	0.0560	0.0585	0.0604	0.0652	0.0666	0.0673	0.0675	0.0675
2.0	0.0000	0.0176	0.0255	0.0324	0.0384	0.0434	0.0474	0.0507	0.0533	0.0553	0.0607	0.0624	0.0634	0.0636	0.0636
2.5	0.0063	0.0125	0.0183	0.0236	0.0284	0.0325	0.0362	0.0393	0.0419	0.0440	0.0504	0.0529	0.0543	0.0547	0.0548
3.0	0.0046	0.0092	0.0135	0.0176	0.0214	0.0249	0.0280	0.0307	0.0331	0.0352	0.0419	0.0449	0.0469	0.0474	0.0476
5.0	0.0018	0.0036	0.0054	0.0071	0.0088	0.0104	0.0120	0.0135	0.0148	0.0161	0.0214	0.0248	0.0283	0.0296	0.0301
7.0	0.0009	0.0019	0.0028	0.0038	0.0047	0.0056	0.0064	0.0073	0.0081	0.0089	0.0124	0.0152	0.0186	0.0204	0.0212
10.0	0.0005	0.0009	0.0014	0.0019	0.0023	0.0028	0.0033	0.0037	0.0041	0.0046	0.0066	0.0084	0.0111	0.0128	0.0139

3. Stress in subgrade with circular load area

(1) Stress of circular area under uniformly distributed load

The vertical stress σ_z at arbitrary point M of subgrade with circular load area subjected to uniformly distributed load is given by

$$\sigma_z = \alpha_0 P \tag{3-47}$$

The vertical stress σ_z at arbitrary depth z right under the center of circle reads as

$$\sigma_z = P\left[1-\left(\frac{1}{1+\frac{R_1}{z^2}}\right)^{3/2}\right] \tag{3-48}$$

where α_0 is a stress factor, which can be referred to Table 3-12 according to the values of r/R_1 and z/R_1, while R_1 is the radius of circle (m), r is the horizontal distance from the center of circle to calculated point (m).

Table 3-12 Stress factor α_r for circular area under uniformly distributed load

z/R_1	r/R_1										
	0.0	0.2	0.4	0.6	0.8	1.0	1.2	1.4	1.6	1.8	2.0
0.0	1.000	1.000	1.000	1.000	1.000	0.5000	0.000	0.000	0.000	0.000	0.000
0.2	0.993	0.991	0.987	0.970	0.890	0.168	0.077	0.015	0.005	0.002	0.001
0.4	0.949	0.943	0.922	0.860	0.712	0.435	0.181	0.065	0.026	0.012	0.006
0.6	0.864	0.852	0.813	0.733	0.591	0.400	0.221	0.113	0.056	0.029	0.016
0.8	0.756	0.742	0.699	0.619	0.504	0.366	0.237	0.142	0.083	0.048	0.029
1.0	0.646	0.633	0.593	0.525	0.434	0.332	0.235	0.157	0.102	0.065	0.042
1.2	0.547	0.535	0.502	0.447	0.337	0.300	0.226	0.152	0.113	0.073	0.053
1.4	0.461	0.452	0.425	0.383	0.329	0.270	0.212	0.161	0.118	0.086	0.062
1.6	0.390	0.383	0.362	0.330	0.288	0.243	0.197	0.156	0.120	0.090	0.068
1.8	0.332	0.327	0.311	0.285	0.254	0.218	0.182	0.148	0.118	0.092	0.072
2.0	0.285	0.280	0.268	0.248	0.224	0.196	0.167	0.140	0.114	0.092	0.074
2.2	0.246	0.342	0.233	0.218	0.198	0.176	0.153	0.131	0.109	0.090	0.074
2.4	0.214	0.211	0.203	0.192	0.176	0.159	0.140	0.122	0.104	0.087	0.073
2.6	0.187	0.185	0.179	0.170	0.158	0.144	0.129	0.113	0.098	0.084	0.071
2.8	0.165	0.163	0.159	0.150	0.141	0.130	0.118	0.105	0.092	0.080	0.069
3.0	0.146	0.145	0.141	0.135	0.127	0.118	0.108	0.097	0.087	0.077	0.067
3.4	0.117	0.116	0.114	0.110	0.105	0.098	0.091	0.084	0.076	0.068	0.061
3.8	0.096	0.095	0.093	0.091	0.087	0.083	0.078	0.073	0.067	0.061	0.055
4.2	0.079	0.079	0.078	0.076	0.073	0.070	0.067	0.063	0.059	0.054	0.050
4.6	0.067	0.067	0.066	0.064	00.063	0.060	0.058	0.055	0.052	0.048	0.045
5.0	0.057	0.057	0.056	0.055	0.054	0.052	0.050	0.048	0.046	0.043	0.041
5.5	0.048	0.048	0.047	0.045	0.0445	0.044	0.043	0.041	0.039	0.038	0.036
6.0	0.040	0.040	0.040	0.039	0.039	0.038	0.037	0.036	0.034	0.033	0.031

(2) Stress for circular area under triangularly distributed load

As shown in Fig. 3-49, the vertical stress σ_z at arbitrary depth z right under the zero pressure point of the circle circumference (see point (1) is given by

$$\sigma_{z1} = \alpha_1 P \tag{3-49}$$

while the vertical stress σ_z of M_2 at depth z (point 2)under the point of the circle circumference with pressure p reads as

$$\sigma_{z2} = \alpha_2 P \tag{3-50}$$

where: P —the maximum of triangularly distributed load (kPa);

α_1, α_2 —stress factors for σ_{z1} and σ_{z2} respectively, which can be referred to in Table 3-13 according to the value of z/R_1.

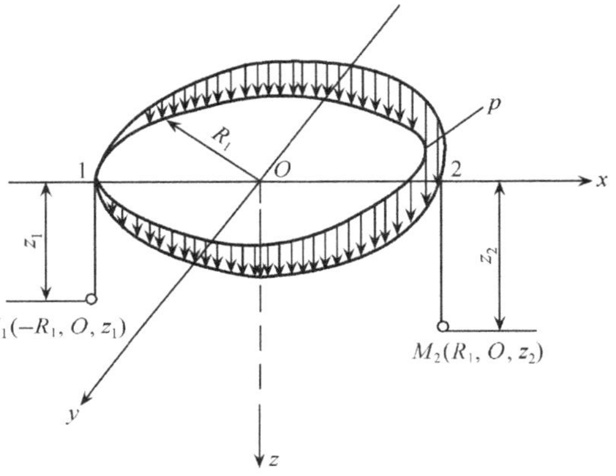

Fig. 3-49 Stress for circular area subjected to triangular distributed load

$$\sigma_{z1} = \alpha_1 P \tag{3-49}$$

Table 3-13 Stress factors α_1 and α_2 at boundary points of circular area under triangularly distributed load

point / z/R_1	1(α_1)	2(α_2)	point / z/R_1	1(α_1)	2(α_2)	point / z/R_1	1(α_1)	2(α_2)	point / z/R_1	1(α_1)	2(α_2)
0.0	0.000	0.500	1.2	0.093	0.205	2.4	0.067	0.091	3.6	0.041	0.051
0.1	0.016	0.465	1.3	0.092	0.190	2.5	0.064	0.086	3.7	0.040	0.048
0.2	0.031	0.433	1.4	0.091	0.177	2.6	0.062	0.081	3.8	0.038	0.046
0.3	0.044	0.403	1.5	0.089	0.165	2.7	0.059	0.078	3.9	0.037	0.043
0.4	0.054	0.376	1.6	0.087	0.154	2.8	0.057	0.074	4.0	0.036	0.041
0.5	0.063	0.349	1.7	0.085	0.144	2.9	0.055	0.070	4.2	0.033	0.038
0.6	0.071	0.324	1.8	0.083	0.134	3.0	0.052	0.067	4.4	0.031	0.034
0.7	0.078	0.300	1.9	0.080	0.126	3.1	0.050	0.064	4.6	0.029	0.031
0.8	0.083	0.279	2.0	0.078	0.117	3.2	0.048	0.061	4.8	0.027	0.029
0.9	0.088	0.258	2.1	0.075	0.110	3.3	0.046	0.059	5.0	0.025	0.027
1.0	0.091	0.238	2.2	0.072	0.104	3.4	0.045	0.055			
1.1	0.092	0.221	2.3	0.070	0.097	3.5	0.043	0.053			

(3) Stress for annular area under uniformly distributed load

Eq.(3-47) and Table 3-12 for circular subsoil can be applied to calculate stress σ_z for annular subsoil (see Fig. 3-50), that is

$$\sigma_z = P(\alpha_{c1} - \alpha_{c2}) \tag{3-51}$$

where α_{c1} can be referred to in Table 3-12 according to r/R_1 and z/R_1 of point M, while α_{c2} can be referred to in Table 3-12 according to r/R_2 and z/R_2 of point M.

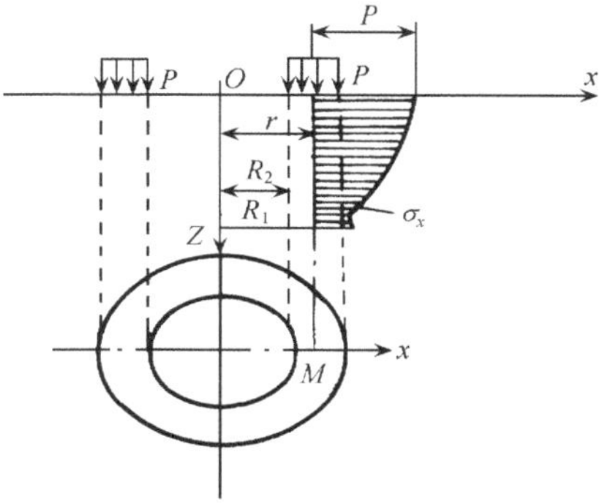

Fig. 3-50 Annular subsoil under uniformly distributed load

3.4.2 General Mechanics of Semi-infinite Elastic Body

Since deep foundation has certain embedded depth, its mechanical problems can be summarized as stress problems of a semi-infinite elastic body. For the purpose of convenient application, stress formulas for seven loading conditions are summed up as below.

1. Semi-infinite elastic body subjected to concentrated vertical force(Fig. 3-51)

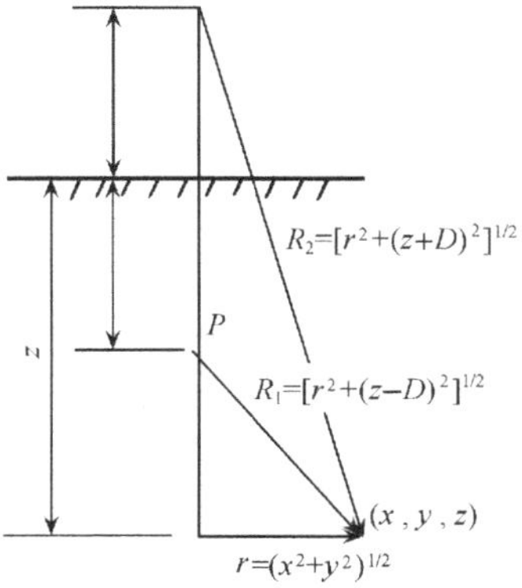

Fig. 3-51 Semi-infinite elastic body subjected to concentrated vertical force

$$
\sigma_z = -\frac{P}{8\pi(1-\mu)}\left\{\frac{(1-2\mu)(z-c)}{R_1^3} - \frac{3x^2(z-c)}{R_1^5}\right.
+\frac{(1-2\mu)[3(z-c)-4\mu(z+c)]}{R_2^3}
-\frac{3(3-4\mu)x^2(z-c)-6c(z+c)[(1-2\mu)z-2\mu c]}{R_2^5}
\left.-\frac{30cx^2z(z+c)}{R_2^7} - \frac{4(1-\mu)(1-2\mu)}{R_2(R_2+z+c)}\left[1-\frac{x^2}{R_2(R_2+z+c)}-\frac{x^2}{R_2^2}\right]\right\} \tag{3-52}
$$

$$
\sigma_y = -\frac{P}{8\pi(1-\mu)}\left\{\frac{(1-2\mu)(z-c)}{R_1^3} - \frac{3y^2(z-c)}{R_1^5}\right.
+\frac{(1-2\mu)[3(z-c)-4\mu(z+c)]}{R_2^3}
-\frac{3(3-4\mu)y^2(z-c)-6c(z+c)[(1-2\mu)z-2\mu c]}{R_2^5}
\left.-\frac{30cy^2z(z+c)}{R_2^7} - \frac{4(1-\mu)(1-2\mu)}{R_2(R_2+z+c)}\left[1-\frac{y^2}{R_2(R_2+z+c)}-\frac{y^2}{R_2^2}\right]\right\} \tag{3-53}
$$

$$
\sigma_z = -\frac{P}{8\pi(1-\mu)}\left[-\frac{(1-2\mu)(z-c)}{R_1^3} + \frac{(1-2\mu)(z-c)}{R_2^1}\right.
\left.-\frac{3(z-c)^3}{R_1^5} - \frac{3(3-4\mu)z(z+c)^2-3c(z+c)(5z-c)}{R_2^5} - \frac{30cz(z+c)^3}{R_2^7}\right] \tag{3-54}
$$

$$
\tau_{xy} = -\frac{Pxy}{8\pi(1-\mu)}\left\{-\frac{3(z-c)}{R_1^5} - \frac{3(3-4\mu)(z-c)}{R_2^5} + \frac{4(1-\mu)(1-2\mu)}{R_2^2(R_2+z+c)}\right.
\left.\left[\frac{1}{R_2+z+c}+\frac{1}{R_2}\right] - \frac{30cz(z+c)}{R_2^7}\right\} \tag{3-55}
$$

$$
\tau_{yz} = -\frac{Py}{8\pi(1-\mu)}\left\{-\frac{1-2\mu}{R_1^3} + \frac{1-2\mu}{R_2^3} - \frac{3(z-c)^2}{R_1^5}\right.
\left.-\frac{3(3-4\mu)z(z+c)-3c(3z+c)}{R_2^5} - \frac{30cz(z+c)^2}{R_2^7}\right\} \tag{3-56}
$$

$$
\tau_{xz} = -\frac{Px}{8\pi(1-\mu)}\left[-\frac{1-2\mu}{R_1^3} + \frac{1-2\mu}{R_2^3} - \frac{3(z-c)^2}{R_1^5}\right.
\left.-\frac{3(3-4\mu)z(z+c)-3c(3z+c)}{R_2^5} - \frac{30cz(z+c)^2}{R_2^7}\right] \tag{3-57}
$$

2. Semi-infinite elastic body subjected to concentrated horizontal force(Fig. 3-52)

$$
\sigma_x = -\frac{Qx}{8\pi(1-\mu)}\left\{-\frac{(1-2\mu)}{R_1^3} + \frac{(1-2\mu)(5-4\mu)}{R_2^3} - \frac{3x^2}{R_1^5} - \frac{3(3-4\mu)x^2}{R_2^5}\right.
-\frac{4(1-\mu)(1-2\mu)}{R_2(R_2+z+c)^2}\times\left[3-\frac{x^2(3R_2+z+c)}{R_2^2(R_2+z+c)}\right]
$$

$$+\frac{6c}{R_2^5}\left[3c-(3-2\mu)(z+c)+\frac{5x^2z}{R_2^2}\right]\Bigg\} \tag{3-58}$$

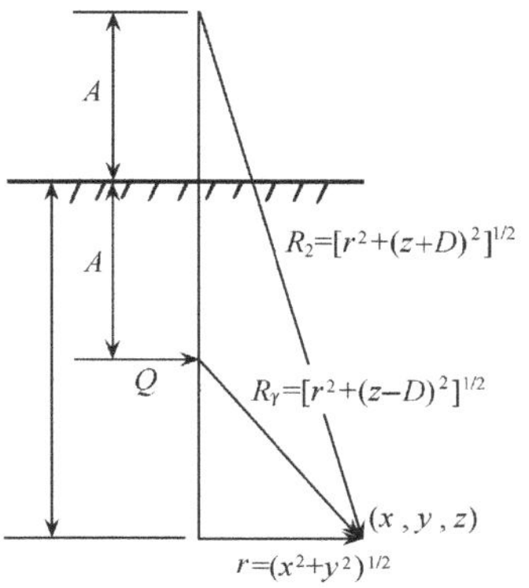

Fig. 3-52 Semi-infinite elastic body subjected to concentrated horizontal force

$$\sigma_y=-\frac{Qx}{8\pi(1-\mu)}\Bigg\{\frac{(1-2\mu)}{R_1^3}+\frac{(1-2\mu)(3-4\mu)}{R_2^3}-\frac{3y^2}{R_1^5}$$
$$-\frac{3(3-4\mu)y^2}{R_2^5}-\frac{4(1-\mu)(1-2\mu)}{R_2(R_2+z+c)^2}\left[1-\frac{y^2(3R_2+z+c)}{R_2^2(R_2+z+c)}\right]$$
$$+\frac{6c}{R_2^5}\left[c-(1-2\mu)(z+c)+\frac{5y^2z}{R_2^2}\right]\Bigg\} \tag{3-59}$$

$$\sigma_z=-\frac{Qx}{8\pi(1-\mu)}\Bigg\{\frac{1-2\mu}{R_1^3}-\frac{1-2\mu}{R_2^3}-\frac{3(z-c)^2}{R_1^5}-\frac{3(3-4\mu)(z+c)^2}{R_2^5}$$
$$+\frac{6c}{R_2^5}\left[c+(1-2\mu)(z+c)+\frac{5z(z+c)^2}{R_2^2}\right]\Bigg\} \tag{3-60}$$

$$\tau_{xy}=-\frac{Qy}{8\pi(1-\mu)}\Bigg\{-\frac{1-2\mu}{R_1^3}+\frac{1-2\mu}{R_2^3}-\frac{3x^2}{R_1^5}-\frac{3(3-4\mu)x^2}{R_2^5}$$
$$-\frac{4(1-\mu)(1-2\mu)}{R_2(R_2+z+c)^2}\left[1-\frac{x^2(3R_2+z+c)}{R_2^2(R_2+z+c)}\right]-\frac{6cz}{R_2^5}\left(1-\frac{5x^2}{R_2^2}\right)\Bigg\} \tag{3-61}$$

$$\tau_{yz}=-\frac{Q_{xy}}{8\pi(1-\mu)}\Bigg\{-\frac{3(z-c)}{R_1^5}-\frac{3(3-4\mu)(z+c)}{R_2^5}$$
$$+\frac{6c}{R_2^5}\left[1-2\mu+\frac{5z(z+c)}{R_2^2}\right]\Bigg\} \tag{3-62}$$

$$\tau_{xz}=-\frac{Q}{8\pi(1-\mu)}\Bigg\{-\frac{(1-2\mu)(z-c)}{R_1^3}+\frac{(1-2\mu)(z-c)}{R_2^3}$$
$$-\frac{3x^2(z-c)}{R_1^5}-\frac{3(3-4\mu)x^2(z+c)}{R_2^5}-\frac{6c}{R_2^5}\left[z(z+c)-(1-2\mu)x^2-\frac{5x^2z(z+c)}{R_2^2}\right]\Bigg\} \tag{3-63}$$

3. Semi-infinite elastic body subjected to uniformly distributed linear vertical pressure P (Fig. 3-53)

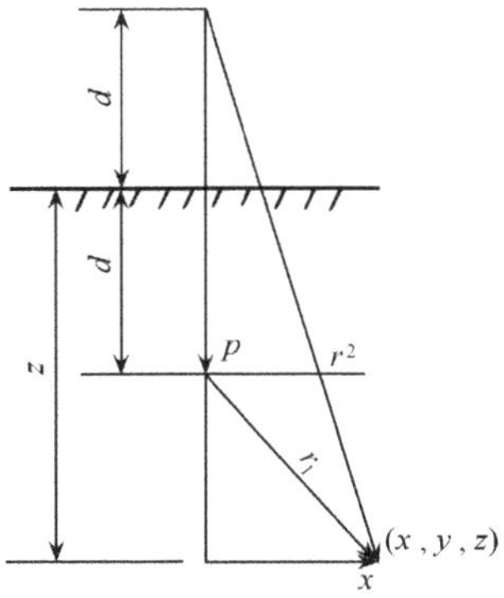

Fig. 3-53 Semi-infinite elastic body subjected to uniformly distributed linear vertical pressure

$$\sigma_x = \frac{p}{\pi}\left\{\frac{1+m}{2m}\left[\frac{(z-d)x^2}{r_1^4} + \frac{(z+d)(x^2+2d^2)-2dx^2}{r_2^4} + \frac{8dz(d+z)x^2}{r_2^6}\right]\right.$$
$$\left. + \frac{m-1}{4m}\left[-\frac{z-d}{r_1^2} + \frac{z+3d}{r_2^2} + \frac{4zx^2}{r_2^4}\right]\right\} \qquad \text{(3-6}$$

$$\sigma_z = \frac{p}{\pi}\left\{\frac{m+1}{2m}\left[\frac{(z-d)^3}{r_1^4} + \frac{(z+d)(z^2+d^2+4dz)}{r_2^4} - \frac{8dz(d+z)x^2}{r_2^6}\right]\right.$$
$$\left. + \frac{m-1}{4m}\left[\frac{z-d}{r_1^2} + \frac{3z+d}{r_2^2} - \frac{4zx^2}{r_2^4}\right]\right\} \qquad \text{(3-6}$$

$$\tau_{xz} = \frac{px}{\pi}\left\{\frac{m+1}{2m}\left[\frac{(z-d)^2}{r_1^4} + \frac{z^2-2dz-d^2}{r_2^4} + \frac{8dz(d+z)^2}{r_2^6}\right]\right.$$
$$\left. + \frac{m-1}{4m}\left[\frac{1}{r_1^2} - \frac{1}{r_2^2} + \frac{4z(d+z)}{r_2^4}\right]\right\} \qquad \text{(3-6}$$

in which $m = \dfrac{1-\mu}{\mu}$.

4. Semi-infinite elastic body subjected to uniformly distributed linear horizontal pressure q (Fig. 3-54)

$$\sigma_x = \frac{qx}{\pi}\left\{\frac{m+1}{2m}\left[\frac{x^2}{r_1^4} + \frac{x^2+8dz+6d^2}{r_2^4} + \frac{8dz(d+z)^2}{r_2^6}\right]\right.$$
$$\left. + \frac{m-1}{4m}\left[\frac{1}{r_1^2} + \frac{3}{r_2^2} - \frac{4z(d+z)}{r_2^4}\right]\right\} \qquad \text{(3-67)}$$

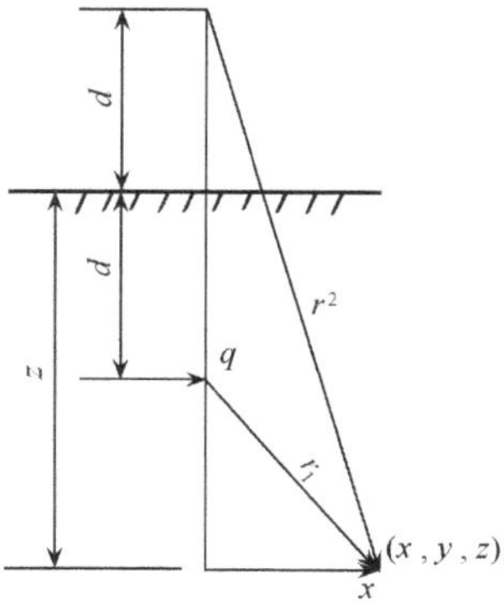

Fig. 3-54 Semi-infinite elastic body subjected to uniformly distributed linear horizontal pressure

$$\sigma_z = \frac{qx}{\pi}\left\{\frac{m+1}{2m}\left[\frac{(z-d)^2}{r_1^4} - \frac{d^2 - z^2 + 6zd}{r_2^4} + \frac{8dzx^2}{r_2^6}\right] - \frac{m-1}{4m}\left[\frac{1}{r_1^2} - \frac{1}{r_2^2} - \frac{4z(d+z)}{r_2^4}\right]\right\} \tag{3-68}$$

$$\tau_{xz} = \frac{q}{\pi}\left\{\frac{m+1}{2m}\left[\frac{(z-d)x^2}{r_1^4} + \frac{(2dz + x^2)(d+z)}{r_2^4} - \frac{8dz(d+z)x^2}{r_2^6}\right] + \frac{m-1}{4m}\left[\frac{z-d}{r_1^2} + \frac{3z+d}{r_2^2} - \frac{4z(d+z)^2}{r_2^4}\right]\right\} \tag{3-69}$$

in which $m = \dfrac{1-\mu}{\mu}$.

5. Semi-infinite elastic body subjected to uniformly distributed linear vertical pressure along the vertical axis (Fig. 3-55)

$$\sigma_r = -\frac{P}{8\pi(1-\mu)D^2}\left\{\frac{1-2\mu}{A} + \frac{(7-2\mu) - 12(1-\mu)\frac{m}{n}\left(\frac{m}{n} + \frac{1}{n}\right)}{B} - \frac{4(2-\mu) - 12(1-\mu)\left(\frac{m}{n}\right)^2}{F} - \frac{n^2}{A^3} + \frac{4n^2 - 2m^2 + 2(1+2\mu)\left(\frac{m}{n}\right)^2 m^2}{F^5} - \frac{3n^2 - 2m^2 + 2(1+2\mu)\frac{m}{n}(m+1)^2\left(\frac{m}{n} + \frac{1}{n}\right)}{B^3} + \frac{6\left[n^2m^2 - m^4\left(\frac{m}{n}\right)^2\right]}{F^5} + \frac{6\left[\frac{m}{n}(m+1)^4\left(\frac{m}{n} + \frac{1}{n}\right) - m^2n^2\right]}{B^5} + 4(1-\mu)(1-2\mu)\left[\frac{1}{F+m} - \frac{1}{B+m+1}\right]\right\} \tag{3-70}$$

$$\sigma_\theta = -\frac{P}{8\pi(1-\mu)D^2}\left\{\frac{1-2\mu}{A} + \frac{6-(1-2\mu)(3-4\mu)+6(1-2\mu)\dfrac{m}{n}\left(\dfrac{m}{n}+\dfrac{1}{n}\right)}{B}\right.$$

$$+\frac{2(1-2\mu)^2-6(1-2\mu)\left(\dfrac{m}{n}\right)^2-6}{F} + \frac{2m^2-4\mu n^2+2(1+2\mu)\dfrac{m}{n}(m+1)^2\left(\dfrac{m}{n}+\dfrac{1}{n}\right)}{B^3}$$

$$\left.-\frac{4\mu n^2-2m^2-2(1+2\mu)m^2\left(\dfrac{m}{n}\right)^2}{F^3} - 4(1-\mu)(1-2\mu)\times\left(\frac{1}{F+m}-\frac{1}{B+m+1}\right)\right\} \quad (3\text{-}71)$$

$$\sigma_z = -\frac{P}{8\pi(1-\mu)D^2}\left\{-\frac{2(2-\mu)}{A} + \frac{2(2-\mu)+2(1-2\mu)\dfrac{m}{n}\left(\dfrac{m}{n}+\dfrac{1}{n}\right)}{B}\right.$$

$$-\frac{(1-2\mu)2\left(\dfrac{m}{n}\right)^2}{F} + \frac{n^2}{A^3} + \frac{4m^2-4(1+\mu)\left(\dfrac{m}{n}\right)^2 m^2}{F^3}$$

$$+\frac{4m(1+\mu)(m+1)\left(\dfrac{m}{n}+\dfrac{1}{n}\right)^2-(4m^2+n^2)}{B^3} + \frac{6m^2\left(\dfrac{m^4-n^4}{n^2}\right)}{F^5}$$

$$\left.+\frac{6m\left[mn^2-\dfrac{1}{n^2}(m+1)^5\right]}{B^5}\right\} \quad (3\text{-}72)$$

$$\tau_{rz} = -\frac{nP}{8\pi(1-\mu)D^2}\left\{\frac{(1-2\mu)\dfrac{1}{n}\left(\dfrac{m}{n}-\dfrac{1}{n}\right)}{A} + \frac{(m-1)\left(\dfrac{m}{n}-\dfrac{1}{n}\right)^2}{A^3}\right.$$

$$+\frac{(1-2\mu)\dfrac{1}{n}\left(\dfrac{m}{n}+\dfrac{1}{n}\right)-\dfrac{6}{n}\left(\dfrac{m}{n}\right)^2\left(\dfrac{m}{n}+\dfrac{1}{n}\right)}{B}$$

$$+\frac{12m-4\mu m+(m+1)^3\left[\left(\dfrac{1}{n}\right)^2+12\dfrac{m^2}{n^4}\right]}{B^3}$$

$$-\frac{6\left(\dfrac{m}{n}\right)^2(m+1)^3\left(\dfrac{m}{n}+\dfrac{1}{n}\right)^2+6mn^2}{B^5} + \frac{6\left(\dfrac{m}{n}\right)^3\left(\dfrac{1}{n}\right)-2(1-2\mu)\dfrac{m}{n^2}}{F}$$

$$\left.+\frac{4\mu m-12m-m^3\left[\dfrac{2}{n^2}+12\dfrac{m^2}{n^4}\right]}{F^3} + \frac{6mn^2+6m^3\left(\dfrac{m}{n}\right)^4}{F^5}\right\} \quad (3\text{-}73)$$

in which

$$\left.\begin{aligned} n &= \frac{r}{D}, m = \frac{z}{D} \\ F^2 &= n^2 + m^2 \\ A^2 &= n^2 + (m-1)^2 \\ B^2 &= n^2 + (m+1)^2 \end{aligned}\right\} \tag{3-74}$$

6. Vertical linearly varying linear load acting along the vertical axis in a semi-infinite body (Fig. 3-56)

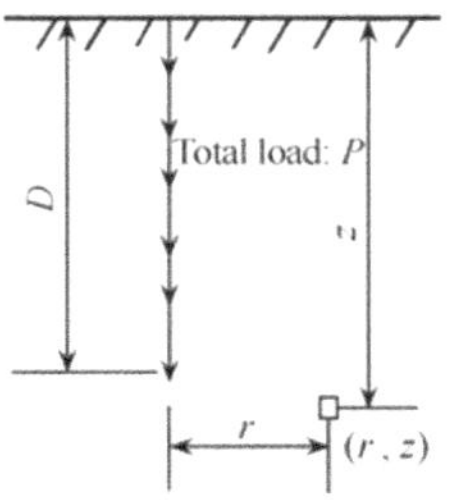

Fig. 3-55 Semi-infinite elastic body subjected to uniformly distributed linear vertical pressure (along the vertical axis)

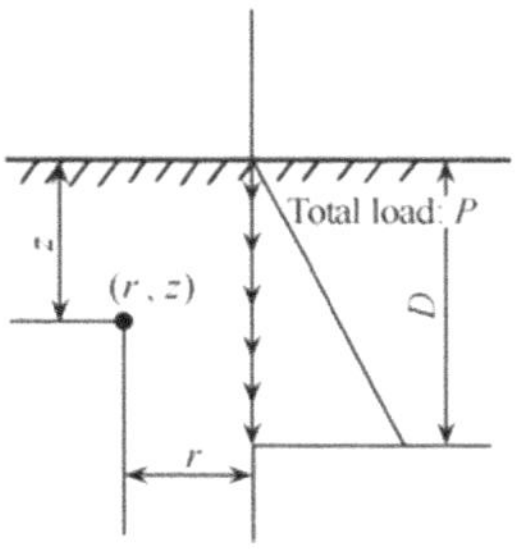

Fig. 3-56 Semi-infinite body subjected to linearly & vertically varying vertical load (along the vertical axis)

$$\begin{aligned} \sigma_r = -\frac{P}{4\pi(1-\mu)D^2}\Bigg\{ & \frac{1-2\mu}{A} + \frac{(7-2\mu) - 12m + 12(1-\mu)\left(\dfrac{m}{n}\right)^2(m+1)}{B} \\ & + \frac{12m - 12(1-\mu)\dfrac{m^2}{n^2}}{F} - \frac{(m-1)^3 + mn^2}{A^3} \\ & + \frac{3(m+1)^3 - 2m^3 + (21-4\mu)mn^2 + 2(5+2\mu)\left(\dfrac{m}{n}\right)^2(m+1)^3}{B^3} \\ & - \frac{2(5+2\mu)\dfrac{m^5}{n^2} + 4(5-\mu)mn^2}{F^3} + \frac{6mn^2(m^2-n^2) - 12\left(\dfrac{m}{n}\right)^2(m+1)^5}{B^5} \\ & - \frac{6mn^2(m^2-n^2) - 12\dfrac{m^7}{n^2}}{F^5} + (1-2\mu)\ln\frac{A+m-1}{F+m} + [(1-2\mu)^2 - 6] \\ & \ln\frac{B+m+1}{F+m} + 2(1-\mu)(1-2\mu)\left[\frac{m-1}{B+m+1} - \frac{m}{F+m}\right]\Bigg\} \end{aligned} \tag{3-75}$$

$$\sigma_\theta = -\frac{P}{4\pi(1-\mu)D^2}\left\{\frac{1-2\mu}{A} - \frac{(1-2\mu)(3-4\mu)+6(1-2\mu)\left(\dfrac{m}{n}\right)^2(m+1)+6(2m-1)}{B}\right.$$

$$+\frac{6(1-2\mu)\dfrac{m^2}{n^2}+12m}{F} - (1-2\mu)\frac{2(m+1)^3+4mn^2-2\left(\dfrac{m}{n}\right)^2(m+1)^3}{B^3}$$

$$+\frac{2(m+1)^3+6mn^3-2m^3-6\left(\dfrac{m}{n}\right)^2(m+1)^3}{B^3} + \frac{2m^3+4mn^2-2\left(\dfrac{m^5}{n^2}\right)(1-2\mu)}{F^3}$$

$$-\frac{6mn^2-6\dfrac{m^5}{n^2}}{F^5} + (1-2\mu)\ln\frac{A+m-1}{F+m} + [(1-2\mu)^2-6]$$

$$\left.\times\ln\frac{B+m+1}{F+m} - 2(1-\mu)(1-2\mu)\left[\frac{m-1}{B+m+1} - \frac{m}{F+m}\right]\right\} \tag{3-76}$$

$$\sigma_z = -\frac{P}{4\pi(1-\mu)D^2}\left[\frac{-2(2-\mu)}{A} + \frac{2(2-\mu)(4m+1)-2(1-2\mu)\left(\dfrac{m}{n}\right)^2(m+1)}{B}\right.$$

$$+\frac{2(1-2\mu)\dfrac{m^2}{n^2}-8(2-\mu)m}{F} + \frac{mn^2+(m-1)^3}{A^3}$$

$$+\frac{4\mu n^2 m+4m^3-15n^2m-2(5+2\mu)\left(\dfrac{m}{n}\right)^2(m+1)^3+(m+1)^3}{B^3}$$

$$+\frac{2(7-2\mu)mn^2-6m^3+2(5+2\mu)\left(\dfrac{m}{n}\right)^2 m^3}{F^3} + \frac{6mn^2(n^2-m^3)+12\left(\dfrac{m}{n}\right)^2(m+1)^5}{B^5}$$

$$\left.-\frac{12\left(\dfrac{m}{n}\right)^2 m^5+6mn^2(n^2-m^2)}{F^5} - 2(2-\mu)\ln\left(\frac{A+m-1}{F+m}\times\frac{B+m+1}{F+m}\right)\right] \tag{3-77}$$

$$\tau_{yz} = -\frac{nP}{4\pi(1-\mu)D^2}\left\{\frac{2(2-\mu)+(1-2\mu)\dfrac{m}{n^2}(m-1)}{A} - \frac{6\left(\dfrac{m}{n}\right)^4}{F}\right.$$

$$-\frac{2(2-\mu)+(1-2\mu)\dfrac{m}{n^2}(m+1)-6\dfrac{m^3}{n^2}(m+1)}{B} + \frac{\dfrac{m}{n^2}(m-1)^3-n^2}{A^3}$$

$$-\frac{(3-4\mu)\left[\dfrac{m}{n^2}(m+1)^3+m^3\right]+17m^2-n^2+12\dfrac{m^3}{n^4}(m+1)^3}{B^3}$$

$$+\frac{2(1-2\mu)\frac{m^4}{n^2}+4(5-\mu)m^2+12\frac{m^6}{n^4}}{F^3}+\frac{6\frac{m^3}{n^4}(m+1)^5-6\frac{m}{n^2}(m+1)^5+12m^2n^2}{B^5}$$

$$\left.-\frac{6\frac{m^8}{n^4}-6\frac{m^6}{n^2}+12m^2n^2}{F^5}\right\} \tag{3-78}$$

7. A Semi-infinite elastic body (Fig. 3-57)

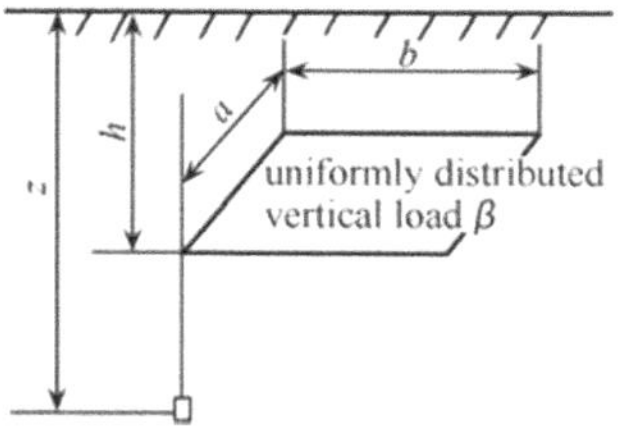

Fig. 3-57 uniformly distributed vertical load acting on a rectangular horizontal area in a semi-infinite elastic body

The stress σ_z at arbitrary point right beneath the angular point of the rectangular area can be expressed as follows

$$\sigma_z=\frac{p}{4\pi(1-\mu)}\left\{(1-\mu)\left[\mathrm{tg}^{-1}\frac{ab}{(z-h)R_1}+\mathrm{tg}^{-1}\frac{ab}{(z+h)R_2}\right]+\frac{(z-h)aR_1}{2br_1^2}-\frac{a(z-h)^3}{2br_3^2R_1}\right.$$

$$+\frac{[(3-4\mu)z(z+h)-h(5z-h)]aR_2}{2(z+h)br_2^2}-\frac{[(3-4\mu)z(z+h)^2-h(z+h)(5z-h)]a}{2br_4^2R_2}$$

$$\left.+\frac{2hz(z+h)aR_2^3}{b^3r_2^4}+\frac{3hzaR_2r_5^2}{(z+h)b^3r_2^2}-\frac{hz(z+h)^2a}{br_4^4R_2}\left[\frac{2b^2-(z+h)^2}{b^2}-\frac{a^2}{R_2^2}\right]\right\} \tag{3-79}$$

where

$$R_1^2=a^2+b^2+(z-h)^2 \qquad R_2^2=a^2+b^2+(z+h)^2$$

$$r_1^2=a^2+(z-h)^2 \qquad r_2^2=a^2+(z+h)^2$$

$$r_3^2=b^2+(z-h)^2 \qquad r_4^2=b^2+(z+h)^2$$

$$r_5^2=b^2-(z+h)^2$$

3.4.3 Simplified Calculations of Stress Distribution of Pile Foundation

(1) Based on Mindlin's theoretical equation for Stress calculation of load acting inside the subsoil, i.e. stress analysis of semi-infinite body, Gedder derived and tabulated vertical stress factors for three loading conditions through simplified calculations (Fig. 3-58), which can be

used to compute vertical stress distributions in subsoil under the load of one pile or pile group, which can also be used to calculate the settlement of pile foundation.

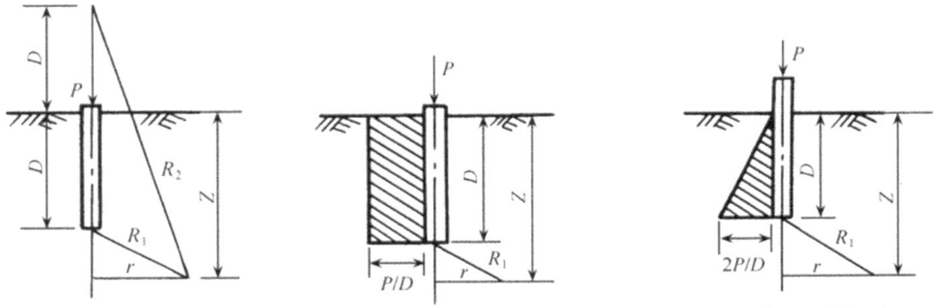

Loading condition 1 concentrated load (end-bearing pile)

Loading condition 2 constant surface friction

Loading condition 3 linearly varying surface friction

Fig. 3-58 Pile-subgrade system for subgrade's stress calculation by Mindlin solution

Transforming Eqs. (3-54) and (3-57) into polar coordinates yields

$$\sigma_r = \frac{P}{8\pi(1-\mu)}\left\{-\frac{(1-2\mu)(z-D)}{R_1^3}+\frac{(1-2\mu)(z-D)}{R_2^3}-\frac{3(z-D)^3}{R_1^5}\right.$$
$$\left.-\left[\frac{3(3-4\mu)z(z+D)^2-3D(z+D)(5z-D)}{R_2^5}\right]-\frac{30zD(z+D)^3}{R_2^7}\right\} \tag{3-80}$$

Shear stress is given by

$$\tau = \frac{Pr}{8(1-\mu)}\left\{-\frac{1-2\mu}{R_1^3}+\frac{1-2\mu}{R_2^3}-\frac{3(z-D)^3}{R_1^7}\right.$$
$$\left.-\left[\frac{3(3-4\mu)z(z+D)-3D(3z+D)}{R_2^5}\right]-\frac{30zD(z+D)^2}{R_2^7}\right\} \tag{3-81}$$

$$R_1^2 = r^2+(z-D)^2$$
$$R_2^2 = r^2+(z-D)^2$$

Other formulas are omitted. When using computer for calculation, it can be expressed with dimensionless formulasas

$$n=\frac{r}{D};\ m=\frac{z}{D};\ F^2=m^2+n^2$$
$$R_1=n^2+(m-1)^2;\ R_2=n^2+(m+1)^2$$

And a stress factor is introduced for obtaining the vertical stress

$$\sigma_z=\frac{P}{D^2}K=\frac{P_P}{D^2}k_P+\frac{P_{us}}{D^2}k_a+\frac{P_{vs}}{D^2}k_v \tag{3-82}$$

in which, for loading condition 1, i.e. end-bearing pile with a concentrated load, the stress factor K_p is

$$K_P = \frac{1}{8\pi(1-\mu)}\left[-\frac{(1-2\mu)(m-1)}{R_1} + \frac{(1-2\mu)(m-1)}{R_2} - \frac{3(m-1)^3}{R_1} - \frac{3(3-4\mu)m(m+1)^2 - 3(m+1)(5m-1)}{R_2^5} - \frac{30m(m+1)^3}{R_2^7}\right] \tag{3-83}$$

for loading condition 2, i.e. friction pile with uniformly distributed surface friction, the vertical stress factor is

$$K_\mu = \frac{1}{8\pi(1-\mu)}\left[-\frac{2(2-\mu)}{R_1} + \frac{2(2-\mu) + 2(1-2\mu)\frac{m}{n}\left(\frac{m}{n}+\frac{1}{n}\right)}{R_2} - \frac{(1-2\mu)2\left(\frac{m}{n}\right)^2}{F} + \frac{n^2}{R_1^3} + \frac{4m^2 - 4(1+\mu)\left(\frac{m}{n}\right)^2 m^2}{F^3} + \frac{4m(1+\mu)(m+1)\left(\frac{m}{n}+\frac{1}{n}\right)^2 - (4m^2+n^2)}{R_2^3} + \frac{6m^2\left(\frac{m^4-n^4}{n^2}\right)}{F^5} + \frac{6m\left[mn^2 - \frac{1}{n^2}(m+1)^5\right]}{R_2^5}\right] \tag{3-84}$$

for loading condition 3, i.e. friction pile with linearly varying surface friction, the vertical stress factor is

$$K_V = \frac{1}{4\pi(1-\mu)}\left[-\frac{2(2-\mu)}{R_1} + \frac{2(2-\mu)(4m+1) - 2(1-2\mu)\left(\frac{m}{n}\right)^4 (m+1)}{R_2} + \frac{2(1-2\mu)\frac{m^3}{n^2} - 8(2-\mu)m}{F} + \frac{mn^2 + (m-1)^3}{R_1^3} + \frac{4\mu n^2 m + 4m^3 - 15n^2 m - 2(5+2n)\left(\frac{m}{n}\right)^2 (m+1)^3 + (m+1)^3}{R_2^3} + \frac{2(7-2\mu)mn^2 - 6m^3 + 2(5+2\mu)\left(\frac{m}{n}\right)^2 m^3}{F^3} + \frac{6mn^2(n^2-m^2) + 12\left(\frac{m}{n}\right)(m+1)^5}{R_2^5} - \frac{12\left(\frac{m}{n}\right)^2 m^5 + 6mn^2(n^2-m^2)}{F^6} - 2(2-\mu)\ln\left(\frac{R_1+m-1}{F+m}\frac{R_2+m+1}{F+m}\right)\right] \tag{3-85}$$

In Table 3-14—Table 3-16, values for $m<1.00$ are not listed for loading conditions 1 and 3 based on the fact that tension stress can not be induced although gravity can cause downward flow of subsoil. Though computation shows that the subgrade's gravity may generate deformation, in these cases the subgrade's gravity is usually not taken into consideration. The stresses in subgrade beneath the tip of the pile can induce settlement, while the subgrade's deformation above the tip of the pile is limited to pile's elastic compression which is computed to in the way of aP_aL/AE. What should be paid attention to in tabulation is $n=0.002^+$ be adopted since $n=0.0$ may cause incontinuity in computation.

Table 3-14 Stress factor for loading condition 1, i.e. concentrated force, where (−) indicates compression stress

m/n	0.0	0.1	0.2	0.3	0.4	0.5	0.75	1.0	1.5	2.0
	Poisson ration $\mu=0.2$									
1.0		−0.0960	−0.0936	−0.0897	−0.0846	−0.0785	−0.0614	−0.0448	−0.0208	−0.0089
1.1	−17.9689	−8.7753	−0.6188	−0.2238	−0.1332	−0.0999	−0.0659	−0.0467	−0.0222	−0.0099
1.2	−4.5510	−2.7458	−1.0005	−0.3937	−0.2035	−0.1325	−0.0724	−0.0490	−0.0236	−0.0110
1.3	−2.0809	−1.5287	−0.9233	−0.4788	−0.2672	−0.1681	−0.0811	−0.0520	−0.0249	−0.0119
1.4	−1.1858	−1.0382	−0.7320	−0.1652	−0.0926	−0.1930	−0.0905	−0.0555	−0.0263	−0.0129
1.5	−0.7722	−0.7153	−0.5682	−0.4114	−0.2875	−0.2025	−0.0985	−0.0592	−0.0277	−0.0138
1.6	−0.5548	−0.5238	−0.4457	−0.3518	−0.2664	−0.1997	−0.1038	−0.0625	−0.0290	−0.0147
1.7	−0.1188	−0.4018	−0.3669	−0.2984	−0.2399	−0.1893	−0.1061	−0.0651	−0.0303	−0.0156
1.8	−0.3294	−0.3193	−0.2918	−0.2539	−0.2133	−0.1755	−0.1057	−0.0668	−0.0315	−0.0164
1.9	−0.2673	−0.2609	−0.2431	−0.2177	−0.1890	−0.1606	−0.1033	−0.0675	−0.0325	−0.0172
2.0	−0.222	−0.2180	−0.2060	−0.1883	−0.1676	−0.1462	−0.0995	−0.0673	−0.0334	−0.0179
m/n	0.0	0.1	0.2	0.3	0.4	0.5	0.75	1.0	1.5	2.0
	Poisson ration $\mu=0.3$									
1.0		−0.1013	−0.0986	−0.0944	−0.0889	−0.0824	−0.0641	−0.0463	−0.0209	−0.0087
1.1	−19.3926	−3.9054	−0.5978	−0.2123	−0.1287	−0.0986	−0.0668	−0.0475	−0.0222	−0.0097
1.2	−4.9099	−2.9275	−1.0358	−0.4001	−0.202	−0.1303	−0.0722	−0.0493	−0.0235	−0.0106
1.3	−2.2222	−1.7467	−0.9757	−0.4970	−0.2717	−0.1637	−0.0808	−0.0519	−0.0247	−0.0116
1.4	−1.2777	−1.1152	−0.7805	−0.1891	−0.3032	−0.1974	−0.0908	−0.0555	−0.0260	−0.0125
1.5	−0.8377	−0.7686	−0.6070	−0.4356	−0.3012	−0.2098	−0.0999	−0.0594	−0.0274	−0.0134
1.6	−0.5968	−0.5626	−0.4768	−0.3738	−0.2809	−0.2086	−0.1093	−0.0631	−0.0288	−0.0143
1.7	−0.4500	−0.4312	−0.3819	−0.3177	−0.2538	−0.1988	−0.1094	−0.0661	−0.0302	−0.0152
1.8	−0.3536	−0.3424	−0.3122	−0.2706	−0.2262	−0.1849	−0.1096	−0.0682	−0.0315	−0.0161
1.9	−0.2806	−0.2795	−0.2600	−0.2321	−0.2006	−0.1697	−0.1076	−0.0693	−0.0326	−0.0169
2.0	−0.2380	−0.2333	−0.2201	−0.2007	−0.1780	−0.1547	−0.1039	−0.0694	−0.0336	−0.0177

continued

m/n	0.0	0.1	0.2	0.3	0.4	0.5	0.75	1.0	1.5	2.0
	Poisson ration $\mu=0.4$									
1.0		-0.1083	-0.1054	-0.1008	-0.0947	-0.0876	-0.0676	-0.0483	-0.0212	-0.0083
1.1	-21.2910	-4.0788	-0.5699	-0.1970	-0.1228	-0.0970	-0.0680	-0.0486	-0.0223	-0.0093
1.2	-5.3884	-3.1699	-1.0829	-0.4820	-0.1989	-0.1274	-0.0720	-0.0496	-0.0233	-0.0102
1.3	-2.4373	-1.9040	-1.0455	-0.5200	-0.2776	-0.1695	-0.0804	-0.0519	-0.0244	-0.0111
1.4	-1.4002	-1.2179	-0.8438	-0.5208	-0.3173	-0.2032	-0.0913	-0.0554	-0.0256	-0.0120
1.5	-0.9172	-0.8395	-0.6587	-0.4678	-0.3194	-0.2196	-0.1017	-0.0596	-0.0270	-0.0129
1.6	-0.6527	-0.6143	-0.5181	-0.4033	-0.3001	-0.2205	-0.1095	-0.0638	-0.0284	-0.0138
1.7	-0.4915	-0.4705	-0.4152	-0.3435	-0.2724	-0.2116	-0.1138	-0.0675	-0.0300	-0.0147
1.8	-0.3858	-0.3732	-0.3393	-0.2929	-0.2433	-0.1976	-0.1148	-0.0701	-0.0314	-0.0156
1.9	-0.3123	-0.3044	-0.2825	-0.5212	-0.2161	-0.1818	-0.1123	-0.0717	-0.0328	-0.0166
2.0	-0.2590	-0.2537	-0.2300	-0.2173	-0.1919	-0.1659	-0.1098	-0.0722	-0.0340	-0.0174

Table 3-15 Stress factor for loading condition 2, i.e. uniformly distributed surface friction, where (–) indicates compression stress

m/n	0.00	0.02	0.04	0.06	0.08	0.10	0.15	0.20	0.50	1.0	2.0
	Poisson ration $\mu=0.2$										
1.0		-6.4703	-3.2374	-2.1595	-1.6202	-1.2962	-0.8630	-0.6445	-0.2300	-0.0690	-0.0081
1.1	-1.7781	-1.7342	-1.5944	-1.4178	-1.2418	-1.0850	-0.7953	-0.6138	-0.2283	-0.0730	-0.0096
1.2	-0.9015	-0.8789	-0.8576	-0.8269	-0.7882	-0.7446	-0.631	-0.5307	-0.2231	-0.0759	-0.0111
1.3	-0.5968	-0.5799	-0.3725	-0.5629	-0.5500	-0.5340	-0.4867	-0.4355	-0.2138	-0.0779	-0.0125
1.4	-0.4569	-0.4288	-0.4241	-0.4201	-0.4142	-0.4068	-0.3838	-0.3562	-0.2010	-0.0789	-0.0139
1.5	-0.3482	-0.3359	-0.3334	-0.3313	-0.3282	-0.3242	-0.3113	-0.2952	-0.1862	-0.0790	-0.0152
1.6	-0.2922	-0.2726	-0.2716	-0.2707	-0.2689	-0.2666	-0.2589	-0.2487	-0.1708	-0.0784	-0.0165
1.7	-0.2518	-0.2304	-0.2287	-0.2274	-0.2661	-0.2247	-0.2195	-0.2127	-0.1559	-0.0770	-0.0175
1.8	-0.1772	-0.1953	-0.1949	-0.1942	-0.1936	-0.1925	-0.1891	-0.1844	-0.1420	-0.0750	-0.0185
1.9	-0.1648	-0.1702	-0.1698	-0.1687	-0.1682	-0.1675	-0.1650	-0.1610	-0.1293	-0.0727	-0.0193
2.0	-0.1461	-0.1482	-0.1486	-0.1420	-0.1478	-0.1473	-0.1455	-0.1429	-0.1180	-0.700	-0.0201
m/n	0.00	0.02	0.04	0.06	0.08	0.10	0.15	0.20	0.50	1.0	2.0
	Poisson ration $\mu=0.3$										
1.0		-6.8149	-3.4044	-2.2673	-1.6983	-1.3567	-0.8998	-0.6695	-0.2346	-0.0686	-0.0076
1.1	-1.9219	-1.8611	-1.7027	-1.5134	-1.3211	-1.1503	-0.8368	-0.6419	-0.2335	-0.0728	-0.0091
1.2	-0.9699	-0.9403	-0.9166	-0.8825	-0.8400	-0.7922	-0.6688	-0.5588	-0.2292	-0.0760	-0.0105
1.3	-0.6430	-0.6188	-0.6099	-0.5992	-0.5850	-0.5675	-0.5157	-0.4697	-0.2207	-0.0782	-0.0120
1.4	-0.4867	-0.4558	-0.4507	-0.4461	-0.4396	-0.4316	-0.4063	-0.371	-0.2082	-0.0796	-0.0134
1.5	-0.3766	-0.3561	-0.3533	-0.3510	-0.3476	-0.3432	-0.3291	-0.3115	-0.1934	-0.0800	-0.0148
1.6	-0.3339	-0.2895	-0.2878	-0.2863	-0.2843	-0.2817	-0.2732	-0.2621	-0.1777	-0.0796	-0.0160
1.7	-0.2664	-0.2438	-0.2414	-0.2399	-0.2384	-0.2369	-0.2313	-0.2239	-0.1623	-0.0786	-0.0172
1.8	-0.2025	-0.2065	-0.2054	-0.2044	-0.2038	-0.2026	-0.1989	-0.1956	-0.1419	-0.0766	-0.0182
1.9	-0.1847	-0.1794	-0.1785	-0.1777	-0.1768	-0.1760	-0.1733	-0.1696	-0.1347	-0.0744	-0.0191
2.0	-0.1634	-0.1565	-0.1561	-0.1556	-0.1551	-0.1545	-0.1525	-0.1498	-0.1229	-0.0718	-0.0199

continued

m/n	0.00	0.02	0.04	0.06	0.08	0.10	0.15	0.20	0.50	1.0	2.0
	Poisson ration $\mu = 0.4$										
1.0		−7.2744	−3.6270	−2.4110	−1.8026	−1.4373	−0.9488	−0.7029	−0.2407	−0.0681	−0.0069
1.1	−2.0931	−2.0296	−1.8574	−1.6409	−1.4266	−1.2372	−0.8921	−0.6794	−0.2404	−0.0725	−0.0083
1.2	−1.0486	−1.0209	−0.9947	−0.9567	−0.9091	−0.8556	−0.7181	−0.5964	−0.2373	−0.0760	−0.0098
1.3	−0.6922	−0.6694	−0.6598	−0.6476	−0.6318	−0.6122	−0.5543	−0.4921	−0.2298	−0.0787	−0.0113
1.4	−0.5347	−0.4922	−0.4860	−0.4807	−0.4735	−0.4645	−0.4362	−0.4026	−0.2178	−0.0805	−0.0128
1.5	−0.4020	−0.3823	−0.3798	−0.3771	−0.3734	−0.3684	−0.3527	−0.3332	−0.2029	−0.0813	−0.0142
1.6	−0.3440	−0.3096	−0.3083	−0.3068	−0.3045	−0.3017	−0.2922	−0.2800	−0.1868	−0.0812	−0.0155
1.7	−0.2943	−0.2606	−0.2580	−0.2564	−0.2549	−0.2531	−0.2469	−0.2387	−0.1708	−0.0803	−0.0167
1.8	−0.2114	−0.2207	−0.2189	−0.2181	−0.2174	−0.2161	−0.2119	−0.2063	−0.1558	−0.0787	−0.0178
1.9	−0.1782	−0.1907	−0.1904	−0.1890	−0.1881	−0.1873	−0.1843	−0.1802	−0.1419	−0.0766	−0.0188
2.0	−0.1741	−0.1660	−0.1658	−0.1652	−0.1648	−0.1642	−0.1620	−0.1590	−0.1294	−0.0741	−0.0196

Table 3-16 Stress factor for loading condition 3, i.e. linear varying surface friction, where (−) indicates compression stress

m/n	0.00	0.02	0.04	0.06	0.08	0.10	0.15	0.20	0.50	1.0	2.0
	Poisson ration $\mu = 0.2$										
1.0		−11.5315	−5.3127	−3.3023	−2.3263	−1.7582	−1.0372	−0.7033	−0.1963	−0.0618	−0.0082
1.1	−2.8427	−2.7514	−2.4908	−2.1596	−1.8329	−1.5469	−1.0359	−0.7646	−0.2074	−0.0656	−0.0095
1.2	−1.2853	−1.2541	−1.2158	−1.1620	−1.0930	−1.0162	−0.8211	−0.6529	−0.2141	−0.0689	−0.010
1.3	−0.7673	−0.7753	−0.7585	−0.7420	−0.7195	−0.6928	−0.6142	−0.5312	−0.2139	−0.0717	−0.0123
1.4	−0.5837	−0.5450	−0.5343	−0.5267	−0.5181	−0.5063	−04693	−0.4261	−0.2068	−0.0737	−0.0136
1.5	−0.4485	−0.4051	−0.4059	−0.4006	−0.3960	−0.3901	−0.3704	−0.3460	−0.1947	−0.0750	−0.0143
1.6	−0.3635	−0.3201	−0.3226	−0.3183	−0.3154	−0.3123	−0.3008	−0.2861	−0.1803	−0.0754	−0.0160
1.7	−0.3204	−0.2583	−0.2635	−0.2618	−0.2595	−0.2574	−0.2503	−0.2408	−0.1652	−0.0750	−0.0193
1.8	−0.2533	−0.2222	−0.2239	−0.2206	−0.2181	−0.2166	−0.2122	−0.2059	−0.1506	−0.0739	−0.0186
1.9	−0.2382	−0.1761	0.1855	−0.1880	−0.1878	−0.1853	−0.1827	−0.1782	−0.1371	−0.0722	−0.0188
2.0	−0.1767	−0.1643	−0.1648	−0.1630	−0.1631	−0.1614	−0.1591	−0.1561	−0.1248	−0.0700	−0.0196

m/n	0.00	0.02	0.04	0.06	0.08	0.10	0.15	0.20	0.50	1.0	2.0
	Poisson ration $\mu = 0.3$										
1.0		−12.1310	−5.5765	−3.4591	−2.4320	−1.8346	−1.0774	−0.7276	−0.1997	−0.0616	−0.0077
1.1	−3.0612	−2.9620	−2.6751	−2.3119	−1.9547	−1.6433	−1.0908	−0.7680	−0.2115	−0.0654	−0.0090
1.2	−1.3821	−1.3465	−1.3052	−1.2465	−1.1706	−1.0864	−0.8730	−0.6899	−0.2198	−0.0689	−0.0104
1.3	−0.8262	−0.8305	−0.8130	−0.7949	−0.7705	−0.7411	−0.6548	−0.5639	−0.2212	−0.0720	−0.0117
1.4	−0.5194	−0.5827	−0.5722	−0.5630	−0.5540	−0.5410	−0.5005	−0.4530	−0.2150	−0.0744	−0.0130
1.5	−0.6189	−0.4337	−0.4332	−0.4281	−0.4227	−0.4163	−0.3946	−0.3679	−0.2033	−0.0760	−0.0143
1.6	−0.3841	−0.3415	−0.3449	−0.3955	−0.3361	−0.3327	−0.3202	−0.3039	−0.1887	−0.0768	−0.0155
1.7	−0.3332	−0.2764	−0.2810	−0.2782	−0.2764	−0.2739	−0.2660	−0.2556	−0.1732	−0.0767	−0.0166
1.8	−0.2837	−0.2263	−0.2361	−0.2347	−0.2319	−0.2300	−0.2253	−0.2183	−0.1580	−0.0758	−0.0176
1.9	−0.2654	−0.1873	−0.1963	−0.1991	−0.1988	−0.1965	−0.1937	−0.1987	−0.1439	−0.0742	−0.0186
2.0	−0.1872	−0.1730	−0.1744	−0.1732	−0.1725	−0.1714	−0.1684	−0.1651	−0.1310	−0.0721	−0.0194

continued

m/n	0.00	0.02	0.04	0.06	0.08	0.10	0.15	0.20	0.50	1.0	2.0
	Poisson ration $\mu=0.4$										
1.0		−12.9304	−5.9282	−3.6683	−2.5729	−1.9365	−1.1311	−0.7600	−0.2042	−0.0614	−0.0069
1.1	−3.3525	−3.2423	−2.9209	−2.5144	−2.1171	−1.7719	−1.1641	−0.8125	−0.2170	−0.0652	−0.0083
1.2	−1.5030	−1.4712	−1.4255	−1.3588	−1.2742	−1.1800	−0.9422	−0.7394	−0.2274	−0.0689	−0.0096
1.3	−0.8965	−0.9066	−0.8862	−0.8649	−0.8383	−0.8056	−0.7089	−0.6076	−0.2308	−0.0723	−0.0100
1.4	−0.6753	−0.6350	−0.6222	−0.6120	−0.6018	−0.5874	−0.5419	−0.4890	−0.2260	−0.0752	−0.0123
1.5	−0.5629	−0.4718	−0.4712	−0.4641	−0.4584	−0.4511	−0.4270	−0.3971	−0.2147	−0.0773	−0.0136
1.6	−0.4198	−0.3701	−0.3730	−0.3672	−0.3642	−0.3600	−0.3461	−0.3278	−0.1999	−0.0786	−0.0149
1.7	−0.3752	−0.2840	−0.3039	−0.3011	−0.2984	−0.2956	−0.2870	−0.2754	−0.1838	−0.0788	−0.0161
1.8	−0.3158	−0.2496	−0.2575	−0.2530	−0.2497	−0.2479	−0.2427	−0.2349	−0.1680	−0.0782	−0.0172
1.9	−0.2851	−0.2022	−0.2122	−0.2155	−0.2141	−0.2113	−0.2083	−0.2028	−0.1530	−0.0769	−0.0182
2.0	−0.2012	−0.1929	−0.1878	−0.1854	−0.1850	−0.1837	−0.1807	−0.1771	−0.1393	−0.0749	−0.0191

The values of K are listed in Table 3-14—Table 3-16 for these three loading conditions using different m s and n s with three designated Poisson's ratios μ. With stress superposition these three loading conditions can present the general solution of vertical stress at arbitrary point along the pile. Vertical stress distribution in subgrade around a single pile is illustrated in Fig. 3-60.

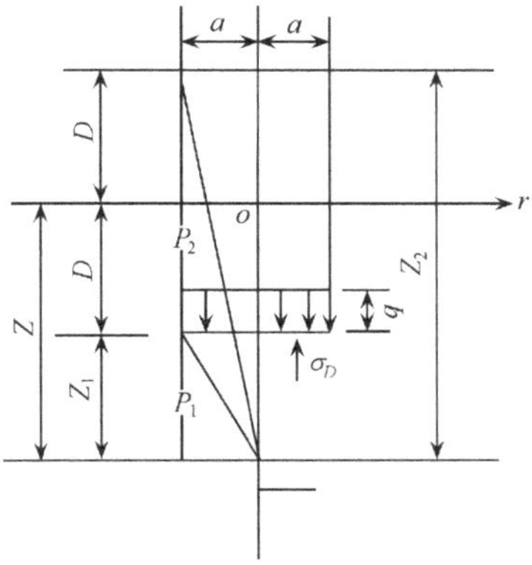

Fig. 3-59 Sketch map of subsoil under uniformly distributed circular vertical load

K_p and K_a are vertical stress factors related to $m=\dfrac{z}{D}$ and $n=\dfrac{r}{D}$, and their values for clay subgrade, when the soil's Poisson's ratio $\mu=0.5$, can be determined by Fig. 3-60, in which D is the pile's length.

The left side indicates stress factor for surface frictional resistance, while the right side indicates stress factor for resistance at the end of the pile, where negative sign indicates tension stress.

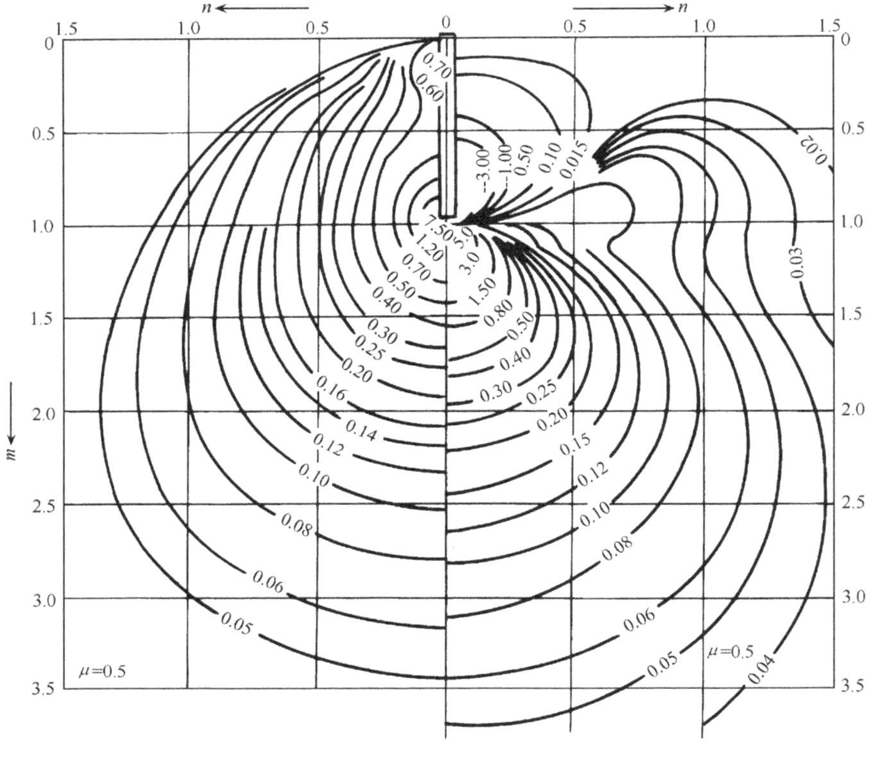

Fig. 3-60 Vertical stress factors for subgrade around a single pile

(2) subsoil subjected to uniformly distributed circular vertical load q (Fig. 3-59).

Vertical compression stress in subgrade at $r=0$ is given as follows

$$\sigma_z = \left[\frac{q}{4(1-\mu)}\right]\left[(1-2\mu)z\left(\frac{1}{\rho_2}-\frac{1}{\rho_1}+\frac{1}{z_1}-\frac{1}{z_2}\right)\right.$$
$$-\left(\frac{z_2^3}{\rho_2^3}-1\right)\{3(3-4\mu)zz_2^2-3Dz_2(4z+z)\}/3z_2^3$$
$$\left.+\left(1-\frac{z^3}{\rho_1^3}\right)+\frac{6Dz}{z^2}(1-z^2/\rho_2^5)\right] \tag{3-86}$$

while the vertical compression stress at $z=D$ is expressed in the form of $\sigma_{zD}(r)=qI_D$, in which the factor I_D is listed in Table 3-17.

Table 3-17 Stress factor for subsoil subjected to uniformly distributed circular load

v	D/n	r/q					
		0.0	0.2	0.4	0.6	0.8	1.0
0.00	0.5	0.889	0.882	0.653	0.115	0.856	0.587
	1.0	0.696	0.692	0.682	0.666	0.646	0.024
	2.0	0.564	0.503	0.662	0.560	0.557	0.554
	4.0	0.517	0.517	0.517	0.517	0.517	0.516
	10.0	0.503	0.503	0.503	0.503	0.503	0.503
	20.0	0.501	0.501	0.501	0.501	0.501	0.501
	50.0	0.500	0.500	0.500	0.500	0.500	0.500
0.25	0.5	0.912	0.904	0.373	0.834	0.799	0.604
	1.0	0.714	0.710	0.600	0.660	0.558	0.636
	2.0	0.570	0.570	0.563	0.566	0.563	0.559
	4.0	0.519	0.519	0.519	0.519	0.518	0.518
	10.0	0.503	0.503	0.503	0.503	0.503	0.503
	20.0	0.501	0.501	0.501	0.501	0.501	0.501
	50.0	0.500	0.500	0.500	0.500	0.500	0.500
0.30	0.5	0.956	0.947	0.920	0.879	0.795	0.797
	1.0	0.750	0.745	0.731	0.708	0.681	0.650
	2.0	0.584	0.583	0.581	0.578	0.574	0.560
	4.0	0.523	0.523	0.523	0.522	0.522	0.522
	10.0	0.504	0.501	0.504	0.504	0.504	0.504
	30.9	0.501	0.501	0.501	0.501	0.501	0.501
	50.0	0.500	0.500	0.500	0.500	0.500	0.400

Note: r/a —1.0<1.0 .

3.5 Stress Distribution in Heterogeneous and Anisotropic Subgrade

3.5.1 Surface Loading for Finite Elastic Layer Over Rigid Foundation Base

1. Circular load area on the surface of the finite elastic layer with uniformly distributed vertical pressure p *(Fig. 3-61)*

The stress σ_x at arbitrary point right under the center of circle can be determined by Fig. 3-62. The stress σ_z at arbitrary point right under the circumference can be determined by Fig. 3-63. The stress σ_r at arbitrary point right under the center of circle can be determined by Fig. 3-64. The stress σ_r at arbitrary point right under the circumference can be determined by Fig. 3-65, while the stress τ_{rz} be determined by Fig. 3-66.

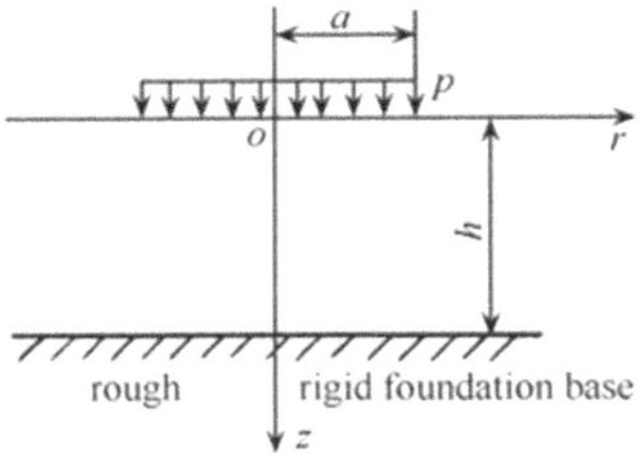

Fig. 3-61 Circular load area subjected to uniformly distributed vertical load

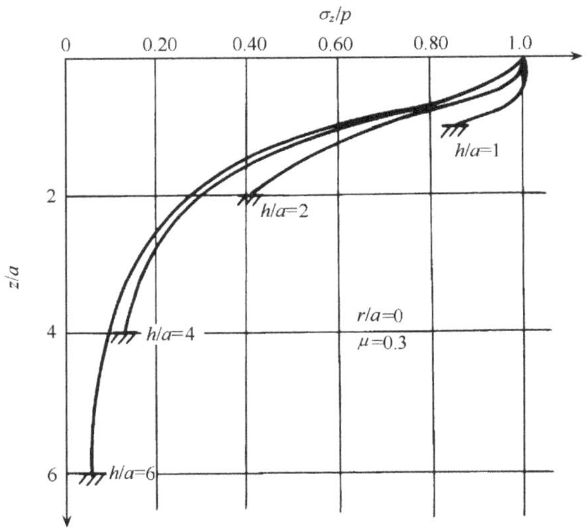

Fig. 3-62 Distribution of σ_x at arbitrary point right under the center of circle (Milovic, 1970)

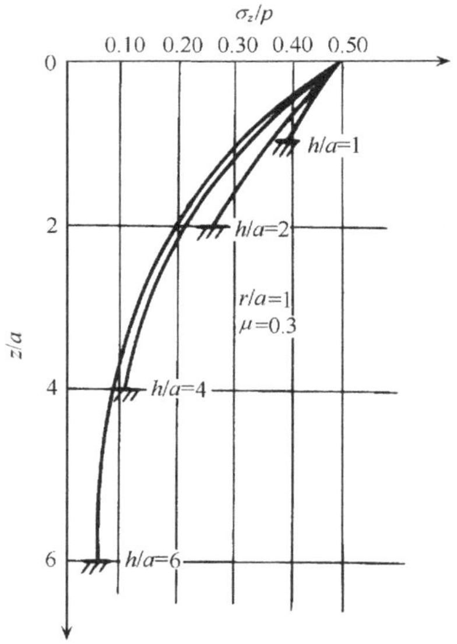

Fig. 3-63 Distribution of σ_z at arbitrary point right under the circumference (Milovic, 1970)

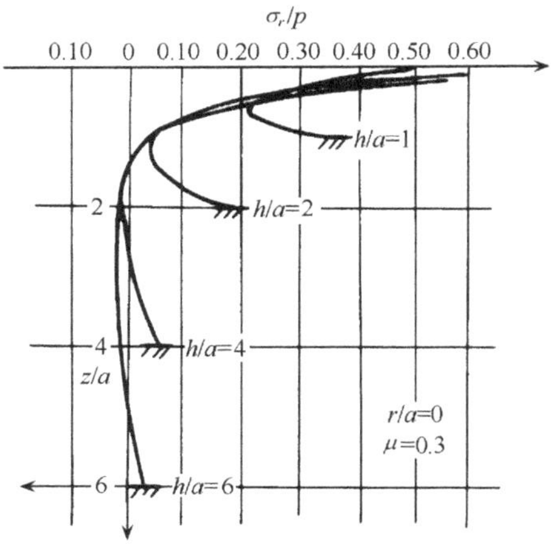

Fig. 3-64 Distribution of σ_r at arbitrary point right under the center of circle (Milovic, 1970)

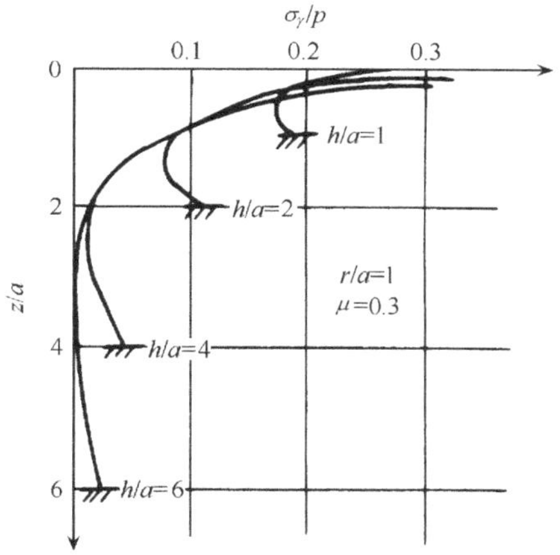

Fig. 3-65 Distribution of σ_r at arbitrary point right under the circumference (Milovic, 1970)

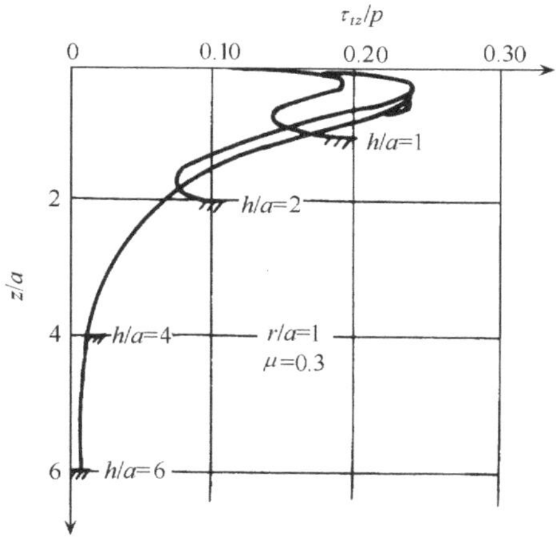

Fig. 3-66 Distribution of τ_{rz} at arbitrary point right under the circumference (Milovic, 1970)

Besides, the vertical displacement of arbitrary point of the circumference is expressed as

$$v_i = \frac{2pa(1-\mu^2)}{E} I_i \tag{3-87}$$

in which I_i is displacement influence factor, which can be referred to in Table 3-18. The vertical displacement of arbitrary point within the circle is given by

$$v_i = \frac{2pa}{E} I_i \tag{3-88}$$

where I_i is a displacement influence factor, which can be referred to in Table 3-19.

Table 3-18 The values of influence factor I_i (Egorov, 1958)

h/a	The interface between the elastic layer and rigid base	
	Smooth (Suitable for all v)	Rough or bonded (only suitable for v=0.3)
0.2	0.005	0.04
0.5	0.12	0.10
1	0.23	0.20
2	0.38	0.34
3	0.45	0.42
5	0.52	0.50
7	0.50	0.54
10	0.58	0.57
∞	0.64	0.64

Table 3-19 values of influence factor I_i (Milovic, 1970)

V	$\frac{b}{a}$	r/a					
		0	0.2	0.4	0.6	0.8	1.0
0.15	1	0.454	0.458	0.441	0.408	0.348	0.208
	2	0.684	0.674	0.645	0.593	0.509	0.348
	4	0.811	0.800	0.768	0.710	0.619	0.463
	6	0.839	0.827	0.794	0.736	0.646	0.501
0.3	1	0.497	0.392	0.379	0.351	0.301	0.173
	2	0.613	0.604	0.578	0.531	0.456	0.305
	4	0.740	0.732	0.703	0.651	0.568	0.420
	6	0.770	0.762	0.733	0.681	0.597	0.458
0.45	1	0.278	0.276	0.267	0.250	0.213	0.109
	2	0.489	0.482	0.461	0.422	0.361	0.229
	4	0.612	0.608	0.585	0.541	0.472	0.340
	6	0.637	0.635	0.612	0.568	0.499	0.374

Note: This table is suitable for the case of rough or bonded interface between elastic layer and rigid foundation base.

2. Rectangular load area on the surface of finite elastic layer with uniformly distributed vertical load (Fig. 3-67)

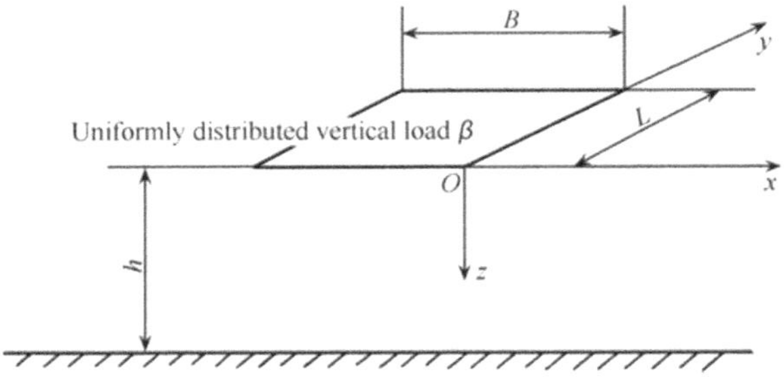

Fig. 3-67 Rectangular load area subjected to uniformly distributed vertical pressure

The stress σ_z at the depth $z = 0.2h$ beneath the four angular points of the rectangle for rough or bonded interface between elastic layer and rigid foundation base, can be determined by Fig. 3-68, in which Poisson's ratio $\mu = 0.4$ for elastic layer is assumed.

Under the condition of smooth interface between the elastic layer and rigid foundation base, the stress σ_z at arbitrary depth within the elastic layer beneath the center of the rectangle can be determined by Fig. 3-69, while the stress σ_z at designated depth beneath some points of the rectangular area can be referred to in Table 3-20, and the vertical displacements of some points of the rectangular area can be determined by Fig. 3-70 (denoted by black dot).

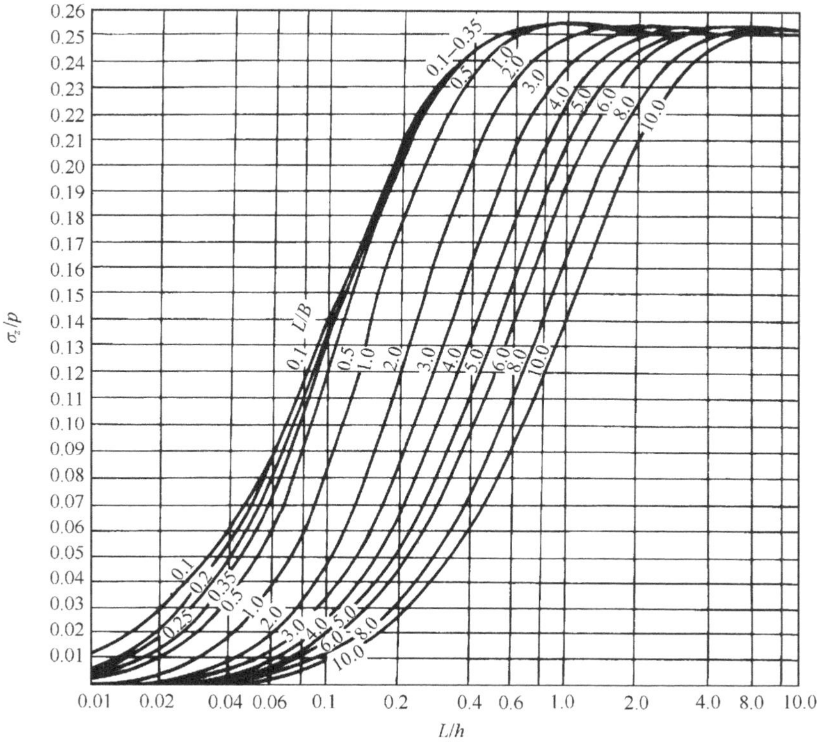

Fig. 3-68 Distribution of σ_z at the depth $0.2h$ beneath the four angular points of the rectangle (Burmister, 1956)

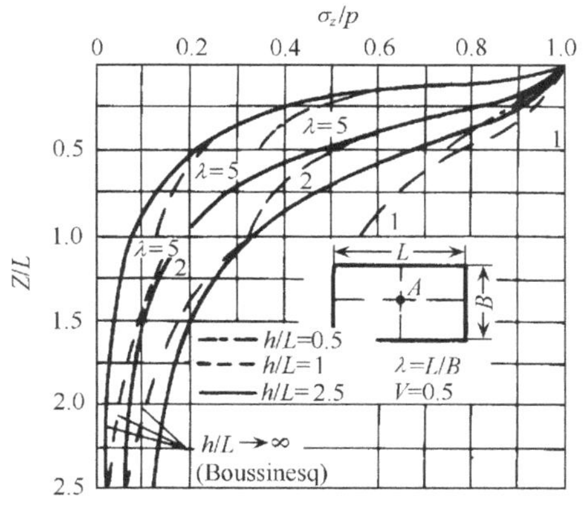

Fig. 3-69 Distribution of σ_z at arbitrary depth beneath the center of rectangle

Table 3-20 The values of σ_z/p (Sovinc, 1961)

$\frac{L}{B}$	$\frac{h}{B}$	Beneath the center of the rectangle		Beneath the midpoint of the short side		Beneath the midpoint of the long side		Beneath the angular point of the rectangle	
		$\frac{z}{h}$=0.5	1	$\frac{z}{h}$=0.5	1	$\frac{z}{h}$=0.5	1	$\frac{z}{h}$=0.5	1
1	1	0.7835	0.5616	0.4571	0.3835	0.4571	0.3835	—	—
	2.5	0.2498	0.1217	0.1938	0.1105	0.1938	0.1105	—	—
	5	0.0744	0.0325	0.0695	0.0317	0.0695	0.0317	0.0616	0.0282
2	1	0.8808	0.7410	0.4412	0.3842	0.5359	0.5110	0.2678	0.2636
	2	0.5097	0.3219	0.2923	0.2197	0.3881	0.2804	0.2256	0.1921
	3	0.1333	0.0622	0.1050	0.0564	0.1242	0.0606	0.0988	0.0552
5	2.5	0.4847	0.3459	0.2032	0.1675	0.3930	0.3199	0.1826	0.1541
	5	0.2294	0.1346	0.1239	0.0894	0.2094	0.1316	0.1205	0.0875
	12.5	0.0526	0.0246	0.0406	0.0214	—	—	—	—

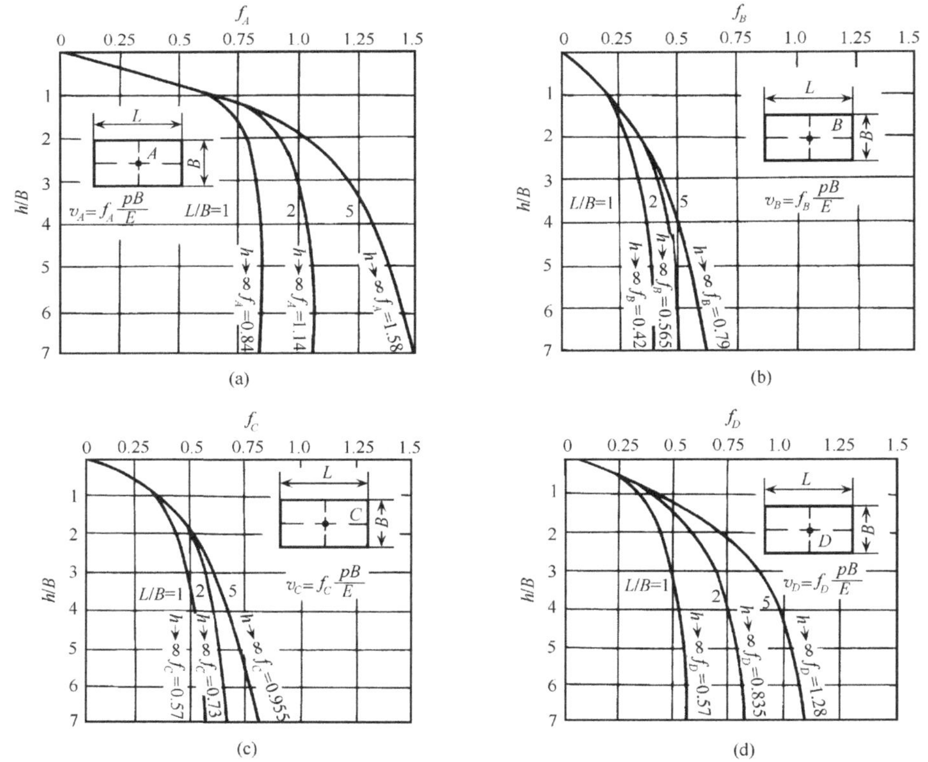

Fig. 3-70 Vertical displacements of black dots on the rectangular area (Sovinc, 1961)

3.5.2 Circular Load Area on the Surface of a Dual-Layer Semi-Infinite Elastic Body with Uniformly Distributed Vertical Pressure *p* (Fig. 3-71)

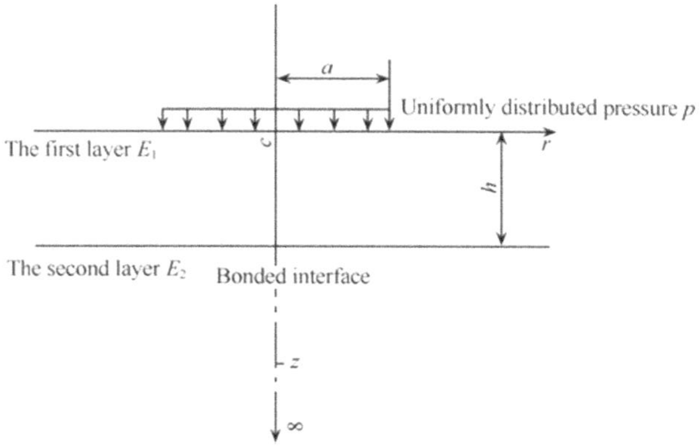

Fig. 3-71 Circular load area on a dual-layer semi-infinite body with uniformly distributed vertical pressure

The vertical stress σ_z can be determined by Fig. 3-72, which is plotted in the form of contours of the percentage of σ_z / p and is only applicable for the case that $E_1 / E_2 = 10$, $\mu_1 = \mu_2 = 0.5$ and $h / a = 1$.

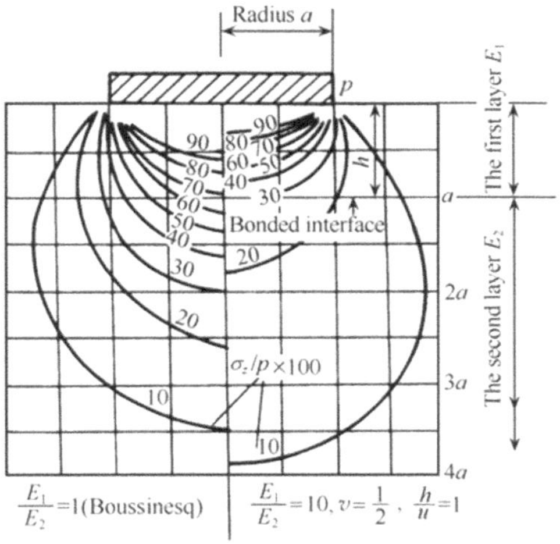

Fig. 3-72 Distribution of vertical stress σ_z (Fox, 1948)

The vertical stress σ_z at the crosspoint of the interface of these two layers and axis z can be determined by Fig. 3-73, from which effect of ratios of E_1 / E_2 and h / a on vertical stress σ_z can be observed. Vertical stresses σ_z at other points of the interface can be determined by Fig. 3-74, which is only suitable for the case that $h / a = 1$.

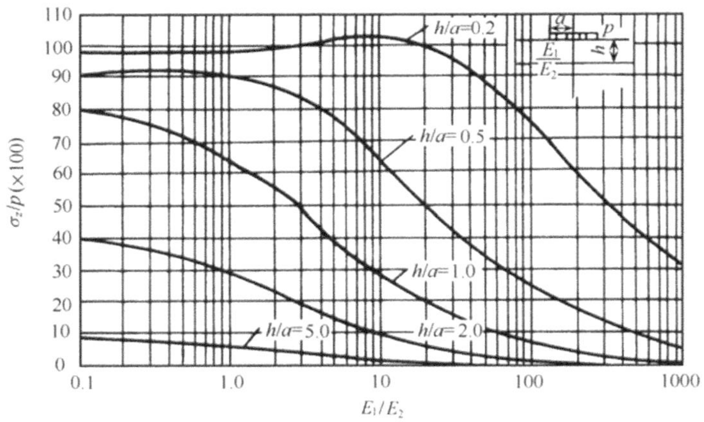

Fig. 3-73 The distribution of vertical stress σ_z at the crosspoint of the interface and axis z (Fox, 1948a)

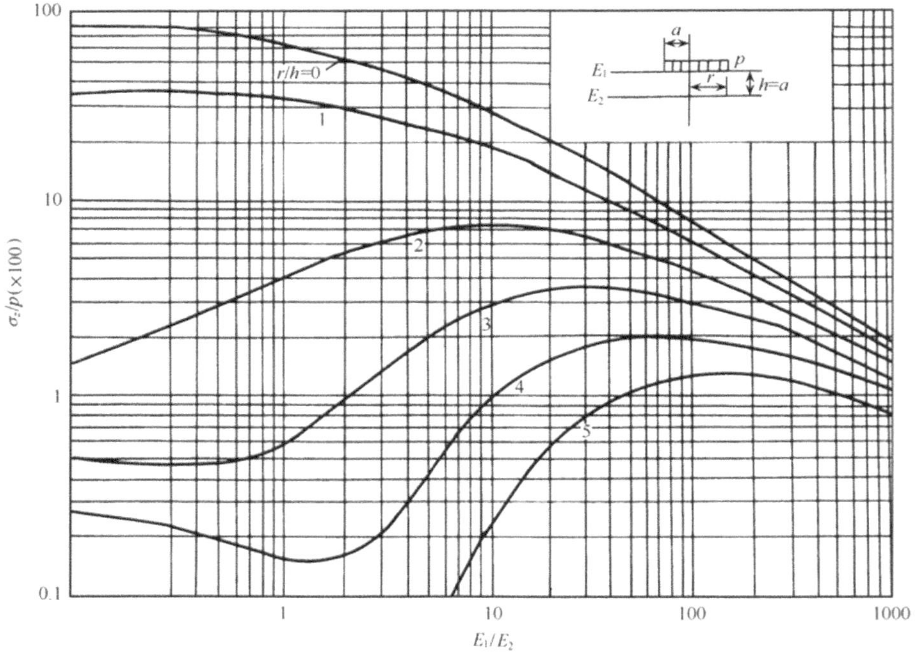

Fig. 3-74 Distribution of vertical stress σ_z at other points of the interface (Fox, 1948a)

The stresses σ_z and $(\sigma_z - \sigma_r)$ in the next layer beneath the interface can be veferred to in Table 3-21 when the interface is completely rough or bonded, on the other side, when the interface is completely smooth, one can refer to Table 3-22 for these stresses. Noticeably, all the readings in these two tables are the percentage of $\dfrac{\sigma_z}{p}$ and $\dfrac{(\sigma_z - \sigma_r)}{p}$.

Table 3-21 Percentages of σ_z/p and $(\sigma_z-\sigma_r)/p$ in the next layer below the completely rough interface of dual-layer system

E_1/E_2	σ_z/p				$(\sigma_z-\sigma_r)/p$			
	1	10	100	1000	1	10	100	1000
The depth beneath the interface					$a/h=1/2$			
0	28.4	10.1	2.38	0.51	26.8	7.6	1.26	0.160
h	8.7	4.70	1.58	0.42	8.6	3.93	1.02	0.185
2h	4.03	2.78	1.17	0.35	4.00	2.48	0.85	0.195
3h	2.30	1.34	0.01	0.31	2.29	1.70	0.71	0.190
4h	1.43	1.29	0.74	0.23	1.48	1.23	0.61	0.185
				$a/h=1$				
0	64.6	29.2	8.1	1.85	53.0	18.8	3.6	0.54
h	28.4	16.8	6.0	1.62	26.8	13.5	3.8	0.71
2h	14.5	10.5	4.6	1.43	14.1	9.2	3.3	0.79
3h	8.7	7.0	3.8	1.24	8.6	6.4	2.8	0.76
4h	5.7	5.0	2.9	1.10	5.6	4.7	2.4	0.73
				$a/h=2$				
0	91.1	64.4	24.5	7.10	53.7	30.4	8.4	1.50
h	64.6	48.0	20.5	6.06	53.0	34.6	11.8	2.52
2h	42.4	34.0	16.5	5.42	38.4	28.2	11.4	2.90
3h	28.4	24.4	13.3	4.80	26.8	21.5	10.2	2.92
4h	20.0	18.1	10.8	4.28	19.2	16.6	8.8	2.82

Table 3-22 Percentages of σ_z/p and $(\sigma_z-\sigma_r)/p$ in the next layer under the completely smooth interface of the dual-layer system

E_1/E_2	σ_z/p				$(\sigma_z-\sigma_r)/p$			
	1	10	100	1000	1	10	100	1000
The depth beneath the interface					$a/h=1/2$			
0	31.0	10.5	2.41	0.51	0.00	0.00	0.00	0.00
1/2h					14.5	4.49		
h	14.1	6.3	1.83	0.45	11.5	4.32	0.96	0.18
2h	6.4	3.67	1.36	0.38	5.9	3.03	0.91	0.18
3h	3.46	2.35	1.05	0.33	3.32	2.08	0.79	0.19
4h	2.12	1.61	0.83	0.29	2.07	1.37	0.66	0.18
				$a/h=1$				
0	72.2	30.5	8.2	1.90	0.00	0.00	0.00	0.00
1/2h					34.7	12.7		
h	43.7	21.7	6.8	1.72	33.1	14.2	3.41	0.59
2h	22.5	13.6	5.25	1.51	20.2	11.0	3.47	0.74
3h	12.8	8.9	4.09	1.33	12.1	7.8	3.05	0.77
4h	8.1	6.2	3.26	1.17	7.8	5.7	2.61	0.75

continued

E_1/E_2	σ_z/p				$(\sigma_z-\sigma_r)/p$			
	1	10	100	1000	1	10	100	1000
	$a/h=2$							
0	102.5	67.7	24.9	6.7	0.00	0.00	0.00	0.00
1/2h					37.8	23.1		
h	86.9	57.6	22.5	6.3	62.6	32.0	9.9	1.96
2h	59.6	42.1	18.6	5.7	48.3	31.7	11.6	2.86
3h	39.6	30.2	15.0	5.10	36.3	25.4	10.9	2.68
4h	27.1	22.0	12.2	4.54	25.7	19.6	9.6	2.86

The vertical displacement v of the center of the circular load area is determined by the following figures. Where Fig. 3-75 is suitable for materials with $\mu_1=0.2$, $\mu_2=0.4$, Fig. 3-76 for materials with $\mu_1=\mu_2=0.5$, while Fig. 3-77 for materials with $\mu_1=\mu_2=0.35$.

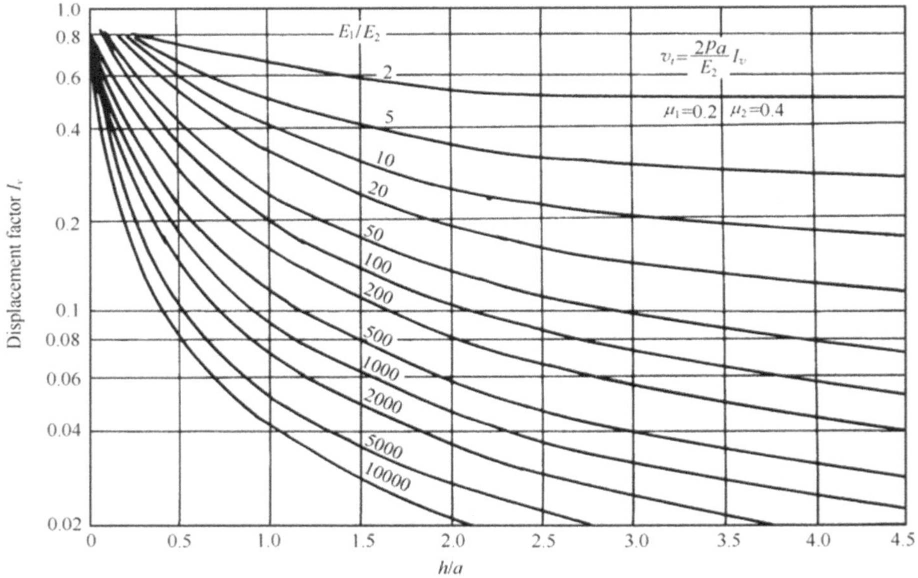

Fig. 3-75 The relation between displacement factor I_v and h/a ($\mu_1=0.2$, $\mu_2=0.4$) (Burmister, 1962)

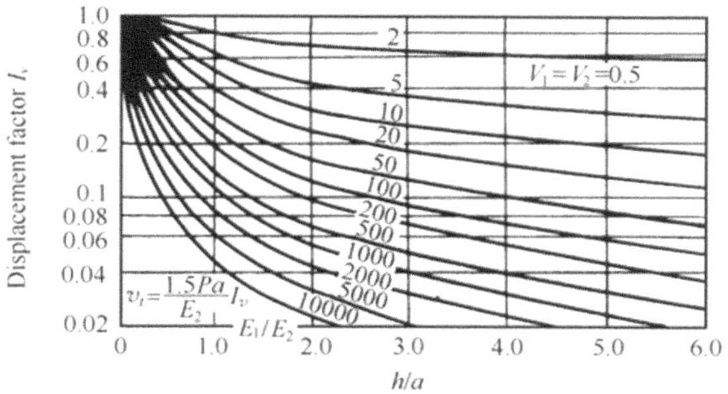

Fig. 3-76 The relation between displacement factor I_v and h/a ($\mu_1=\mu_2=0.5$) (Burmister, 1962)

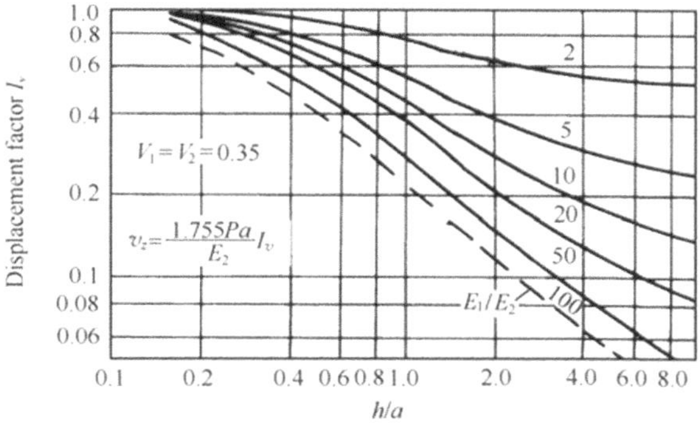

Fig. 3-77 Relation between displacement factor I_v and h/a ($\mu_1=\mu_2=0.35$) (Thenn de Barros, 1962)

3.5.3 Circular Load Area on the Surface of Triple-Layer Semi-Infinite Elastic Body with Uniformly Distributed Vertical Pressure *p* (Fig. 3-78)

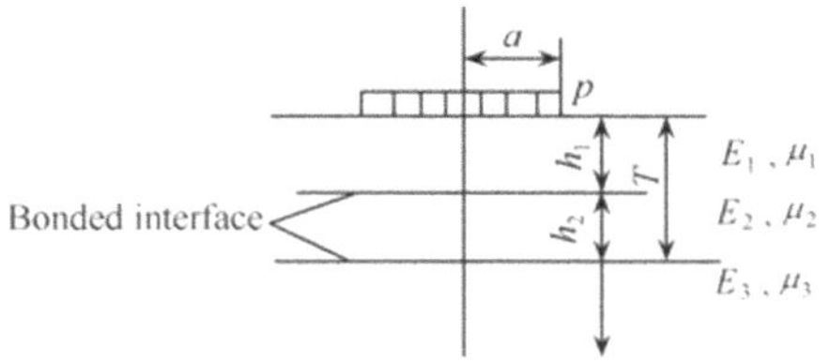

Fig. 3-78 Circular load area on a triple-layer semi-infinite elastic body with uniformly distributed vertical pressure

Stress at the crosspoint of the interface and $z-$axis can be referred to in Table 3-23 and 3-24. Stresses in the former three columns therein belong to the upper interface, while the latter three columns go to the lower interface, where

$$a_1 = a/h_2$$

$$H = h_1/h_2$$

$$k_1 = E_1/E_2$$

$$k_2 = E_2/E_3$$

For the purpose of brevity, the compression stress is taken as positive.

Vertical displacements for the center of the circle and points along the boundary are given by

$$v_s = \frac{1.5pa}{E_3} F_{co} \tag{3-89a}$$

$$v_l = \frac{1.5pa}{E_3} F_{cl} \tag{3-89b}$$

respectively. Where v_c is the vertical displacement of the center of the circle, while v_l is the vertical displacement of points along the circumference. F_{co} and F_{cl} are displacement factors, which can be determined by Fig. 3-79 and 3-80, respectively.

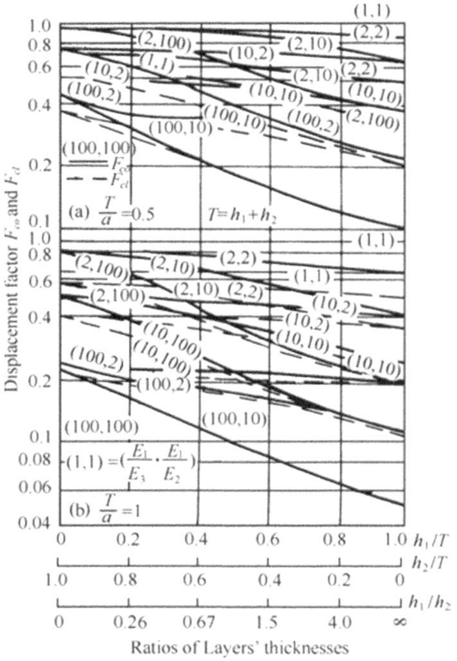

Fig. 3-79 The relation between displacement factor and ratios of layers' thicknesses (Ucshita and Meyerhof, 1967)

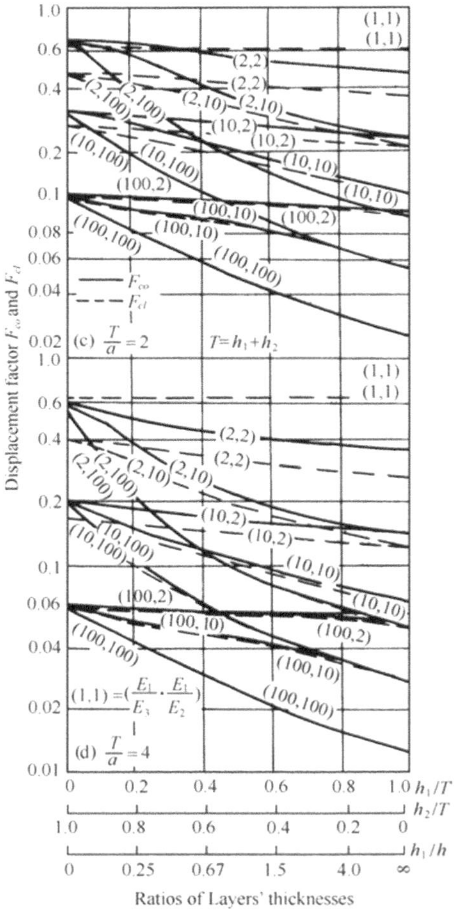

Fig. 3-80 The relation between displacement factor and ratios of layers' thicknesses (Ucshita and Meyerhof, 1967)

The vertical displacement of the center of the circular load area can also be computed precisely by

$$v_c = \frac{1.755pa}{E_3}F \tag{3-89c}$$

where F is a displacement factor, which can be determined from Table 3-25 — Table 3-29, in which

$$n_1 = E_1 / E_2 = 2,5,10,20,50$$
$$n_2 = E_2 / E_3 = 2,5,10$$
$$\mu_1 = \mu_2 = \mu_3 = 0.35$$

Table 3-23 (Jones, 1962)

$H = 0.125$
$k_1 = 2.0$

	a_1	σ_{σ_1}/p	$(\sigma_{\sigma_1}-\sigma_{\eta})/p$	$(\sigma_{\sigma_1}-\sigma_{rsi})/p$	σ_{π_2}/p	$(\sigma_{\sigma_3}-\sigma_{\eta})/p$	$(\sigma_{\sigma_3}-\sigma_{r_3})/p$
	0.1	0.66045	0.12438	0.62188	0.01557	0.00332	0.01659
	0.2	0.90249	0.13546	0.67728	0.06027	0.01278	0.06391
k_2=0.2	0.4	0.95295	0.10428	0.52141	0.21282	0.04430	0.22150
	0.8	0.99520	0.09011	0.45053	0.56395	0.10975	0.54877
	1.6	1.00064	0.08777	0.43884	0.86258	0.13755	0.68777
	3.2	0.99970	0.04129	0.20643	0.94143	0.10147	0.50736
k_2=2.0	0.1	0.66048	0.12285	0.61424	0.00892	0.01693	0.00846
	0.2	0.90157	0.12916	0.64582	0.03480	0.06558	0.03279
	0.4	0.95120	0.08115	0.40576	0.12656	0.23257	0.11629
k_1=0.2	0.8	0.99235	0.01823	0.09113	0.37307	0.62863	0.31432
	1.6	0.99918	−0.04136	−0.20680	0.74038	0.98754	0.49377
	3.2	1.00032	−0.03804	−0.19075	0.97137	0.82102	0.41051
	0.1	0.66235	0.12032	0.60161	0.00258	0.03667	0.00183
	0.2	0.90415	0.11787	0.58933	0.01011	0.14336	0.00717
	0.4	0.95135	0.03474	0.17370	0.03838	0.52691	0.02635
k_2=20.0	0.8	0.98778	−0.14872	−0.74358	0.13049	1.61727	0.08086
	1.6	0.99407	−0.50533	−2.52650	0.36442	3.58944	0.17947
	3.2	0.99821	−0.80990	−4.05023	0.76669	5.15409	0.25770
	0.1	0.66266	0.11720	0.58599	0.00057	0.05413	0.00027
	0.2	0.90370	0.10495	0.52477	0.00226	0.21314	0.00107
	0.4	0.94719	−0.01709	−0.08543	0.00881	0.80400	0.00402
k_3=200.0	0.8	0.99105	−0.34427	−1.72134	0.03259	2.67934	0.01340
	1.6	0.99146	−1.21129	−6.05643	0.11034	7.35978	0.03680
	3.2	0.99332	−2.89282	−14.46408	0.32659	16.22830	0.08114

Table 3-24 (Jones, 1962)

$H = 0.125$
$k_1 = 2.0$

	a_1	σ_{z1}/p	$(\sigma_{z1}-\sigma_{r1})/p$	$(\sigma_{z1}-\sigma_{r2})/p$	σ_{z1}/p	$(\sigma_{z2}-\sigma_{r2})/p$	$(\sigma_{z2}-\sigma_{r3})/p$
$k_2 = 0.2$	0.1	0.43055	0.71614	0.35807	0.01682	0.00350	0.01750
	0.2	0.78688	1.01561	0.50780	0.06511	0.01348	0.06741
	0.4	0.98760	0.83924	0.41962	0.23005	0.04669	0.23346
	0.8	1.01028	0.63961	0.31981	0.60886	0.11484	0.57418
	1.6	1.00647	0.65723	0.32862	0.90959	0.13726	0.68630
	3.2	0.99822	0.38165	0.19093	0.94322	0.09467	0.47335
$k_1 = 0.2$	0.1	0.42950	0.70622	0.36303	0.00896	0.01716	0.00858
	0.2	0.78424	0.97956	0.48989	0.03493	0.06647	0.03324
	0.4	0.98044	0.70970	0.35488	0.12667	0.23531	0.11766
	0.8	0.99434	0.22319	0.11164	0.36932	0.63003	0.31501
	1.6	0.99364	−0.19982	−0.09995	0.72113	0.97707	0.48853
	3.2	0.99922	−0.28916	−0.14461	0.96148	0.84030	0.42015
$k_2 = 20.0$	0.1	0.43022	0.69332	0.34662	0.00228	0.03467	0.00173
	0.2	0.78414	0.92086	0.46048	0.00899	0.13541	0.00677
	0.4	0.97493	0.46583	0.23297	0.03392	0.49523	0.02478
	0.8	0.97806	−0.66535	−0.33270	0.11350	1.49612	0.07481
	1.6	0.96921	−2.82859	−1.41430	0.31263	3.28512	0.16426
	3.2	0.98591	−5.27906	−2.63954	0.68433	5.05952	0.25298
$k_2 = 200.0$	0.1	0.42925	0.67488	0.33744	0.00046	0.04848	0.00024
	0.2	0.78267	0.85397	0.42698	0.00183	0.19043	0.00095
	0.4	0.97369	0.21165	0.10582	0.00711	0.71221	0.00356
	0.8	0.97295	−1.65954	−0.82977	0.02597	2.32652	0.01163
	1.6	0.95548	−6.47707	−3.23855	0.08700	6.26638	0.03133
	3.2	0.96377	−16.67376	−8.33691	0.26292	14.25621	0.07128

Table 3-25 Values of F (Thenn de Barros, 1966) $n_1 = 2$

n_1	h_1/a \ h_2/a	0.156	0.312	0.625	1.25	2.5	5
2	0.312	0.858	0.789	0.662	0.510	0.394	—
	0.625	0.772	0.717	0.616	0.489	0.387	0.323
	1.25	0.669	0.633	0.560	0.460	0.375	0.319
	2.5	—	0.564	0.508	0.428	0.360	0.314
	5	—	—	0.470	0.400	0.343	0.306
5	0.312	0.747	0.651	0.505	0.352	0.240	—
	0.625	0.601	0.537	0.438	0.324	0.231	0.171
	1.25	0.449	0.416	0.359	0.284	0.215	0.166
	2.5	—	0.320	0.287	0.240	0.194	0.158
	5	—	—	0.235	0.202	0.172	0.148

continued

n_1	h_1/a \ h_2/a	0.156	0.312	0.625	1.25	2.5	5
10	0.312	0.664	0.559	0.415	0.274	0.174	—
	0.625	0.500	0.436	0.346	0.246	0.165	0.112
	1.25	0.344	0.315	0.267	0.207	0.150	0.108
	2.5	—	0.221	0.198	0.165	0.130	0.100
	5	—	—	0.149	0.128	0.108	0.0903

Table 3-26 Values of *F* (Thenn de Barros, 1966) $n_1 = 5$

n_1	h_1/a \ h_2/a	0.156	0.312	0.625	1.25	2.5	5
2	0.312	0.830	0.733	0.556	0.372	0.246	—
	0.625	0.745	0.669	0.522	0.359	0.242	0.174
	1.25	0.648	0.593	0.476	0.339	0.235	0.172
	2.5	—	0.528	0.430	0.313	0.224	0.168
	5	—	—	0.394	0.289	0.211	0.163
5	0.312	0.713	0.598	0.427	0.268	0.162	—
	0.625	0.572	0.497	0.378	0.250	0.157	0.101
	1.25	0.429	0.387	0.312	0.223	0.148	0.0989
	2.5	—	0.299	0.249	0.188	0.134	0.0944
	5	—	—	0.202	0.155	0.116	0.0871
10	0.312	0.626	0.508	0.350	0.211	0.122	—
	0.625	0.469	0.401	0.301	0.195	0.118	0.0712
	1.25	0.325	0.291	0.236	0.168	0.109	0.0691
	2.5	—	0.206	0.174	0.134	0.0954	0.0649
	5	—	—	0.130	0.102	0.0779	0.0579

Table 3-27 Values of *F* (Thenn de Barros, 1966) $n_1 = 10$

n_2	h_1/a \ h_2/a	0.156	0.312	0.625	1.25	2.5	5
2	0.312	0.811	0.687	0.483	0.298	0.181	—
	0.625	0.729	0.630	0.457	0.290	0.178	0.116
	1.25	0.634	0.561	0.420	0.275	0.174	0.115
	2.5	—	0.499	0.379	0.255	0.166	0.112
	5	—	—	0.346	0.234	0.156	0.109
5	0.312	0.689	0.553	0.369	0.217	0.123	—
	0.625	0.553	0.467	0.334	0.207	0.121	0.0720
	1.25	0.416	0.367	0.281	0.187	0.115	0.0706
	2.5	—	0.284	0.225	0.160	0.105	0.0679
	5	—	—	0.181	0.130	0.0912	0.0629
10	0.312	0.601	0.467	0.302	0.172	0.0946	—
	0.625	0.405	0.376	0.267	0.163	0.0924	0.0525
	1.25	0.312	0.275	0.214	0.144	0.0876	0.0514
	2.5	—	0.195	0.159	0.117	0.0782	0.0489
	5	—	—	0.117	0.0885	0.0642	0.0442

Table 3-28 Values of *F* (Thenn de Barros, 1966) $n_1 = 20$

n_2	h_2/a \ h_1/a	0.156	0.312	0.625	1.25	2.5	5
2	0.312	0.789	0.629	0.411	0.239	0.136	—
	0.625	0.711	0.583	0.394	0.234	0.135	0.0809
	1.25	0.621	0.523	0.365	0.224	0.132	0.0802
	2.5	—	0.465	0.331	0.209	0.127	0.0788
	5	—	—	0.300	0.191	0.120	0.0764
5	0.312	0.652	0.501	0.313	0.175	0.0953	—
	0.625	0.535	0.433	0.290	0.169	0.0939	0.0528
	1.25	0.404	0.345	0.250	0.167	0.0909	0.0521
	2.5	—	0.267	0.202	0.136	0.0846	0.0506
	5	—	—	0.161	0.112	0.0742	0.0475
10	0.312	0.573	0.419	0.254	0.139	0.0740	—
	0.625	0.434	0.349	0.232	0.134	0.0729	0.0396
	1.25	0.301	0.260	0.193	0.123	0.0703	0.0390
	2.5	—	0.184	0.145	0.102	0.0645	0.0377
	5	—	—	0.106	0.0779	0.0542	0.0348

Table 3-29 Values of *F* (Thenn de Barros, 1966) $n_1 = 50$

n_2	h_2/a \ h_1/a	0.156	0.312	0.625	1.25	2.5	5
2	0.312	0.744	0.538	0.324	0.178	0.0960	—
	0.625	0.677	0.508	0.314	0.175	0.0953	0.0532
	1.25	0.594	0.461	0.297	0.170	0.0940	0.0628
	2.5	—	0.411	0.271	0.161	0.0915	0.0522
	5	—	—	0.245	0.148	0.0868	0.0509
5	0.312	0.612	0.421	0.244	0.131	0.0687	—
	0.625	0.507	0.378	0.233	0.128	0.0681	0.0364
	1.25	0.387	0.311	0.209	0.122	0.0667	0.0361
	2.5	—	0.241	0.173	0.110	0.0637	0.0354
	5	—	—	0.137	0.0915	0.0575	0.0338
10	0.312	0.524	0.348	0.197	0.104	0.0539	—
	0.625	0.410	0.305	0.187	0.102	0.0534	0.0280
	1.25	0.288	0.237	0.164	0.0966	0.0523	0.0277
	2.5	—	0.169	0.128	0.0847	0.0496	0.0272
	5	—	—	0.0926	0.0664	0.0436	0.0258

3.5.4 Subsoil With Deformation Modulus Increased With Depth

For subsoil with deformation modulus increasing with depth, the vertical stress at arbitrary point M of the subgrade subjected to concentrated load p can be expressed in the following semi-empirical equation

$$\sigma_z = \frac{kp}{2\pi R^2}\cos k\theta \tag{3-90}$$

in which k is empirical factor (stress concentration factor). Generally speaking, $k=6$ for sandy soil, $k=3$ for clay soil, while $k=3$—6 for soils lying between sandy soil and clay soil, especially $k=5$ for sandy loam, $k=4$ for sandy clay soil.

3.5.5 Anisotropic Subsoil

Assuming the v s of the subgrade in two directions are identical, while the corresponding deformation moduli are different, one can obtain the stresses in the subgrade subjected to uniformly distributed linear vertical pressure $\overline{p}$ as follows

$$\left.\begin{aligned} \sigma_z &= k\frac{2\overline{p}}{\pi}\frac{z^3}{r^2 r_1^2} \\ \sigma_x &= k\frac{2\overline{p}}{\pi}\frac{x^2 z}{r^2 r_1^2} \\ \tau_{zx} &= k\frac{2\overline{p}}{\pi}\frac{xz^2}{r^2 r_1^2} \end{aligned}\right\} \tag{3-91}$$

where: $r^2 = x^2 + z^2$, $r_1^2 = k^2\left(x^2+z^2\right)$ and $k=\sqrt{\frac{E_x}{E_z}}$, x and z therein are the coordinates of the calculation point, while E_x and E_z are deformation moduli in the horizontal and vertical directions, respectively. When $E_z > E_x$, stress diffusion phenomena occurs in subgrade, while when $E_x > E_z$, stress concentration phenomena arises.

Noticeably, it is too complicated to study completely anisotropic subsoil either from the viewpoint of theoretical studies or from prospect of engineering applications.

3.6 Chapter Summary

In this chapter, some mechanical problems relating to settlements, with stress calculation as its key issue, are studied. Stress calculation formulas for all kinds of boundary conditions and loading conditions, especially the Boussinesq and the Mindlin solutions for half-space problems, are presented. Besides, stress formulas for heterogeneous and anisotropic subsoil are also brought forward. Finally, basic equations of elasticity, as well as some generic loading problems on the boundary plane of a semi-infinite body, are appended.

Appendix Basic Equations of Elasticity

Basic equations of elasticity in rectangular coordinates (x, y, z) are listed as follows.

1. Equilibrium equations

$$\left.\begin{aligned} &\frac{\partial \sigma_z}{\partial x}+\frac{\partial \tau_{xy}}{\partial y}+\frac{\partial \tau_{xz}}{\partial z}+f_x=0 \\ &\frac{\partial \tau_{yx}}{\partial x}+\frac{\partial \sigma_y}{\partial y}+\frac{\partial \tau_{yz}}{\partial z}+f_y=0 \\ &\frac{\partial \tau_{zx}}{\partial x}+\frac{\partial \sigma_{zy}}{\partial y}+\frac{\partial \sigma_z}{\partial z}+f_z=0 \end{aligned}\right\} \tag{A1-1}$$

Equilibrium equations in terms of displacements are given by

$$\left.\begin{aligned} &\frac{F}{2(1+\mu)}\left(\nabla^2 u+\frac{1}{1-2\mu}\frac{\partial e}{\partial x}\right)+f_x=0 \\ &\frac{E}{2(1+\mu)}\left(\nabla^2 v+\frac{1}{1-2\mu}\frac{\partial e}{\partial y}\right)+f_y=0 \\ &\frac{E}{2(1+\mu)}\left(\nabla^2 w+\frac{1}{1-2\mu}\frac{\partial e}{\partial z}\right)+f_z=0 \end{aligned}\right\} \tag{A1-2}$$

in which $\nabla^2=\frac{\partial^2}{\partial x^2}+\frac{\partial^2}{\partial y^2}+\frac{\partial^2}{\partial z^2}$ is Laplacian operator.

2. Generalized Hooke's law

$$\begin{Bmatrix} \sigma_x \\ \sigma_y \\ \sigma_z \\ \tau_{xy} \\ \tau_{yz} \\ \tau_{zx} \end{Bmatrix}=\frac{E}{(1+\mu)(1-2\mu)}\begin{bmatrix} 1-\mu & \mu & \mu & 0 & 0 & 0 \\ v & 1-\mu & \mu & 0 & 0 & 0 \\ v & v & 1-\mu & 0 & 0 & 0 \\ 0 & 0 & 0 & \frac{1-2\mu}{2} & 0 & 0 \\ 0 & 0 & 0 & 0 & \frac{1-2\mu}{2} & 0 \\ 0 & 0 & 0 & 0 & 0 & \frac{1-2\mu}{2} \end{bmatrix} \tag{A1-3}$$

References

Bjerrum L. 1972. Problems of Soil Mechanics and Construction on Soft Clays, State of the Report, Proc. VIII IC-SMFE, Vol.3.

Braja.M.Das. 2008. Advanced Soil Mechanics, Third Edition, McGrew-Hill Book Company, New York.

Chen X.F., Chen M.K., Xu C.P. 1998. Structure Design of High-rise Building in China, Hainan: Hainan Press.

Chen X.F., Zhen B.Z. 1992. Engineering Mechanics, Vols. 1-2, Beijing: Beijing Science and Technology Press.

Chen L.F., Zhen G.X., Gong X.N. 1988. Settlement Calculation Considering the Anisotropy of Foundation, Memoir of the Third National Rock Mechanics Numerical Analysis and Analytic method Conference.

Dunean J.M, Chang C.Y.1970. Nonlinear Settlement Analysis of Stress and Strain in Soils, J.Soil Mech. Found. Div. ASCE, Vol.96, SM 5.

Fan J.H., Gao Y.H. 1989. Mechanics Basis of Nonlinear Continuum, Chongqing: Chongqing University Pre.

Jiang P.G. 1982. Constitutive Relation of the Soil, Beijing: Science Press.

Gong X.N. 1984. Foundation Characters of Tank Soft Clay. Doctoral Dissertation of Zhejiang University.

Lu Z.J. 1989. Deformation Failure Mechanism of Soil and Soil Mechanics Calculation Theory, Journal of Geotechnical Engineering, Vol. 11, No. 6.

Qian W.H., Ye K.Y. 1956. Elastic Mechanics, Beijing: Science Press.

Qin Rong. 2005. Calculation Structural Mechanics, Beijing: Science Press.

Shen Z.J. 2000. Theoretical Soil Mechanics, Beijing: China Water Conservancy and Hydroelectricity Press.

Sowers G. F. 1988. Introduction Soil Mechanics and Foundations, London: Macmilla Balkema.

Tergzghi K. 1943. Theoretical Soil Mechanics, John Wiley & Sons, New York.

Yuan W.B. 1988. Handbook of Mechanical Engineering, Beijing: Coal Industry Press.

Zienkiewicz O.C. 1967. The Finite Element Method in Structural and Continuum Mechanics, London: McGraw-Hill.

Table 3-9 Stress factor α for stress under the angular point of rectangular area subjected to uniformly distributed load

z/B \ A/B	1.0	1.2	1.4	1.6	1.8	2.0	2.2	2.4	2.6	2.8	3.0	4.0	5.0	7.0	9.0	>10.0
0.0	0.2500	0.2500	0.2500	0.2500	0.2500	0.2500	0.2500	0.2500	0.2500	0.2500	0.2500	0.2500	0.2500	0.2500	0.2500	0.2500
0.2	0.2468	0.2489	0.2490	0.2491	0.2491	0.2491	0.2492	0.2492	0.2492	0.2492	0.2492	0.2492	0.2492	0.2492	0.2492	0.2492
0.4	0.2401	0.2420	0.2429	0.2434	0.2437	0.2439	0.2441	0.2442	0.2442	0.2442	0.2442	0.2443	0.2443	0.2443	0.2443	0.2443
0.6	0.2229	0.2275	0.2300	0.2315	0.2324	0.2329	0.2335	0.2337	0.2337	0.2338	0.2339	0.2341	0.2342	0.2342	0.2342	0.2342
0.8	0.1999	0.2075	0.2120	0.2147	0.2165	0.2176	0.2188	0.2192	0.2192	0.2194	0.2196	0.2200	0.2202	0.2202	0.2202	0.2203
1.0	0.1752	0.1851	0.1911	0.1955	0.1981	0.1999	0.2020	0.2026	0.2026	0.2031	0.2034	0.2042	0.2044	0.2045	0.2046	0.2046
1.2	0.1516	0.1626	0.1705	0.1758	0.1793	0.1818	0.1849	0.1858	0.1858	0.1865	0.1870	0.1882	0.1885	0.1888	0.1888	0.1889
1.4	0.1308	0.1423	0.1508	0.1569	0.1613	0.1644	0.1685	0.1696	0.1696	0.1705	0.1712	0.1730	0.1735	0.1739	0.1739	0.1740
1.6	0.1123	0.1241	0.1329	0.1390	0.1445	0.1482	0.1530	0.1545	0.1545	0.1557	0.1567	0.1590	0.1598	0.1602	0.1604	0.1605
1.8	0.0969	0.1083	0.1172	0.1241	0.1294	0.1334	0.1389	0.1408	0.1408	0.1423	0.1434	0.1463	0.1474	0.1480	0.1482	0.1483
2.0	0.0840	0.0947	0.1034	0.1103	0.1158	0.1202	0.1263	0.1284	0.1284	0.1300	0.1314	0.1350	0.1363	0.1371	0.1373	0.1375
2.2	0.0732	0.0832	0.0917	0.0984	0.1039	0.1084	0.1149	0.1172	0.1172	0.1191	0.1205	0.1248	0.1264	0.1274	0.1277	0.1279
2.4	0.0642	0.0734	0.0813	0.0879	0.0934	0.9979	0.1047	0.1071	0.1071	0.1092	0.1108	0.1156	0.1175	0.1188	0.1191	0.1194
2.6	0.0586	0.0651	0.0725	0.0788	0.0842	0.0887	0.0955	0.0981	0.0981	0.1003	0.1020	0.1073	0.1095	0.1111	0.1115	0.1118
2.8	0.0502	0.0580	0.0649	0.0709	0.0761	0.0805	0.0875	0.0900	0.0900	0.0923	0.0942	0.0999	0.1024	0.1040	0.1047	0.1050
3.0	0.0447	0.0519	0.0583	0.0640	0.0696	0.0732	0.0801	0.0828	0.0828	0.0851	0.0870	0.0931	0.0959	0.0980	0.0986	0.0990
3.2	0.0401	0.0467	0.0526	0.0580	0.0627	0.0668	0.0735	0.0762	0.0762	0.0786	0.0806	0.0870	0.0900	0.0923	0.0930	0.0935
3.4	0.0361	0.0421	0.0477	0.0527	0.0571	0.0611	0.0677	0.0704	0.0704	0.0727	0.0747	0.0814	0.0847	0.0873	0.0880	0.0886
3.6	0.0326	0.0382	0.0433	0.0480	0.0523	0.0561	0.0624	0.0651	0.0651	0.0674	0.0694	0.0763	0.0799	0.0826	0.0835	0.0842
3.8	0.0296	0.0348	0.0395	0.0439	0.0479	0.0516	0.0577	0.0603	0.0603	0.0626	0.0646	0.0717	0.0753	0.0784	0.0794	0.0802
4.0	0.0270	0.0318	0.0362	0.0403	0.0441	0.0474	0.0535	0.0560	0.0560	0.0583	0.0603	0.0674	0.0712	0.0745	0.0756	0.0765
4.2	0.0247	0.0291	0.0333	0.0371	0.0407	0.0439	0.0496	0.0521	0.0521	0.0543	0.0563	0.0634	0.0674	0.0709	0.0721	0.0731
4.4	0.0227	0.0268	0.0306	0.0343	0.0376	0.0407	0.0462	0.0485	0.0485	0.0507	0.0527	0.0597	0.0639	0.0676	0.0689	0.0700
4.6	0.0209	0.0247	0.0283	0.0317	0.0348	0.0378	0.0430	0.0453	0.0453	0.0474	0.0493	0.0564	0.0606	0.0644	0.0659	0.0671
4.8	0.0193	0.0229	0.0262	0.0294	0.0324	0.0352	0.0402	0.0424	0.0424	0.0444	0.0463	0.0533	0.0576	0.0616	0.0631	0.0645
5.0	0.0179	0.0212	0.0243	0.0274	0.0302	0.0328	0.0376	0.0397	0.0397	0.0417	0.0435	0.0504	0.0547	0.0589	0.0606	0.0620
6.0	0.0127	0.0151	0.0174	0.0196	0.0218	0.0238	0.0276	0.0293	0.0293	0.0310	0.0325	0.0388	0.0431	0.0479	0.0500	0.0521
7.0	0.0094	0.0112	0.0130	0.0147	0.0164	0.0180	0.0210	0.0224	0.0224	0.0238	0.0251	0.0306	0.0346	0.0396	0.0421	0.0449
8.0	0.0073	0.0087	0.0101	0.0114	0.0127	0.0140	0.0165	0.0176	0.0176	0.0187	0.0198	0.0246	0.0283	0.0332	0.0359	0.0394
9.0	0.0053	0.0069	0.0080	0.0091	0.0102	0.0112	0.0132	0.0142	0.0142	0.0152	0.0161	0.0202	0.0235	0.0282	0.0310	0.0351
10.0	0.0047	0.0056	0.0065	0.0074	0.0083	0.0092	0.0108	0.0116	0.0116	0.0124	0.0132	0.0167	0.0198	0.0242	0.0270	0.0316

Chapter 4 Theoretical Analysis of Subgrade Deformation of Deep Foundations of Super High-Rise Buildings

The characteristics of super high-rise buildings are the great height, heavy load, and big settlement. The loads are delivered to the subgrade through foundations, and introduce stress diffusion in the subgrade. For the reason that the subgrade is compressible, deformation, whose main component is vertical deformation, is produced in the subgrade under the action of induced stress, then the settlement or inclination of foundation are induced to super-high buildings. The values of deformation depend on the physical and mechanical properties of subgrade and loads, and is also related to the area , depth of foundation and the shoring structures of the pit. Even foundation settlement of super high-rise buildings has little influence on the safety of structures, but excessive settlement would affect the function and appearance, especially for elevators, pipelines and equipments. If foundation settlement is uneven, the crack, distortion or inclination might be induced, which will affect structure's safety and even results in collapse when serious. This kind of collapse happens both home and abroad. So the problem of subgrade deformation must be carefully researched and considered, and the settlement must be accurately predicted when constructing super high-rise buildings.

In order to make sure the normal use and safety of super high-rise buildings, the design of most foundation must satisfy certain settlement requirements. Subgrade deformation is one of the most important factors of super high-rise building design. Therefore, apart from the research on subgrade stress variation behavior, the following must also be researched: subgrade compressibility, subgrade deformation behavior, practical and reliable calculation methods of foundation's total settlement and the relationship between settlement and time duration.

4.1 The Compression Properties and Mechanical Index of Subgrade

4.1.1 The Conception of Compression Properties of Subgrade

The subgrade compressibility: ① compression of solid particles, ② compression of water and air in voids, ③ extrusion of water and air from voids. Among these, water is uncompressible, and the compression of solid particles is negligible. Test shows that the volume change of solid particles is less than 1/400 of the whole volume, when the pressure is 100—600 kPa. Therefore, the compression of water and solid particles can both be neglected, and the compressibility of subgrade mainly comes from decrease of the volume of voids, i.e. parts of the water and air are extruded from the voids, the closed air is compressed, and the solid particles are removed and realigned correspondingly. For saturated subgrade, its compression mainly comes from the extrusion of water from the voids.

The compression of subgrade is shown as the vertical deformation and lateral deformation. Generally, vertical deformation is the main part, so lots of research puts emphasis on it. Under the action of loads, for saturated cohesionless subgrade with good permeability, e.g. sand, the compression process can be finished in a short time. But for cohesive subgrade with poor permeability, water is extruded slowly, so more time is needed for compression to get stable. This compressing process is called subgrade consolidation. For saturated cohesive subgrade, consolidation problem is very important, because almost all deep foundations of super high-rise buildings are buried in saturated subgrade.

The subgrade compressibility index is the most important one used for calculating subgrade settlement. In common projects, the laboratory compression test with lateral deformation (lateral confined) is adopted to test compressibility index of subgrade sample. It is obvious that this real status of subgrade is disturbed, so the in-situ test should be conducted if possible.

4.1.2 Compression Curve and Compressibility Index

1. Compression curve

Compression curve comes from laboratory compression tests of subgrade, which is the relation curves between subgrade void ratio and pressure, e.g. the *e*-*p* curve (Fig. 4-1) and *e*-log *p* curve (Fig. 4-2).

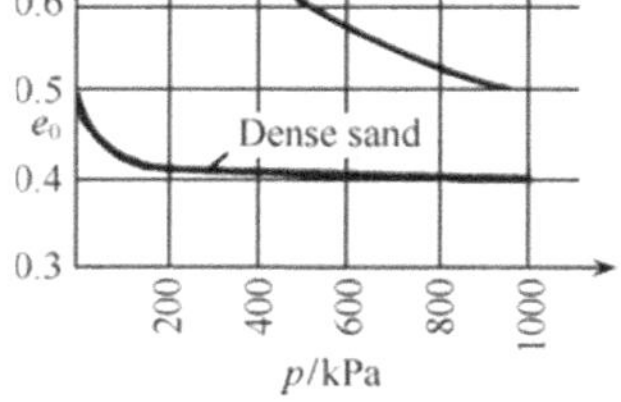

Fig. 4-1 *e*-*p* curve

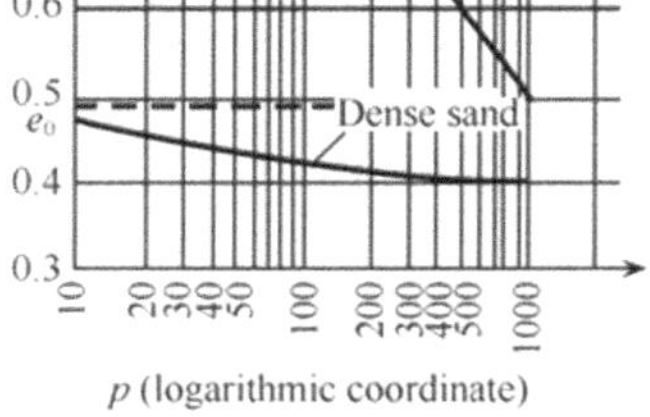

Fig. 4-2 *e*-log *p* curve

2. Compressibility coefficient and compressibility index of subgrade

Subgrade compressibility changes in different subgrade groups, so does the curve. The steeper the curve is, the more obvious the void ratio decreases when the pressure is increasing, and the better the subgrade compressibility is. The subgrade compressibility coefficient is expressed as

$$\Delta\sigma_1 = \sigma_2 \tag{4-1}$$

where: α —the subgrade compressibility coefficient (kPa ^{1} or MPa ^{1});

P_1—generally, it represents the vertical geostatic stress in a certain depth of subgrade;

P_2—the sum of gravity stress and induced stress in a certain depth of subgrade;

e_1—the void ratio when the compression process is stable under the action of P_1;

e_2—the void ratio when the compression process is stable under the action of P_2.

The compressibility coefficient can be determined by *e-p* curve, see Fig. 4-3.

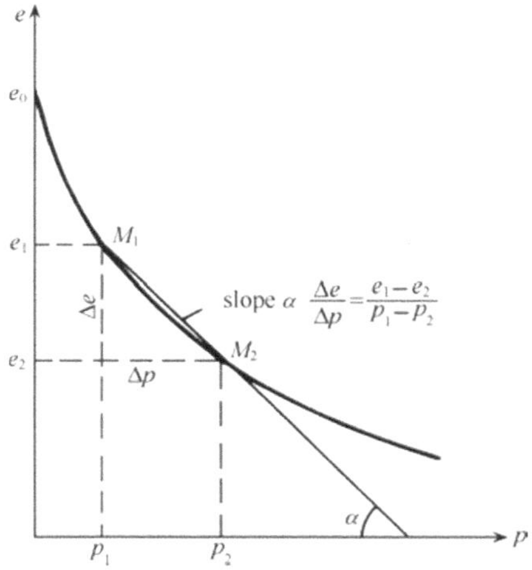

Fig. 4-3 Determining compressibility coefficient based on *e-p* curve

In engineering projects, the subgrade compressibility can be valued by the compressibility coefficient $a_{1\text{-}2}$ which is obtained by adding pressure from p=100kPa (0.1MPa) to 200kPa (0.2MPa).

When $a_{1\text{-}2}$<0.1MPa^{-1}, the subgrade is of low compressibility;

When 0.1MPa^{-1}$\leqslant a_{1\text{-}2}$<0.5MPa^{-1}, the subgrade is of medium compressibility;

When $a_{1\text{-}2}\geqslant$0.5MPa^{-1}, the subgrade is of high compressibility.

Re-plot the *e-p* curve to semilogarithmic compression curve *e*-log *p*, since the second part is close to straight line, see Fig. 4-4, its slope C_c is express as:

$$C_c = \frac{e_1 - e_2}{\log p_1 - \log p_2} = (e_1 - e_2)/\log\frac{p_2}{p_1} \tag{4-2}$$

where: C_c — the subgrade compressibility index. It is different from the subgrade compressibility coefficient α.

The meanings of other symbols are the same as the foregoing equations.

Like the compressibility coefficient α, the bigger the compressibility index is, the higher the subgrade compressibility is. C_c value is generally smaller than 0.2 for the slightly compressible subgrade; while C_c value is bigger than 0.4 for the highly compressible subgrade. The influence of the stress history on the highly compressible subgrade compressibility is analyzed abroad through curve.

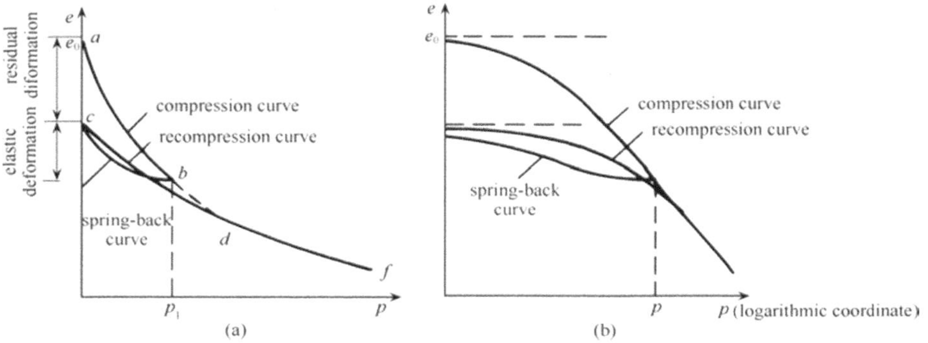

Fig. 4-4 Solve C_c based on *e*-log *p* curve

3. Modulus of compressibility (under the lateral confined condition)

Based on the *e-p* curve, another compressibility index, modulus of compressibility E_s, can be solved. It is the ratio of the vertical induced stress to the corresponding strain increment under the condition of complete lateral confined condition. This modulus E_s can be calculated by the equation:

$$E_s = \frac{1+e_2}{a} \tag{4-3}$$

where: E_s —the subgrade modulus of compressibility (kPa or MPa);

α —the subgrade coefficient of compressibility (kPa^{-1} or MPa^{-1}).

This expression shows that the subgrade compressive strain increment is in direct ratio with the subgrade compressive stress increment, and the proportion is $\frac{1+e_2}{a}$, where the proportional coefficient E_s is just the subgrade modulus of compressibility, or lateral confined modulus of compressibility exactly to differentiate from the compressive elastic modulus under the unconfined condition.

The modulus of compressibility for subgrade is another important compressibility index. The smaller it is, the higher the subgrade compressibility is.

4. Subgrade spring-back curve and recompression curve

Because that both the area and the depth of deep foundation of super high-rise buildings are great, the spring-back is induced for subgrade expansion caused by the decreased pressure (stress relief) after excavation of foundation pit. Therefore, such influence should be considered when calculating settlement of foundation. The e-log p curve of compression, spring-back and recompression is used here to analyze the influence of stress history on subgrade compressibility. Such action of spring-back and recompression is very complex (groundwater effect and drainage of foundation pit), so it is hard to calculate the influence of subgrade spring-back and recompression on the final settlement theoretically and accurately. In practical project, actual measurement is adopted to consider this influence synthetically. The test results of subgrade spring-back curve and recompression curve are shown in Fig.4-5.

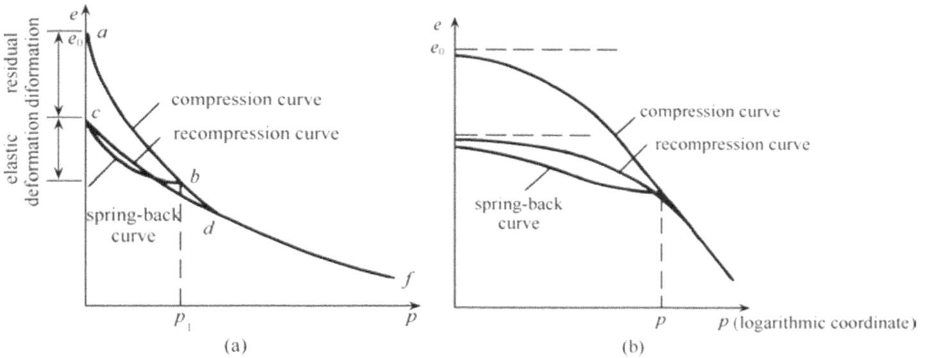

Fig. 4-5 Subgrade spring-back curve and recompression curve

4.1.3 Subgrade Modulus of Deformation

It is more accurate to get the subgrade compressibility index from the field in-situ test data than from the laboratory compression test.

1. Determine the subgrade modulus of deformation through field in-situ loading test

According to the loading test and the measured corresponding state settlement value, the relation curve, p-s curve, between load and stable settlement can be drawn on proper scale, and the relation curve, s-t curve, between each grade of settlement and time can also be drawn. The beginning part of the p-s curve is close to straight line, and the ending point of the straight part's corresponding load p_1 is just the proportional limit load of subgrade, which is also the plastic limit load, see Fig. 4-6.

The design value of subgrade bearing capacity is close to or a little beyond the proportional limit value. It is obvious that the elastic mechanics formula, which is as below, can be adopted, when the subgrade is on the stage of linear deformation, i.e. elastic deformation stage.

$$E_0 = \omega(1-\mu^2)\frac{p_1 b}{s_1} \tag{4-4}$$

where: ω—for the rigid bearing board, its value is ω_r, for the square bearing board, its value is 0.88, while for the round bearing board, its value is 0.79;

b—the side length or diameter of the bearing board;

s_1—the corresponding settlement to the set proportional limit p_l. In some situation, the p-s curve dose not have the starting part of straight line. For the medium, high compressibility silty subgrade and cohesive subgrade, its value is s_1=0.02b and the corresponding load is p_1. For the low compressibility silty subgrade and cohesive subgrade, gravel subgrade, and sandy subgrade, its value is s_1= (0.010—0.015)b and the corresponding load p_1 can be brought into the formula above to calculate E_0.

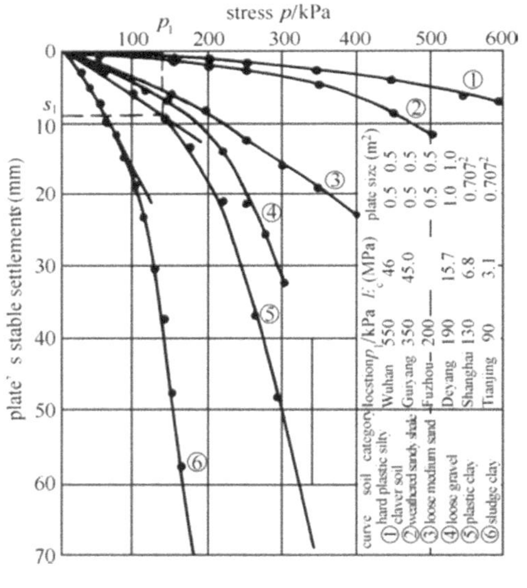

Fig. 4-6 Example curves for several kinds of subgrade

Loading test is generally adopted for the shallow subgrade. The influence depth is about 1.5—2.5b, so the test results can basically show the subgrade compressibility. When the loading board is bigger, the situation is more similar with the practical foundation, so some standards abroad require that the compressibility index used in the equation for foundation settlement calculation should be determined by in-situ loading test. This test needs great work, time and cost. According to empirical practice, the consolidation degree it indicates is equivalent to the early settlement when the building construction is just finished. The loading test, with round rigid board in bored hole of deep subgrade, is very meaningful while there is no groundwater. But when there is groundwater, it is difficult to carry out the slag removal work on the bored hole base, additionally, the stress condition is complicated, so it is hard to get a satisfactory result. Maybe it is more meaningful to carry out loading test on the pit base after the foundation pit is excavated if possible.

2. The relationship between deformation modulus and compressibility modulus

The subgrade deformation modulus E_0 is the ratio of stress to strain under the condition of no lateral confinement. The subgrade compressibility modulus E_s is the ratio of effective stress to strain under the complete lateral confined condition(Table 4-1 and Table 4-2). According to the elastic theory, the relation equation of E_0 and E_s can be expressed as:

$$E_0 = \beta E_s \tag{4-5}$$

where: $\beta = 1 - \dfrac{2\mu^2}{1-\mu} = 1 - 2\mu K_0$;

K_0—the lateral pressure coefficient or pressure coefficient of earth at rest. Its value can be measured by test, given the proper test condition, or adopt empirical value. This value is commonly less than 1, but it can be bigger than 1 under some specific condition (e.g. over consolidation).

Table 4-1 The empirical relation between deformation modulus E_0 and compressibility modulus E_s

Subgrade category	$K = E_0/E_s$
Subgrade with high compressibility	1—2
Subgrade with slight compressibility	≤10
Loess	2—5

Table 4-2 The empirical relation between deformation modulus E_0 and compressibility modulus E_s

Subgrade category		$K = E_0/E_s$	
		Normal range	Average value
Old cohesive subgrade		1.45—2.80	2.11
Normal cohesive subgrade	$I_p>10$	0.60—2.80	1.35
	$I_p<10$	0.54—2.68	0.98
Recently deposited cohesive subgrade		0.35—1.94	0.93
Sludge or mucky cohesive subgrade		1.05—2.97	1.90
Red clay		1.04—4.87	2.36

In practice, the equation above can not indicate exactly the real relationship between E_0 and E_s, because several factors can not be considered in the measuring process of E_0 from the field in-situ loading test and E_s from laboratory compression test. Sometimes value of E_0 is probably several times of βE_s, and the harder the subgrade is, the bigger the ratio is. But the values are close each other for soft subgrade.

4.1.4 The Subgrade Elastic Deformation and Residual Deformation

The subgrade elastic deformation includes the deformation of pellicle water, subgrade particles, the structural changes of subgrade, and the compression or dissolution of the sealed air. The subgrade residual deformation means the deformation part that can not be recovered after the removal of pressure, which includes the relative displacement of particles, the crushing of some particles, and the extrusion of water and air in voids. The elastic deformation speed is different from the residual deformation speed(Fig. 4-7). The subgrade particles' elastic deformation completes soon, while deformation caused by the extrusion process of the free water from voids takes a long time. Therefore, the time history of subgrade deformation differs from elastic body, for both loading and unloading process.

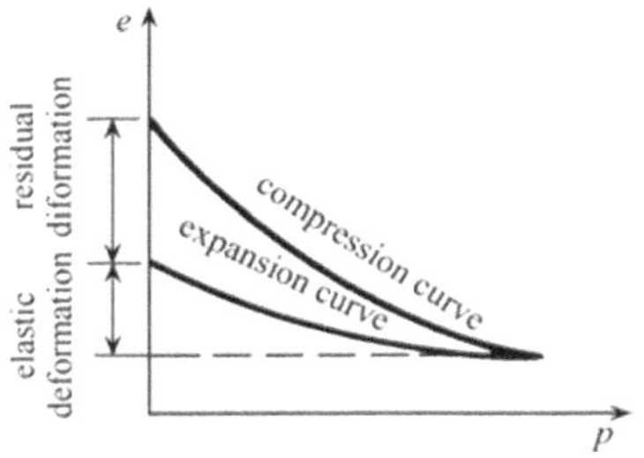

Fig. 4-7 The soil elastic and residual deformation

4.1.5 The Natural Consolidated State and Preconsolidation Pressure

In compression test of cohesive subgrade, the compression curve is different from the standard compression curve. It is because that the subgrade has been preloaded before the unloading when sampling.

Preconsolidation pressure is the effective pressure on the subgrade, and it is already consolidated and stable through the geological history. This load, which once acted on the subgrade, can be bigger, less than or equal to the geostatic stress. According to this, the subgrade consolidation state can be determined by comparing preconsolidation pressure p_c with present overlaying subgrade's geostatic stress p_o. If $p_c > p_o$, this state is over-consolidation, which represents that large pressure once acted on the subgrade to consolidate it during the natural deposition process. If $p_c = p_o$, this is moderate consolidation state, and the subgrade of such state is moderately consolidated subgrade. If $p_c < p_o$, this is slight consolidation state, and such kind of subgrade is slightly consolidated subgrade. The ratio of p_c/p_o is defined as over-consolidation ratio, and 1) for normally consolidated subgrade, OCR=1; 2) for over consolidated subgrade, OCR>1; 3) for slightly consolidated subgrade, OCR<1. It is obvious that the bigger OCR is, the stronger the over consolidation action is, and the compressibility is poorer, given the same condition. The previous consolidation pressure is an index to show the natural stress state of subgrade. If load on the subgrade is less than or equal to the previous consolidation pressure of subgrade, the subgrade deformation would be very small, even can be ignored. Contrarily, if this load is bigger than the previous consolidation pressure of subgrade, the deformation would be obvious. Hence, the previous consolidation pressure of subgrade can be treated as a critical index of deformation change under the load action, that is, critical pressure, which is taken into account in settlement calculation.

At present, the main method for calculating the previous consolidation pressure of subgrade is the Aasagrande method (Aasagrande, 1936).

4.1.6 The Relationship Between Stress and Strain for Foundation

The foundation stress-strain relation is very complex. For the general situation, *p-s* curve can be divided into: ① linear deformation stage (subgrade compression stage); ② local and shear deformation stage (plastic deformation gradual developing; ③ complete failure stage (shear failure). Obviously, these three deformation stages have different characteristics.

For sand subgrade and dense cohesive subgrade foundation, there are two obvious deformation stages. For soft soil subgrade, if the embedded depth is deep, the above three deformation stages are not obvious, so it is difficult to find the clear extrusion failure phenomenon on site.

4.1.7 Elastic Modulus

Compressibility modulus and deformation modulus are both the ratio of normal stress to total strain of subgrade. Considering the subgrade elasticity and initial strain, the ratio of normal stress to corresponding subgrade elastic strain is just the subgrade elastic modulus. The subgrade elastic modulus E is adopted as the calculation of foundation deformation under initial loads. For the reason that the subgrade elastic strain is far less than the subgrade total strain, the subgrade elastic modulus is far more than the subgrade compressibility modulus or deformation modulus. The subgrade elastic modulus can be got through repeated loading and unloading processes in the lateral unconfined compression test and non-drainage triaxial shear test. When test data are short, see the reference data in Table 4-3.

Table 4-3 The subgrade elastic modulus *E*

Subgrade category	The value of *E*(MPa)
Gravel, crushed stone, and pebble	40—56
Coarse sand	40—48
Medium sand	32—46
Dry fine sand	24—32
Saturated fine sand	8—16
Hard plastic sub-clayey and light sub-clayey subgrade	32—40
Plastic sub-clayey and light sub-clayey subgrade	8—16
Hard clayey soil	80—160
Hard elastic clayey soil	40—56
Elastic clayey soil	8—16

4.1.8 The Soil Lateral Pressure Coefficient and Poisson Ratio

If the equipment which can measure the horizontal pressure is embedded and settled in the confined compression device, then the corresponding increment $\mathrm{d}\sigma_x$ of horizontal pressure σ_x ($\sigma_x = \sigma_y$) induced by the arbitrary increment $\mathrm{d}\sigma_x$ of vertical pressure σ_z can be measured. The ratio of horizontal pressure increment $\mathrm{d}\sigma_x$ to vertical pressure increment $\mathrm{d}\sigma_x$ is just the subgrade lateral pressure coefficient ξ or earth pressure at rest coefficient K_0, i.e.

$$\xi = K_0 = \frac{\mathrm{d}\sigma_x}{\mathrm{d}\sigma_z} \tag{4-6}$$

The integration of the expression above is

$$\sigma_x = \xi\sigma_z + C \tag{4-7}$$

where: *C*—the integral constant, which is relevant to the original boundary condition. Test reveals that: for loose sand, *C*=0; for sand which is pounded in metal canister, *C*>0; for clayey soil, *C*<0.

Practically, *C* is ignored for simplification, then

$$\sigma_x = \xi\sigma_z \tag{4-8}$$

or

$$\xi = \frac{\sigma_x}{\sigma_z} \tag{4-9}$$

The subgrade lateral pressure coefficient is relevant to the subgrade categories and the ξ value for subgrade of the same category is relevant to its void ratio, moisture content, loading condition, degree of consolidation etc. It can be determined by test, when the test data is not available, see the reference data in Table 4-4.

Table 4-4 The subgrade lateral pressure coefficient ξ and Poisson ratio μ

Subgrade category and state	ξ	μ
Crushed stone subgrade	0.18—0.25	0.15—0.2
Sandy soil	0.25—0.33	0.20—0.25
Silty soil	0.33	0.25
Silty clayey soil:		
Hard state	0.33	0.25
Plastic state	0.43	0.30
Soft plastic or flow state	0.53	0.35
Clayey soil:		
Hard state	0.33	0.25
Plastic state	0.53	0.35
Soft plastic or flow state	0.72	0.42

The subgrade Poisson ratio μ (lateral expansion coefficient) is the ratio of subgrade lateral strain to vertical strain, and it is relevant to the subgrade lateral pressure coefficient. The relationship can be derived according to the principles in material mechanics:

When the subgrade is compressed, three stresses, i.e. $\sigma_x, \sigma_y, \sigma_z$, act on any point in the subgrade. Assuming that the relationship between stress and strain is linear, the subgrade strain in three directions can be expressed as below, according to the Hooke law.

$$\left.\begin{aligned} \lambda_s &= \frac{1}{E_0}\left[\sigma_s - \mu\left(\sigma_y + \sigma_z\right)\right] \\ \lambda_y &= \frac{1}{E_0}\left[\sigma_y - \mu\left(\sigma_x + \sigma_z\right)\right] \\ \lambda_s &= \frac{1}{E_0}\left[\sigma_z - \mu\left(\sigma_x + \sigma_y\right)\right] \end{aligned}\right\} \tag{4-10}$$

where: E_0—the subgrade deformation modulus.

For precondition of confined compression, there is no lateral deformation. Therefore, the horizontal strain should be zero, i.e.

$$\lambda_x = \lambda_y = 0$$

And according to the symmetric relation, $\sigma_x = \sigma_y$

It can be derived as

$$\sigma_x = \sigma_y = \frac{\mu}{1-\mu}\sigma_z \tag{4-11}$$

Because of $\sigma_y = \xi\sigma_z$, it can be derived as

$$\xi = \frac{\mu}{1-\mu} \tag{4-12}$$

or

$$\mu = \frac{\xi}{1-\xi} \tag{4-13}$$

It is inconvenient to measure the subgrade Poisson ratio directly from the test. Usually, the subgrade lateral pressure coefficient is measured first, and then calculate Poisson ratio. When test data is not available, see the reference data in Table 4-4.

4.2 The Conception of Foundation's Final Settlement Calculation

Under the action of loads, there will be deformations in three directions, i.e. *x*, *y*, *z*, in the subgrade. Among them, it is the settlement induced by vertical deformation of foundation that we concern most. According to the temporal sequence, the total settlement of foundation which is built on saturated cohesive subgrade is divided into ① initial settlement; ② consolidation settlement, ③ secondary consolidation settlement. The three settlements are all related to time, see Fig. 4-8. Initial settlement is induced by the subgrade distortion under the action of loads, and it happens immediately after loading. It is the settlement that is induced immediately after the building is finished. The consolidation settlement is formed by the extrusion of water in voids, and this process is relatively slow. These two parts of settlement make up of most of the total settlement. The secondary consolidation settlement is induced by the creep under the action of constant effective stress after the dissipation of excess hydrostatic pressure. This classification is suitable for cohesive subgrade. For sandy soil subgrade, the consolidation process is very fast for its good permeability, so it is hard to distinguish initial settlement from consolidation settlement. Sandy soil subgrade's elastic modulus grows along with its depth, and it does not match practice well using the elastic theory. Therefore, empirical method should be used for the settlement calculation of sandy soil subgrade besides the numerical analysis method, and the engineering examples are very important.

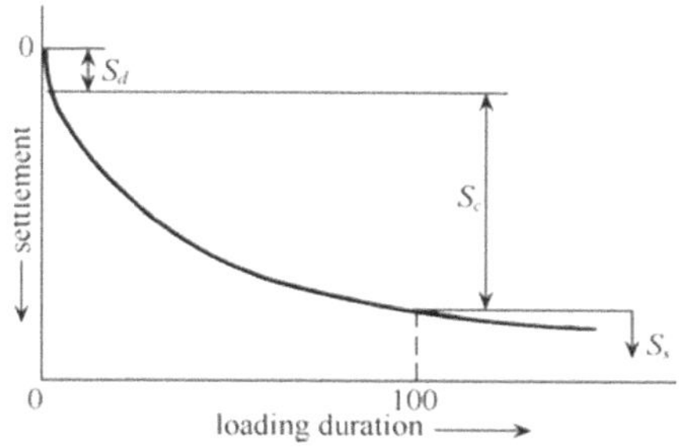

Fig. 4-8 Relationship curve of time and settlement

The calculating methods of foundation settlement can be classified to be: ① elastic mechanics method (i.e. direct method); ② engineering method (i.e. indirect method); ③ empirical method; ④ numerical solution (Finite Element method, Difference method, Boundary Element method etc.). Elastic mechanics method is strict in theory, and its mathematic solution is accurate for the elastic homogeneous isotropic half-space body. But its constitutive relation does not fit practice sometimes, so solution differs from measured value, so this is usually used for the calculation of initial settlement. Engineering method includes compression instrument method (1957), stress path method (Lambe, 1963, 1967), state boundary surface method (Burland, 1969, 1971; Roscoe, 1969) etc. These methods still use elastic theory to calculate the additional stress in foundation, and use test results (so called indirect method) to get the stress-strain relation. The settlement calculating result can be regarded as the combination of initial settlement and consolidation settlement. The third method includes empirical or half-empirical formula. It can still meet the engineering requirement adopting the in-situ test result to derive the practical foundation settlement, for the situation of sandy soil subgrade. Numerical solution method mainly includes finite element method, finite difference method, and lumped parameter method, the essential of these methods is still elastic theory, so the result is not satisfactory. Here we can get a revelation, i.e. the engineering and practical geologic condition must be considered in the research of foundation settlement to get the half-theoretical and half-empirical method.

The Mechanism for Calculation of Foundation Settlement

1. The mechanism of foundation deformation and settlement under three-dimensional stress

Under the action of local loadings on the surface of earth, subgrade is in the state of three-dimensional stress, and the extrusion of water in voids is three-dimensional too. If it is circular loading, then the deformation mechanism for the subgrade unit body of point *M* on the medial axel can be explained as below.

The circular loading p_0 induces principal stress increment $\Delta\sigma_1 = \sigma_z$ and minor principal stress increment $\Delta\sigma_3 = \sigma_r = \sigma_x = \sigma_y$ on point *M*. When the subgrade is saturated, on the moment of the action of loading, since the water in voids can not been extruded immediately, the subgrade volume change $\Delta V = 0$, and the point *M*'s initial pore water pressure increment (excess hydrostatic pressure) $\Delta\mu$ can be expressed as below according to the Skempton formula.

$$\Delta\mu = \Delta\sigma_3 + A(\Delta\sigma_1 - \Delta\sigma_3) \tag{4-14}$$

The expression above indicates that the increase of saturated subgrade's initial pore water pressure is the sum of two components. There are the void pressure increment $\Delta\mu_3 = \Delta\sigma_3$ induced by the isotropic pressure increment $\Delta\sigma_3$ and the pore water pressure increment $\Delta\mu_1 = A(\Delta\sigma_1 - \Delta\sigma_3)$ induced by the deviation stress increment $\Delta\sigma_1 - \sigma_3$, in the state of axisymmetric stress. A is the pore water pressure coefficient, and its value is determined by the tri-axial compression test.

Although the saturated subgrade can not be compressed on the moment of loading, but shear distortion is caused immediately by the shear stress increment $(\Delta\sigma_1 - \Delta\sigma_3)/2$. The subgrade is compressed for the extrusion of water from voids with time, the void pressure dissipates and transfers to the subgrade skeleton, and the effective stress adds from zero to $\Delta\sigma' = \Delta\mu$ when the consolidation is finished. Since $\Delta\sigma'$ and $\Delta\mu$ are both isotropic, the subgrade body is compressed in the isotropic way, The even compression in all directions of subgrade is shown as the dashed line in Fig. 4-9(c) under the action of $\Delta\sigma'$. Now the subgrade volume changes to be

$$\varepsilon_v = \frac{\Delta V}{V} = \frac{\Delta\sigma'}{K} = \frac{\Delta u}{K} \tag{4-15}$$

where: *K*—the subgrade volume modulus, and its expression is $K = \frac{1}{3}E_0/(1-2\mu)$, according to elastic mechanics.

The permeating consolidation deformation that is under the action of constant effective stress is called consolidation deformation. When permeating consolidation process is finished, the subgrade can still be compressed for creep under the action of constant effective stress. This is relevant to the extrusion of bounding water around the subgrade particles and the compression or yielding of the subgrade skeleton, and such kind of subgrade deformation is called secondary consolidation deformation.

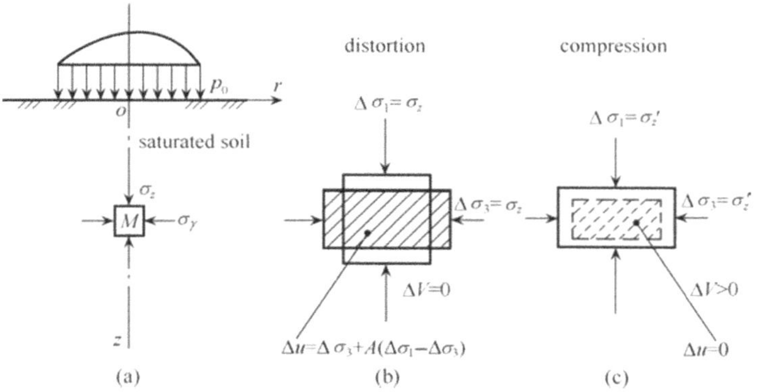

Fig. 4-9 The soil stress and deformation under the center point of circular loading

In the three-dimensional stress condition, total deformations of subgrade include immediate compression deformation, principal and secondary consolidation deformation. The foundation's total settlement s can be expressed as below, under the action of local loading in deep foundation pit.

$$s = s_d + s_c + s_s = \sum_{i=1}^{3} s_i \tag{4-16}$$

According to the *s*-*t* curve, the foundation total settlement and time relationship curve, which is measured from the beginning of the building construction, the expression's three components can be expressed clearly as three settlement stages in Fig.4-10.

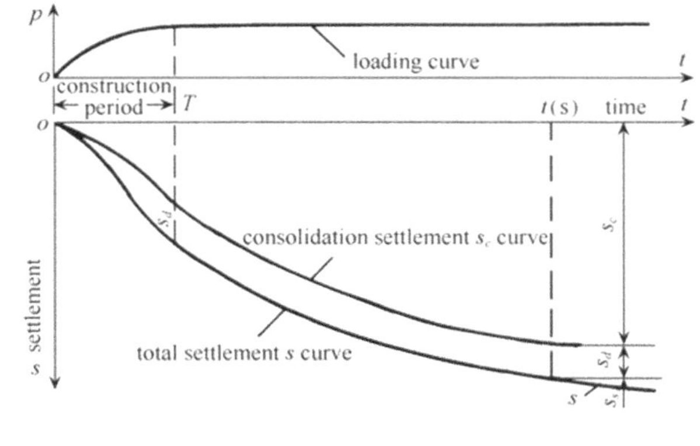

Fig. 4-10 The three components of foundation settlement

(1) The mechanism of initial settlement (s_d)

The initial settlement is called instant settlement or non-drainage settlement. It is usually the combination of all settlements that happen before the finishing of the construction of super high-rise buildings. Because of concentrated stress on the edge of the deep foundation, the initial settlement could happen even the load is small at the beginning of construction. The settlement increment will increase with the adding of loads, until the end of the construction period, and the building loads will stay the same then. For foundation with small size in soft and thick subgrade under heavy loads, the initial settlement will take a big proportion of total settlement. For example, the percentage that the initial settlement takes in the total settlement is more than 50% for middle-sized structures built on the soft subgrade.

(2) The mechanism of consolidation settlement (s_c)

The consolidation settlement is the foundation deformation process that begins after the completion of construction, under the action of dead load. It increases with the gradual extrusion of water from voids. It will not stop until the initial pore water pressure dissipates completely. Generally the consolidation settlement is the main part of the foundation total settlement.

The foundation's final consolidation settlement depends on the distribution of initial pore water pressure. In the three-dimensional stress state, the subgrade initial pore water pressure and normal stress increment are relevant to partial stress increment, so its distribution is quite different from one-dimensional consolidation theory.

(3) The mechanism of secondary consolidation settlement (S_s)

The secondary consolidation settlement process, which is related to the creep of subgrade skeleton, is more complex. It is the slow consolidation of subgrade after the dissipation of pore pressure and stabilization of effective stress. The rate of secondary consolidation settlement is irrelevant to the extrusion rate of the free water in subgrade pore and the subgrade thickness of secondary consolidation. Generally, the secondary consolidation settlement is much smaller than the consolidation settlement, and even can be ignored sometimes. But for soft subgrade, the secondary consolidation settlement should be considered when the ratio of additional stress to gravity stress is small in the compressible layer of deep part in subgrade.

2. The conception of the calculating method for initial settlement

Skempton (Skempton, 1955) etc. first suggested to use formulas of elastic mechanics to calculate foundation initial settlement, and this suggestion was confirmed by laboratory test of large-scale model and site exploration research. It is required that the settlement which is induced by the compression of volume should not be included in the initial settlement, and the volumetric strain should be 0, the Poisson ratio μ should be 0.5. This non-drainage Poisson ratio's ideal value has not yet been confirmed through practical exploration, because of the natural subgrade's characters of heterogeneity and nonlinearity, but it is still adopted now since the error is small.

In engineering, the layered property, heterogeneity, and the total thickness for foundation deformation calculation should all be considered except for simplified calculation methods, so the linear deformation layerwise summation method is recommended. This method is for the corner point settlement under uniform rectangular flexible load to consider the influence of nearby load using corner point method, and the linear deformation sum method's formula for rigid foundation is no longer suitable. The calculating formula for initial settlement is

$$s_d = 0.75 p_0 \sum_{i=1}^{n} \frac{1}{E_i}(z_i C_i - z_{i-1} C_{i-1}) \tag{4-17}$$

The form of the formula above is completely the same as the formula of uniaxial compression layerwise summation method, only that the average additional stress coefficient α is replaced by foundation vertical deformation coefficient *C*, and *C* is the function of rectangular load face's ratio of length to width $\alpha = l/b$, depth ratio $\beta = l/b$, and Poisson ratio μ.

The initial tangent modulus E_i determined through the stress-strain curve, which is measured through the laboratory tri-axial compression test or uniaxial compression test under the condition of non-drainage, is usually adopted as the non-drainage elastic modulus *E* in the calculation of initial settlement.

3. The conception of the calculating method for consolidation settlement

The subgrade's three-dimensional stress state is considered in linear deformation summation method which is based on the solution of vertical displacement of elastic half-space. If the subgrade deformation modulus E_0 and Poisson ratio are adopted as deformation parameters here, the derived stress is the final total settlement which includes the initial settlement. The consolidation settlement is then derived by subtracting the initial settlement. The settlement calculation formula which directly adopts the solution of elastic half-space theory assumes the subgrade body to be continuous medium of linear deformation, the consolidation character, the inducing and dissipating processes of pore water pressure and its converting to effective stress in three-dimensional stress state for saturated subgrade is not considered. Therefore the foundation consolidation settlement which is controlled by the distribution of initial pore pressure is hard to be correctly estimated, and the shoring structure's action is not considered further.

Obviously, it is difficult to comprehensively analyse the initial pore pressure distribution at every point of the subgrade and to accurately calculate the foundation consolidation settlement in the state of three-dimensional stress. For engineering practicality, A.W. Skempton-L.Bjerrum (1957) put forward a half-theoretical and half-empirical formula which modified the result of single-axial compression summation method, and took the triaxial compression consolidation settlement into account. They replaced the volume strain ε_v and volume modulus K with vertical strain ε_z and compression modulus E_s in confined condition, based on the consolidation settlement in the center point of the circular load in the axisymmetric subject, then get

$$\varepsilon_z = \frac{\Delta u}{E_s} \tag{4-18}$$

Skempton-Bjerrum thought that such simplification's error is less than 20%. Put $\Delta\mu$ into the equation above, it can be got to be

$$\begin{aligned}\varepsilon_z &= \frac{1}{E_s}\left[\Delta\sigma_3 + A(\Delta\sigma_1 + \Delta\sigma_3)\right] \\ &= \frac{1}{E_s}\left[\Delta\sigma_x + A(\Delta\sigma_z + \Delta\sigma_x)\right] \\ &= \frac{1}{E_s}\left[\Delta\sigma_z + (1-A)\sigma_x\right]\end{aligned} \tag{4-19}$$

Considering three-dimensional stress state, the consolidation settlement can be derived as below, assuming that subgrade's coefficients E_s and A do not change with the depth within the compressed layer's thickness H.

$$s_c = \frac{A_z}{E_s}\left[A + (1-A)\frac{A_z}{A_s}\right] \tag{4-20}$$

where: $A_z = \int_0^H \sigma_z \mathrm{d}z$ and $A_x = \int_0^H \sigma_x \mathrm{d}z$ are respectively the distributing maps' areas for induced stress σ_z and σ_x;

A—pore pressure coefficient, which is measured by triaxial test. When the single-axial compression settlement is $s' = \frac{A_z}{E_s}$, the equation above can be changed to be

$$S_c = \xi S' \tag{4-21}$$

where: ξ—three-dimensional correction coefficient of foundation consolidation settlement

$$\xi = A + (1-A)\frac{A_z}{A_s}$$

The smaller the value of A (or the bigger the subgrade over consolidation ratio) is, the smaller the correction coefficient ξ is. Skempton and Bjerrum give the relationship between consolidation settlement's correction coefficient ξ and pore pressure coefficient A for the square (circular) foundation and strip foundation built on saturated compressed subgrade with limited thickness, according to elastic mechanics. This method's calculating result and measured data show that: ① the calculating result of single-axial compression summation method overestimates the consolidation settlement on over consolidated soil subgrade (its deviation degree increases along with the over consolidated ratio); ② it underestimates the consolidation settlement on high sensitive clayey soil subgrade.

Although the method above considers the influence of three-dimensional stress distribution of initial pore pressure based on the calculation of single-axial compression settlement, its result is hard to conform to the reality. The biggest difficulty here is that the pore pressure coefficient A is hard to be accurately measured. Therefore its application is affected.

4. The conception of the calculating method for secondary consolidation settlement

Many results of laboratory test and site exploration indicate that the void ratio and time relationship curve is close to a straight line in the semilog plot when subgrade is under the action of dead load, in the process of secondary consolidation inducing after the principal consolidation. So the void ratio change induced by secondary consolidation can be approximately expressed as

$$\Delta e = C_a \log \frac{t}{t_1} \tag{4-22}$$

where: C_a — the straight slope in semilogarithmic coordinate, also called secondary consolidation coefficient;

t—the time of secondary consolidation settlement, account from the moment of load;

t_1 — the time when the principal consolidation percentage is 100%, which is superpolated according to slops of e-log$t$ curves of principal consolidation and secondary consolidation.

The layerwise summation method for the calculation of foundation secondary consolidation settlement is

$$s_s = \sum_{i=1}^{n} \frac{H_i}{1+e_{1i}} C_{ai} \log \frac{t}{t_1} \tag{4-23}$$

According to many results of laboratory and site tests, the value of C_a mainly depends on the subgrade's natural moisture content ω, and $C_a = 0.018\omega$ for approximate calculation.

5. The conception of calculating succedent settlement by observed settlement data

For most projects, secondary consolidation settlement is not very important compared with consolidation settlement. Therefore, the final settlement usually is the sum of initial settlement and consolidation settlement, i.e. $s=s_d+s_c$. Accordingly, T time after the finish of building construction, the settlement value is

$$s_t=s_d+s_{ct} \quad \text{or} \quad s_t=s_d+U_z s_c \tag{4-24}$$

The settlement of the equations above is normally calculated according to the one-dimensional consolidation theory, and its result does not conform to the measured one. Therefore, it is with important engineering significance to calculate succedent settlement (including final settlement) using the observed settlement data. Its empirical methods include hyperbola method, logarithmic curve method etc. logarithmic curve method (i.e. three point method) can separate initial settlement s_d from total settlement s_t.

One common expression can summary the calculating formula of consolidation degree U_z in different conditions, i.e.

$$U_z = 1 - A\exp(-Bt) \tag{4-25}$$

where: A and B—two parameters to be determined.

Comparing the equation above with the theoretical formula of one-dimensional consolidation, it is revealed that parameter A is the constant value $8/\pi^2$, and B is relevant to time factor T_v's consolidation coefficient and drainage path. It can be got as below, making A and B as the parameters of the measured settlement-time relation curve, and there values are to be determined.

$$s_t = s_\infty\left[1 - A\exp(-Bt)\right] + s_d A\exp(-Bt) \tag{4-26}$$

where

$$A = 8/\pi^2 \qquad B = \frac{1}{t_2 - t_1}\ln\frac{s_{t2} - s_{t1}}{s_{t3} - s_{t2}}$$

$$s_\infty = \frac{s_{t3}\left(s_{t2} - s_{t1}\right) - s_{t2}\left(s_{t3} - s_{t2}\right)}{\left(s_{t2} - s_{t1}\right) - \left(s_{t3} - s_{t2}\right)} \qquad s_d = \frac{s_{t1} - s_\infty\left[1 - A\exp\left(Bt_1\right)\right]}{A\exp\left(-Bt_1\right)} \tag{4-27}$$

The succedent settlement s_t of any time can be calculated according to next equation.

6. The conception of foundation's final settlement

(1) Calculating according to the layerwise summation method

When using the layerwise summation method to calculate the final settlement of foundation, the subgrade should be divided into several layers within the calculating depth to calculate each layer's compression value and then sum up. Each layer's calculating method for compression value is the same as the settlement calculation method of thin compressed layer foundation.

If the buried depth of the uncompressible rock is shallow, and the thickness of the compressible subgrade is $H<0.5b$ (b is the width of subgrade), this is called thin compressed layer foundation. The geostatic stress and additional stress change little in the thin layer, and only small lateral deformation happens when the subgrade is compressed, because of the confining action of foundation base frictional resistance and rock's inter-layer frictional resistance. So this situation is considered to be close to the force and deformation situation (single-axial compression) of the subgrade sample in the compression instrument. The foundation's final settlement can be calculated directly by the equation below:

$$S = \frac{e_1 - e_2}{1 + e_1}H \tag{4-28}$$

where: *H*—the thickness of the thin compressive subgrade layer;

e_1—the corresponding void ratio in the subgrade compression curve according to the average value of the geostatic stress σ_z (i.e. the initial pressure p_l) from the top to the base of the thin subgrade layer;

e_2—the corresponding void ratio in the subgrade compression curve according to the sum of σ_c and induced stress's average value σ_z.

Most soft subgrade's compressive subgrade layer's thickness is more than twice of the foundation width, so these factors should be considered, i.e. the attenuation of the induced stress along with the depth's adding, the layered character of the foundation, and the variability of the compressibility in the same subgrade layer. So the distribution of subgrade induced stress and compressibility can be considered to be even, if the subgrade is divided into several thin layers.

The single-axial compression layerwise summation assumes that: ① the induced pressure of foundation base is considered to be local flexible load on earth's surface, and for non-homogeneous subgrade, its induced stress's distribution can be calculated according to the homogeneous foundation method; ② the shear stress can be ignored, and only the action of vertical induced stress compresses the subgrade layer and induces foundation settlement; ③ there is no lateral deformation when the subgrade is compressed.

In the assumptions above, the subgrade of each layer is just like the subgrade in the compression instrument, being in the state of single-axial compression, so the compression index got in lateral confined condition should be adopted to calculate subgrade compression.

Under long-term action of geostatic stress, subgrade compressibility increases with the adding of depth while the induced stress raised by local loads decreases. The deformation of the subgrade which is under certain depth is very small, so is the settlement. The certain depth of subgrade is called foundation effective compressed layer, and this depth is just the calculating depth of foundation settlement or the thickness of foundation compressed layer. The lower limit for foundation settlement calculating depth is usually confined to the place where the foundation induced stress is 20% or 10% of geostatic stress, and their accounting precisions are both ±5kPa. The settlement calculating depth determined by stress ratio method is small sometimes, but it is big for small foundation.

The thickness of stratification is 0.4*b* or 1～2 m, within the settlement calculating depth. The layered subgrade's interfaces and the surface of groundwater are absolute interface for layering. After being layered, the average of each layer's geostatic stress and induced stress can both be calculated. It is obvious that the problem of effective depth for foundation compressed layer has not yet been really settled.

(2) Calculating according to the standard method

The calculating method for foundation final settlement recommended by "*Code for Design of Building Foundation*" is actually layerwise summation method in a different form. It adopts the compression index in lateral confined condition, uses average induced stress coefficient; and regulates the standard for foundation settlement's calculating depth, puts forward regional empirical coefficient for foundation settlement calculation to make the result more close to engineering measured value.

This method's most distinctive feature is to adopt the regional empirical correction coefficient.

7. Theoretical issues of calculation of foundation final settlement

(1) Assumption issues of layerwise summation method

The primary purpose of all kinds of layerwise summation method is basically to solve the calculating difficulties which come from the layered and non-homogeneous characteristics of foundation. Therefore, it is assumed that the whole foundation has a half-space of homogeneous linear deformation which shears the same deformation coefficient with this layer. This means that all the layerwise summation methods consider it to be acceptable to use homogeneous elastic half-space theory as a replacement to solve the induced stress distribution in non-homogeneous foundation under the action of loads. Then according to the purpose and requirement of settlement calculation, it is convenient to choose one-dimensional or three-dimensional stress state's calculating method, to adopt linear or non-linear stress-strain relation which is more suitable to the subgrade engineering character, to select appropriate subgrade deformation coefficient to calculate according to available test condition. Because the layerwise summation method can solve stress ahead before the calculation of deformation, the effect of foundation's initial stress and stress increment on the subgrade deformation coefficient can be considered, and the calculation accuracy can be improved for changing the non-linear problem to be linear problem through dividing thin layers.

It is unharmonious for the layerwise summation method to calculate the deformation of non-homogeneous foundation by the homogenous elastic half-space's stress, and its error has not been adequately tested through theory and practice. But practice shows that it depends more directly on whether the method can reflect the foundation's characteristics of layered and non-homogeneous, consider the non-linear characteristic of the subgrade stress-strain relationship, than the stress calculating accuracy to judge whether the calculation of foundation settlement is right. So the layerwise summation method is till widely used in engineering practice, although this method is not reasonable.

(2) The problem of each layerwise summation method and its application

The single-axial compression layerwise summation method uses non-linear stress compression relation measured by compression test, then stratify and linearize it to calculate foundation settlement. The measurement and calculating methods of the subgrade deformation coefficients needed for this method are easy and practical, so this method is widely used in engineering, and many experiences are accumulated. single-axial compression layerwise summation method fits best for the foundation of thin compressive layer under large area loadings, because its situation of stress and deformation is close to the complete lateral confined state, in which the subgrade body only has volume deformation, and the calculating result is the foundation's final consolidation settlement, i.e. foundation's final settlement for thin compressed layer foundation, when compress one subgrade sample. For general foundation, the compressed layer's thickness is equivalent with the foundation base size, it can not be treated as thin layer, so if the single-axial compression layerwise summation method is still used to calculate, the initial settlement that is caused by the distortion from subgrade shear stress would be ignored, for having not considered the affection of the foundation's three-dimensional stress state. Theoretically speaking, the result got by this is just the foundation's final consolidation settlement, so the calculating result of the single-axial compression layerwise summation method is grossly considered to be foundation's final settlement, and the initial settlement is not considered further.

For the traditional and standard referenced single-axial compression layerwise summation methods, considering the calculation method, the former is based on the induced stress, and the later is based on the area of induced stress curve. If the settlement's calculating depths are equal, and without the empirical correction, then there is no difference in work and result. The distinctive characteristic of standard method is introduced into empirical coefficient for settlement calculation to correct the calculating result's error compared with the measured value. The calculating empirical coefficient provided by the standard takes as the basis for tabulation the settlement's calculating value got by foundation settlement calculating depth determined by the deformation ratio method. Therefore, it may not be appropriate to correct the settlement's calculating value got from stress ratio method using the empirical coefficient's tabular value.

For the calculation of over-consolidated subgrade's settlement, the historical stress's effect should be considered. In order to determine the early consolidation pressure more reliable in the curve, little increment loading between the present subgrade geostatic pressure and predicted early consolidation pressure should be adopted in the compression laboratory.

The linear deformation layerwise summation method considers the second degree stress condition under the acing of local rigid load, based on the elastic half-space vertical displacement's solution. The result of rigid foundation's final settlement and inclination calculated by the deformation modulus and Poisson ratio which is measured in drainage condition indicates the sum of two components, i.e. the initial settlement or inclination induced by the subgrade shear distortion and then consolidation settlement or inclination induced by the volume compression. The deformation modulus needed in the calculation can be measured by the triaxial apparatus, and rigid foundation's linear deformation can be got by lookup table according to the Poisson ratio. The layerwise summation method formula can not consider the near load's linear deformation, while the layerwise summation method can not only consider the influence of the near load, but also unify the linear deformation summation method's formula which considers three-dimensional stress state and the uniaxial compression summation method which is recommended by the standard, and make the later to be a special case of the former.

When calculate the settlement and inclination of the rigid foundation, the influence of the foundation's rigidity has been taken into account. For continuous foundation's settlement calculation with different rigidity, the influence of foundation rigidity can be calculated by combining linear deformation or single-axial compression layerwise summation methods for numerical analysis, based on the theory of interaction between foundation and subgrade.

The sandy subgrade's settlement induced by the subgrade volume deformation and shear distortion is almost finished synchronously in short time. Because the sandy subgrade's deformation modulus increases along with the increase of depth, and it is difficult to sample and measure it, the settlement calculation for sandy subgrade are generally through the empirical method put forward by H.J. Simo terman based on the data of in-situ penetration test.

(3) The calculating depth problem for foundation settlement

The significance of determining the calculating depth for foundation settlement is determining the subgrade depth extension within which the foundation settlement is influenced, i.e. the depth of compressive layer to satisfy the accuracy demand for settlement calculation. The preexistence of *Code for Design of Building Foundation (*GBJ 7-89*)—Code* TJ 7-74 puts forward to determine the settlement's calculating depth by the deformation ratio method for the first time. Its difference with GBJ 7-89 in that the nth layer's thickness adopts 1 m for different foundation width. GBJ 7-89 indicates that its calculating accuracy various for foundations with different width, and uses depth of $0.3(1+\ln b)$ to replace the regulation in *Code* TJ 7-74. But some provincial or urban codes and *Technical Code for Building Pile Foundation* still adopt the traditional stress ratio method after the publishing of GBJ 7-89. Then stress ratio and deformation ratio methods coexist in the codes.

4.3 The Elastic Mechanics Method of Foundation Deformation Calculation

4.3.1 The Foundation Deformation Calculation under Flexible Load

The vertical displacement $\omega(x, y, z)$ of any point $M(x, y, z)$ on the half-space can be solved according to the foundation stress analysis, when vertical concentrated load P acts on the elastic half-space surface. If the point M's z=0, the vertical displacement $M(x, y, 0)$ of any point on half-space surface is just the settlement s of the foundation surface.(see Fig. 4-11)

$$s = \omega(x, y, 0) = \frac{P(1-\mu^2)}{\pi E_0 r} \tag{4-29}$$

where: s—the settlement of any point on the foundation surface under the action of vertical concentrated load P;

r—the distance form any point on the foundation surface to the acting point of the vertical concentrated load;

E_0—the deformation modulus of the subgrade;

μ—the Poisson ratio of the subgrade.

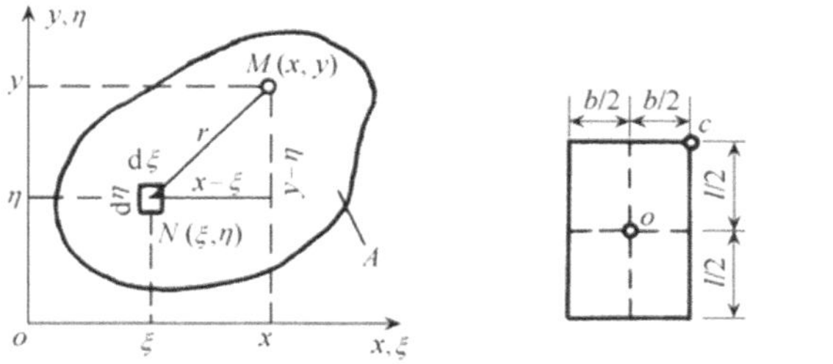

(a) Arbitrary load surface (b) Rectangular load surface

Fig. 4-11 the calculation of subgrade surface settlement under the local loading

For foundation settlement under the action of the local flexible loads (i.e. the subgrade pressure when the foundation's flexural stiffness is zero), the expression above can be used to calculate it according to the superposition principle. Let the distributing load on the point of $N(\xi, \eta)$ in the load surface be $p_0(\xi, \eta)$, then this point's elementary area $d\xi d\eta$'s distributing load can be replaced by the concentrated load $P = p_0(\xi, \eta) d\xi d\eta$. Then the settlement of point $M(x, y)$, from which to point N the distance is $r = \sqrt{(x-\xi)^2 + (y-\eta)^2}$, is

$$S(x, y) = \frac{1-\mu^2}{\pi E_0} \iint \frac{p_0(\xi, \eta) d\xi d\eta}{\sqrt{(x-\xi)^2 + (y-\eta)^2}} \tag{4-30}$$

For uniform rectangular load, $p_0(\xi,\eta)=p_0$ is constant, based on the integral equation above, the integral of its corner point C's settlement is

$$S=\delta_c p_0=\frac{1-\mu^2}{E_0}\omega_c b p_0$$

where: $\omega_c=\frac{1}{\pi}\left[m\ln\frac{1+\sqrt{m^2+1}}{m}+\ln\left(m+\sqrt{m^2+1}\right)\right]$, it is called corner point settlement coefficient, in which $m=l/b$.

Using the expression above, it is easy to solve any point' settlement on the foundation surface under the action of uniform rectangular load. For example, the center point of rectangle's settlement is the summation of corner point's settlement of the same four small rectangles which are divided to be by the dashed lines in the figure. Because the small rectangle's length-width ratio is the same as the origin rectangle one, the settlement of the center point is

$$S=4\cdot\frac{1-\mu^2}{E_0}\omega_c\left(\frac{b}{2}\right)p_0=2\cdot\frac{1-\mu^2}{E_0}\omega_c b p_0 \tag{4-31}$$

That is, the center point's settlement is twice of that of the corner point, let $\omega_0=2\omega_c$ be the influence coefficient of the center point, then

$$S=\frac{1-\mu^2}{E_0}\omega_c b p_0 \tag{4-32}$$

The calculation result and the practical experience of the corner point method indicates that the settlement only happens within the extension of load area under the action of flexible loads, it also happens beyond load area. The subgrade deformation after settlement is in dishing shape. Because almost every foundation has flexural stiffness in a certain degree and the foundation base's settlement stabilizes based on the foundation rigidity, foundation settlement under the action of center load can be approximated as the foundation base's average settlement under the action of flexural load, i.e.

$$S=\left(\iint_A S(x,y)\mathrm{d}x\mathrm{d}y\right)/A \tag{4-33}$$

where: A—the area of foundation base.

For the uniform rectangular load, the integral of the expression above is

$$S=\frac{1-\mu^2}{E_0}\omega_n b p_0 \tag{4-34}$$

where: S—the average settlement influence coefficient.

For the convenience of calculation, the expression above is uniformed as the elastic mechanics formula for foundation settlement:

$$S = \frac{1-\mu^2}{E_0}\omega b p_0 \tag{4-35}$$

where: b—the width of rectangular load or the diameter of the circular load;

ω—the influence coefficient for settlement, which is determined by the stiffness, subgrade surface shape and the position of the calculating point.

4.3.2 The Settlement of Rigid Foundation

For the rigid foundation under the center load, because of the unlimited flexural stiffness, there is normally no deflection after the settlement of foundation under loading, therefore, the settlement of the foundation base is equal everywhere, i.e., S is a constant. Combined with the foundation's static balance condition, the foundation base reaction p_0 and settlement S can be solved, and $p_0=P/A$. rigid foundation's settlement influence coefficient ω_r is adopted as ω, its value is close to the flexible load's ω_m.

The settlement influence coefficient ω_z can be used to get the simplified method for the settlement of layered subgrade for the rigid foundation. Assuming that there are n horizontal natural subgrade layers within the calculating depth for foundation settlement, and the foundation settlement caused by deformation of the ith layer subgrade whose layer base depth is z_i can be expressed as $\Delta S_i = S_i - S_{i-1}$, where S_i and S_{i-1} are respectively the rigid foundation settlement of the calculating depth z_i and z_{i-1}. when calculate the S_i and S_{i-1}, assuming the whole elastic half-space is the homogeneous foundation with the same deformation parameters(E_{oi}, v_i) as the ith subgrade layer. Then the rigid foundation's settlement is the summation of each layer's deformation, i.e.

$$S = \sum_{i=1}^{n} \Delta S_i = b p_0 \cdot \sum_{i=1}^{n} \frac{1-\mu^2}{E_{0i}} (\omega_{zi} - \omega_{zi-1}) \tag{4-36}$$

where the foundation settlement influence coefficient ω_{zi} and ω_{zi-1} can be got by lookup the table, according to the depth-width ratio. This method is called linear deformation layerwise summation method.

4.3.3 The Inclination of Rigid Foundation

When there is eccentric load on the rigid foundation, the foundation base is an inclined surface after settlement. The centroid of the foundation base's settlement can be calculated according to the expression above. For rigid foundation's inclination, the numerical method considering the reaction between foundation and ground can be adopted. For rigid foundation on homogeneous elastic half-space, if only the soil deformation within the extension of foundation perforating depth is considered, the foundation inclination can be express as

$$\theta \approx \tan\theta = k \cdot \frac{1-\mu^2}{E_0} \cdot \frac{P \cdot e}{b^3} \tag{4-37}$$

where: θ—foundation's inclination angle;

P, e—the resultant force of the foundation eccentric loads and its eccentricity;

b, l—the rectangular foundation base's side length in eccentric direction of load and the other direction;

k—the inclination influence coefficient for rigid foundation;

E_0, μ—the deformation modulus and Poisson ratio of the subgrade within the extension of settlement calculating depth.

For the rigid foundation on the horizontal layered subgrade, the inclination can be calculated by layerwise summation method, i.e.

$$\theta = \sum_{i=1}^{n} \Delta\theta_i = \frac{p \cdot e}{b^3} \cdot \sum_{i=1}^{n} \frac{1-\mu^2}{E_{0i}} (k_i - k_{i-1}) \tag{4-38}$$

where: subscript i—the layer number in the sequence of from top to bottom.

The inclination influence coefficients k_i and k_{i-1} are respectively founded in figure according to the depth ratio and side length of rectangular foundation.

The elastic mechanics formula for the calculation of foundation settlement is based on the solution of the vertical displacement with the concentrated load on the surface of the homogeneous elastic half-space. Therefore, the three-dimensional stress state induced by the local load in the foundation can be considered, and this can be used for the calculation of foundation's final settlement, subgrade's deformation modulus, Poisson ratio and initial settlement.

4.4 Calculation of Initial Settlement

The experience of site exploration home and abroad indicates that the initial settlement of buildings constructed on the cohesive soil subgrade takes a considerable part of the total settlement, so it can not be ignored, and can be estimated by elastic theory. If the initial settlement is big, it indicates that the subgrade's plastic deformation area is too large, the foundation design is not suitable, and should be adjusted.

4.4.1 Practical Calculation Methods of Initial Settlement

Assuming the subgrade to be a half-infinite linear deformable body, with circular or rectangular distributed load on the surface, then the initial settlement can be calculated by elastic theory formula.

1. The homogeneous foundation (Schleicher, 1926)

Assuming it as homogeneous foundation, then its initial settlement's calculation formula is

$$S_d = C_d pb \frac{1-\mu^2}{E} \tag{4-39}$$

where: S_d—any point on the loading area's surface vertical settlement or initial settlement under the action of circular or rectangular uniform distributed load;

p—the uniform distributed load;

b—the diameter or width of the loading area;

C_d—the parameter for the calculation shape of the loading area and the position of the calculation point;

E, μ —the subgrade elastic modulus and Poisson ratio respectively.

2. Layered foundation

Actually, the subgrade is made up of different soil stratums. Then, the calculation should be based on three different situations below.

1) When the thickness of the top stratum is bigger than the size of the loading area, the initial surface displacement still can be calculated according to the formula above, considering it as homogeneous foundation. If the top stratum is thin, then the layered influence should be considered, especially when it is rock or hard subsoil stratum under the compressible soft subsoil layer.

2) When it is rigid subgrade under the compressible cohesive subsoil stratum (its thickness is H), the initial settlement can still be calculated according to the formula above, but the coefficient should be corrected (by lookup of table).

3) When it is hard subsoil stratum with limited thickness over thick compressible subsoil stratum, Burmister (1965) calculates the surface displacement value on the center point of the circular uniform distributed loading area, and the result can be expressed by homogeneous foundation's surface displacement value, i.e.

$$S_{d1} = aS_{d\infty} \tag{4-40}$$

where: S_{d1}—the surface displacement on the center point of the circular uniform distributed loading area which is on the surface of the upper hard subgrade with elastic modulus E_1, Poisson ratio v_1, and thickness H (it is compressive subsoil layer with infinite thickness, elastic modulus E_2 and Poisson ratio μ_2 below);

$S_{d\infty}$ —the surface displacement on the center point of the circular uniform distributed loading area which is on the surface of the homogeneous half-space with elastic parameters E_2 and μ_2;

a—correcting coefficient (see the table).

Except for the situation above, there are other calculating methods for the surface displacement of the layered system.

3. Inclination of perfectly rigid foundation

When there is eccentric load on rigid foundation, not only settlement, but also inclination induced by settlement difference happens in the foundation. The average value of settlement can be calculated according to the layerwise summation method, and the calculating formulas for inclination are as below respectively.

(1) For rectangular foundation

When the inclination is along the long side of the foundation

$$\tan\theta = \frac{8Pe}{l^3}\frac{K_2}{C} \tag{4-41}$$

When the inclination is along the long side of the foundation

$$\tan\theta = \frac{8Pe}{b^3}\frac{K_2}{C} \tag{4-42}$$

where: θ —the inclination angle of the foundation;

P—the vertical load;

e—the eccentricity;

l, b—the long and short side of the foundation;

K_1, K_2 —the dimensionless coefficients for the calculation of the foundation inclination;

C—the foundation's deformation coefficient, $C = \dfrac{E}{1-\mu^2}$.

(2) For circular foundation

$$\tan\theta = \frac{6Pe}{d^3 C} \tag{4-43}$$

where: d—the diameter of the circular foundation, the other signals are the same as above.

4. The uplift of excavation

During the excavation of foundation pit, the phenomenon of pit base's uplift happens a lot, the uplift value is very important for the later recompression settlement value induced by the action of loading, especially when design partial or complete compensation box (raft) foundation, it is more important. Baladi (1968) solved the uplift problem of the strip excavation subgrade in the elastic medium. For the strip excavation with rectangular section, its uplift value or resilience value can be determined by the expression as below:

$$R_d = \Delta_{\text{strip}}\frac{rd^2}{E} \tag{4-44}$$

where: Δ_{strip}—the dimensionless excavation coefficient, its value can be determined by the size of excavation and position of the calculating resilience. For excavation, its finite length should be considered, and its uplift value is determined by the formula below:

$$R_d = C_d'' \cdot \Delta_{strip} \cdot \frac{rd^2}{E} \tag{4-45}$$

where: C_d''—the shape coefficient.

4.4.2 Values of the Calculation Coefficients

The values of initial settlement and excavation are directly relevant to the values of the elastic parameters. Because cohesive subgrade is not linear elastic material, the values of E and μ are not constant, they are changing with stress.

For saturated cohesive subgrade, on the moment of loading, because its deformation happens without volume change, it is considered to be uncompressible, and $\mu = 0.5$ can be assumed. Although it is different from reality, it has slight influence on the result of initial settlement.

Therefore, the key problem is the determination of the elastic modulus E. Usually, elastic modulus E is solved by triaxially non-drainage test or unconfined compression test. The value got by this way is small, and just counts a small part of the measured one on site. The present solution is the triaxial consolidation non-drainage test using the original subgrade sample with good quality, and let the consolidation pressure be isotropic and equal to the average value of effective pressure obtained by site exploration. When consolidation is finished, add axial loading on non-drainage condition and then increase the axial pressure to meet the in-situ situation, and then decrease it to zero. Repeat this loading and unloading process for several times, usually five or six times to determine the value. The initial settlement got by this way is much closer to the practically measured one.

The elastic modulus can also be connected with the strength got by the non-drainage tri-axial test to estimate the value indirectly.

$$E = (250 — 500)(\sigma_1 - \sigma_3)_f \tag{4-46}$$

where: $(\sigma_1 - \sigma_3)_f$—the principal stress difference when the sample is failure.

The calculating result differs a lot if the elastic modulus value is not determined appropriately. The elastic modulus from in-situ test is more reliable.

4.4.3 The Modification of Initial Settlement When the Development of the Plastic Zone is Large

It is difficult to get correct initial settlement using the elastic mechanics' formula, when there is large plastic deformation zone under loading, and this could induce that the measured value of initial settlement is bigger than the calculating result sometimes.

When the plastic deformation zone is considered, the modification solution of the initial settlement is given already by D'Appolinia (1971). Let the ratio of in-situ shear stress to non drainage shear strength c_u be

$$f = \frac{\sigma_v - \sigma_h}{2} / c_u = \frac{1 - K_0}{\frac{2c_u}{c_v}} \tag{4-47}$$

where, σ_v, σ_h —initial effective vertical stress and horizontal stress;

K_0—the coefficient of lateral earth pressure at rest.

Because c_u and σ_v of cohesive subgrade are in direct ratio, f is constant for homogeneous foundation.

Deducing the foundation's ultimate load P according to the non-drainage strength, the stress horizontal ratio is P/P_u, given the loading P. The correction coefficient a can be derived according to P/P_u and f.

Therefore, when there is plastic deformation in the foundation, the foundation's initial settlement S'_d is

$$S'_d = \frac{S_d}{a} \tag{4-48}$$

The general cohesive subgrade's initial settlement is small compared with the consolidation settlement. For the buildings set up on the subgrade with thick cohesive soil, its initial settlement is probably big, so it should be considered adequately.

4.5 Calculation of Consolidation Settlement

4.5.1 Layerwise Summation Method

The layerwise summation method has three assumptions. ① There is no lateral expansion in subgrade when compressed. ② The calculation is based on the induced stress under the center point of the foundation. ③ The foundation's final (consolidation) settlement is the summation of each layer's compression below the subgrade, within the extension of compressive layer.

The *i*th layer subsoil's stress state, which is below the subgrade, within the extension of compressive layer, before and after the building construction is completed, there is only geostatic stress before construction, while there is induced stress further after construction. In most situations, the deformation process is finished under the geostatic stress, so only induced stress *A* can bring to new subgrade deformation, cause foundation settlement. For the assumption of no lateral expansion, its forced state is the same as the confined compression test's subgrade sample. The *i*th layer's subsoil compression value can be expressed as:

$$S_i = \frac{e_{1i} - e_{2i}}{1 + e_{1i}} h_i$$

and the total settlement is

$$S = \sum_{i=1}^{n} S_i = \sum_{i=1}^{n} \frac{e_{1i} - e_{2i}}{1 + e_{1i}} h_i \tag{4-49}$$

where: S—foundation's final settlement;

e_{1i}—the *i*th layer's void ratio when the compression is stable under the action of subsoil average geostatic stress before the building construction;

e_{2i}—the *i*th layer's void ratio when the compression is stable under the action of subsoil average geostatic stress and average induced stress after the building construction;

h_i—the *i*th layer subsoil's original thickness (cm);

n—the number of subsoil layers within the extension of compressed layer.

4.5.2 The Layerwise Summation Method's Calculating Formula Which is Recommended by the Standards in China

The final settlement value got by layerwise summation method is usually different from the measured value, even has big difference. Summarizing amounts of measured data of the building settlement from projects, the settlement calculation's empirical coefficient is introduced to correct the calculation result, then the calculation formula for settlement recommended by China is derived, i.e.

$$S = \psi_s S' = \psi_s \sum_{i=1}^{n} \frac{p_0}{E_{si}} \left(\sum_{i=1}^{n} z_i \bar{a}_i - z_{i-1} \bar{a}_{i-1} \right) \tag{4-50}$$

where: S—foundation's final settlement (mm), which is derived by multiplying foundation settlement S' which is calculated by layerwise summation method by empirical coefficient ψ_s;

ψ_s—the empirical coefficient for settlement calculation, which is determined by regional settlement's measured data and experience;

n—the number of subsoil layers that the foundation's compression subsoil is divided into;

p_0—the additional pressure on the subgrade for the load effect quasi-permanent combination;

E_{si}—the compression modulus of the ith layer under the foundation base, which is determined according to actual stress extension;

z_i, z_{i-1}—the distance from the foundation base to the ith and ($i-1$)th layer subsoil base;

$\overline{a}_i$, $\overline{a}_{i-1}$—the average induced stress coefficient in the extension of the foundation base's calculating point's ith and ($i-1$)th.

The advantage of this method is that it reflects the compressibility of each layer within the compressed layer, and it's simple and convenient to use. But there is an assumption that no lateral deformation happens in the subgrade, and the actual situation is close to this assumption only when the building's foundation area is big and the compressible subsoil layer's thickness is thin. Generally speaking, its calculation result is small. Besides, the induced stress under the center point of the foundation is adopted and the settlement of the center point of the foundation is adopted as the whole foundation's settlement, it makes the calculation result big. Therefore, it is difficult to estimate the error. In addition, the rigidity influence of the upper structure and action of the foundation pit's shoring structure are not considered, so there is usually a certain gap between the calculated value and the measured value. In the half-theory and half-experience formula that is recommended by China's "*Code for Design of Building Foundation*", the foundation settlement's calculating result is made to be closer to the measured value by selecting the empirical coefficient ψ_s for settlement calculation. This empirical coefficient is regional and needs analysis for amounts of measured data to determine.

4.5.3 Calculate Consolidation Settlement According to Preconsolidation Pressure

Subgrade can be classified to be normally consolidated subgrade, under-consolidated subgrade, and over-consolidated subgrade, according to the experienced geological history, i.e. the consolidation degree. The settlement calculation is divided to be three situations accordingly.

It has to be considered that the pressure-void ratio relationship curve got from the laboratory compression test is different from what is got from the in-situ test (Fig. 4-12). The laboratory result indicates that these two curves intersect constantly at the point $0.42e_0$ (Schmertmann, 1957).

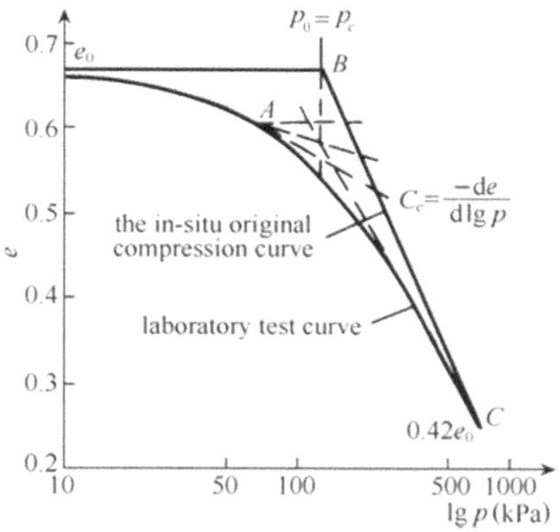

Fig. 4-12 The e-lg p curve of the normally-consolidated soil

1. The settlement calculation of the normally consolidated subgrade ($p_c= p_0$)

The in-situ subgrade's natural void ratio is e_0 and the vertical effective geostatic stress is p_0, these are both available already, which are expressed by the point *B*'s. The subgrade's pre-consolidation pressure p_0 can be determined according to the foregoing method. For normally-consolidated subgrade, $p_c= p_0$. It is easy to find the point *C* on the curve where the void ratio is 0.42 e_0. Connecting point *B* and *C*, the test curve is rebuilt to be the in-situ initial compression curve, and its slope is just the compression index $C_c = -\dfrac{\mathrm{d}e}{\mathrm{d}\lg p}$.

The *i*th layer subgrade's compression value Δs_i, in the compressed layer, is expressed as:

$$\Delta s_i = \frac{\Delta e_i}{1+e_{0i}} h_i \tag{4-51}$$

where: Δe_i—the change of void ratio on the center point of the *i*th layer subgrade.

The consolidation settlement s_c equals the summation of each layer's compression, i.e.

$$s_c = \sum_{i=1}^{n} \Delta s_i = \sum_{i=1}^{n} \frac{h_i}{1+e_{0i}} C_{c_i} \lg\left(\frac{p_0+\Delta p}{p_0}\right) \tag{4-52}$$

2. The settlement calculation for the over-consolidated subgrade

For over-consolidated subgrade, the point *B* can be determined by its natural void ratio e_0 and vertical effective geostatic stress p_0. Plot line *BD* which is parallel to the compression curve's test springback's average slope C_s, intersects the vertical line p_c at point *D*. after determining the point *C*, plot *DC* line, then *BD* and *DC* are just the rebuilt in-situ original compression curve (Fig. 4-13). Because the subgrade's additional stress Δp could be either bigger or smaller than (p_c−p_0), the foregoing method is needed for the settlement calculation respectively.

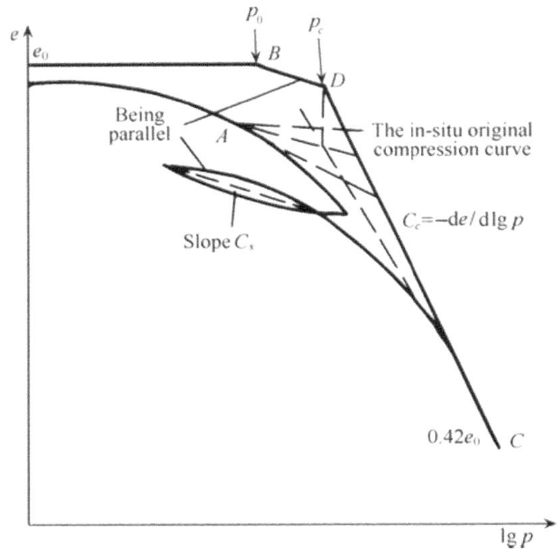

Fig. 4-13 The e-lg p curve of the over-consolidated subgrade

3. The settlement calculation for the under-consolidated subgrade (p_c<p_0)

The settlement of the under-consolidated subgrade (Fig. 4-14) should be the sum of the compression value which is induced by the under-consolidated part of geostatic stress and the compression value which is induced by the building's loads, i.e.

$$s = \sum_{i=1}^{n} C_{c_i} \frac{h_i}{1+e_{0i}} \log\left[\frac{p_0+\Delta p}{p_0}\right] \tag{4-53}$$

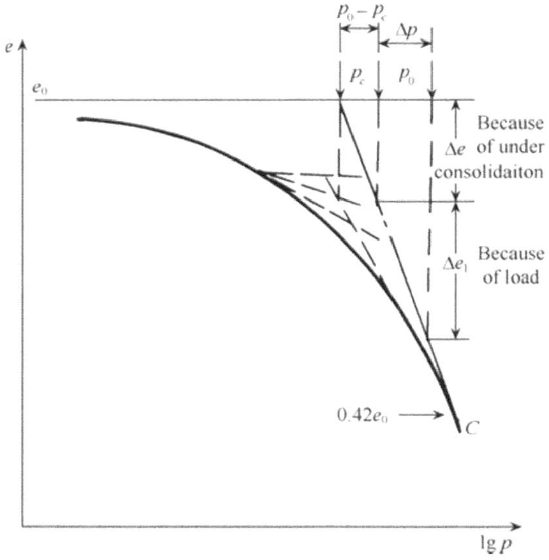

Fig. 4-14 The e-lg p curve of the under-consolidated subgrade

4.5.4 The Calculation of Consolidation Settlement Value Considering Lateral Deformation

When the compressible subgrade layer's thickness is bigger than the foundation size, e.g. the soft subgrade of Shanghai and Tianjin, the lateral deformation influences consolidation settlement a lot, and directly affects the settlement value and speed. Although the numerical solution has provided way for consideration of lateral deformation, it is not adopted yet. Therefore, the half-theory and half-experience method is more effective, in which Skempton-Bjerrum method is the most popular one. This method is based on the two assumptions below:

1) Consolidation settlement comes from the dissipation of the subgrade's excess pore water pressure, and can be expressed as:

$$s_c = \int_0^H \Delta u \frac{a}{1+e_0} \mathrm{d}z \tag{4-54}$$

where: H—the thickness of the compressible subgrade layer;

Δu—the excess water pressure of voids in certain depth, which is induced by the loads acting on the surface;

e_0—the subgrade's initial void ratio;

a—the subgrade's single-axial compression coefficient.

2) For the axisymmetric situation, $\Delta\sigma_2 = \Delta\sigma_3$, any point in the subgrade's pore water pressure, change, which is induced by the induced principal stress change surface $\Delta\sigma_1$ and $\Delta\sigma_2$, satisfies the Skempton saturated soil formula:

$$\Delta u = \Delta\sigma_3 + A(\Delta\sigma_1 - \sigma_3) \tag{4-55}$$

where: A—the void pressure coefficient.

This assumption simplifies pore water pressure three-directional effect to make the settlement calculation be unidirectional.

If a and A do not change with calculating depth, and lateral deformation is considered for the calculation of consolidation settlement, then it can be expressed by the consolidation settlement s_c which is obtained by the single-axial compression test, e.g.

$$\left.\begin{aligned} s_{3c} &= \lambda s_c \\ s_c &= \int_0^H \Delta\sigma_1 \frac{a}{1+e_0} \mathrm{d}z \\ \lambda &= A + a(1-A) \end{aligned}\right\} \tag{4-56}$$

and

$$a = \frac{\int_0^H \Delta\sigma_3 \mathrm{d}z}{\int_0^H \Delta\sigma_1 \mathrm{d}z} \tag{4-57}$$

where: s_{3c}—the consolidation settlement which considers the influence of lateral deformation.

The value of a is determined by the shape of the loading area and the upper layer's thickness. The American Highway Research Committee gives the relation curve between λ and OCR (Fig.4-15).

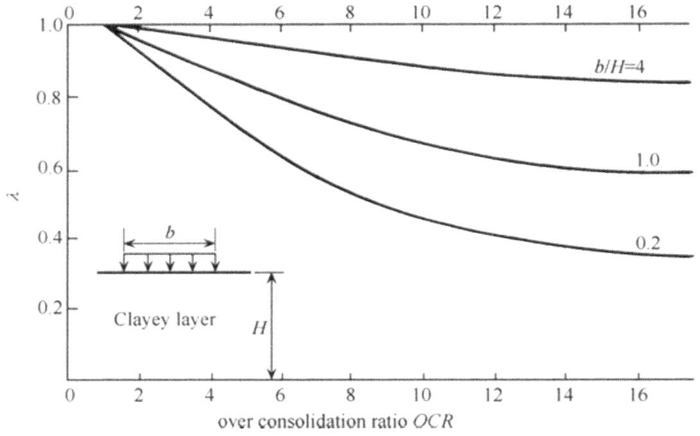

Fig. 4-15 The relation curve between λ and OCR

4.6 Calculation Method for Secondary Consolidation Settlement of Clayey Subgrade

The secondary consolidation of the cohesive subgrade is the subgrade volume's compression process along with the increment of time when the effective stress is basically the same. Although there is still small excess pore water pressure actually which makes the water to move slowly in voids during the secondary consolidation process, the value of this excess water pressure is too small to be measured. The secondary consolidation's volume change rate is irrelevant to the extrusion rate of the water in voids. The cohesive subgrade's in-situ secondary consolidation rate can be estimated directly by laboratory test. The secondary consolidation process happens after the principal consolidation, and its relation with time is close to a straight line in the semilogarithmic coordinate plot. The void ratio change Δe induced by secondary consolidation can be expressed as

$$\Delta e = C_a \log \frac{t_1}{t_2} \tag{4-58}$$

where: C_a—the straight line segment's slope in the semilogarithmic coordinate curve, which is called secondary consolidation coefficient. When no test data is available, we can select C_a from C_a=0.005~0.02 (for normally-consolidated subgrade), $C_a \geqslant 0.03$ (for subgrade with big plasticity), $C_a \leqslant 0.01$ (for over-consolidated soil, $OCR>2$). Because secondary consolidation settlement can not be ignored, C_a can also be estimated by water content ($C_a = 0.018\,\omega$);

t_1—the time when the principal consolidation is finished completely;

t_2—the time of secondary consolidation that need to be calculated.

For the same kind of day subgrade, the smaller the ratio of stress increment to initial stress, the bigger the ratio of secondary consolidation settlement to principal consolidation settlement. For coarse grained subgrade, the water of voids penetrates fast, and the excess hydrostatic pressure dissipates fast too, so there is basically no secondary consolidation settlement (Fig. 4-16).

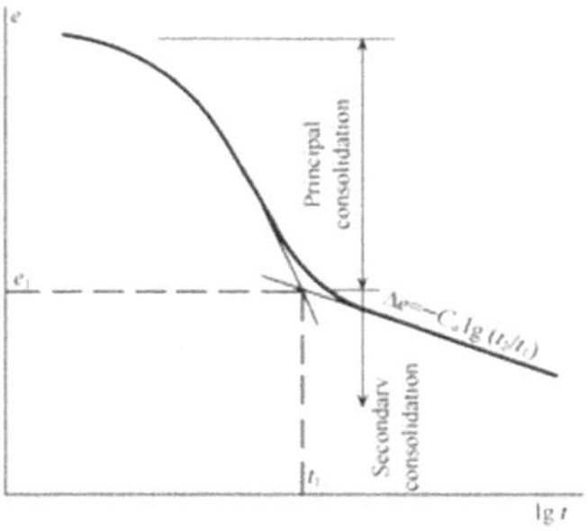

Fig. 4-16 The secondary consolidation curve

4.7 Calculation of Consolidation Settlement for Sandy Subgrade

Because the sand subgrade's shear and compression deformation all happen fast, it is difficult to distinguish the initial consolidation settlement from consolidation settlement. The sandy subgrade's elastic modulus increases with the depth of foundation, so it dose not accord with reality to calculate using the method of elastic mechanics. There is no reasonable calculating method thus far, so can only depend on kinds of half-theory and half-experience method. In America, the most common method is the empirical relation formula, between load test's bearing board's settlement and appropriate foundation settlement, which is recommended by Terzaghi and Peck, i.e.

$$s = s_0 \frac{4}{(1 + b_0 / b)^2} \tag{4-59}$$

where: s, b—the settlement and minimum size of foundation;

s_0, b_0—the settlement and minimum size of bearing board (b=0.3m).

Practice indicates that the settlement result estimated by the expression above is small, sometimes even to the extent of 5 times. There are still many problems after kinds of correction.

The calculating result of the half-theory and half-experience method put forward by Sckmertmann is close to different places' measured value, tested by practice. This method is got by combination of analysis, laboratory test and site measurement.

1) When there is local uniform distributed load on the surface of linear homogeneous semi-infinite body, the center point of the foundation base area's vertical-down strain can be calculated by the expression below:

$$\varepsilon_z = \frac{p}{E} I_z \tag{4-60}$$

where: p—uniform load's strength;

E—the elastic modulus of the semi-infinite linear sandy subgrade;

I_z—the strain inductance, which depends on the Poisson ratio and the position of the calculating strain point.

2) Through model tests and the analysis of non-linear finite element, it is testified that: the measured curve of the strain distribution is similar to the curve got by theoretical analysis, it is just that the maximum vertical strain's position is slightly lower, about at 40% of the foundation width.

Therefore, Schmertmann puts forward: practically, the distribution of the vertical strain in sandy subgrade can be expressed according to the formula above, and the value of E changes with depth, which is assumed to be triangular distribution. In the z/b=0.5 place, its maximum value is 0.6, while in the z/b=2 place, I_z=0, so it is called "2b-0.6" distribution.

Sand subgrade's settlement is just the initial settlement which equals the vertical strain's integral along the depth, i.e.

$$s_d = \int_0^{\infty} \varepsilon_z \mathrm{d}z \tag{4-61}$$

If the settlement's calculating depth is 2b, then the expression above is changed to be

$$s_d = \int_0^{2d} \frac{PI_z}{E} \mathrm{d}z = p \int_0^{2d} \frac{I_z}{E} \mathrm{d}z \tag{4-62}$$

If use layerwise summation method, the expression above can be simplified to be

$$s_d = C_1 C_2 p \sum_{i=1}^{n} \left(\frac{I_z}{E} \right)_i \Delta z_i \tag{4-63}$$

where: p—the additional pressure on the foundation base surface;

I_z—the strain inductance;

E_i—the elastic modulus on the center of the ith subgrade;

C_1 ,C_2—the correction coefficient. C_1 is the foundation's springback action, maximum value of I_z's influence $C_1 = 1 - 0.5\left(\frac{p'_0}{\Delta p}\right)$. C_2 is the influence of the sand subgrade's settlement's increasing with time, $C_2 = 1 + 0.2\log\left(\frac{t}{0.1}\right)$, where p'_0 is the subgrade's gravity pressure in certain depth of the subgrade, Δp is subgrade's static force, t is time. Because $p'_0/\Delta p$ is less than 1, C_1 is bigger than 0.5.

The value above considers the axisymmetric foundation. For the plane strain problem, considering that the stress in certain depth of subgrade increases, the elastic modulus increases too, and these influence can be mutually offset. For both axisymmetric and plane strain problems, there is no obvious difference on the point of strain's changing with depth.

In the calculation, the estimation of the E value in various depths of the sandy subgrade is needed. Because it is difficult to get undisturbed subgrade sample to take the laboratory test, the static cone penetration test can be adopted. If the sandy subgrade has nerve been preloaded by the force which is bigger than the overlying subgrade's gravity stress, Schmertmann suggests to estimate according to the expression below, i.e.

$$E=2p_s \tag{4-64}$$

where: p_s—the cone resistance.

For the preloaded sandy subgrade, the estimation value got from the formula above may be small.

Although static pone penetration test is more reliable than the standard penetration test, the later has been commonly used. When there is no static pone penetration test's equipments, the standard penetrating number $N_{63.5}$ can be used to estimate the value of p_s. but $N_{63.5}$ should be selected as much as possible to reduce the error that is brought to the correlation for less data.

4.8 Theoretic Formula for Deformation of Saturated Subgrade

Terzaghi (1925) put forward the one-dimensional consolidation theory first, and Rendulic (1936) extended it to three-dimension under the assumption that the total stress is the same during the consolidation process. The theory above has not considered the interaction between skeleton and pore water, and the consolidating equation finally got has only one variable, pore pressure, its equation form is the same as heat conduction equation or diffusion equation. Biot (1941) created strict consolidating theory which considers the interaction between skeleton and pore water, and extended this problem to be dynamic problem to complete the basic framework of elastic pore medium deformation theory. The succeeding development mainly considers the skeleton deformation's rheology, non-linearity and large deformation etc. After 1957, Trusdell etc. put forward cross theory, and regard preserving water porous medium as one kind of mixture to deduce the consolidation formula anew. There is no essential difference between Trusdell's mixture theory and Biot's consolidation theory. Biot consolidation theory takes the subgrade body as the research object, and pore water is the floating medium in it, while mixture theory takes solid particle and pore water as separate object, then combine them to be subgrade body. The research thinking of these two theories can be expressed to be:

Mixture theory: skeleton soil+pore water→subgrade body

Biot theory: subgrade body-pore water→skeleton solid

The subgrade body as a whole is concerned most in project, and its balance and movement are considered first. Secondly, when skeleton and pore water are investigated separately, their interaction is external force, and its calculating equation is more complex. Therefore, the mixture theory has little practical value for geotechnical engineer and structure engineer.

4.8.1 Biot Consolidation Equation

For the Biot consolidation formula under the situation of small strain, let u_x, u_y, u_z be the displacement components of differential subgrade body's skeleton (Fig. 4-17), and $\omega_x, \omega_y, \omega_z$ be the subgrade's liquid's relative displacement components to subgrade skeleton. The subgrade body's equilibrium differential equation is

$$\left.\begin{aligned}&\frac{\partial \sigma_x}{\partial x}+\frac{\partial \tau_{xy}}{\partial y}+\frac{\partial \tau_{xz}}{\partial z}+\rho \ddot{u}_x+\rho_f \ddot{\omega}_x=0\\&\frac{\partial \tau_{yz}}{\partial x}+\frac{\partial \sigma_y}{\partial y}+\frac{\partial \tau_{xz}}{\partial z}+\rho \ddot{u}_y+\rho_f \ddot{\omega}_x=0\\&\frac{\partial \tau_{zx}}{\partial x}+\frac{\partial \tau_{zy}}{\partial y}+\frac{\partial \tau_{z}}{\partial z}+\rho \ddot{u}_z+\rho_f \ddot{\omega}_z+\rho g=0\end{aligned}\right\} \quad (4\text{-}65)$$

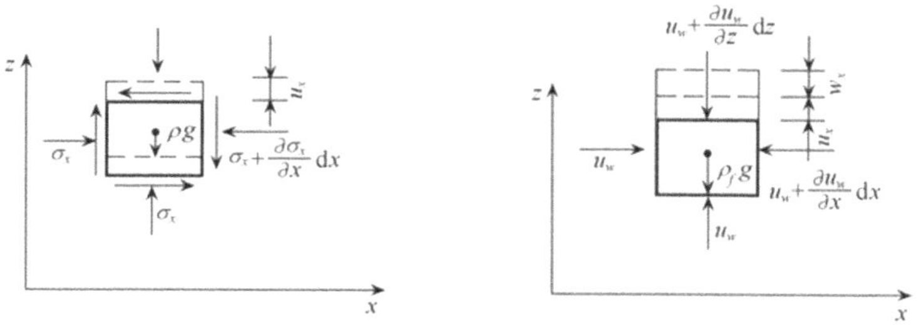

(a) the equilibrium of soil body (b) the equilibrium of liquid

Fig. 4-17 The equilibrium of differential body

From effective stress principle, it can be got as

$$\sigma_x = \sigma'_\omega + u_x,\ \sigma_y = \sigma'_x + u_\omega,\ \sigma_z = \sigma'_z + u_\omega \tag{4-66}$$

The subgrade body's stress-strain relation is

$$\{\sigma'\} = f(\{\varepsilon\}) \tag{4-67}$$

or

$$\{\sigma'\} = [D](\{\varepsilon\} - \{\varepsilon_0\}) \tag{4-68}$$

where $\{\varepsilon_0\}$ is the initial strain which is introduced for considering non-linearity.

The deformation's geometric relation is

$$\left.\begin{aligned} \varepsilon_x &= -\frac{\partial u_x}{\partial x} & \gamma_{xy} &= -\left(\frac{\partial u_x}{\partial y} + \frac{\partial u_y}{\partial x}\right) \\ \varepsilon_y &= -\frac{\partial u_y}{\partial y} & \gamma_{yz} &= -\left(\frac{\partial u_x}{\partial z} + \frac{\partial u_z}{\partial y}\right) \\ \varepsilon_z &= -\frac{\partial u_z}{\partial z} & \gamma_{zx} &= -\left(\frac{\partial u_z}{\partial x} + \frac{\partial u_x}{\partial z}\right) \end{aligned}\right\} \tag{4-69}$$

or

$$\{\varepsilon\} = -[B]\{u\} \tag{4-70}$$

The liquid's equilibrium formula in subgrade voids:

$$\left.\begin{aligned} -\frac{\partial u_\omega}{\partial x} &= \frac{\rho_f g}{k_x}\omega_x + \rho_f \ddot{u}_x + \rho_f \ddot{\omega}_x / n \\ -\frac{\partial u_\omega}{\partial y} &= \frac{\rho_f g}{k_y}\omega_y + \rho_f \ddot{u}_y + \rho_f \ddot{\omega}_y / n \\ -\rho_f g - \frac{\partial u_\omega}{\partial z} &= \frac{\rho_f g}{k_z}\omega_z + \rho_f \ddot{u}_z + \rho_f \ddot{\omega}_z / n \end{aligned}\right\} \tag{4-71}$$

Ignoring the right side's acceleration item, the Darcy law is derived.

Continuity equation of flow:

$$-\frac{\partial \omega_x}{\partial x} - \frac{\partial \omega_y}{\partial y} - \frac{\partial \omega_z}{\partial z} = \frac{\partial u_x}{\partial x} + \frac{\partial u_y}{\partial y} + \frac{\partial u_z}{\partial z} + \frac{n}{K_f} u_\omega \tag{4-72}$$

where: K_f—the compression modulus of liquid, i.e. the reciprocal value of C_f.

According to the analysis of Zinkiewicz, the inertial force of liquid which is relative to subgrade skeleton's movement can be ignored, except for the situation of high frequency vibration. In this situation, the continuity formula of flow above is deformed to be:

$$\frac{\partial}{\partial x}\frac{k_x}{\rho_f g}\frac{\partial u_w}{\partial x}+\frac{\partial}{\partial y}\frac{k_y}{\rho_f g}\frac{\partial u_w}{\partial y}+\frac{\partial}{\partial z}\frac{k_z}{\rho_f g}\frac{\partial u_w}{\partial z}+\frac{\partial k_z}{\partial z}-\frac{n}{K_f}u_w$$
$$-\left(\frac{\partial u_x}{\partial x}+\frac{\partial u_y}{\partial y}+\frac{\partial u_z}{\partial_z}\right)+\frac{1}{g}\left(k_x\frac{\partial \ddot{u}_x}{\partial x}+k_y\frac{\partial \ddot{u}_y}{\partial y}+k_z\frac{\partial \ddot{u}_z}{\partial_x}\right)=0$$

Then get:

$$\left.\begin{aligned}
&d_{11}\frac{\partial^2 u_x}{\partial x^2}+d_{44}\frac{\partial^2 u_z}{\partial y^2}+d_{66}\frac{\partial^2 u_x}{\partial z^2}+(d_{14}+d_{41})\frac{\partial^2 u_x}{\partial x\partial y}+(d_{46}+d_{64})\frac{\partial^2 u_x}{\partial y\partial z}\\
&\quad+(d_{16}+d_{61})\frac{\partial^2 u_x}{\partial z\partial x}+d_{14}\frac{\partial^2 u_y}{\partial x^2}+d_{42}\frac{\partial^2 u_y}{\partial y^2}+d_{65}\frac{\partial^2 u_y}{\partial z^2}+(d_{12}+d_{44})\frac{\partial^2 u_y}{\partial x\partial y}\\
&\quad+(d_{46}+d_{62})\frac{\partial^2 u_y}{\partial y\partial z}+(d_{15}+d_{64})\frac{\partial^2 u_y}{\partial z\partial x}+d_{16}\frac{\partial^2 u_z}{\partial x^2}+d_{45}\frac{\partial^2 u_z}{\partial y^2}+d_{63}\frac{\partial^2 u_z}{\partial z^2}\\
&\quad+(d_{15}+d_{46})\frac{\partial^2 u_z}{\partial x\partial y}+(d_{43}+d_{65})\frac{\partial^2 u_z}{\partial y\partial z}+(d_{13}+d_{66})\frac{\partial^2 u_z}{\partial z\partial x}\\
&\quad-\frac{\partial u_\omega}{\partial x}+X^0=\rho\ddot{u}_x\\
&d_{41}\frac{\partial^2 u_x}{\partial x^2}+d_{24}\frac{\partial^2 u_x}{\partial y^2}+d_{56}\frac{\partial^2 u_x}{\partial z^2}+(d_{21}+d_{44})\frac{\partial^2 u_x}{\partial x\partial y}+(d_{26}+d_{54})\frac{\partial^2 u_x}{\partial y\partial z}\\
&\quad+(d_{46}+d_{51})\frac{\partial^2 u_x}{\partial z\partial x}+d_{44}\frac{\partial^2 u_y}{\partial x^2}+d_{22}\frac{\partial^2 u_y}{\partial y^2}+d_{55}\frac{\partial^2 u_y}{\partial z^2}+(d_{24}+d_{42})\frac{\partial^2 u_y}{\partial x\partial y}\\
&\quad+(d_{25}+d_{52})\frac{\partial^2 u_y}{\partial y\partial z}+(d_{45}+d_{54})\frac{\partial^2 u_y}{\partial z\partial x}+d_{46}\frac{\partial^2 u_x}{\partial x^2}+d_{25}\frac{\partial^2 u_z}{\partial y^2}+d_{53}\frac{\partial^2 u_z}{\partial z^2}\\
&\quad+(d_{26}+d_{45})\frac{\partial^2 u_z}{\partial y\partial y}+(d_{23}+d_{55})\frac{\partial^2 u_z}{\partial y\partial z}+(d_{43}+d_{56})\frac{\partial^2 u_z}{\partial z\partial x}\\
&\quad-\frac{\partial^2 u_w}{\partial y}+Y^0=\rho\ddot{u}_y\\
&d_{61}\frac{\partial^2 u_x}{\partial x^2}+d_{54}\frac{\partial^2 u_x}{\partial y^2}+d_{36}\frac{\partial^2 u_x}{\partial z^2}+(d_{51}+d_{64})\frac{\partial^2 u_x}{\partial x\partial y}+(d_{34}+d_{56})\frac{\partial^2 u_x}{\partial y\partial z}\\
&\quad+(d_{31}+d_{66})\frac{\partial^2 u_x}{\partial z\partial x}+d_{54}\frac{\partial^2 u_y}{\partial x^2}+d_{52}\frac{\partial^2 u_y}{\partial y^2}+d_{35}\frac{\partial^2 u_y}{\partial z^2}+(d_{54}+d_{62})\frac{\partial^2 u_y}{\partial x\partial y}\\
&\quad+(d_{32}+d_{55})\frac{\partial^2 u_y}{\partial y\partial z}+(d_{34}+d_{65})\frac{\partial^2 u_y}{\partial z\partial x}+d_{66}\frac{\partial^2 u_x}{\partial x^2}+d_{55}\frac{\partial^2 u_z}{\partial y^2}+d_{33}\frac{\partial^2 u_z}{\partial z^2}\\
&\quad+(d_{56}+d_{65})\frac{\partial^2 u_z}{\partial x\partial y}+(d_{35}+d_{53})\frac{\partial^2 u_z}{\partial y\partial z}+(d_{36}+d_{63})\frac{\partial^2 u_z}{\partial z\partial x}\\
&\quad-\frac{\partial u_w}{\partial z}+Z^0=\rho(\ddot{u}_z+g)
\end{aligned}\right\}\tag{4-73}$$

where: X^0, Y^0 and Z^0—the equivalent nodes force induced by initial strain $\{\varepsilon_0\}$;

$d_{11}, d_{12}, d_{13}, d_{14}, d_{15}, d_{16}, d_{21}, d_{22},\cdots,d_{66}$—the elements of matrix $[D]_{6*6}$. For the linear elastic medium whose permeability coefficient is constant, the expression above can be simplified as

$$\left.\begin{aligned}
&\frac{k}{\rho_f g}\left(\frac{\partial^2 u_w}{\partial x^2}+\frac{\partial^2 u_w}{\partial y^2}+\frac{\partial^2 u_w}{\partial z^2}\right)+\frac{k}{g}\left(\frac{\partial \ddot{u}_x}{\partial x}+\frac{\partial \ddot{u}_y}{\partial y}+\frac{\partial \ddot{u}_z}{\partial z}\right)-\left(\frac{\partial u_x}{\partial x}+\frac{\partial u_y}{\partial y}+\frac{\partial u_z}{\partial z}\right)-\frac{n}{K_f}u_w=0\\
&2G\frac{1-v}{1-2v}\frac{\partial^2 u_x}{\partial x^2}+G\frac{\partial^2 u_x}{\partial y^2}+\frac{\partial^2 u_x}{\partial z^2}+G\frac{1}{1-2v}\frac{\partial^2 u_y}{\partial x\partial y}+G\frac{1}{1-2v}\frac{\partial^2 u_z}{\partial z\partial x}-\frac{\partial u_w}{\partial x}=\rho\ddot{u}_x\\
&G\frac{\partial^2 u_y}{\partial x^2}+2G\frac{1-v}{1-2v}\frac{\partial^2 u_y}{\partial y^2}+G\frac{\partial^2 u_y}{\partial z^2}+G\frac{1}{1-2v}\frac{\partial^2 u_x}{\partial x\partial y}+G\frac{1}{1-2v}\frac{\partial^2 u_x}{\partial z\partial y}-\frac{\partial u_w}{\partial y}=\rho\ddot{u}_y\\
&G\frac{\partial^2 u_z}{\partial x^2}+G\frac{\partial^2 u_z}{\partial y^2}+2G\frac{1-v}{1-2v}\frac{\partial^2 u_z}{\partial z^2}+G\frac{1}{1-2v}\frac{\partial^2 u_x}{\partial x\partial z}+G\frac{1}{1-2v}\frac{\partial^2 u_y}{\partial z\partial y}-\frac{\partial u_w}{\partial z}=\rho(\ddot{u}_z+g)
\end{aligned}\right\}\tag{4-74}$$

The expression above is just the familiar Biot dynamic consolidation equation, and corresponding boundary condition is:

Displacement boundary: $u_x=\bar{u}_x, u_y=\bar{u}_y, u_z=\bar{u}_z$.

Stress boundary: $\{\sigma\}^T\{n\}=\{\bar{t}\}$.

Pore pressure boundary: $u_w=\bar{u}_w$.

Impulse boundary: $\dfrac{-k\partial u_w}{\rho_f g\partial n}+k\dfrac{\partial z}{\partial n}=\bar{q}$.

For common impervious boundary: $\dfrac{\partial u_w}{\partial n}=\rho_f g\dfrac{\partial z}{\partial n}$.

n: normal direction of boundary.

4.8.2 Terzaghi-Rendulic Consolidation Formula

For static problem and uncompressible fluid, $K_f=\infty$, then

$$\frac{\partial^2 u_x}{\partial x^2}+\frac{\partial^2 u_y}{\partial y^2}+\frac{\partial^2 u_z}{\partial z^2}=-\frac{\rho_f g}{K}\varepsilon_v \tag{4-75}$$

where: $\varepsilon_v=-\left(\dfrac{\partial u_x}{\partial x}+\dfrac{\partial u_y}{\partial y}+\dfrac{\partial u_z}{\partial z}\right)$ is volumetric strain, let the subgrade's compression formula be $\varepsilon_v=m_v(\sigma_n-\mu_w)$, which can be deformed to be

$$\frac{\partial^2 u_w}{\partial x^2}+\frac{\partial^2 u_w}{\partial y^2}+\frac{\partial^2 u_w}{\partial z^2}=-C_v(\sigma_m-u_w) \tag{4-76}$$

where: $C_v=\rho_f g m_v/k$ is a consolidation coefficient. When the total stress σ_m is constant, the following Terzaghi-Rendulic diffusion formula can be got.

$$\frac{\partial^2 u_w}{\partial x^2}+\frac{\partial^2 u_w}{\partial y^2}+\frac{\partial^2 u_w}{\partial z^2}=C_v u_w \tag{4-77}$$

This expression has only one variable u_w, and can be solved independently form the soil deformation.

For one and two dimensional problem, if define $m_{v1}=\frac{\varepsilon_v}{\sigma_1-u_w}$ and $m_{v2}=\frac{\varepsilon_v}{\frac{1}{2}(\sigma_1-\sigma_2)-u_w}$, under the assumption of σ_1 and $\sigma_1+\sigma_3$ are constant, the equation above is correct, but the compression coefficient is different for three different situation, i.e.

$$m_{v1}=\frac{E(1-\mu)}{(1+\mu)(1-2\mu)};\ m_{v2}=\frac{E}{2(1+\mu)(1-2\mu)};\ m_{v3}=\frac{E}{3(1-2\mu)}$$

Divide u_w to be hydrostatic pressure u_{w0} and excess hydrostatic pressure u_{w1}, for hydrostatic pressure, there is $\dot{u}_{w0}=0$, then get

$$\left.\begin{aligned}&\frac{\partial^2 u_{w1}}{\partial x^2}+\frac{\partial^2 u_{w1}}{\partial y^2}+\frac{\partial^2 u_{w1}}{\partial z^2}=C_v\dot{u}_{w1}\\&\frac{\partial^2 u_{w0}}{\partial x^2}+\frac{\partial^2 u_{w0}}{\partial y^2}+\frac{\partial^2 u_{w0}}{\partial z^2}=0\end{aligned}\right\} \tag{4-78}$$

The method of dividing the pore water pressure into hydrostatic pressure and excess hydrostatic pressure is very convenient for the subgrade consolidation problem, because the coordinate points are on the subgrade surface. But for the problem whose calculating area's shape is complex, the solution is very difficult. Then take the water head as variable, can get

$$-k\frac{\partial h}{\partial n}=\bar{q} \tag{4-79}$$

This is only for subgrade consolidation problems.

4.8.3 The Solution of Terzaghi Consolidation Equation

1. Equation's general solution

If $\dot{\sigma}_m=f(x,y,z,t)$ is only induced by the change of external load, and is also a known quantity, then Terzaghi consolidation equation's most common form could be

$$\frac{\partial^2 u_w}{\partial x^2}+\frac{\partial^2 u_w}{\partial y^2}+\frac{\partial^2 u_w}{\partial z^2}=C_v\left[\frac{\partial u_w}{\partial_t}+f(x,y,z,t)\right] \tag{4-80}$$

The general solution which satisfies equation above and the initial condition, $u_w|_{t=0}=\varphi(x,y,z)$, is

$$u_w=\frac{1}{(4\pi c_v t)^{n/2}}\int_{-\infty}^{\infty}\int_{-\infty}^{\infty}\int_{-\infty}^{\infty}\varphi(\xi,\eta,\zeta)\exp\left[-\frac{(x-\xi)^2+(y-\eta)^2+(z-\zeta)^3}{4c_v t}\right]\mathrm{d}\zeta\mathrm{d}\eta\mathrm{d}\xi$$
$$+\frac{1}{(4\pi c_v)^{n/2}}\int_0^t\int_{-\infty}^{\infty}\int_{-\infty}^{\infty}\int_{-\infty}^{\infty}\frac{f(\xi,\eta,\zeta,t)}{(t-\pi)^2}\exp\left[-\frac{(x-\xi)^2+(y-\eta)^2+(z-\zeta)^3}{4c_v(t-\tau)}\right]\mathrm{d}\zeta\mathrm{d}\eta\mathrm{d}\xi\mathrm{d}\tau$$

(4-81)

where: n is the dimension, i.e. n=1 for one-dimensional problem, n=2 for two-dimensional problem, n=3 for three-dimensional problem. For two and one dimensional problems, the integral multiplicity should be two and one respectively. The right side of this equation is made up of two parts, the first part is the solution when external load is constant and f=0, the second part is initial pore pressure function's solution u_{w2} when $\varphi = 0$. For the linear equation's characteristics of superposition, the solution process can be divided into two steps, first solve u_{w1}, then solve u_{w2}.

Our country's scholars researched the situation that computational domain (x, y) is infinite, and computational domain in z direction is within a certain thickness, and then got the general solution. The thinking for this problem's solution has two kinds:

1) Using sine function's integrity, the infinite integral in z direction can be changed to be the infinite items series. Decompose initial function $\varphi(x, y, z)$ into Foruier series, and the solution can satisfy boundary condition for the feature of sine function.

2) Extending $\varphi(x, y, z)$ to be periodic function directly along direction, then the subgrade body consolidation's general solution can be got by discrete $\varphi(x, y, z)$.

2. One-dimensional consolidation

(1) Single layered subgrade

The one-dimensional subgrade's consolidation degree is

$$U = 1 - \frac{1}{u_0}\int_0^{2H} u_w \mathrm{d}z = 1 - \sum_{m=1,3,5}^{\infty} \frac{8}{m^2\pi^2} \exp\left[-\left(\frac{m\pi}{2H}\right)^2 C_v t\right] \tag{4-82}$$

The solution given by Schiffman for the one-dimensional consolidation problem is

$$u_w = \sum_{m=1,3,5}^{\infty} \frac{16 r_0 H^2}{c_v m^3 \pi^3} \sin\frac{m\pi}{2H} z \left\{1 - \exp\left[-\left(\frac{m\pi}{2H}\right)^2 C_v t\right]\right\} \tag{4-83}$$

(2) Double layered subgrade consolidation's Gray solution

Gray first solved the consolidation problem for double layered subgrade, but the condition set is too simple. Let H be the total thickness of double layered subgrade, h_1 and h_2 be the soil thicknesses of the first and second layer, each layer's pore pressure coefficient, consolidation coefficient be u_{w1}, k_{v1}, C_{v1} and u_{w2}, k_{v2}, C_{v2} respectively, then the consolidation equation for double layered subgrade would be

$$\left.\begin{aligned} \frac{\partial u_{w1}}{\partial t} &= C_{v1}\frac{\partial^2 u_{w1}}{\partial z^2} + r(t) \\ \frac{\partial u_{w2}}{\partial t} &= C_{v2}\frac{\partial^2 u_{w2}}{\partial z^2} + r(t) \end{aligned}\right\} \tag{4-84}$$

Boundary condition and interface continuous condition are respectively

$u_{w1}|_{z=0}=0;$

$u_{w1}|_{z=h_1}=u_{w2}|_{z=h_1};$

$k_{v1}\dfrac{\partial u_{w1}}{\partial z}=k_{v2}\dfrac{\partial u_{w2}}{\partial z};$

$\dfrac{\partial u_{w2}}{\partial z}|_{z=h}=0$ (bottom surface is impermeable) or $u_{w2}=0$ (bottom surface is permeable);

$u_{w1}|_{t=0}=u_{10}(z); u_{w2}|_{t=0}=u_{210}(z)$.

Finally, according to the principle that the pore pressure induce by load change is uniform distributed and the solution induced by initial pore pressure must satisfy initial condition, the result is got to be:

Single drainage

$$u_{w2}=q_0\sum_{m=1}^{\infty}\frac{c_m\sin(\lambda_m)}{\cos\left(\mu\dfrac{h_2}{h_1}\lambda_m\right)}\cos\left(\mu\lambda_m\frac{H-z}{h_1}\right)\mathrm{e}^{\frac{-\lambda^2 m}{h_1^2}c_{v1}t} \tag{4-85}$$

Double drainage

$$u_{w2}=q_0\sum_{m=1}^{\infty}\frac{c_m\sin(\lambda_m)}{\sin\left(\mu\dfrac{h_2}{h_1}\lambda_m\right)}\sin\left(\mu\lambda_m\frac{H-z}{h_1}\right)\mathrm{e}^{\frac{-\lambda^2 m}{h_1^2}c_{v1}t} \tag{4-86}$$

where

Single drainage

$$C_m=\frac{2\cos^2\left(\mu\dfrac{h_2}{h_1}\lambda_m\right)}{\lambda_m\left[\cos^2\left(\mu\dfrac{h_2}{h_1}\lambda_m\right)+\dfrac{m_{v2}h_2}{m_{v1}h_1}\sin^2(\lambda_m)\right]}$$

Double drainage

$$C_m=\frac{2\sin^2\left(\mu\dfrac{h_2}{h_1}\lambda_m\right)+\sqrt{\dfrac{k_{v2}m_{v2}}{k_{v1}m_{v1}}}\sin^2(\lambda_m)\sin^2\left(\mu\dfrac{h_2}{h_1}\lambda_m\right)}{\lambda_m\left[\sin^2\left(\mu\dfrac{h_2}{h_1}\lambda_m\right)+\dfrac{m_{v2}h_2}{m_{v1}h_1}\sin^2(\lambda_m)\right]}$$

This is the solution given by Gray.

3. The finite subgrade layer's consolidation problem under local load

(1) The solution under concentrated load

For saturated elastic medium whose v=0.5, the average stress distribution is as below within finite thickness under concentrated load P.

$$\frac{1}{3}(\sigma_x+\sigma_y+\sigma_z)=\frac{P}{2\pi}\frac{z}{(x^2+y^2+z^2)^{3/2}} \tag{4-87}$$

This equation is the distribution of initial stress in subgrade base. If P changes with the rule:

$$P=P_0+rt \tag{4-88}$$

Then when load linearly increases, pore pressure' solution is

$$\begin{aligned}u_w=&\frac{P_0}{2\pi(4\pi C_v t)^{3/2}}\int_{-\infty}^{\infty}\int_{-\infty}^{\infty}\frac{\zeta}{(\xi^2+\eta^2+\zeta^2)^{3/2}}\left[\exp\left(-\frac{(x-\xi)^2+(y-\eta)^2+(z-\zeta)^2}{4C_v t}\right)\right.\\&\left.-\exp\left(-\frac{(x-\xi)^2+(y-\eta)^2+(z-\zeta)^2}{4C_v t}\right)\right]\mathrm{d}\eta\mathrm{d}\xi\\&+\frac{r}{2\pi(4\pi C_v t)^{3/2}}\int_{-\infty}^{\infty}\int_{-\infty}^{\infty}\frac{\zeta}{(\xi^2+\eta^2+\zeta^2)^{3/2}}\frac{1}{(t-\tau)^{3/2}}\\&\times\left[\exp\left(-\frac{(x-\xi)^2+(y-\eta)^2+(z-\zeta)^2}{4C_v(t-\tau)}\right)\right.\\&\left.-\exp\left(-\frac{(x-\xi)^2+(y-\eta)^2+(z-\zeta)^2}{4C_v(t-\tau)}\right)\right]\mathrm{d}\eta\mathrm{d}\xi\mathrm{d}\tau\end{aligned} \tag{4-89}$$

The expression above satisfies the condition of double drainage. For the problem of non-drainage on bottom surface, change integral domain from 0—$2H$ to 0—H, and change f_1 to f_2.

(2) The solution under distributed load.

For the distributed load on the subgrade surface

$$p(x,y)=p_0(x,y)(1+rt) \tag{4-90}$$

Pore pressure's solution can be get as below by integral (Fig. 4-18):

$$\begin{aligned}u_w=&\frac{p_0}{2\pi(4\pi C_v t)^{3/2}}\int_{-\infty}^{\infty}\int_{-\infty}^{\infty}\int_0^{2H}\frac{\zeta}{(\xi^2+\eta^2+\zeta^2)^{3/2}}\mathrm{Exp}\left[-\frac{(x-\xi)^2+(y-\eta)^2}{4C_v t}\right]\times f_1(z,\zeta,t)\mathrm{d}\zeta\mathrm{d}\eta\mathrm{d}\xi\\&+\frac{r}{2\pi(4\pi C_v t)^{3/2}}\int_0^{t}\int_{-\infty}^{\infty}\int_{-\infty}^{\infty}\int_0^{2H}\frac{\zeta}{(\xi^2+\eta^2+\zeta^2)^{3/2}}\frac{1}{(t-\tau)^{3/2}}\\&\times\exp\left[-\frac{(x-\xi)^2+(y-\eta)^2}{4C_v(t-\tau)}\right]f_1(z,\zeta,t,\tau)\mathrm{d}\zeta\mathrm{d}\eta\mathrm{d}\xi\mathrm{d}\tau\end{aligned} \tag{4-91}$$

Three dimensional problem's solution can be get by the integral along y direction. This figure indicates that the one, two and three dimension's pore pressure differ little (Fig. 4-18).

4.8.4 The Solution of Biot Consolidation Equation

1. The general solution of Biot equation

Considering $\varepsilon_v = -(\frac{\partial u_x}{\partial x} + \frac{\partial u_y}{\partial y} + \frac{\partial u_z}{\partial z})$, then it can be got as below, for complete saturated subgrade's static consolidation problem.

$$\left.\begin{aligned} &\frac{k}{\rho_f g}\nabla^2 u_w = \frac{\partial \varepsilon_v}{\partial t} \\ &G\nabla^2 u_x - G\frac{1}{1-2\mu}\frac{\partial \varepsilon_v}{\partial x} - \frac{\partial u_w}{\partial x} = 0 \\ &G\nabla^2 u_y - G\frac{1}{1-2\mu}\frac{\partial \varepsilon_v}{\partial y} - \frac{\partial u_w}{\partial y} = 0 \\ &G\nabla^2 u_z - G\frac{1}{1-2\mu}\frac{\partial \varepsilon_v}{\partial z} - \frac{\partial u_w}{\partial z} = \rho g \end{aligned}\right\} \tag{4-92}$$

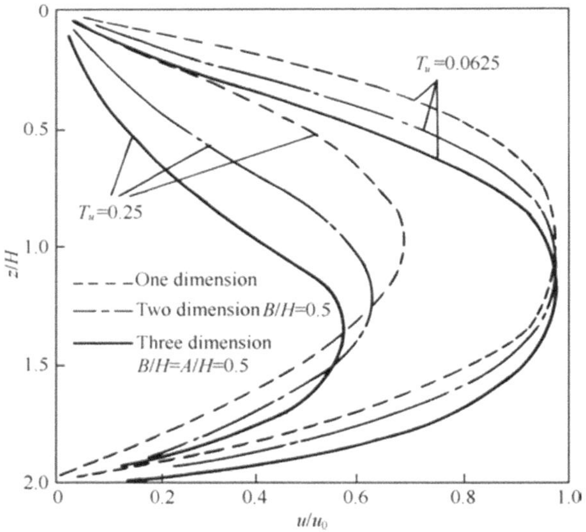

Fig. 4-18 The load center's void pressure under uniform load

Then get

$$\nabla^2 u_w = -2G\frac{1-\mu}{1-2\mu}\nabla^2 \varepsilon_v \tag{4-93}$$

and get

$$\overline{C}_v \nabla^2 \varepsilon_v = \frac{\partial \varepsilon_v}{\partial t} \tag{4-94}$$

Or after considering $\varepsilon_v = m_v\sigma'_m$, get

$$\overline{C}_v\nabla^2\sigma'_m = \frac{\partial\sigma'_m}{\partial t} \tag{4-95}$$

But Terzaghi equation's unknown quantity is u_w, and its boundary condition is easy to be determined, while volumetric strain ε_w and average strain σ'_m' boundary conditions are unknown. This is the difficult point for the solution of Biot consolidation equation. Biot solved the half-infinite subgrade's consolidation problem under strip load then. Mc Namme and Gibson etc. solved several special problems' solution further. Zape got the solution of half-infinite subgrade under concentrated load. But there is still no effective general solution now. Recently, our country's scholar Huang Chuanzhi made big progress in this aspect.

2. The solution of Biot function under the action of linear load

Let the soil thickness be $2H$, and then the top and bottom surface's boundary conditions are

$$\sigma'_{mf}\,|_{z=0} = p_1(x);\ \sigma'_{mf}\,|_{z=2H} = p_2(x)$$

Its exact solution is

$$u_w = \frac{p_2}{\pi}(1-v)\int_0^{\infty}\cos\lambda x\int_0^{\infty}\left[\left(\frac{\mathrm{sh}(2H-z)\lambda}{\mathrm{sh}2H\lambda} - f_b\right)\varphi_1 + \left(\frac{\mathrm{sh}z\lambda}{\mathrm{sh}2H\lambda} - f_d\right)\varphi_2 - f_a\psi_1 - f_c\psi_2\right]\mathrm{d}\alpha\mathrm{d}\lambda$$

$$\begin{aligned}\sigma'_z + u_w = {} & \frac{1}{2}\sigma''_z + \frac{p}{2\pi}\int_0^{\infty}\frac{\mathrm{sh}(2H-z)}{\mathrm{sh}2H\lambda}\cos\lambda x\mathrm{d}\lambda \\ & + \frac{p_2}{\pi}(1-v)\int_0^{\infty}\cos\lambda x\int_0^{\infty}\left\{\left[z\lambda\mathrm{ch}(2H-z)\lambda - \frac{2H\lambda}{\mathrm{sh}2H\lambda}\mathrm{sh}z\lambda\right]\varphi_1\right. \\ & \left. -\left[z\lambda\mathrm{ch}z\lambda - (1+2H\lambda\mathrm{cth}2H\lambda)\mathrm{sh}2\lambda\right]\varphi_2\right\}\frac{1}{\mathrm{sh}2H\lambda}\mathrm{d}\alpha\mathrm{d}\lambda \\ & - \frac{p_2}{\pi}(1-2v)\int_0^{\infty}\cos\lambda x\int_0^{\infty}\frac{\lambda^2}{\alpha}\left[f_a\varphi_1 + f_c\varphi_2 + \left(\frac{\mathrm{sh}(2H-z)}{\mathrm{sh}2H\lambda} - f_b\right)\varphi_1\right. \\ & \left. + \left(\frac{\mathrm{sh}z\lambda}{\mathrm{sh}2H\lambda} - f_d\right)\varphi_2\right]\mathrm{d}\alpha\mathrm{d}\lambda\end{aligned}$$

$$\begin{aligned}u_w = {} & \frac{1}{2}\sigma''_x - \frac{p}{2\pi}\int_0^{\infty}\frac{\mathrm{sh}(2H-z)\lambda}{\mathrm{sh}2H\lambda}\cos\lambda x\mathrm{d}\lambda \\ & + \frac{p_2}{\pi}(1-v)\int_0^{\infty}\cos\lambda x\int_0^{\infty}\left\{\left[2\mathrm{sh}(2H-z)\lambda - z\lambda\mathrm{ch}(2H-z)\lambda + \frac{2H\lambda}{\mathrm{sh}2H\lambda}\mathrm{sh}z\lambda\right]\varphi_1\right. \\ & \left. + \left[z\lambda\mathrm{ch}z\lambda + (1-2H\lambda\mathrm{cth}2H\lambda)\mathrm{sh}2\lambda\right]\varphi_2\right\}\frac{1}{\mathrm{sh}2H\lambda}\mathrm{d}\alpha\mathrm{d}\lambda \\ & + \frac{p_2}{\pi}(1-2v)\int_0^{\infty}\cos\lambda x\int_0^{\infty}\left\{\left(f_b - \frac{\lambda^2}{\alpha}f_a\right)\varphi_1 + \left(f_d - \frac{\lambda^2}{\alpha}f_c\right)\varphi_2\right. \\ & \left. + \left[f_a - \frac{\lambda^2}{\alpha}\left(\frac{\mathrm{sh}(2H-z)\lambda}{\mathrm{sh}2H\lambda} - f_b\right)\right]\varphi_1 + \left[f_c - \frac{\lambda^2}{\alpha}\left(\frac{\mathrm{sh}z\lambda}{\mathrm{sh}2H\lambda} - f_d\right)\right]\varphi_2\right\}\mathrm{d}\alpha\mathrm{d}\lambda\end{aligned}$$

$$\tau_{zx}=\frac{1}{2}\tau''_{zx}+\frac{p}{2\pi}\int_0^{\infty}\frac{\mathrm{ch}(2H-z)\lambda}{\mathrm{sh}2H\lambda}\sin\lambda x\mathrm{d}\lambda$$
$$+\frac{p_2}{\pi}(1-\nu)\int_0^{\infty}\sin\lambda x\int_0^{\infty}\left\{\left[z\lambda\mathrm{sh}(2H-z)\lambda+\frac{2H\lambda}{\mathrm{sh}2H\lambda}\mathrm{ch}z\lambda-\mathrm{ch}(2H-z)\lambda\right]\varphi_1\right.$$
$$\left.+\left[z\lambda\mathrm{sh}z\lambda-2H\lambda\mathrm{cth}2H\lambda\mathrm{ch}z\lambda\right]\varphi_2\right\}\frac{1}{\mathrm{sh}2H\lambda}\mathrm{d}\alpha\mathrm{d}\lambda$$
$$-\frac{p_2}{\pi}(1-2\nu)\int_0^{\infty}\sin\lambda x\int_0^{\infty}\frac{\lambda}{\alpha}\left\{\left(A_0g_a-B_0g_b\right)\varphi_1-\left(A_0g_c-B_0g_d\right)\varphi_2\right.$$
$$\left.+\left[\lambda\frac{\mathrm{ch}(2H-z)\lambda}{\mathrm{sh}2H\lambda}-A_0g_b-B_0g_a\right]\varphi_1-\left[\lambda\frac{\mathrm{sh}z\lambda}{\mathrm{sh}2H\lambda}-A_0g_d-B_0g_c\right]\varphi_2\right\}\mathrm{d}\alpha\mathrm{d}\lambda$$
$$u_z=\frac{1}{2}u''_z+\frac{1+\nu}{E}\frac{p}{2\pi}\int_0^{\infty}\frac{1}{\lambda}\frac{\mathrm{ch}(2H-z)\lambda}{\mathrm{sh}2H\lambda}\cos\lambda x\mathrm{d}\lambda$$
$$+\frac{1+\nu}{E}\frac{p_2}{\pi}(1-\nu)\int_0^{\infty}\frac{1}{\lambda}\cos\lambda x\int_0^{\infty}\left\{\left[z\lambda\mathrm{sh}(2H-z)\lambda+\frac{2H\lambda}{\mathrm{sh}2H\lambda}\mathrm{ch}z\lambda\right]\varphi_1\right.$$
$$\left.+\left[z\lambda\mathrm{sh}z\lambda-(1+2H\lambda\mathrm{cth}2H\lambda)\mathrm{ch}z\lambda\right]\varphi_2\right\}\frac{1}{\mathrm{sh}2H\lambda}\mathrm{d}\alpha\mathrm{d}\lambda$$
$$-\frac{1+\nu}{E}\frac{p_2}{\pi}(1-2\nu)\int_0^{\infty}\cos\lambda x\int_0^{\infty}\left\{\left(A_0g_a-B_0g_b\right)\varphi_1-\left(A_0g_c-B_0g_d\right)\varphi_2\right.$$
$$\left.+\left[\lambda\frac{\mathrm{ch}(2H-z)\lambda}{\mathrm{sh}2H\lambda}-A_0g_b-B_0g_a\right]\varphi_1-\left[\lambda\frac{\mathrm{sh}z\lambda}{\mathrm{sh}2H\lambda}-A_0g_d-B_0g_c\right]\varphi_2\right\}\frac{1}{\alpha}\mathrm{d}\alpha\mathrm{d}\lambda$$
$$u_x=\frac{1}{2}u''_x+\frac{1+\nu}{E}\frac{1}{2\pi}\int_0^{\infty}\frac{1}{\lambda}\frac{\mathrm{sh}(2H-z)\lambda}{\mathrm{sh}2H\lambda}\sin\lambda x\mathrm{d}\lambda+\frac{1+\nu}{E}\frac{p_2}{\pi}(1-\nu)$$
$$\times\int_0^{\infty}\frac{1}{\lambda}\sin\lambda x\int_0^{\infty}\left\{\left[\mathrm{sh}(2H-z)\lambda-z\lambda\mathrm{ch}(2H-z)\lambda+\frac{2H\lambda}{\mathrm{sh}2H\lambda}\mathrm{sh}z\lambda\right]\varphi_1\right.$$
$$\left.+\left[z\lambda\mathrm{sh}z\lambda-2H\lambda\mathrm{cth}2H\lambda\mathrm{sh}z\lambda\right]\varphi_2\right\}\frac{1}{\mathrm{sh}2H\lambda}\mathrm{d}\alpha\mathrm{d}\lambda$$
$$+\frac{1+\nu}{E}\frac{p_2}{\pi}(1-2\nu)\int_0^{\infty}\sin\lambda x\int_0^{\infty}\left[f_a\varphi_1+f_c\varphi_2+\left(\frac{\mathrm{sh}(2H-z)\lambda}{\mathrm{sh}2H\lambda}-f_b\right)\varphi_1\right.$$
$$\left.+\left(\frac{\mathrm{sh}z\lambda}{sh2H\lambda}-f_d\right)\varphi_2\right\}\frac{\lambda}{\alpha}\mathrm{d}\alpha\mathrm{d}\lambda \tag{4-96}$$

where, $\sigma''_x,\sigma''_z,\tau''_{xz},u''_z,u''_x$ are elastic theoretical solutions of finite depth subgrade.

$$\psi_1=\frac{1}{\alpha\left(R_1^2+R_2^2\right)}\left(Q_2\sin\alpha\overline{C}_{\nu}t-Q_1\cos\alpha\overline{C}_{\nu}t\right)$$
$$\psi_2=\frac{1}{\alpha\left(R_1^2+R_2^2\right)}\left(Q_4\sin\alpha\overline{C}_{\nu}t-Q_3\cos\alpha\overline{C}_{\nu}t\right)$$
$$f_a=\frac{1}{C_0}\left[\mathrm{sh}(4H-z)A_0\sin B_0z-\mathrm{sh}A_0z\sin(4H-z)B_0\right]$$
$$f_b=\frac{1}{C_0}\left[\mathrm{ch}(4H-z)A_0\cos B_0z-\mathrm{ch}A_0z\cos(4H-z)B_0\right]$$

$$f_c = \frac{1}{C_0}\left[\text{sh}(2H+z)A_0\sin(2H-z)B_0 - \text{sh}(2H-z)A_0\sin(2H+z)B_0\right]$$

$$f_d = \frac{1}{C_0}\left[\text{ch}(2H+z)A_0\cos(2H-z)B_0 - \text{ch}(2H-z)A_0\cos(2H+z)B_0\right]$$

$$g_a = \frac{1}{C_0}\left[\text{ch}(4H-z)A_0\sin B_0 z + \text{ch}A_0 z\sin(4H-z)B_0\right]$$

$$g_b = \frac{1}{C_0}\left[\text{sh}(4H-z)A_0\cos B_0 z + \text{sh}A_0 z\cos(4H-z)B_0\right]$$

$$g_c = \frac{1}{C_0}\left[\text{ch}(2H+z)A_0\sin(2H-z)B_0 + \text{ch}(2H-z)A_0\sin(2H+z)B_0\right]$$

$$g_d = \frac{1}{C_0}\left[\text{sh}(2H+z)A_0\cos(2H-z)B_0 + \text{sh}(2H-z)A_0\cos(2H+z)B_0\right]$$

For half-infinite subgrade, the expression above is simplified to be

$$u_w = \frac{2p_2}{\pi}(1-\mu)\int_0^\infty\int_0^\infty\left[\varphi\sin z\beta + \psi(\cos z\beta - e^{-z\lambda})\right]\cos\lambda x\,\mathrm{d}\beta\,\mathrm{d}\lambda$$

$$\sigma_z' + u_w = \sigma_2'' - \frac{2p_2}{\pi}(1-\mu)\int_0^\infty\int_0^\infty \psi z\lambda e^{-z\lambda}\cos\lambda x\,\mathrm{d}\beta\,\mathrm{d}\lambda$$
$$+\frac{2p_2}{\pi}(1-2\mu)\int_0^\infty\int_0^\infty\frac{\lambda^2}{\lambda^2+\beta^2}\left[\varphi\sin z\beta + \psi(\cos z\beta - e^{-z\lambda})\right]\cos\lambda x\,\mathrm{d}\beta\,\mathrm{d}\lambda$$

$$\sigma_z' + u_w = \sigma_2'' - \frac{2p_2}{\pi}(1-\mu)\int_0^\infty\int_0^\infty \psi(z - z\lambda)e^{-z\lambda}\cos\lambda x\,\mathrm{d}\beta\,\mathrm{d}\lambda$$
$$+\frac{2p_2}{\pi}(1-2\mu)\int_0^\infty\int_0^\infty\frac{1}{\lambda^2+\beta^2}\left[\varphi\beta^2\sin z\beta + \psi(\beta^2\cos z\beta + \lambda e^{-z\lambda})\right]\cos\lambda x\,\mathrm{d}\beta\,\mathrm{d}\lambda$$

$$\tau_{zx} = \tau_{zx}'' + \frac{2p_2}{\pi}(1-\mu)\int_0^\infty\int_0^\infty\psi(1-z\lambda)\,e^{-z\lambda}\sin\lambda x\,\mathrm{d}\beta\,\mathrm{d}\lambda - \frac{2p_2}{\pi}(1-2\mu)$$
$$\times\int_0^\infty\int_0^\infty\frac{\lambda}{\lambda^2+\beta^2}\left[\varphi\beta\cos z\beta - \psi(\sin z\beta - \lambda e^{-z\lambda})\right]\sin\lambda x\,\mathrm{d}\beta\,\mathrm{d}\lambda \tag{4-97}$$

where $\sigma_z'', \sigma_x'', \sigma_{zx}''$ are elastic theoretical solutions of half-infinite subgrade.

$$\varphi = \left[\frac{\beta}{\lambda^2+\beta^2} + \frac{(1-v)v\beta}{v^2\lambda^2+(1-\mu)^2\beta^2}\right]\exp\left[-\overline{C}_v t(\lambda^2+\beta^2)\right]$$

$$\varphi = \left[\frac{\lambda}{\lambda^2+\beta^2} + \frac{v^2\beta}{v^2\lambda^2+(1-\mu)^2\beta^2}\right]\exp\left[-\overline{C}_v t(\lambda^2+\beta^2)\right]$$

3. The Biot equation's solution under the action of concentrated load

The subgrade layer with finite depth's consolidation problem under the action of concentrated load can be solved using the forgoing method, and its result is as below:

$$u_w = \frac{p_3}{\pi}(1-\mu)\int_0^\infty\int_0^\infty\cos x\alpha\cos y\beta\int_0^\infty\left[\left(\frac{\text{sh}(2H-z)r}{\text{sh}2Hr} - f_b\right)\varphi_1\right.$$
$$\left.+\left(\frac{\text{sh}zr}{\text{sh}2Hr} - f_d\right)\varphi_2 - f_a\psi_1 - f_c\psi_2\right]\mathrm{d}\lambda\,\mathrm{d}\beta\,\mathrm{d}\alpha$$

$$\sigma_z' + u_w = \frac{1}{2}\sigma_z'' + \frac{p_2}{2\pi}\int_0^\infty\int_0^\infty \frac{\mathrm{sh}(2H-z)r}{\mathrm{sh}2Hr}\cos x\alpha\cos y\beta\,\mathrm{d}\beta\,\mathrm{d}\alpha$$
$$+\frac{p_3}{\pi}(1-\mu)\int_0^\infty\int_0^\infty \frac{1}{\mathrm{sh}2Hr}\cos x\alpha\cos y\beta\int_0^\infty\left\{\left[zr\mathrm{ch}(2H-z)r-\frac{2H\lambda}{\mathrm{sh}2Hr}\mathrm{sh}z\lambda\right]\varphi_1\right.$$
$$\left.-\left[zr\mathrm{ch}zr-(1+2Hr\mathrm{ch}2Hr)\mathrm{sh}zr\right]\varphi_2\right\}\mathrm{d}\lambda\,\mathrm{d}\beta\,\mathrm{d}\alpha$$
$$-\frac{p_3}{\pi}(1-2\mu)\int_0^\infty\int_0^\infty \cos x\alpha\cos y\beta\int_0^\infty\frac{r^2}{\lambda}\left[f_a\varphi_1+f_c\varphi_2\right.$$
$$\left.+\left(\frac{\mathrm{sh}(2H-z)r}{\mathrm{sh}2Hr}-f_b\right)\psi_1+\left(\frac{\mathrm{sh}zr}{\mathrm{sh}2Hr}-f_d\right)\psi_2\right]\mathrm{d}\lambda\,\mathrm{d}\beta\,\mathrm{d}\alpha$$

$$\sigma_x' + u_w = \frac{1}{2}\sigma_z'' - \frac{p_2}{2\pi}\int_0^\infty\int_0^\infty \frac{\alpha^2}{r^2}\frac{\mathrm{sh}(2H-z)r}{\mathrm{sh}2Hr}\cos x\alpha\cos y\beta\,\mathrm{d}\beta\,\mathrm{d}\alpha$$
$$+\frac{p_3}{\pi}(1-\mu)\int_0^\infty\int_0^\infty \frac{\alpha^2}{r^2}\cos x\alpha\cos y\beta\cdot\frac{1}{\mathrm{sh}2Hr}$$
$$\times\left\{\left[\left(1+\frac{r^2}{\alpha^2}\right)\mathrm{sh}(2H-z)r-zr\mathrm{ch}(2H-z)r+\frac{2Hr}{\mathrm{sh}2Hr}\mathrm{sh}zr\right]\int_0^\infty\varphi_1\mathrm{d}\lambda\right.$$
$$\left.+\left[\left(\frac{r^2}{\alpha^2}-2Hr\mathrm{cth}Hr\right)\mathrm{sh}zr+zr\mathrm{ch}zr\right]\int_0^\infty\varphi_2\mathrm{d}\lambda\right\}\mathrm{d}\beta\,\mathrm{d}\alpha$$
$$-\frac{p_3}{\pi}(1-2\mu)\int_0^\infty\int_0^\infty \cos x\alpha\cos y\beta\int_0^\infty\left[\left(f_b-\frac{\alpha^2}{\lambda}f_a\right)\varphi_1+\left(f_d-\frac{\alpha^2}{\lambda}f_c\right)\varphi_2\right.$$
$$\left.+\left(f_a+\frac{\alpha^2}{\lambda}f_b-\frac{\alpha^2}{\lambda}\frac{\mathrm{sh}(2H-z)r}{\mathrm{sh}2Hr}\right)\psi_1+\left(f_c+\frac{\alpha^2}{\lambda}f_d-\frac{\alpha^2}{\lambda}\frac{\mathrm{sh}zr}{\mathrm{sh}2Hr}\right)\psi_2\right]\mathrm{d}\lambda\,\mathrm{d}\beta\,\mathrm{d}\alpha$$

$$\tau_{xy} = \frac{1}{2}\tau_{xy}'' + \frac{p_2}{2\pi}\int_0^\infty\int_0^\infty \frac{\mathrm{sh}(2H-z)r}{\mathrm{sh}2Hr}\sin x\alpha\sin y\beta\,\mathrm{d}\beta\,\mathrm{d}\alpha$$
$$-\frac{p_3}{\pi}(1-\mu)\int_0^\infty\int_0^\infty \frac{\alpha\beta}{r^2}\sin x\alpha\sin y\beta\cdot\frac{1}{\mathrm{sh}2Hr}$$
$$\times\left\{\left[\mathrm{sh}(2H-z)r-zr\mathrm{ch}(2H-z)r+\frac{2Hr}{\mathrm{sh}2Hr}\mathrm{sh}zr\right]\int_0^\infty\varphi_1\mathrm{d}\lambda+\left[(zr\mathrm{ch}zr\right.\right.$$
$$\left.\left.-2Hr\mathrm{cth}Hr)\mathrm{sh}zr\right]\int_0^\infty\varphi_2\mathrm{d}\lambda\right\}\mathrm{d}\beta\,\mathrm{d}\alpha-\frac{p_3}{\pi}(1-2\mu)\int_0^\infty\int_0^\infty\sin x\alpha\sin y\beta\int_0^\infty\frac{\alpha\beta}{\lambda}$$
$$\times\left[f_a\varphi_1+f_c\varphi_2+\left(\frac{\mathrm{sh}(2H-z)r}{\mathrm{sh}2Hr}-f_b\right)\psi_1+\left(\frac{\mathrm{sh}zr}{\mathrm{sh}2Hr}-f_d\right)\psi_2\right]\mathrm{d}\lambda\,\mathrm{d}\beta\,\mathrm{d}\alpha$$

$$\tau_{yz}=\frac{1}{2}\tau''_{yz}+\frac{p_2}{2\pi}\int_0^{\infty}\int_0^{\infty}\frac{\operatorname{sh}(2H-z)r}{\operatorname{sh}2Hr}\cos x\alpha\sin y\beta\mathrm{d}\beta\mathrm{d}\alpha$$

$$-\frac{p_3}{\pi}(1-\mu)\int_0^{\infty}\int_0^{\infty}\frac{\beta}{r^2}\cos x\alpha\sin y\beta\cdot\frac{1}{\operatorname{sh}2Hr}$$

$$\times\left\{\left[zr\operatorname{sh}(2H-z)r-\operatorname{ch}(2H-z)r+\frac{2Hr}{\operatorname{sh}2Hr}\operatorname{ch}zr\right]\int_0^{\infty}\varphi_1\mathrm{d}\lambda\right.$$

$$\left.+\left[zr\operatorname{sh}zr-2Hr\operatorname{cth}Hr\operatorname{ch}zr\right]\int_0^{\infty}\varphi_2\mathrm{d}\lambda\right\}\mathrm{d}\beta\mathrm{d}\alpha-\frac{p_3}{\pi}(1-2\mu)$$

$$\times\int_0^{\infty}\int_0^{\infty}\cos x\alpha\sin y\beta\int_0^{\infty}\frac{\beta}{\lambda}\left[\left(A_0g_a-B_0g_b\right)\varphi_1-\left(A_0g_c-B_0g_d\right)\varphi_2\right.$$

$$\left.+\left(r\frac{\operatorname{ch}(2H-z)r}{\operatorname{sh}2Hr}-A_0g_b-B_0g_a\right)\psi_1-\left(r\frac{\operatorname{ch}zr}{\operatorname{sh}2Hr}-A_0g_c-B_0g_d\right)\psi_2\right]\mathrm{d}\lambda\mathrm{d}\beta\mathrm{d}\alpha$$

$$\tau_{zx}=\frac{1}{2}\tau''_{zx}+\frac{p_2}{2\pi}\int_0^{\infty}\int_0^{\infty}\frac{\alpha}{r}\frac{\operatorname{sh}(2H-z)r}{\operatorname{sh}2Hr}\sin x\alpha\cos y\beta\mathrm{d}\beta\mathrm{d}\alpha$$

$$+\frac{p_3}{\pi}(1-\mu)\int_0^{\infty}\int_0^{\infty}\frac{\alpha}{r}\sin x\alpha\cos y\beta\cdot\frac{1}{\operatorname{sh}2Hr}$$

$$\times\left\{\left[zr\operatorname{sh}(2H-z)r-\operatorname{ch}(2H-z)r+\frac{2Hr}{\operatorname{sh}2Hr}\operatorname{ch}zr\right]\int_0^{\infty}\varphi_1\mathrm{d}\lambda\right.$$

$$\left.+\left[zr\operatorname{sh}zr-2Hr\operatorname{ch}Hr\operatorname{ch}zr\right]\int_0^{\infty}\varphi_2\mathrm{d}\theta\right\}\mathrm{d}\beta\mathrm{d}\alpha-\frac{p_3}{\pi}(1-2\mu)$$

$$\times\int_0^{\infty}\int_0^{\infty}\sin x\alpha\cos y\beta\int_0^{\infty}\frac{\alpha}{\lambda}\left[\left(A_0g_a-B_0g_b\right)\varphi_1-\left(A_0g_c-B_0g_d\right)\varphi_2\right.$$

$$\left.+\left(r\frac{\operatorname{ch}(2H-z)r}{\operatorname{sh}2Hr}-A_0g_b-B_0g_a\right)\psi_1-\left(r\frac{\operatorname{ch}zr}{\operatorname{sh}2Hr}-A_0g_d-B_0g_c\right)\psi_2\right]\mathrm{d}\lambda\mathrm{d}\beta\mathrm{d}\alpha$$

$$u_z=\frac{1}{2}u''_z+\frac{1+v}{E}\frac{p_2}{2\pi}\int_0^{\infty}\int_0^{\infty}\frac{1}{r}\frac{\operatorname{ch}(2H-z)\lambda}{\operatorname{sh}2Hr}\cos x\alpha\cos y\beta\mathrm{d}\beta\mathrm{d}\alpha$$

$$+\frac{1+v}{E}\frac{p_3}{2\pi}(1-\mu)\int_0^{\infty}\int_0^{\infty}\frac{1}{r}\cos x\alpha\cos y\beta\frac{1}{\operatorname{sh}2Hr}$$

$$\times\left\{\left[zr\operatorname{sh}(2H-z)r+\frac{2Hr}{\operatorname{sh}2Hr}\operatorname{ch}zr\right]\int_0^{\infty}\varphi_1\mathrm{d}\lambda\right.$$

$$\left.+\left[z\lambda\operatorname{sh}zr-(1+2Hr\operatorname{ch}2Hr)\operatorname{ch}zr\right]\int_0^{\infty}\varphi_2\mathrm{d}\lambda\right\}\mathrm{d}\beta\mathrm{d}\alpha$$

$$-\frac{1+\mu}{E}\frac{p_3}{\pi}(1-2\mu)\int_0^{\infty}\int_0^{\infty}\cos x\alpha\cos y\beta\int_0^{\infty}\frac{1}{\lambda}[(A_0g_a-B_0g_a)\varphi_1$$

$$-(A_0g_c-B_0g_d)\varphi_2+\left[r\frac{\operatorname{ch}(2H-z)r}{\operatorname{sh}2Hr}-A_0g_b-B_0g_a\right]\psi_1$$

$$\left.-\left(r\frac{\operatorname{ch}zr}{\operatorname{sh}2Hr}-A_0g_d-B_0g_c\right)\psi_2\right]\mathrm{d}\lambda\mathrm{d}\beta\mathrm{d}\alpha$$

$$
\begin{aligned}
u_x = & \frac{1}{2}u_x'' + \frac{p_3}{2\pi}\int_0^\infty\int_0^\infty \frac{a}{r^2}\sin x\alpha\cos y\beta\frac{\mathrm{sh}(2H-z)r}{\mathrm{sh}2Hr}\mathrm{d}\beta\mathrm{d}\alpha \\
& -\frac{1+\mu}{E}\frac{p_3}{\pi}(1-\mu)\int_0^\infty\int_0^\infty \frac{\alpha}{r^2}\sin x\alpha\cos y\beta\frac{1}{\mathrm{sh}2Hr} \\
& \times\left\{\left[\mathrm{sh}(2H-z)r - zr\mathrm{ch}(2H-z)r + \frac{2Hr}{\mathrm{sh}2Hr}\mathrm{sh}zr\right]\int_0^\infty \varphi_1\mathrm{d}\lambda\right. \\
& \left.+[zr\mathrm{ch}zr - 2Hr\mathrm{cth}2Hr - \mathrm{sh}zr]\int_0^\infty \varphi_2\mathrm{d}\lambda\right\}\mathrm{d}\beta\mathrm{d}\alpha \\
& -\frac{1+\mu}{E}\frac{p_3}{\pi}(1-2\mu)\int_0^\infty\int_0^\infty \sin x\alpha\cos y\beta\int_0^\infty\frac{\alpha}{\lambda}[f_a\varphi_1 + f_c\varphi_2 \\
& +\left(\frac{\mathrm{sh}(2H-z)r}{\mathrm{sh}2Hr} - f_b\right)\psi_1 + \left(\frac{\mathrm{sh}zr}{\mathrm{sh}2Hr} - f_d\right)\psi_2\Bigg]\mathrm{d}\lambda\mathrm{d}\beta\mathrm{d}\alpha \\
u_y = & \frac{1}{2}u_y'' + \frac{1+\mu}{E}\frac{p_2}{2\pi}\int_0^\infty\int_0^\infty \frac{\beta}{r^2}\cos x\alpha\sin y\beta\frac{\mathrm{sh}(2H-z)r}{\mathrm{sh}2Hr}\mathrm{d}\beta\mathrm{d}\alpha \\
& -\frac{1+\mu}{E}\frac{p_3}{\pi}(1-\mu)\int_0^\infty\int_0^\infty \frac{\beta}{r^2}\cos x\alpha\sin y\beta\frac{1}{\mathrm{sh}2Hr} \\
& \times\left\{\left[\mathrm{sh}(2H-z)r - zr\mathrm{ch}(2H-z)r + \frac{2Hr}{\mathrm{sh}2Hr}\mathrm{sh}zr\right]\int_0^\infty \varphi_1\mathrm{d}\lambda\right. \\
& \left.+[zr\mathrm{ch}zr - 2Hr\mathrm{cth}2Hr - \mathrm{sh}zr]\int_0^\infty \varphi_2\mathrm{d}\lambda\right\}\mathrm{d}\beta\mathrm{d}\alpha \\
& -\frac{1+\mu}{E}\frac{p_3}{\pi}(1-2\mu)\int_0^\infty\int_0^\infty \cos x\alpha\sin y\beta\int_0^\infty\frac{\beta}{\lambda}[f_a\varphi_1 + f_c\varphi_2 \\
& +\left(\frac{\mathrm{sh}(2H-z)r}{\mathrm{sh}2Hr} - f_b\right)\psi_1 + \left(\frac{\mathrm{sh}zr}{\mathrm{sh}2Hr} - f_d\right)\psi_2\Bigg]\mathrm{d}\lambda\mathrm{d}\beta d\alpha
\end{aligned} \tag{4-98}
$$

where

$$
\begin{aligned}
\varphi_1 &= \frac{1}{R_\lambda}(Q_1\sin\lambda C_v t + Q_2\cos\lambda C_v t) \\
\varphi_2 &= \frac{1}{R_\lambda}(Q_3\sin\lambda C_v t + Q_4\cos\lambda C_v t) \\
\psi_1 &= \frac{1}{R_\lambda}(Q_2\sin\lambda C_v t - Q_1\cos\lambda C_v t) \\
\psi_2 &= \frac{1}{R_\lambda}(Q_4\sin\lambda C_v t - Q_3\cos\lambda C_v t) \\
R_\lambda &= \lambda(R_1^2 + R_2^2) \\
R_1 &= g_1^2 - h_1^2 + g_2 g_3 + h_2^2 \\
R_2 &= 2h_1 g_1 + h^2 g_3 - h_2 g_2
\end{aligned}
$$

$$
Q_1 = (R_1 g_2 + R_2 h_2)\mathrm{cth}2Hr - (R_1 g_1 + R_2 h_1)\frac{1}{\mathrm{sh}2Hr}
$$

$$
Q_2 = (R_2 g_2 - R_1 h_2)\mathrm{cth}2Hr - (R_2 g_1 - R_1 h_1)\frac{1}{\mathrm{sh}2Hr}
$$

$$Q_3 = (R_1g_1 + R_2h_1)\text{cth}2Hr + (R_1g_1 - R_2h_2)\frac{1}{\text{sh}2Hr}$$

$$Q_4 = (R_2g_1 - R_1h_1)\text{cth}2Hr + (R_2g_3 + R_2h_2)\frac{1}{\text{sh}2Hr}$$

$$g_1 = (1-\mu)\frac{2Hr}{\text{sh}2Hr}(\text{th}2Hr + 2(1-2\mu)\frac{r}{\lambda C_0}$$
$$\times(B_0\text{sh}2HA_0\cos 2HB_0 - A_0\text{ch}2HA_0\sin 2HB_0)$$

$$h_1 = (1-2\mu)\frac{r}{\lambda}\left[\frac{2}{C_0}(A_0\text{sh}2HA_0\cos 2HB_0 + B_0\text{ch}2HA_0\sin 2HB_0) - \frac{r}{\text{sh}2Hr}\right]$$

$$g_2 = (1+\mu)\left(\text{cth}2Hr + \frac{2Hr}{\text{sh}^2 2Hr}\right) + (1-2\mu)\frac{r}{\lambda C_0}(B_0\text{sh}4HA_0 - A_0\sin 4HB_0)$$

$$h_2 = (1-2\mu)\frac{r}{\lambda}\left[\frac{1}{C_0}(A_0\text{sh}4HA_0 + B_0\sin 4HB_0) - r\text{cth}2Hr\right]$$

$$g_3 = (1+\mu)\left(\text{cth}2Hr - \frac{2Hr}{\text{sh}^2 Hr}\right) - (1-2\mu)\frac{r}{\lambda C_0}(B_0\text{sh}4HA_0 - A_0\sin 4HB_0)$$

$$A_0 = \sqrt{\frac{\sqrt{\lambda^2 + r^4} + r^2}{2}}$$

$$B_0 = \sqrt{\frac{\sqrt{\lambda^2 + r^4} - r^2}{2}}$$

$$C_0 = \text{ch}4HA_0 - \cos 4HB_0$$

$$r = \sqrt{\alpha^2 + \beta^2}$$

4.9 Practical Numerical Analysis for Foundation Deformation (Finite Element Method)

Terzaghi put forward effective stress principle and one-dimensional consolidation theory in 1942, and it marked the birth of modern subgrade mechanics. Foundation's consolidation analysis has been one of the important subjects in subgrade mechanics. Further more, consolidation theory's general equation is just the multiphase continuum mechanics' general equation. Therefore, the consolidation analysis has certain universal significance.

1. The brief introduction of foundation deformation

In Terzaghi one-dimensional consolidation theory, except for the subgrade's assumption of homogeneity and small deformation, there are other assumptions as below:① subgrade is completely saturated; ② subgrade particles and water are uncompressible; ③ subgrade compresses and pore water is extruded only in one direction; ④ the flowing of pore water follows Darcy law; ⑤ in the consolidation process, permeability coefficient and compression coefficient are all constant; ⑥ the relation between subgrade's void ratio and effective stress does not change with time. Based on these assumptions, Terzaghi one-dimensional consolidation equation can be expressed to be

$$C_v \frac{\partial^2 p_w}{\partial z^2} = \frac{\partial p_w}{\partial t} \tag{4-99}$$

where: C_v—consolidation coefficient, $C_v = k(1+e)/\rho_w a_v$, where e is initial void ratio, k is permeability coefficient, ρ_w is volume density of water , a_v is compression coefficient.

p_w—the pore water pressure.

Extending Terzaghi one-dimensional consolidation theory into two-dimensional and three dimensional problems, Terzaghi-Rendulic diffusion equation can be obtained, and its three-dimensional form is

$$\frac{\partial p_w}{\partial t} = C_v \left(\frac{\partial^2 p_w}{\partial x^2} + \frac{\partial^2 p_w}{\partial y^2} + \frac{\partial^2 p_w}{\partial z^2} \right) \tag{4-100}$$

For simple geometry and boundary condition, the diffusion equation can get analytical solution, while for complex geometry and boundary condition, the numerical analysis (e.g. finite element method and finite difference method) is needed.

According to the effective stress principle, the subgrade's continuous condition and equilibrium equation, the consolidation theory is put forward. The consolidation equation is made up of dynamic equilibrium equation and continuity equation. The continuity equation is:

$$\frac{1-2\mu}{E} \frac{\partial(\Theta - 3p_w)}{\partial t} + \frac{k_x}{\rho_w} \frac{\partial^2 p_w}{\partial x^2} + \frac{k_x}{\rho_w} \frac{\partial^2 p_w}{\partial y^2} + \frac{k_x}{\rho_w} \frac{\partial^2 p_w}{\partial z^2} = 0 \tag{4-101}$$

where: Θ —the volumetric total pressure, $\Theta = \overline{\sigma}_x + \overline{\sigma}_y + \overline{\sigma}_z$.

The difference between Biot consolidation theory and Terzaghi-Rendulic quasi consolidation theory is: the former considers subgrade body's average total stress's change with time in the consolidation process, while the later assumes that the subgrade body's average total stress keeps invariant. If let the expression's $\partial\Theta/\partial t = 0$, i.e. subgrade body's total stress keeps invariant, then get:

$$C_v = \frac{kE}{3\rho_w(1+\mu)(1-2\mu)} \tag{4-102}$$

Under the one-dimensional consolidation condition, $\varepsilon_x = \varepsilon_z = 0$, then get

$$C_v = \frac{kE}{3\rho_w(1-2\mu)} \tag{4-103}$$

In uni-dimensional consolidation, total stress $\overline{\sigma}_z$ should be equal to subgrade surface load. If this load is invariant, then the condition that $\overline{\sigma}_z$ is invariant can be satisfied. In this situation, Biot consolidation theory is same to the Terzaghi consolidation theory, and so, Terzaghi consolidation theory is correct. In general case, especially in three-dimensional problems, it is difficult to satisfy the condition that total stress keeps constant in the consolidation process, so the calculating result may have big error. Especially Rendulic quasi consolidation theory can not explain Mandel-Oryer effect (Mandel-Oryer effect is that the pore pressure dose not dissipate, but increases, in the subgrade which is having initial consolidation, under certain condition). Because the calculation is simplified a lot for the Terzaghi-Rendulic quasi consolidation theory's assumption that pore water pressure change is irrelevant to subgrade's skeleton deformation, it is still applied in engineering.

Biot consolidation theory is more reasonable than Terzaghi-Rendulic quasi consolidation theory, and it can explain Mandel-Oryer effect. But for the difficulties of mathematics, the analytical solution can only be obtained for few simple boundary value problems using series method and integral transformation method. For the development of numerical method and computer, the Biot consolidation theory is more and more commonly applied in engineering, which also impels development of itself. Terzaghi one-dimensional consolidation theory's assumptions are cancelled one by one, and many scholars put forward some more common consolidation theories. For example, the consolidation method put forward by Schiffmann not only considers the nonlinear relation between stress and strain, permeability's change with effective stress, but also considers the situation of large strain.

It is put forward by Sandhu and Wilson first to solve Biot consolidation equation by finite elements. They select quadratic interpolation mode for displacement, and linear mode for pore water pressure, use variational principle to get consolidation theory's finite element equation. Yin Zongze etc. get the similar equation according to the conception of flow equilibrium, and combining virtual displacement principle. Gong Xiaonan deduces Biot consolidation theory's continuity equation based on the cohesive saturated condition of equivalent node flow equal to equivalent node compression amount. Recently, it is common to use finite element method to solve foundation consolidation problem.

Not only finite element method, but also boundary element method is adopted to solve Biot consolidation equation. But compared with finite element method, boundary element method fits worse in the aspects of treating non-homogeneous material, nonlinear stress-strain relation and complex boundary condition, and its mathematical derivation is complex, sometimes has difficulties in solution.

2. The finite elementary solution of consolidation equation

According to effective stress principle, the Biot consolidation equation got by motion equilibrium differential equation and flow continuity equation is continuum mechanics' general equation, i.e.

$$\left.\begin{aligned}&d_1\frac{\partial^2 u_x}{\partial x^2}+d_3\frac{\partial^2 u_z}{\partial z^2}+(d_2+d_3)\frac{\partial^2 u_x}{\partial x\partial z}-\rho_f g\frac{\partial h}{\partial x}+z^0=\rho\ddot{u}_x\\&d_3\frac{\partial^2 u_x}{\partial x^2}+d_1\frac{\partial^2 u_z}{\partial x^2}+(d_2+d_3)\frac{\partial^2 u_x}{\partial z\partial x}-\rho_f g\frac{\partial h}{\partial x}+z^0=\rho\ddot{u}_x+(\rho-\rho_f)g\\&\frac{\partial}{\partial x}k_x\frac{\partial h}{\partial x}+\frac{\partial}{\partial z}k_z\frac{\partial h}{\partial z}-\beta h+\left(\frac{\partial u_x}{\partial x}+\frac{\partial u_z}{\partial z}\right)+\rho_f\left(\frac{\partial}{\partial x}k_x\ddot{u}_x+\frac{\partial}{\partial z}\ddot{u}_z\right)=0\end{aligned}\right\}\tag{4-104}$$

After discretization, Biot consolidation equation can be expressed as

$$\left.\begin{aligned}&[K]\{u\}+[Q]\{h\}=\{F_1\}+\{F_0\}\\&[Q]^T\{u\}+[S]\{h\}+[H]\{h\}=\{F_2\}\end{aligned}\right\}\tag{4-105}$$

The expression above is time's first order differential equation, and it is generally solved by the tow points progressive scheme. Let t_n and t_{n+1} be two points in the time domain, and $\{u\}_n$, $\{u\}_{n+1}$, $\{h\}_n$, $\{h\}_{n+1}$ be corresponding variant. Then let $\{u\}=\{\Delta u\}/\Delta t$ and $\{h\}=\{\Delta h\}/\Delta t$, at the time of $\Delta t=t_{n+1}-t_n$, and adopt the linear interpolating formula below:

$$\left.\begin{aligned}&\{u\}=\{u\}_n+\frac{\tau}{\Delta t}\{\Delta u\}\\&\{h\}=\{h\}_n+\frac{\tau}{\Delta t}\{\Delta h\}\\&\{F_0\}=\{F_0\}_n+\frac{\tau}{\Delta t}\{\Delta F_0\}\\&\{F_1\}=\{F_1\}_n+\frac{\tau}{\Delta t}\{\Delta F_1\}\\&\{F_3\}=\{F_2\}+\frac{\tau}{\Delta t}\{\Delta F_2\}\\&\text{where } \tau:0\rightarrow\Delta t\end{aligned}\right\}\tag{4-106}$$

Calculate the integral for τ from 0 to $\Delta\tau$, then get

$$\left.\begin{aligned}&\theta[K]\{\Delta u\}+[Q]\{\Delta h\}=\theta\{\Delta F_1\}+\theta\{\Delta F_0\}-([K]\{u\}_n+[Q]\{h\}_n-\{F_1\}_n-\{F_0\}_n)\\&\frac{1}{\Delta t}[Q]^{\mathrm{T}}\{\Delta u\}+\frac{1}{\Delta t}[S]^{\mathrm{T}}\{\Delta h\}+\theta[H]\{\Delta h\}=\theta\{\Delta F_2\}-([H]\{h\}_n-\{F_2\}_n)\end{aligned}\right\}\tag{4-107}$$

where

$$\theta=\int_0^{\Delta r}\omega\tau\mathrm{d}\tau/\Delta t\int_0^{\Delta r}\omega\mathrm{d}\tau$$

ω —is the weight function for integral.

If the system is satisfied at the time of t_n, change stiffness matrix $[K]$ to be tangent matrix $[K_t]$, and delete initial strain's equivalent force $\{\Delta F_0\}$, i.e. let $[K_t]\{\Delta u\}=[K]\{\Delta u\}-\{\Delta F_0\}$, get

$$\left.\begin{aligned}&[K_t]\{\Delta u\}=[Q\{\Delta h\}]=\{\Delta F_1\}\\&[Q]^T\{\Delta u\}+([S]+\theta\Delta t[H])\{\Delta h\}=(\{F_2\}_n+\theta\{\Delta F_2\})\Delta t-[H]\Delta t\{h\}_n\end{aligned}\right\}\tag{4-108}$$

For saturated subgrade's situation of $[S]=0$

$$\left.\begin{aligned}&\theta[K]\{\Delta u\}+[Q]\{\Delta h\}=\theta\{\Delta F_1\}+\theta\{\Delta F_0\}-\left([K]\{u\}_n+[Q]\{h\}_n-\{F_1\}_n-\{F_0\}_n\right)\\&\frac{1}{\Delta t}[Q]^{\mathrm{T}}\{\Delta u\}+\frac{1}{\Delta t}[S]^{\mathrm{T}}\{\Delta h\}+\theta[H]\{\Delta h\}=\theta\{\Delta F_2\}-\left([H]\{h\}_n-\{F_2\}_n\right)\end{aligned}\right\}\quad(4\text{-}109)$$

When set weight function ω to be constant, $\theta=\frac{1}{2}$, such time difference scheme equals to center difference scheme, is Orank-Nicholson form. When $\omega=\tau$, $\theta=\frac{2}{3}$, and this is a common difference scheme now. Experience indicates even mutation happens at the time period Δt, error dose not change obviously. $\theta=1$ equals to fully implicit difference. The advantage of adopting this difference scheme is that stable seepage result can be solved further. Now set $\Delta t\to\infty$, then the items that do not have Δt can be ignored. Considering $\{h\}_n+\{\Delta h\}=\{h\}_{n+1}$ and $\{F_2\}_n+\{\Delta F_2\}=\{F_2\}_{n+1}$, then

$$[H]\{h\}_{n+1}=\{F_2\}_{n+1}\quad(4\text{-}110)$$

This seepage equation $\theta<\frac{1}{2}$'s difference scheme is unstable, and should not be used.

3. The selection of element form and period

Sandhu and Wilson adopt $\theta=\frac{1}{2}$ and triangular element for solution of Biot consolidation equation, six nodes e.g. quadratic shape function for displacement, 3 nodes' first shape function for pore water pressure whose accuracy equals to pore water pressure's. Such element is just composite element. Shen Zhujiang etc. adopt the same shape function's standard element for displacement and pore water pressure.

Nishizaki etc. make detailed comparison among kinds of element forms, which include incompatible element form, i.e. add two additional degrees of freedom in the element, except for the displacement's four nodes. In order to promote the calculating accuracy of pore water pressure, artificial smoothing method can be adopted to process the calculating result. But if some spatial measures can be used in the selection of period Δt and element mesh arrangement, big error can be avoided. The arrangement of element should follow the principle of intense mesh in the high gradient of pore water pressure area. Δt's value can not be set to be too small, but too large would induce fluctuation of pore water pressure(Fig. 4-19). The appropriate period can be determined by the expression below:

$$\Delta t=\left(1-\frac{1}{4}\right)\frac{L^2}{C_v}\quad(4\text{-}111)$$

where: L—the size of the element which is near the drainage surface in the flow direction;

C_v—soil's consolidation coefficient.

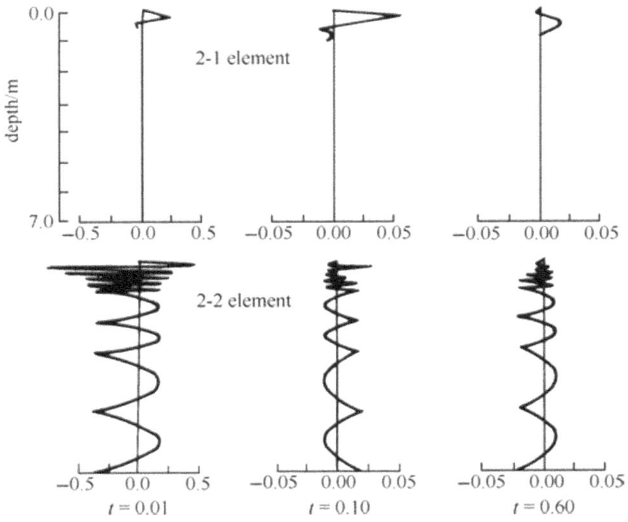

Fig. 4-19 The error of void water pressure

4. The boundary condition

In the Biot consolidation's analysis, the degree of freedom for node has two category: one is node displacement's degree of freedom, the other is node pore water pressure's degree of freedom. The category and processing method of the displacement boundary condition in consolidation analysis are generally the same to finite element's boundary condition in general elastic mechanics problems, only that the boundary condition of pore water pressure is added.

Firstly, discuss displacement's boundary condition. Taking plane problem as example, node's displacement degree of freedom is two: horizontal and vertical degree of freedom. For a certain degree of freedom, node's displacement condition may has the following situations: the first is the complete constrained condition, i.e. the displacement is zero, the second is node's displacement equals to a known value, under certain constraint condition, the third is without constraint, node can have free displacement, the fourth is between complete constraint and non-constrain, i.e. half constraint condition, such as spring bearing. Former two situations both have the node displacement known already. General constraint condition and Semi-permeable boundary condition for node are seldom met in calculation.

Compared with displacement boundary condition, pore water pressure's boundary condition has several situations too: the first is the full-permeable boundary condition, and node's pore water pressure is zero, the second is node's pore water pressure is a known value, the third is full-impermeable boundary condition, the fourth is between full-permeable and full-impermeable, which is called half-permeable boundary. Strictly speaking, the boundary that is intercepted as subgrade layer extends outward uniformly is half-permeable boundary. However, when the boundary's intercepted area is large, it dose not influence the main analysis's zone a lot to simplify it to be full-permeable or full-impermeable boundary. Considering the difficulty of processing half-permeable boundary, in practical engineering analysis, they are most treated as full-permeable or full-impermeable boundary. The displacement boundary condition on the boundary which is intercepted as subgrade layer extends outward uniformly is also similar to pore water pressure boundary condition, and usually be processed as complete constraint, or one-directional complete constraint with displacement in the other direction. The former two situations above belong to the situation that node pore water pressure is known.

For the situation that node displacement or pore water pressure is known, there are two solutions: ① still number degree of freedom, but displace the solved displacement value with known value before re-back substitution; ② change known value' degree of freedom to be zero, then the algebraic equation is divided into two parts as below,

$$\begin{bmatrix} [A_{11}] & [A_{12}] \\ [A_{21}] & [A_{22}] \end{bmatrix} \begin{Bmatrix} x_1 \\ \tilde{x}_2 \end{Bmatrix} = \begin{Bmatrix} b_1 \\ b_2 \end{Bmatrix} \tag{4-112}$$

where: $\tilde{x}_2$—the unknown boundary value. Only build equation for x_1 in calculation, i.e.

$$[A_{11}]\{x_1\} = \{b_1\} - [A_{21}]\{\tilde{x}_2\} \tag{4-113}$$

The right side item $[A_{21}]\{\tilde{x}_2\}$ can be got as calculating each element. In most situation, the known boundary is zero, then the expression above can be simplified to be

$$[A_{11}]\{x_1\} = \{b_1\} \tag{4-114}$$

The determination of boundary condition for foundation's consolidation analysis mainly depends on foundation's geological structure, symmetric conditions, subgrade conditions, etc.

Except for flexible foundation, the influence of foundation and its superstructure's rigidity should be considered, i.e. the interaction of subgrade, foundation and superstructure is mainly considered in calculation. In the boundary between subgrade and foundation, sometimes boundary elements are needed to set.

If for rigid foundation, elements are commonly divided in foundation, and deal with it as elastic material with large elastic modulus. The nodes on the interface between foundation and subgrade satisfy compatibility conditions, i.e. there is no disengagement phenomenon in the deformation of ground and foundation. Another feasible method is numbering each node's degree of freedom on the interface to be unified number. Each point's displacement is completely the same for the calculating result. For the rigid interface that can rotate, this rigid body's displacement's degree of freedom can be used to replace the interface's displacement's degree of freedom. Let $\{x_2\}$ be the degree of freedom on the rigid interface, and $\{x_1\}$ be other freedom, $\{x_3\}$ be rigid body variation's freedom, e.g. $\{x_2\}$ and $\{x_3\}$ have the relation of $\{x_2\}=[R]\{x_3\}$, then

$$\begin{bmatrix}[A_{11}] & [A_{13}] \\ [A_{31}] & [A_{33}]\end{bmatrix}\begin{Bmatrix}x_1 \\ x_3\end{Bmatrix}=\begin{Bmatrix}b_1 \\ b_3\end{Bmatrix} \tag{4-115}$$

where: $[A_{31}]=[R]^{\mathrm{T}}[A_{21}]$、$[A_{33}]=[R]^{\mathrm{T}}[A_{22}]$、$[b_3]=[R]^{\mathrm{T}}[b_2]$. This method can avoid the increment of calculating error induced by large difference of two kinds of material when divide elements in rigid members.

For two-dimensional and three-dimensional consolidation problem, finite elements method can also be used. For two-dimensional problem, let *u*, *v* and *h* be horizontal and vertical displacements and pore water head respectively, then finite elements interpolating formula is

$$\left.\begin{aligned} u&=\sum_{i=1}^{n} N_i u_i \\ v&=\sum_{i=1}^{n} N_i v_i \\ h&=\sum_{i=1}^{n} \overline{N}_i h_i \end{aligned}\right\} \tag{4-116}$$

where: u_i, v_i and h_i —node variants.

The expression above is suitable for individual element and whole computational domain. For the former, n is the element's number of nodes, while for the later, n is the total number of nodes.

4.10 Chapter Summary

This chapter researches the subgrade's compressibility, deformation law, physical mechanical indexes, and foundation settlement mechanism and consolidation theory in details, gives the calculating method for foundation settlement and its applicable conditions, and discusses the problem of solving consolidation function in finite elements method.

References

Black C. A. 1965. Methods of Soil Analysis, Agronomy, No.9, ASAM, Wedison, Wisc.

Chen X.F., Liao S.M., Kong X.P. 2003. Modern Geotechnical Engineering, Shanghai: Tongji University Press.

Chen X.F., Yuan W.B. 1990. Progress of Geotechnical Mechanics, Beijing: China Prospect Press.

Dunean J. M., Chang C. Y. 1970. Nonlinear Analysis of Stress and Strain in Soils, J. Soil. Mech. Found. Div., ASCE,Vol.96.

Hou X.Y., Liu G.B. 1996. Deformation Control Design of Soft Soil Shoring of Trench Structure, Theory and Engineering Practice of Subgrade Deformation Control Design , Shanghai: Tongji University Press.

Huang W.X. 1983. Engineering Properties of Soil, Beijing: China Water Conservancy and Hydroelectricity Press.

Huang X.L., Qin B.J., et al., 1981. Design and Calculation of the Foundation, Beijing: China Building Industry Press.

Huang X.L. Design Specifications of Building Foundation, GB5007-2002.

Huang Y.X., Liu Guo bin, Hou Xueyuan. 2000. Active Earth Pressure Research of Deep Foundation with Support in Soft Subgrade, Tunnel and Underground Engineering, No.3.

Huang Yun fei. 1996. Practical Technology of Deep Foundation Engineering, Beijing: Ordnance Press.

Ladd C. C., Foott R. 1974. New Design Procedure for Stability of Soft J. Geotech. Eng. Div., JGED, ASCE No.GT7.

Liu J.H., Hou Xueyuan. 1997. Handbook of Foundation Engineering, Beijing: China Building Industry Press.

Liu S.M. 1988. Research of the Soft Clay Secondary Consolidation Deformation Characteristics, Doctoral Dissertation of Zhejiang University.

Lu Z.J. 1999. Present State and Perspectives of Clay Shear Strength Research, Journal of Civil Engineering.

P. V. Lade, J. M. Duncan. 1975. Elastoplastic Stress-Strain Theory for Soil Cohesion, J. Geotech. Engng, ASCE, Vol.101, GT.

Singh A, 1976, Soil Engineering in Theory and Practice, 2nd Edition, New York: Asia Publishing House.

Vesic A. S. 1975. Bearing Capacity of Shallow Foundations, Foundation Engineering Handbook, Edited by Winterkorn H.F. and Fang H.Y., Van Nostrand Reinhold Company.

Zeng G. X., Xie K. H. 1989. New Development of the Vertical Drain Theories, Proc, XII ICSMFE, Vol.2.

Chapter 5 Settlement Calculation Methods and Case Studies of Box and Raft Foundations of Super High-Rise Buildings

As far as high-rise or super high-rise buildings are concerned, foundations must ensure the stability of buildings and meet the anti-inclining and anti-sliding requirements given the demands of wind-resistance and earthquake-resistance. So it is necessary to have enough buried depth for foundations. The basements need to not only satisfy the demand of buried depth, but also make full use of underground space. Therefore, box and raft foundations, also called compensating foundations, are mostly adopted in the foundation design of super high-rise buildings if the subgrade conditions allow. According to experiences, the basement depth required in complete compensating foundations of high-rise or super high-rise buildings refers to Table 5-1.

Table 5-1 Number of basement levels of complete compensating foundations adopted in box and raft foundations

Number of stories of high-rise buildings	20	30	40	50	Remarks
Required number of basement levels	1	2	3	4	Pile-box foundations are usually for buildings with over 50 stories

Box foundations are spatial structures with very big stiffness which consist of reinforced concrete roof, floor board, and internal and external crossbar walls (Fig. 5-1). Box foundations work with subgrade and surrounding subsoil together to enhance the entire stability and anti-seismic capacity of buildings. This kind of foundation is called compensating foundation because the additional pressure at foundation bottom is alleviated by digging out subgrade with certain thickness. There are over 50 super high-rise buildings in China which are constructed on natural subgrade with box foundations.

Box foundations of super high-rise buildings are rather more complicated and have lots of differences with the ordinary box foundations given the heavy loading, deep buried depth and large bottom area. There are lots of factors to be comprehensively taken into account including geological conditions, construction procedure, operating requirements, resilience and recompression at foundation pit bottom, interaction among subgrade, foundation, and superstructure, influence of nearby buildings, and so on. Even though there are specifications about box foundation settlement calculation in *Technical Code for Box and Raft Foundations of High-rise Buildings* (JGJ 6-99), the influence of support structures in deep foundation pits on settlement hasn't been considered so far. In this chapter, some new methods, like comprehensive coefficient method, layer-summation method of inclined-layer-step, and settlement calculation method considering the effect of support structures in deep foundation pits, are firstly proposed besides studies on box foundation settlement calculation methods. The results from these new methods are very close to the real measured values.

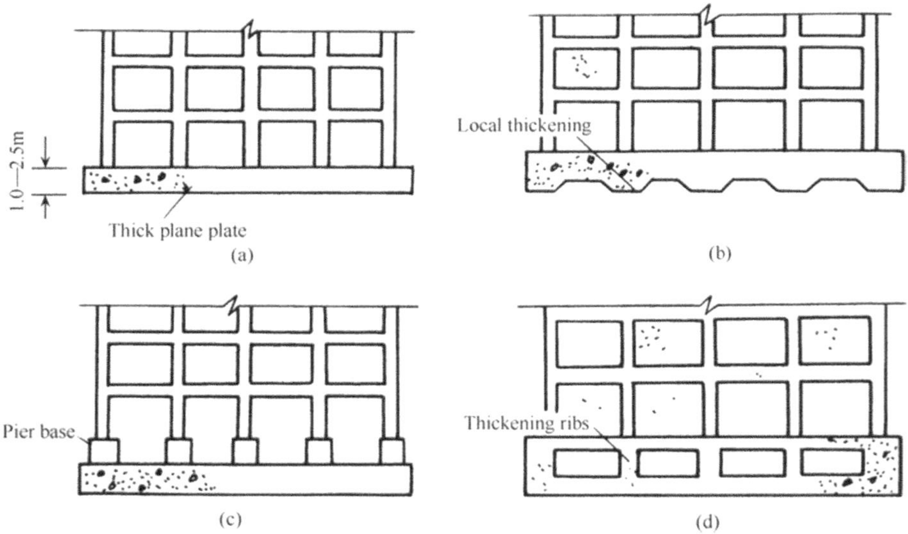

Fig. 5-1 Box foundation

5.1 Problems Considered in Box Foundation Settlement Calculation of Super High-Rise Buildings

5.1.1 Problems about Subgrade Compensation and Box Foundation Settlement

1. Application of subgrade compensation principle

Because the basement of super high-rise building is of at least three-levels in height, its buried depth D is usually rather large and the summation p_c of subgrade gravity pressure p_D at foundation pit bottom and hydraulic pressure p_W ($p_c = p_D + p_W$) is numerically rather great, which can partially compensate foundation pressure P, shown as Fig. 5-2. If p_c is equal to P, the additional foundation pressure is zero and the effective stress and hydraulic pressure in subgrade during the construction procedure are constant, and consequently there is no settlement of foundation. Actually, because the resilience of based subgrade resulting from digging and the recompression resulting from reloading, when $p > p_c$, it will be called lack compensation; when $p < p_c$, it will be called excess compensation which can give rise to probable floating of buildings and should be considered in the design of compensative box and raft foundations of super high-rise buildings.

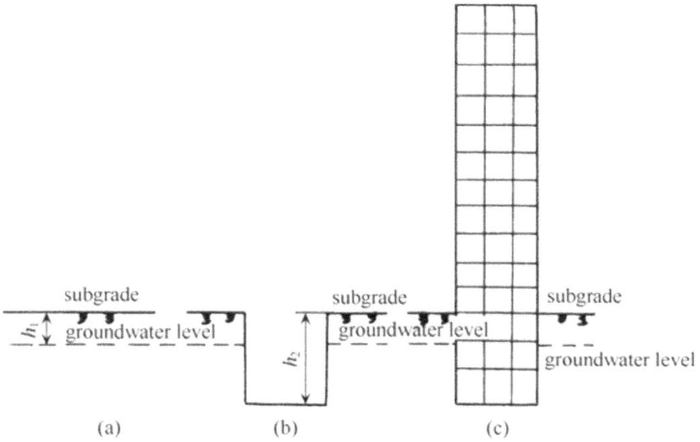

Fig. 5-2 Stress balance in compensation foundation

2. Relations between box foundation area and settlement deformation

The influence of box foundation area to settlement deformation is very complicated. The relation curve is drawn in Fig. 5-3 after experiment and summary real measured settlement deformation data of foundation areas in various dimensions.

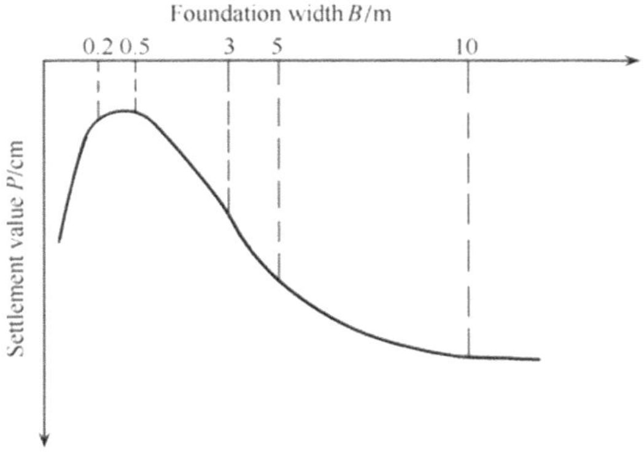

Fig. 5-3 Relation curve of foundation width and settlement deformation

As shown in Fig. 5-3, when foundation width B <0.2m, the plastic deformation occupies most part of settlement because of small base area. Therefore, foundation settlement increases while plastic-deformation area decreases along with the minimization of foundation width; When B is from 0.5m to 3m, foundation deformation conforms with linear relation in elastic theory; when B >10m, the curve is approximately becoming horizontal line. This phenomenon is caused by foundation deformation modulus increasing with depth, that is, load pressure decreasing with depth. Therefore, the box foundation width of high-rise building is usually over 10 meters. The deformation calculation of box foundations of high-rise buildings is rather complicated and differs with ordinary box foundations of small and medium constructions.

3. Utilization of groundwater buoyancy

If super high-rise buildings are built on soft-soil subgrade where groundwater level is a little high, such as in Shanghai, Tianjin, etc, the big groundwater buoyancy can be rationally and scientifically utilized.

4. Allowable digging depth of soft-soil foundation pit

When digging deep foundation in soft soil areas, chances are that there are lumps at the bottom of pits resulting from soil plastic-flow. In terms of layering sedimentary subgrade or soft subgrade, the sliding surface is much closer to the pit bottom, for example, the support structure of deep foundation pit of National Square in Zhuhai has collapsed because of the overall instability caused by sliding of soft layer below pit bottom. Without considering the shear of vertical sliding soil, the following equation can be got based on limit equilibrium principle:

$$K\sigma_d = K(\gamma d + q_0) = 5.7s = 5.7c \tag{5-1}$$

The allowable digging depth d is:

$$d = \frac{1}{\gamma}\left(\frac{5.7c}{K} - q_0\right) \tag{5-2}$$

where: K—safety factor, can be taken as 2;

c—average cohesion of saturated soft soil at the pit bottom;

$\bar{\gamma}$ — average value of specific gravity of soils above pit bottom which is weighted according to the soil layer thickness;

q_0—uniform load on the subgrade surface.

5.1.2 Stress and Strain Station of Digging Deep Foundation Pits

There is great change in stress and strain stations after digging deep foundation pit, especially for deeper pits. For analysis, the vertical loads in digging subgrade are simply put on half-space surface, and are got from integral calculation of Boussinesq's Equation. Because the objective effect of curve surface boundary is not taken into account, there are much bigger errors in this method. The half-space analysis with curve surface boundary under surface and body forces belongs to spatial problems, most of which haven't got analytic solutions (of course there are numerical solutions) except for rare axisymmetric problems. In cylindrical deep foundation pits, there are linear distributed normal load on internal walls, and the stress of any point in subgrade is:

$$\left.\begin{aligned}\sigma_r &= \gamma z\left(1-\frac{r_0^2}{r^2}\right)K_0 + qz\frac{r_0^2}{r^2}\\ \sigma_\theta &= \gamma z\left(1+\frac{r_0^2}{r^2}\right)K_0 - qz\frac{r_0^2}{r^2}\end{aligned}\right\} \tag{5-3}$$

where: $K_0 = \dfrac{r_0}{1-r_0}$, lateral pressure factor, $r=\sqrt{x^2+y^2}$;

γ —subgrade specific gravity(kN/m^2);

r_0 —radius of cylindrical foundation pit.

In numerical analysis, spatial finite element is used to handle this problem. However, for real projects, these spatial problems can be simplified into plane problems with curve boundary under boundary force and body force, and then the methods for elastic mechanics plane problems can be used to get solutions (refer to pit time-space effect principle of Liu Guobin and Hou Xueyuan).

5.1.3 Resilience and Recompression after Digging Deep Foundation Pits

1. Importance of resilience and recompression problems

There is much bigger resilience deformation at pit bottom caused by subgrade unloading after digging the foundation pit. The dashed curve in Fig. 5-4 is the theoretical resilience curve and the solid one represents the observed resilience deformation. This resilience can influent areas outside the pit, even the nearby buildings. When there are some support structures, the curve will differ a little bit. Therefore, the effect of resilience deformation to foundation settlement cannot be neglected. On the other hand, it is inevitable to occur resilience and recompression in foundation deformation of super high-rise buildings. For instance, the area of box foundation of ward building in Chinese Traditional Medicine Hospital of Beijing is 87m×12.6m and the depth of its pit is 5.7m. According to the observed results, there is a medium and light intersect layers of sand and clay under the foundation. About 9 meters below the subgrade surface, there are many kinds of sand-clay subgrade layers, and about 12—20m, there is sand-cobble layer. More deeper, there are several sediment cycles of clay and sand subgrade, till the hard slate of tertiary under 80—90 meters. The resilience and recompression curve of its foundation is shown in Fig. 5-5.

For another example, International Communication Building in Japan, has 32 stories above the ground and a basement with 3 levels. The buried depth of its foundation is about 20 meters and the subgrade is Tokyo conglomerate. its foundation resilience curve is shown in Fig. 5-6.

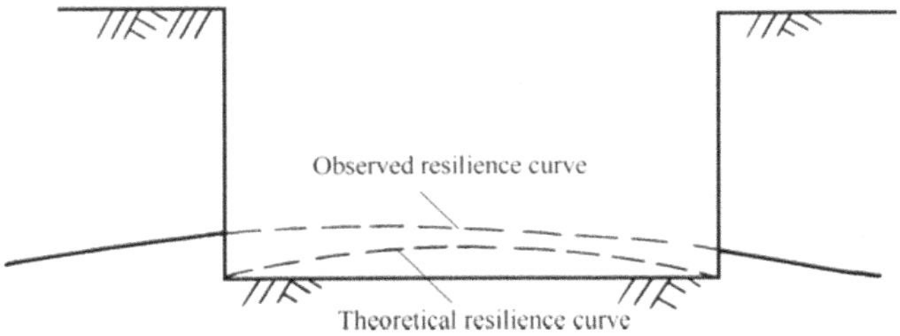

Fig. 5-4 Resilience deformations in the pits of super high-rise buildings

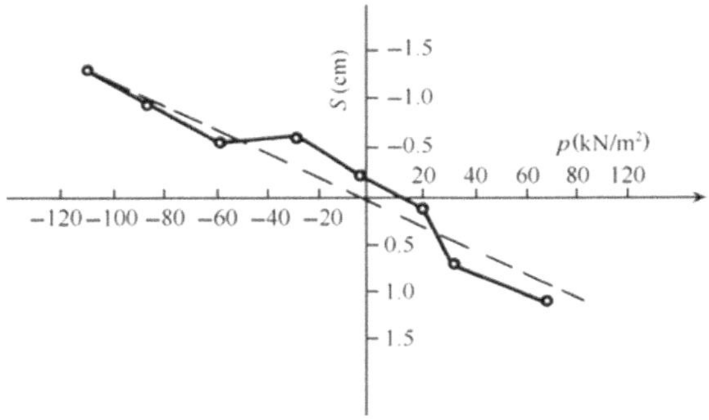

Fig. 5-5 Observed resilience recompression and additional settlement of the foundation of ward building in Chinese Traditional Medicine Hospital of Beijing

The total settlements of these two buildings mentioned above are not very big, but the subgrade resilience accounts for over 50% of total settlements. Lots of observations of deep foundations home and abroad show that the subgrade gravity pressure (so called digging-unloading pressure) at the bottom of ordinary box foundation takes over 50% of total foundation bottom pressure. As far as deep foundations of super high-rise buildings are concerned, the unloading pressure from digging deep foundation pit usually accounts for 20%—30%. In soft subgrade, the resilience-recompression can take 10%~30% of the total settlement after completion. The complexity of this problem lies in the difficulty of counting resilience of deep foundation pit accurately, and it is much more difficult to estimate resilience especially for those pits with support structures (can refer to "*Handbook for foundation pit projects*" compiled by Jianhang Liu and Xueyuan Hou).

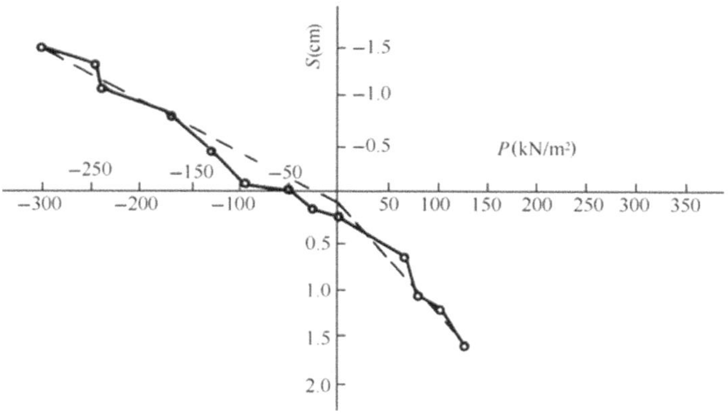

Fig. 5-6 The resilience curve of the foundation of International Communication Building in Japan

2. Simplified method for resilience calculation

The resilience of deep foundation pit can be calculated by finite element and boundary element methods, but the results are not satisfactory. An practical approach is to multiply regional modified coefficient to the analytic solution or the simplified calculation results, which can usually meet the demands of projects. Besides the methods proposed by Tongji University and Hou Yuyuan, the resilience can also be counted by the following method:

The pre-estimation of resilience can be counted given the assumption of half-plane elastic theory with hemicycle gap. In planar strain problems, the strain components in any point M(x, y) are:

$$\left.\begin{aligned} \sigma_x &= \gamma y\left(1-\frac{R^2x^2}{r^2}\right) \\ \sigma_{yx} &= \gamma y\left(1-\frac{R^2y^2}{r^2}\right) \\ \sigma_{xy} &= \gamma y\left(1-\frac{R^2xy}{r^2}\right) \end{aligned}\right\} \tag{5-4}$$

where: $r^2 = x^2 + y^2$.

Based on generalized hook law, the vertical strain is:

$$\begin{aligned} \varepsilon_y &= \frac{1+\mu_0}{E_0}\left[(1-\mu_0)\sigma_y - \mu_0\sigma_x\right] \\ &= \frac{\gamma y(1+\mu_0)}{E_0}\left[1-2\mu_0 - \frac{(1-2\mu_0)R^2y^2}{r^2} + \frac{\mu_0R^2x^2}{r^2}\right] \end{aligned} \tag{5-5}$$

The resilience deformation in the boundary can be obtained by integrating ε_r from certain effective effect depth y_0 to the points on the boundary:

$$S' = \frac{\gamma R^2(1-\mu_0)}{E_0}\left[\frac{x^2}{2(x^2+y^2)} - \frac{x^2}{2(x^2+y^2)} - \frac{1-\mu_0}{2}\ln\frac{x^2+y_0^2}{x^2+y^2}\right] \tag{5-6}$$

where x and y are the coordinates of boundary point. y_0 determines the uniform load with 2R width as the equal-weight substitution for hemicycle soil unloading. In terms of rectangular or trapezoid form digging sections, they can be equivalent to hemicycle sections with radius $R = \sqrt{2Q/(\pi y)}$ under the circumstances of equal total weight Q of unit thickness. The resilience at the central point in pit bottom is simply evaluated as:

$$S_0' = 2.3Q\left(1-u_0^2\right)/\pi E_0 = 0.732\left(1-u_0^2\right)/E_0 \tag{5-7}$$

This result is a little bigger than the actual spatial problems, but much smaller than unloading calculation.

5.1.4 Depth Calculation of Subgrade Compression Layer under Box Foundation

The calculation depth of subgrade compression layer under box foundation is one of the key factors that determine whether the calculation of foundation settlement is correct or not. There are mainly two theories for calculation of depth of subgrade compression layer in domestic projects, namely stress ratio method and strain ratio method. In stress ratio method, the depth of subgrade compression layer is determined by the ratio of additional pressures. This method take much more considerations of load effect on the depth of subgrade compression layer regardless of subgrade compression properties, subgrade categories, and foundation area, and so on. Some real measured data show that loads only influent subgrade compression layer a little bit. In Fig. 5-7, there are the observed relation curves between loads and foundation and subgrade compression layer of Xiao Yanta Hotel in Xi'an, which illuminate the unobvious influence between load and subgrade compression layer.

In addition, strain ratio method is stipulated in our new national code for subgrade & foundation design (GB 0007-2002), in which the depth of subgrade compression layer is determined by the ratio of the settlement in the place 1 meter above the calculation layer thickness to the total settlement, that is what we called, strain ratio. This method gives rise to calculation errors of subgrade compression layer, and at the same time, doesn't consider the effect of different subgrade categories which can result the errors. The observed data show that the calculation results are bigger when it comes to individual and bar foundations, and are only a little bigger for small foundations, and are close to the observed values for big box foundations (width b=10—50m). Based on these facts, it is supposed to use $0.3(1+\ln b)$ m to substitute the old specification of 1 meter above calculation layer thickness, which can be called as modified strain ratio method.

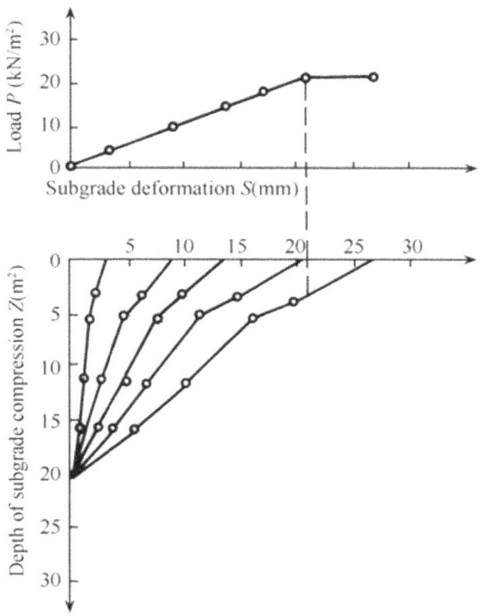

Fig. 5-7 Observed curve of the relation between depth of subgrade compression layer and foundation load of Xiao Yanta Hotel in Xi'an

The width of box foundation of super high-rise building is usually bigger than 10 meters, so there is very close relation between the depth of subgrade compression layer and the foundation width and subgrade categories. The curve of the relation between different foundation widths and depths of subgrade compression layer is shown in Fig. 5-3. According to this curve, it is approximately linear when the foundation width ranges from 10 to 30 m and the empirical formulation for calculating the depth of subgrade compression layer is drawn from this curve. The foundation settlement calculation depth in the central point of foundation can be simplified as:

$$z_n = b(2.5 - 0.4\ln b) \tag{5-8}$$

1) For square and rectangular foundations:

$$z_n = m(z_0 + \xi B) \tag{5-9}$$

where: B—width of foundation bottom (m);

m—adjustment factor, for sandy subgrade, m=0.5, for normal clay, m=0.75; for soft subgrade, m=1.0, for granite eluvial subgrade which is between sandy subgrade and clay, m=0.7; the value of z_0 and ξ can be queried from Table 5-2, in which, L represents the length of foundation bottom.

2) For bar foundation of $\frac{L}{B} > 5$:

$$z_n = m(10.5 + 0.87B) \tag{5-10}$$

The depth of subgrade compression layer z_n calculated by the above formula is compared with observations in projects and it is relatively close to the real measurement. So it can be used as the calculation depth of subgrade compression layer of super high-rise building and the settlement calculation depth is counted by the formulation prescribed in the code of *JGJ*6-99.

Table 5-2 The value of z_0 and ξ

$n=\frac{L}{B}$	1	2	3	4	5
z_0	11.6	12.4	12.5	12.7	13.2
ξ	0.42	0.49	0.53	0.60	0.62

5.1.5 The Effect of Box Foundation Stiffness of Super High-Rise Buildings on Foundation Deformation

Identifying the stiffness of box foundation is also a complicated problem. In the past calculation, the stiffness is calculated only with the consideration of the structure of foundation itself, yet without concern of the effect of superstructure's spatial stiffness. There are different judgment standards for foundation stiffness. The foundation is regarded as absolute rigid one when the ratio of length L to height h of box foundation, that is, L/h>0.7; on the contrary, it is called soft foundation. The soft index is often used to make judgment: when $\gamma = \frac{LBE_0}{D(1-u_0^{\ 2})} \leqslant \frac{8}{\sqrt{L/B}}$, the foundation is rigid. This method doesn't conform with the practice in which superstructure and foundation are individually separated and the foundation is taken as an independent structure without integration with superstructure. For some big foundations, like box foundation or raft foundation, no matter rigid or soft they are considered, foundation and superstructure are taken into account together as a integration. In this way, the foundation and the superstructure of super high-rise building are getting together to bear forces and operate. Therefore, the interaction among support structure in deep foundation pit, foundation and subgrade has to be taken into account.

The observation data of box foundation projects of super high-rise buildings in China indicate that the vertical bend of normal foundation is about 3‱, and the maximum value is 3.5‱. The vertical bend of raft foundation with friction piles is 3.6‱. Because of the great stiffness of cast-in-place super high-rise building plus basement, the vertical bend is approximately zero. Given the effect of superstructure on foundation of super high-rise building, the vertical bend is usually very small. Therefore, the ordinary box or raft foundations can be regarded as rigid foundations.

5.2 Box Foundation Settlement Calculation of Super High-Rise Buildings without Consideration of Support Structure in Deep Foundation Pit

At present, the effect of support structures in deep foundation pit is not taken into account in all box foundation settlement calculation of super high-rise buildings at home and abroad. The relatively practical methods for foundation settlement calculation include layering-summation method and elastic theory method, mostly aiming at the total settlement calculation. Under normal circumstances, the subgrade stays in a three-dimensional stress situation and the subgrade is divided into several layers. So the deformation of subgrade occurs only in the scope of effective compression layer depth. Lots of studies on the subgrade deformation in three-dimensional stress situation have been carried by many scholars without considering the effect of support structure in deep foundation pit. Based on elastic theories, the effects of some factors on foundation deformation, such as three-dimensional stress situation in subgrade, effective compression layer, stiffness, shape and dimensions of the foundation are considered to calculate the approximate solution of rectangular rigid foundation and the accurate solution of bar rigid foundation under uniform loads (refer to "*Design and Construction of High-rise buildings*" compiled by Guangqian He).

Meanwhile, other methods including semi-theoretical and semi-empirical method, semi-analytic and semi-numerical method and many empirical analysis and regional calculation formula are proposed. They are not listed here one by one and more attention is only paid to specification calculation method and two simplified methods.

5.2.1 Specification Calculation Method

According to layering-summation method, the final settlement from linear-elastic deformation of box foundation's effective compression layer can be counted as the following equation:

$$S=\psi_s S'=\psi_s\sum_{i=1}^{n}\frac{p_0}{E_{si}}\left(Z_i\bar{a}_i-Z_{i-1}\bar{a}_{i-1}\right) \tag{5-11}$$

where: S —final settlement (mm);

S' —subgrade settlement calculation by layering-summation method;

ψ_s —settlement calculation empirical coefficient which is identified by settlement observation and experiences, also can be obtained from Table 5-3;

n —number of subgrade layer in the depth scope of subgrade deformation calculation;

p_0 —additional pressure at the foundation bottom under load effect quasi-permanent combination (kPa);

E_{si} —compression modulus of the ith subgrade layer at foundation bottom (MPa), taking value from actual stress range, which is from gravity pressure to the summation of gravity pressure and additional pressure;

Z_i, Z_{i-1} —the distance from the ith and i-1th subgrade layer bottom to the foundation bottom (m)

$\bar{a}_i$, $\bar{a}_{i-1}$ —average additional stress coefficients in the range from the from the ith and i-1th subgrade layer bottom to the calculated point at the foundation bottom, which can be taken values from the table in the specification.

$\bar{E}_s$ in the table 5-3 represents the equivalent value of compression modulus in the settlement calculation range, which can be counted as the following equation:

$$\bar{E}_s = \sum A_i / \sum \frac{A_i}{E_{si}} \tag{5-12}$$

where: A_i —integral of additional stress coefficient of the ith subgrade layer along with the subgrade thickness.

Table 5-3 Settlement calculation empirical coefficient ψ_s

Subgrade type \ $\bar{E}_s$		2.5	4.0	7.0	15.0	20.0
Clay subgrade	$P_0 = f_{nk}$ [1)]	1.4	1.3	1.0	0.4	0.2
	$P_0 < f_{nk}$	1.1	1.0	0.7	0.4	0.2
Sandy subgrade	—	1.1	1.0	0.7	0.4	0.2

1) f_{nk} is subgrade bearing eigenvalue, which is defined as the allowable value for ensuring the normal function in the new specification

5.2.2 Modified Layering-Summation Method

The resilience and recompression of box foundation in quaternary subgrade usually account for 30%—60% of the total settlement after completion, which should be individually considered by separating from the total settlement. In recent decades, He Yihua and others gradually established an effective and practical segmentation-summation method for resilience compression and additional settlement calculation in Beijing area after lots of comparison analysis between calculation results and actual observations in Beijing. This method is still based on layering-summation method, but has some modified improvements as follows:

1. Better solution for identifying the resilience recompression modulus

The resilience and recompression is counted by layering-summation method according to the gravity at foundation bottom, and the key problem in this calculation is to identify the resilience recompression modulus. In consolidation experiment, the relation between E_{or} and oedometric modulus E_{s1} (from laboratory test under 100kPa additional pressure):

$$E_{or} = C_r E_{s1}\left(\frac{\overline{\sigma'_h}}{\sigma'_{h0}}\right)^{b_r} \tag{5-13}$$

where: C_r, b_r —statistical parameters, for quaternary subgrade, $C_r = 6.92 + 0.066z - 0.26\overline{\omega}_p$, $b_r = 2021 - 22.1/z$, where z is the soil layer depth, ranging from 10% to 50%, $\overline{\omega}_p$ is plastic limit (%), ranging from 15% to 25%;

$\overline{\sigma}'_h$, $\overline{\sigma}'_{h0}$ —average effective horizontal stress and natural effective horizontal stress during the process of unloading and resilience.

2. Modifying the vertical stress distribution in the additional settlement calculation

As mentioned above, the depth of ground deformation calculation only takes an limit value. Therefore, the soil below the calculation depth can be regarded as incompressible layer which give rise to an upward concentration of vertical stress, just as the dashed curve shown in Fig. 5-8 and proved by observation. By inducing the modified coefficient R_r for vertical stress, the modified vertical stress p'_z is:

$$p'_z = p_0\left[1 + R_p(a_z - 1)\right] \tag{5-14}$$

$$R_p = \frac{a_{0.75H} - 1}{a_H - 1} \tag{5-15}$$

where: p'_z —modified vertical stress in the middle depth of limit elastic layer in the load area, if the calculated point is out of the load area, $p'_z = R_p P_z$, which is counted based on the elastic half-space formulation;

p_0 —effective additional pressure at foundation bottom;

R_p —modified coefficient for vertical stress, R_p =1 means taking elastic half-space into account, R_p =0 means vertical stress is an constant p_0, representing winkler foundation;

a_z —vertical stress coefficient in the depth z under the center of elastic half-space load area;

H —calculation depth of subgrade deformation.

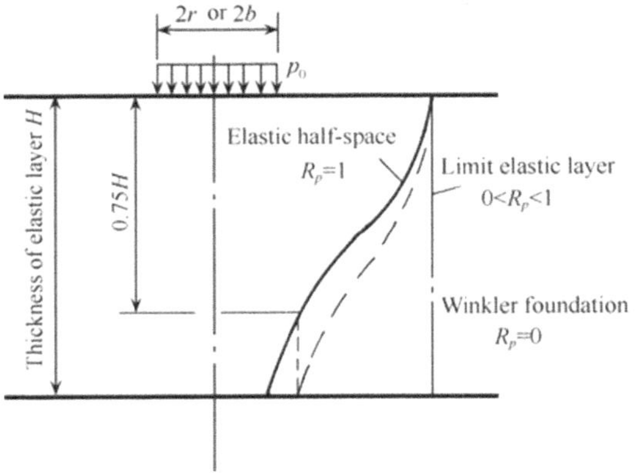

Fig. 5-8 Sketch of modified distribution of vertical stress

For different relative thickness H/b , R_p is shown in Table 5-4.

Table 5-4 Modified coefficient R_p of vertical stress in limit elastic

H/r or H/b	2	3	4	5	6	8	10
circle	0.805	0.894	0.935	0.957	0.969	0.982	0.989
bar	0.737	0.823	0.870	0.899	0.917	0.940	0.953

Notice: H is the thickness of elastic layer, r means the radius of load area, b represents the half width of bar load area.

3. Determining the statistical proportion relation between short-term settlement (just after completion) and long-term settlement (after final stability) of normal quaternary subgrade

$$S_\infty = S_t / C_t \tag{5-16}$$

where: S_t —the summation of resilience compression settlement and additional settlement;

C_t —statistical coefficient, it is 0.85 for sandy cobble subgrade, 0.70 for sandy clay, 0.55 for silty clay.

Even the whole complicated settlement process in soft soil regions also includes three phases as gravity stress, additional stress and constant stress, at present the former two phases are integrated by layering-summation method, and the final settlement is determined by regional empirical formula.

5.2.3 Егоров Theorem for Box Foundation Settlement

Егоров proposed equation for rigid rectangular foundation settlement based on elastic theory:

$$S = M'Bp\sum_{i=1}^{n}(1-\nu_{\sigma i})\frac{K_i - K_{i-1}}{E_{\sigma i}} \tag{5-17}$$

where: B—Width of rectangular foundation $L \times B$;

p—Additional pressure of foundation bottom;

$E_{\sigma i}, \nu_{\sigma i}$ —The deformation modulus and passion ratio of the ith subgrade layer;

K_i— $K_i = f(L/B, z_i/B, \nu_{\sigma i})$, Dimensionless coefficient;

M' —Modified coefficient based on compression layer depth, shown in Table 5-5.

Taking $\nu_{\sigma i}$=0.3 and $M = 0.7M'$, and using total foundation pressure, the equation above is simplified as:

$$S = MBP\sum_{i=1}^{n}\frac{K_i - K_{i-1}}{E_{\sigma i}}$$

where: the coefficient K_i is shown in Table 5-6, the modified coefficient M is in Table 5-5.

Because box foundation usually has the larger buried depth, when it comes to small buried depth, the resilience recompression can be ignored and hereby P is taken as P_0.

Table 5-5 Values of modified coefficient M' and M

H/B	0—0.25	0.25—0.5	0.5—1.0	1.0—1.5	1.5—2.5	2.5 以上
M'	1.5	1.4	1.3	1.2	1.1	1.0
$M = 0.7M'$	1.0	0.95	0.90	0.80	0.75	0.70

Notice: H —the depth of compression layer or bedrock; B—the width of foundation

Table 5-6 Calculation coefficient K_i

Z/B	Circle foundation (B=2r)	Rectangular foundation $n=L/B$									Bar foundation $n \geqslant 0$
		n=1.0	n=1.4	n=1.5	n=1.8	n=2.0	n=2.4	n=3.0	n=3.2	n=5.0	
0.0	0.000	0.000	0.000	0.000	0.000	0.000	0.000	0.000	0.000	0.000	0.000
0.2	0.090	0.100	0.100	0.100	0.100	0.100	0.100	0.100	0.100	0.100	0.104
0.4	0.179	0.200	0.200	0.200	0.200	0.200	0.200	0.200	0.200	0.200	0.208
0.6	0.266	0.299	0.300	0.300	0.300	0.300	0.300	0.300	0.300	0.300	0.311
0.8	0.348	0.380	0.394	0.395	0.397	0.397	0.397	0.397	0.397	0.397	0.412
1.0	0.411	0.446	0.472	0.476	0.482	0.484	0.486	0.486	0.486	0.486	0.511
1.2	0.461	0.499	0.538	0.543	0.556	0.561	0.565	0.566	0.567	0.567	0.605
1.4	0.501	0.542	0.593	0.601	0.618	0.626	0.635	0.640	0.640	0.640	0.687
1.6	0.532	0.577	0.637	0.647	0.671	0.682	0.696	0.706	0.707	0.709	0.763
1.8	0.558	0.606	0.676	0.688	0.717	0.730	0.759	0.764	0.768	0.772	0.831
2.0	0.579	0.630	0.708	0.722	0.756	0.773	0.796	0.816	0.820	0.830	0.892
2.2	0.596	0.650	0.735	0.751	0.789	0.808	0.837	0.861	0.862	0.883	0.949
2.4	0.611	0.668	0.759	0.776	0.819	0.841	0.873	0.902	0.908	0.932	1.001

continued

Z/B	Circle foundation (B=2r)	Rectangular foundation $n=L/B$									Bar foundation $n\geqslant 0$
		n=1.0	n=1.4	n=1.5	n=1.8	n=2.0	n=2.4	n=3.0	n=3.2	n=5.0	
2.6	0.624	0.683	0.780	0.798	0.844	0.868	0.904	0.939	0.948	0.977	1.050
2.8	0.635	0.697	0.798	0.818	0.867	0.893	0.933	0.971	0.981	1.018	1.095
3.0	0.645	0.708	0.814	0.836	0.887	0.913	0.958	1.000	1.011	1.056	1.138
3.2	0.653	0.719	0.828	0.850	0.904	0.934	0.980	1.027	1.031	1.090	1.178
3.4	0.661	0.728	0.841	0.863	0.920	0.951	1.000	1.051	1.065	1.122	1.215
3.6	0.668	0.736	0.852	0.875	0.935	0.967	1.019	1.073	1.088	1.152	1.251
3.8	0.674	0.744	0.863	0.887	0.948	0.981	1.036	1.099	1.109	1.180	1.285
4.0	0.679	0.751	0.872	0.897	0.960	0.995	1.051	1.111	1.128	1.205	1.316
4.2	0.684	0.757	0.881	0.906	0.970	1.007	1.065	1.128	1.146	1.229	1.347
4.4	0.689	0.762	0.888	0.914	0.980	1.017	1.078	1.144	1.162	1.251	1.376
4.6	0.693	0.768	0.896	0.922	0.989	1.027	1.089	1.158	1.178	1.272	1.404
4.8	0.697	0.772	0.902	0.929	0.998	1.036	1.100	1.171	1.192	1.291	1.431
5.0	0.700	0.777	0.908	0.935	1.005	1.045	1.110	1.183	1.205	1.309	1.456

Notice: z—the distance from foundation bottom to the subgrade layer bottom; L, B—the length and width of rectangular foundation; r is the radius of circle foundation.

5.2.4 Japanese Method for Initial Settlement Calculation

In Japanese Foundation Engineering Design Criteria AIJ, the settlement S is divided into initial settlement S_e, consolidation settlement S_c, that is $S= S_e + S_c$. Based on the compression index from e-log$p$ curve, S_c is counted by layering-summation method, and S_e is counted by Еропов theorem:

$$S = q\sqrt{A}\sum_{i=1}^{n}(\xi_i - \xi_{i-1})/E_i \tag{5-18}$$

where: E_i—elastic modulus of subgrade layer;

A—foundation bottom area;

q—average pressure of foundation bottom, in Japanese method, it is taken as additional pressure;

ξ_i—an calculation coefficient related to the subgrade passion ratio, the distance from foundation bottom to subgrade layer bottom, and foundation shape, shown in Table 5-7.

Table 5-7 Calculation coefficient ξ_i

μ_0	L/B	$H/\sqrt{A}$						Remarks
		0.5	1.0	2.0	3.0	5.0	∞	
0.5	1	0.125	0.267	0.413	0.479	0.537	0.631	Saturated clay
	2	0.125	0.257	0.395	0.458	0.516	0.609	
	3	0.122	0.223	0.331	0.385	0.436	0.529	
0.3	1	0.214	0.379	0.537	0.607	0.688	0.766	Sandy guandong powder subgrade
	2	0.210	0.364	0.514	0.582	0.642	0.739	
	3	0.195	0.313	0.433	0.491	0.547	0.642	
0.15	1	0.259	0.433	0.594	0.664	0.716	0.823	guandong powder subgrade with large void ratio
	2	0.254	0.416	0.569	0.637	0.688	0.794	
	3	0.231	0.357	0.480	0.539	0.595	0.690	

Notice: μ_0—passion ratio of subgrade, L, B—foundation's length and width; A—area of foundation bottom; H—distance from foundation bottom to the subgrade layer bottom, if H is zero , then ξ =0.

Now the application scopes of these four simplified methods mentioned above are hardly distinguished, and it'd better take more than two methods to calculate and compare, in which the key part is to reasonably determine the calculation modulus.

Box foundation of super high-rise building has larger compensations and the unloading pressure can account for over 30% of total pressure. In this condition, specification calculation method is apt for settlement calculation. When it comes to quaternary subgrade, the modified layering-summation method or simplified Егоров method can be used. The deformation modulus E_0 is from the result of in-place load plate test, and β , the ratio of E_0 to E_s is referred to Table 5-8.

Table 5-8 The relation between β of clay subgrade and void ratio *e*

β \ e / Subgrade type	0.41—0.50	0.51—0.60	0.61—0.70	0.71—0.80	0.81—0.90	0.91—1.00	1.01—1.10	1.01—1.20	1.21—1.30	1.31—1.40	1.41—1.50
Clay	4.2	4.2	3.7	3.0	2.2	—	—	—	—	—	—
Silty clay	5.0	4.8	4.5	3.9	3.2	2.6	2.1	—	—	—	—
Silty powder	—	—	6.0	6.0	5.8	5.4	4.8	4.1	3.4	2.7	2.0

For Beijing region or similar quaternary subgrade, wave velocity modulus E_V (MPa) can be got from in-place wave velocity test:

$$E_V = 2\left(1+\mu_0\right)\rho V_s^2 \tag{5-19}$$

where: ρ—subgrade mass density, which is the ratio of subgrade specific gravity to gravity acceleration $0.002\text{MN}\cdot\text{s}^2\cdot\text{m}^{-4}$;

μ_0—passion ratio of subgrade, usually is taken as 0.4;

V_s—observed shear wave velocity of subgrade.

The modified modulus $R_v E_v$ which is obtained from modifying wave velocity modulus E_v with modified coefficient R, can be used as deformation modulus E_0 in the settlement calculation. The statistical equation of modified coefficient is:

$$R_v = 0.686 - 0.0848\ln(\Delta p) - 0.1933R_p \tag{5-20}$$

where: Δp—additional pressure at foundation bottom;

R_p—stress adjustment coefficient, which can be queried in the table.

When box foundation of super high-rise building is close to full-compensation or extra-compensation foundations, it is insignificant to consider additional pressure because the settlement is controlled by resilience recompression. Here segmentation-summation method (only considering the part of resilience recompression) and simplified Егоров method are used to calculate the settlement by considering the total load and deformation modulus which are regulated in the specification. The modulus used in all these methods is resilience recompression modulus.

5.3 Settlement Calculation of Box or Raft Foundations of Super High-Rise Buildings Considering the Effect of Support Structures in Deep Foundation Pits

There are many methods for settlement calculation of box or raft foundations of super high-rise buildings, which all have weakness and merits, and application conditions. No matter what kind of method, the difference between theoretical result and real observation is rather obvious, and this problem has been completely solved so far. All analytic analyses are based on elastic theory with the assumption that subgrade is an linear-elastic even continuous body. On the other hand, all numerical analyses, such as finite element method, boundary element method, weighted-residual method, discrete element method, unbounded element method, etc., will encounter great difficulties not in these method themselves, but in the accurate identification of calculation parameters even all kinds of subgrade properties and calculation boundary conditions can be taken into account in these methods. Therefore, a few experts and professors have paid more concentration on the study about semi-theoretical and semi-empirical method and the case study of projects. This approach is also adopted into the national specification for design of building subgrade foundation GB50007-2002 to use modified layering-summation method with empirical coefficients to calculate settlement for better services for projects. In this procedure, the effect of support structures in deep foundation pits is not considered resulting in differences between theoretical value and real observation of settlement, which sometimes are very large. The main reason for these differences is not to take into account the effect of support structures in extra-deep foundation pits, except for other influential factors (such as wrong selection of calculation parameters and subgrade models, incomplete acknowledgement of geological conditions, bad operation of calculation methods, and so on).

5.3.1 Characteristics of Box Foundation of Super High-Rise Building

It is very indispensable for each box foundation of super high-rise building to have a basement and support structures in deep foundation pit, which usually are buried and inserted into subgrade much deeper (in shanghai, the support structure is buried as the same deep as the foundation). Under this circumstance, the settlement calculation has great difference with ordinary multi-story or medium-high buildings and its characteristics include:

1. Big height and large gravity of super high-rise buildings and good site condition

According to the regulations of Construction Ministry, a building exceeding 150 meters in height is defined as super high-rise building. The former specifications in box foundation codes aimed at multi-story and medium-high buildings less than 100 meters high. Given the large gravity load of super high-rise buildings, the geological conditions around box foundations are usually better. For example, Guangdong International Mansion with 63 floors and 200.15 m height has a four-level basement and a box foundation with 16.8 m buried depth. Its subgrade is natural rock. The total weight of the superstructure is about 1,600,000 kN and the gravity weight is about 12,000,000 kN. The average weight of each story is 14.5kPa. The maximum settlement is 7.21cm and the minimum one is 4.18cm. The settlement difference is 3.03cm which indicates a rather even settlement.

2. Deeper buried depth of box foundation of super high-rise building

According to the specifications of the latest box foundation code *JGJ*6-99, the foundation depth for natural subgrade is at least 1/15 of building height in seismic fortified areas, and when it comes to pile-box foundation, the depth shouldn't be less than 1/18 of building height. If the building height is over 200 meters, the minimum depth of box foundation is 13 meter. Most box foundations in China now are buried below 10 meters. There are only two super high-rise buildings exceeding 200 meters in height, China Bank Tower in Qingdao and Guangdong International Tower. There are also several super high-rise buildings with box foundations and exceeding 150 meters in height, for example, Beiing Town Mansion, with 52 floors and 183.5 meter height, has four-level basement and the buried depth of its box foundation is 23.5m.

3. Effect of support structure in deep foundation pit of super high-rise building

Till now, effect of support structure in deep foundation pit is not taken into account in any settlement calculation methods and models (including codes). In terms of settlement calculation of super high-rise buildings, the main effects of support structure in deep foundation pit include: ① lateral restraint of insert-into- subgrade part of the support structure; ② smaller resilience and lump at the foundation bottom resulting from the lateral restraint effect, even these resilience and lump caused by unloading have ignorable influence to partial foundation deformation, especially for super high-rise buildings; ③ groundwater buoyancy effect in groundwater areas; ④ friction damp between outside walls of basement and support structures, which cannot be ignored no matter what type of support structure and construction techniques. Based on these points mentioned above, the effect of support structure in deep foundation pit should be considered in the settlement calculation.

5.3.2 Calculating Diagram of Considering the Effect of Support Structure

There are several different calculating diagrams for settlement calculation of box foundation of super high-rise building with support structure in deep foundation pit, varying with the relations between outside walls of basement and support structures, and construction techniques.

1. Diagram of separating basement and support structures

For super high-rise buildings, if basement outside walls are separated from support structures, there is usually 900mm space. The support structure is composed of subgrade walls or row piles with pre-stressed anchor rods, and is inserted into the subgrade to certain depth which is determined by specific calculation. After finishing digging the foundation pit, the box foundation is constructed from the pit bottom. Under this circumstance, the calculating diagram is illuminated as Fig. 5-9. According to this diagram, several factors should be considered including groundwater buoyancy, friction damp of basement outside walls, lateral restraint of support structures, and the lateral friction damp under additional stress.

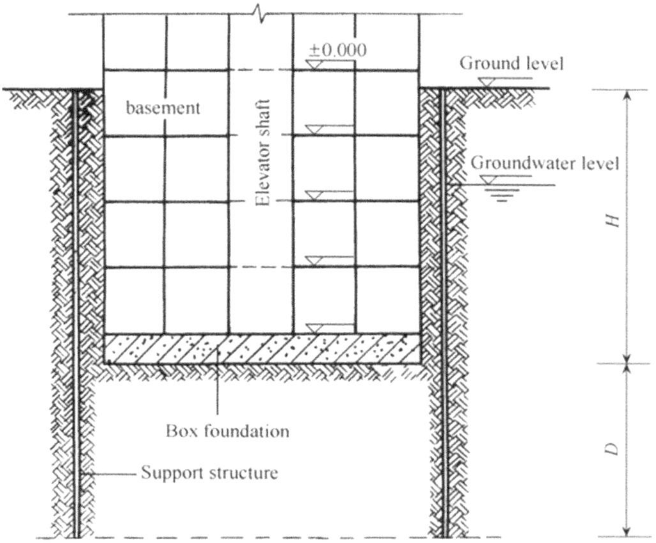

Fig. 5-9 Calculating diagram of separating basement and support structures

2. Diagram of combining basement and support structures

Combining basement outside walls with support structures is often called as "*Two walls integration*". In this situation, the support structures can not only block subgrade, but also serve as basement outside walls. The horizontal beams and plates of basement and the box foundation are completely embedded in support structures and work together as an combination. After beams and plates of each level are embedded in support structures, it is necessary to set shear blocks under beams and plates. At the same time, it needs to be set a vertical "*coherent layer*" inside the support structures to integrate outside walls. Then the support structures and basement are combined into an entity to work together. The diagram of settlement calculation in this situation is shown in Fig. 5-10. Compared with Fig. 5-9, the internal friction damp of inset-into-subgrade parts of support structures is bigger and cannot be ignored except for groundwater buoyancy. This kind of "reverse bucket shape" is beneficial for minimizing settlement. This kind of support structure is usually composed of diaphragm walls with pre-stressed anchor rods or internal-support structures. Meanwhile, down-top method should be adopted for basement construction. On the other hand, if the basement is constructed by "top-down" method, the uniform pile foundation under temporary bearing columns and inner-tub walls cannot be ignored because they can obviously influent the control of box foundation settlement even these piles are very sparse. Therefore, the settlement should be counted as the model of "box + sparse piles".

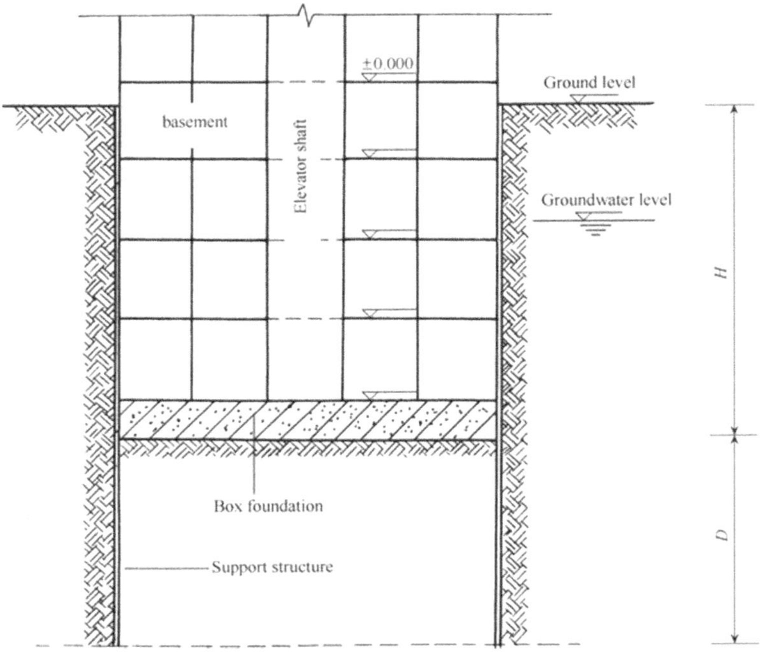

Fig. 5-10 Calculating diagram of combining basement and support structures

3. Settlement calculating diagram of box foundation on rock subgrade

If the box foundation of super high-rise buildings is directly established on rocks, the settlement calculation model will get very simple, just as shown in Fig. 5-11. The compression deformation of rocks is the only factor that should be considered in settlement calculation whether there are support structures or not. For example, Chongqing Industrial Products Trade Center and Guangdong International Tower are both established on rock subgrade.

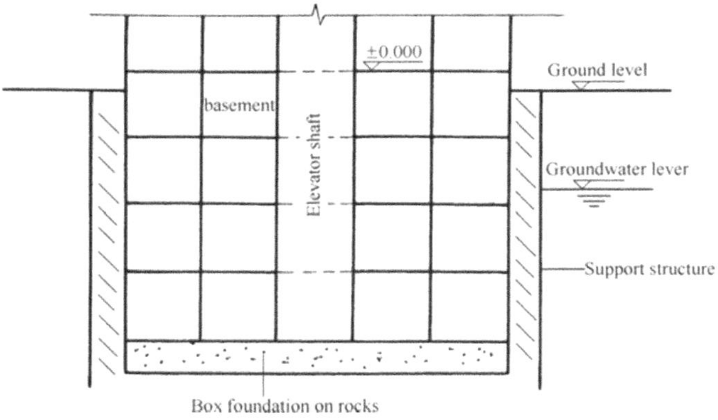

Fig. 5-11 Settlement calculation diagram of box foundation on rocks

5.3.3 Subgrade Model for Settlement Calculation and Spline Sub-domain Method Analysis for Layering Subgrade

As for subgrade models for settlement calculation of box foundations of super high-rise buildings, it is very difficult to reflect the actual operating situation of subgrade for all these present over 60 models, all of which have certain limitations given the complexity. Box foundations of super high-rise buildings are often used on even and good-condition subgrade. Therefore three models mentioned in Chapter one, which are all linear deformation body models, are more apt for settlement calculation of box foundation. If finite element method is adopted, settlement calculation models also include subgrade elastic-plastic model, isotropic elastic model and other models. If considering the effect of support structures in deep foundation pit, the semi-theoretical and semi-empirical method should be used and its calculation model is identified as follows:

1. Winkler foundation model and its improved version

In this model, the shear stress in foundation is ignored and foundation settlement is assumed only happening in the scope of foundation bottom, which is not accord with the facts. However, because of the great simplicity and easy application, this method is often used in real projects. Even in finite element analysis, uniaxial compression model and linear deformation-layering model are sometimes applied. Improved Winkler models (such as Forasovo double-parameter model, generalized Winkler three-parameter model) are rarely used in projects because the foundation parameters increases from one to tow or three, which are sometimes very difficult to be identified.

2. Elastic half-space foundation model

In this model, the layering of subgrade, uneven property, nonlinear relation between stress and strain of subgrade are not taken into account. The calculation settlement by using this model is often larger than observed results. On the other hand, all kinds of layering-summation methods are based on the stress and strain solutions of even elastic half-space.

3. Linear deformation layering subgrade model (including uniaxial compression model)

This model is very easy to be used and its calculated result is also close to actual observation. In addition, the horizontal isotropic characteristics of subgrade layers are considered in this model. This model is the basis of all kinds of layering-summation methods and is widely used by engineers.

There are certainly other models, like finite compression foundation model, model considering the consolidated creep deformation and elastic-plastic model. Except for the first model, the other two models are rarely used.

Here more emphases are placed on spline function analysis method for layering subgrade.

4. Layering subgrade analysis

Winkler subgrade model and semi-infinite elastic subgrade model are usually used for elastic subgrade, sometimes BAacoB subgrade model is also used. These subgrade models place important roles in elastic subgrade structure analysis and still be widely used till now. However, all these models are based on an assumption that subgrade is an even isotropic elastic body, but actually it is uneven and layering. Therefore, it is necessary to study layering subgrade firstly to make subgrade models more conformed to reality.

There have been studies on layering subgrade since 1940s. In 1945, a scholar issued his research on layering subgrade. Since then, many researchers started researching layering subgrade home and abroad. In China, these studies begun at the end of 1950s, and Xu Zhilun proposed his achievements about layering subgrade in 1960. In recent years, more and more researchers have been focusing on this field and putting forward much achievements.

Here more attention is paid to introduction of spline sub-domain method for layering subgrade analysis.

(1) Plane elastic layering subgrade. The calculated model of plan elastic layering subgrade is illuminated in Fig. 5-12. Each layer is assumed as an even isotropic elastic body which is analyzed by spline sub-domain method. Each layer is looked and firstly analyzed as one sub-domain, and is then further analyzed as integration (Fig. 5-13).

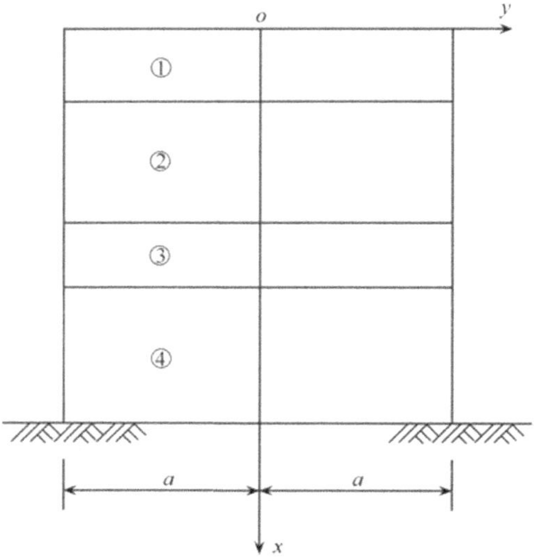

Fig. 5-12 Plate layering subgrade

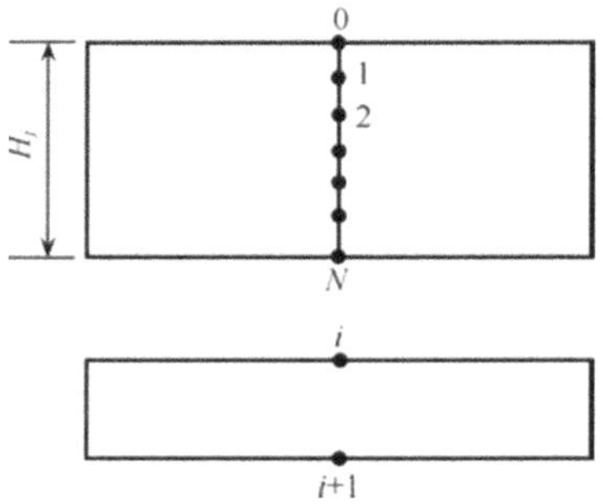

Fig. 5-13 Spline plate subdomain

1) Sub-domain displacement function. Supposed displacement function of the jth sub-domain as:

$$u=\sum_{m=1}^{r}[\varphi]X_m(y)\{a\}_m;\quad v=\sum_{m=1}^{r}[\varphi]Y_m(y)\{b\}_m \tag{5-21}$$

where

$$\{a\}_m=\begin{bmatrix}u_0 & a_1 & a_2 & \ldots & a_{N-1} & u_N\end{bmatrix}_m^{\mathrm{T}}$$

$$\{b\}_m=\begin{bmatrix}v_0 & b_1 & b_2 & \cdots & b_{N-1} & v_N\end{bmatrix}_m^{\mathrm{T}}$$

$$[\varphi]=\begin{bmatrix}\varphi_0 & \varphi_1 & \varphi_2 & \cdots & \varphi_N\end{bmatrix}$$

$$\left.\begin{aligned}X_m&=\sin\frac{m\pi(y+b)}{2b}\\ Y_m&=\cos\frac{m\pi(y+b)}{2b}\end{aligned}\right\}\text{(For vertical load)} \tag{5-22}$$

or

$$\left.\begin{aligned}X_m&=\cos\frac{m\pi(y+b)}{2b}\\ Y_m&=\sin\frac{m\pi(y+b)}{2b}\end{aligned}\right\}\text{(For horizontal load)} \tag{5-23}$$

$\varphi_i(x)$ is a set of basis functions related to cubic-b-spline function, that is

$$[\varphi]=[\varphi_{3k}][Q]\quad k=-1,0,1,2,\cdots,N+1 \tag{5-24}$$

where

$$\varphi_{3k}(x)=\varphi_3\left(\frac{x-x_k}{k}\right)=\varphi_3\left(\frac{x-x_0}{h}-k\right) \tag{5-25}$$

$$[\,Q\,]=\mathrm{diag}\left([\,g\,],[\,I\,],[\,h\,]\right) \tag{5-26}$$

$[I]$ is $(N-1)\,(N-1)$ unit matrix, $[g]=\begin{pmatrix}-6 & 0\\ 3 & \dfrac{-1}{4}\\ 0 & 1\end{pmatrix}$, $[h]=\begin{pmatrix}1 & 0\\ \dfrac{-1}{4} & 3\\ 0 & -6\end{pmatrix}$。Equation (5-21) can be

changed

as

$$\{V\}=[N]\{\delta\} \tag{5-27}$$

$\{V\}=\begin{bmatrix}u & v\end{bmatrix}^{\mathrm{T}}$,

$$[N]=\begin{bmatrix}[N]_1 & [N]_2 & \cdots & [N]_r\end{bmatrix}$$

$$\{\delta\}=\begin{bmatrix}\{\delta\}_1^{\mathrm{T}} & \{\delta\}_2^{\mathrm{T}} & \cdots & \{\delta\}_r^{\mathrm{T}}\end{bmatrix}^{\mathrm{T}}$$

where

$$\left.\begin{aligned}&\{\delta\}_m=\begin{bmatrix}\delta_0^{\mathrm{T}} & \delta_1^{\mathrm{T}} & \cdots & \delta_N^{\mathrm{T}}\end{bmatrix}_m^{\mathrm{T}}\\&\delta_{0m}=\begin{bmatrix}u_0 & v_0\end{bmatrix}_m^{\mathrm{T}} \quad \delta_{Nm}=\begin{bmatrix}u_N & v_N\end{bmatrix}_m^{\mathrm{T}}\\&\delta_{im}=\begin{bmatrix}a_i & b_i\end{bmatrix}_m^{\mathrm{T}} \quad i=1,2,\cdots,N-1\\&[N]_m=[\varphi]\otimes[\Gamma]_m=\begin{bmatrix}\varphi_i[\Gamma]_m\end{bmatrix} \quad [\Gamma]_m=\mathrm{diag}(X_m,Y_m)\end{aligned}\right\} \tag{5-28}$$

In Eq.(5-21), $\varphi_i(x)$ is

$$\begin{aligned}\varphi_i(x)=&\frac{10}{3}\varphi_3\left(\frac{x}{h}-i\right)-\frac{4}{3}\varphi_3\left(\frac{x}{h}-i+\frac{1}{2}\right)-\frac{4}{3}\varphi_3\left(\frac{x}{h}-i-\frac{1}{2}\right)\\&+\frac{4}{6}\varphi_3\left(\frac{x}{h}-i+1\right)+\frac{4}{6}\varphi_3\left(\frac{x}{h}-i-1\right) \quad i=0,1,2,\cdots,N\end{aligned} \tag{5-29}$$

Based in Eq.(5-29), $\varphi_i\left(x_j\right)=\delta_{ij}$.

2) Sub-domain analysis. The total potential energy functional of sub-domain is:

$$\Pi=\frac{1}{2}\int_{\Omega}\left(\{\varepsilon\}^{\mathrm{T}}\{\sigma\}-2\{V\}^{\mathrm{T}}\{q\}\right)\mathrm{d}\Omega \tag{5-30}$$

where

$$\{\varepsilon\}=\begin{bmatrix}\varepsilon_x & \varepsilon_y & \gamma_{xy}\end{bmatrix}^{\mathrm{T}} \quad [q]=\begin{bmatrix}q_x & q_y\end{bmatrix}^{\mathrm{T}}$$
$$\{\sigma\}=\begin{bmatrix}\sigma_x & \sigma_y & \tau_{xy}\end{bmatrix}^{\mathrm{T}} \quad \{V\}=\begin{bmatrix}u & v\end{bmatrix}^{\mathrm{T}}$$

where: q_x and q_y are generalized uniform loads.

For plane problems in elastic theory, then:

$$\{\varepsilon\}=[A]\{\delta\} \quad \{\sigma\}=[R]\{\varepsilon\}=[R][A]\{\delta\} \tag{5-31}$$

where

$$\begin{gathered}[A]=\begin{bmatrix}[A]_1 & [A]_2 & \cdots & [A]_r\end{bmatrix}\\ [A_m]=\begin{bmatrix}A_0 & A_1 & A_2 & \cdots A_N\end{bmatrix}_m\\ A_{im}=\begin{bmatrix}\varphi' iX_m & 0\\ 0 & \varphi_i Y_m'\\ \varphi_i X_m' & \varphi_i' Y_m\end{bmatrix}\end{gathered} \tag{5-32}$$

$$[R]=\begin{bmatrix}R_1 & R_2 & 0\\ R_2 & R_1 & 0\\ 0 & 0 & R_4\end{bmatrix} \tag{5-33}$$

For isotropic elastic body:

$$R_1=\frac{2(1-\mu)}{1-2\mu}G, \quad R_2=\frac{\mu}{1-\mu}R_1, \quad R_4=G \tag{5-34}$$

where: μ and G —passion ratio and shear modulus of subgrade.

To take equation (5-27) and (5-31) into equation (5-30), then:

$$II=\frac{1}{2}\{\delta\}^{\mathrm{T}}[G]\{\delta\}-\{\delta\}^{\mathrm{T}}\{f\} \tag{5-35}$$

The stiffness equation of sub-domain can be got based on variation principle:

$$[G]\{\delta\}=\{f\} \tag{5-36}$$

$[G]$ and $\{f\}$ in this equation represent respectively stiffness matrix and load vector, that is:

$$[G]=\left[[G]_{mn}\right] \quad m,n=1,2,3,\cdots r \tag{5-37}$$

$$\{f\}=\int_{\Omega}[N]^{\mathrm{T}}\{q\}\mathrm{d}\Omega \tag{5-38}$$

That is

$$\{f\}=\left[\{f\}_1^{\mathrm{T}} \quad \{f\}_2^{\mathrm{T}} \quad \cdots \quad \{f\}_r^{\mathrm{T}}\right]^{\mathrm{T}} \tag{5-39}$$

where

$$[G]_{mn}=\left[(S_{ik})\right]_{mn} \quad m,n=1,2,\cdots,r \tag{5-40}$$

$$(S_{ik})_{mn}=\begin{bmatrix} S_{uu} & S_{uv} \\ S_{vu} & S_{vv} \end{bmatrix}, S_{vu}=S_{uv}^{\mathrm{T}} \tag{5-41}$$

where

$$\left.\begin{aligned} &S_{uu}=R_1C_{ik}F_{y1}+R_4F_{ik}C_{y1}, S_{uv}=R_zH_{ik}^{\mathrm{T}}L_y+R_4H_{ik}H_{y1}^{\mathrm{T}} \\ &S_{vv}=R_1F_{ik}C_{y2}+R_4C_{ik}F_{y2} \end{aligned}\right\} \tag{5-42}$$

and

$$\left.\begin{aligned} &C_{y1}=\int_{-b}^{b}X_mX_n'\mathrm{d}y \quad F_{y1}=\int_{-b}^{b}X_mX_n\mathrm{d}y \\ &C_{y2}=\int_{-b}^{b}Y_m'Y_n'\mathrm{d}y \quad F_{y2}=\int_{-b}^{b}Y_mY_n\mathrm{d}y \\ &L_y=\int_{-b}^{b}X_mY_n'\mathrm{d}y \quad H_{y1}=\int_{-b}^{b}Y_mX_n'\mathrm{d}y \end{aligned}\right\} \tag{5-43}$$

where: C_{ik}、F_{ik}、H_{ik} and $H_{ik}{}^{\mathrm{T}}$—the element of the ith row and kth column in matrix $[C_z]$、$[F_z]$、$[H_z]$ and $[H_z]^{\mathrm{T}}$, that is:

$$\left.\begin{aligned} &[C_x]=[Q]^{\mathrm{T}}C_x[Q]=[C_{ik}] \quad [F_x]=[Q]^{\mathrm{T}}F_x[Q]=[F_{ik}] \\ &[H_x]=[Q]^{\mathrm{T}}H_x[Q]=[H_{ik}] \end{aligned}\right\} \tag{5-44}$$

where: C_z, F_z and F_y can be counted by Eq. 5-43.

Because X_m and Y_m are orthogonal functions, so when $m\neq n$:

$$C_{y1}=C_{y2}=F_{y1}=F_{y2}=L_y=H_{y1}=0$$

As mentioned above, when $m\neq n$, $[G]_{mn}=[0]$. Therefore, Eq.(5-35) and (5-36) can be separated into r independent equations:

$$\Pi_m=\frac{1}{2}\{\delta\}_m^{\mathrm{T}}[G]_m\{\delta\}_m-\{\delta\}_m^{\mathrm{T}}\{f\}_m \quad m=1,2,\cdots,r \tag{5-45}$$

$$[G]_m\{\delta\}_m=\{f\}_m \quad m=1,2,\cdots,r \tag{5-46}$$

where

$$[G]_m=[G]_{mn} \tag{5-47}$$

$$\left.\begin{aligned}&\{f\}_m=[f_0^{\mathrm{T}}\ \ f_2^{\mathrm{T}}\ \ f_2^{\mathrm{T}}\ \ \cdots\ \ f_N^{\mathrm{T}}]_m^{\mathrm{T}}\\&f_{im}=[f_u\ \ f_v]^{\mathrm{T}}\\&f_u=\int_\Omega\varphi_i(x)X_mq_x\mathrm{d}\Omega,\ \ f_v=\int_\Omega\varphi_i(x)Y_mq_y\mathrm{d}y\end{aligned}\right\}\tag{5-48}$$

Because Eq. 5-45 and 5-46 represent calculation for each item, so $[G]_m$ and $[f]_m$ represent the mth sub-domain stiffness matrix and sub-domain load vector.

3) Integral analysis When sub-domain stiffness matrix $[G]_m$ and sub-domain load vector $[f]_m$ have been established, the integral stiffness equation of subgrade, which is composed of r independent equations, can be identified based on displacement coordination relation among sub-domains. After this, the displacement and stress of subgrade will be counted (it is necessary to introduce boundary conditions to solve integral stiffness equations).

(2) Spatial elastic layering subgrade. Fig. 5-14 illuminates a calculating diagram of spatial elastic layering subgrade in which each layer is regarded as an even isotropic elastic body, and also is regarded as a sub-domain (shown in Fig. 5-15). In the z direction, cubic-b-spline function is adopted, and in the x and y directions, trigonometric functions are used.

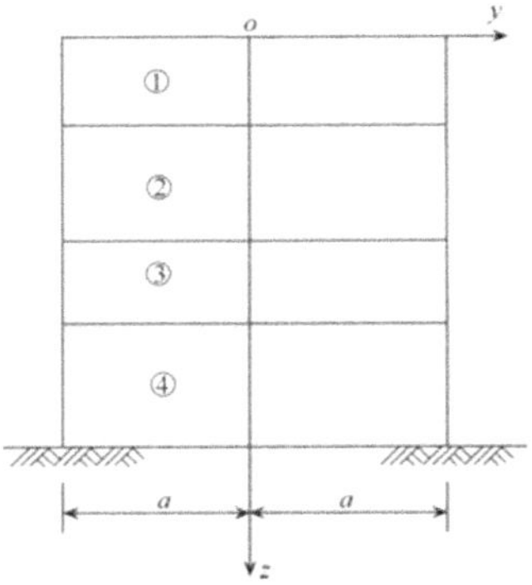

Fig. 5-14 Spatial layering ground

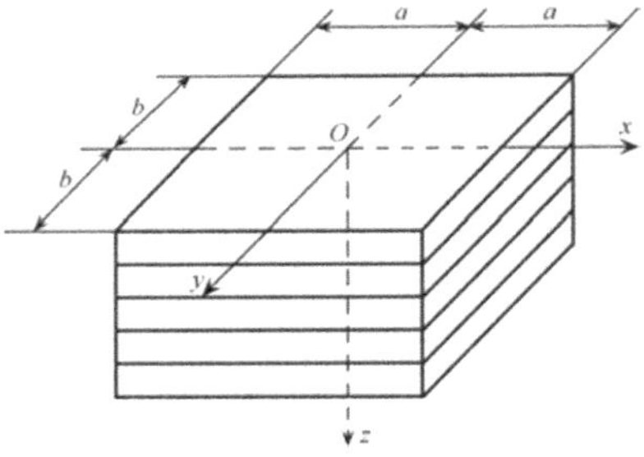

Fig. 5-15 Spline-patial subdomain

1) Sub-domain displacement function. Assume the kth sub-domain displacement function as:

$$\left.\begin{aligned}&u=\sum_{m=1}^{r}\sum_{n=1}^{s}[\varphi]\{a\}_{mn}X_mX_n\quad v=\sum_{m=1}^{r}\sum_{n=1}^{s}[\varphi]\{b\}_{mn}Y_mY_n\\&\omega=\sum_{m=1}^{r}\sum_{n=1}^{s}[\varphi]\{c\}_{mn}Z_mZ_n\end{aligned}\right\}\tag{5-49}$$

where: $[\ ]=[(z)]$, which has the same style of equation 5-24. For horizontal load, X_m, Y_m, Z_m, and X_n, Y_n, Z_n are :

$$\left.\begin{aligned} X_m &= \sin\frac{m\pi(x+a)}{2a} & X_n &= \cos\frac{n\pi(y+b)}{2b} \\ Y_m &= \cos\frac{m\pi(x+a)}{2a} & Y_n &= \sin\frac{n\pi(y+b)}{2b} \\ Z_m &= \cos\frac{m\pi(x+a)}{2a} & Z_n &= \cos\frac{n\pi(y+b)}{2b} \end{aligned}\right\} \tag{5-50}$$

For vertical loads:

$$\left.\begin{aligned} X_m &= \cos\frac{m\pi(x+a)}{2a} & X_n &= \sin\frac{n\pi(y+b)}{2b} \\ Y_m &= \sin\frac{m\pi(x+a)}{2a} & Y_n &= \cos\frac{n\pi(y+b)}{2b} \\ Z_m &= \sin\frac{m\pi(x+a)}{2a} & Z_n &= \sin\frac{n\pi(y+b)}{2b} \end{aligned}\right\} \tag{5-51}$$

$$\{A\}_{mn} = [V_0 \quad A_1 \quad A_2 \quad \cdots \quad A_{N-1} \quad V_N]_{mn}^{\mathrm{T}}$$

where

$$A = a,b,c \quad V = u,v,w$$

Eq.(5-49)can be altered as:

$$\{V\} = [u \quad v \quad w]^{\mathrm{T}} = \sum_{m=1}^{r}\sum_{n=1}^{s}[N]_{mn}\{\delta\}_{mn} = [N]\{\delta\} \tag{5-52}$$

where

$$\left.\begin{aligned} [N] &= [[N]_{11}[N]_{12}\cdots[N]_{1s}\cdots[N]_{r1}[N]_{r2}\cdots[N]_{rs}] \\ \{\delta\} &= [\{\delta\}_{11}^{\mathrm{T}}\{\delta\}_{12}^{\mathrm{T}}\cdots\{\delta\}_{1s}^{\mathrm{T}}\cdots\{\delta\}_{r1}\{\delta\}_{r2}\cdots\{\delta\}_{rs}] \end{aligned}\right\} \tag{5-53}$$

$$\left.\begin{aligned} &\{\delta\}_{mn} = [\{\delta\}_0^{\mathrm{T}} \quad \{\delta\}_1^{\mathrm{T}} \quad \{\delta\}_2^{\mathrm{T}}\cdots\{\delta\}_N^{\mathrm{T}}]_{mn}^{\mathrm{T}} \\ &\{\delta\}_{0mn} = [u_0 \quad v_0 \quad w_0]_{mn}^{\mathrm{T}} \quad \{\delta\}_{Nmn} = [u_N \quad v_N \quad w_N]_{mn}^{\mathrm{T}} \\ &\{\delta\}_{imn} = [a_i \quad b_i \quad c_i]_{mn}^{\mathrm{T}} \quad i = 1,2,\cdots,N-1 \end{aligned}\right\} \tag{5-54}$$

$$\left.\begin{aligned} [N]_{mn} &= [\varphi]\otimes[\Gamma]_{mn} = [\varphi_i[\Gamma]_{mn}] \\ [\Gamma]_{mn} &= \mathrm{diag}(X_mX_n, Y_mY_n, Z_mZ_n) \end{aligned}\right\} \tag{5-55}$$

2) Sub-domain analysis. The total potential energy functional of sub-domain has the same style of Eq.(5-30), in which:

$$\{\varepsilon\} = [\varepsilon_x \quad \varepsilon_y \quad \varepsilon_z \quad \gamma_{xy} \quad \gamma_{yz} \quad \gamma_{zx}]^{\mathrm{T}}$$

$$\{\sigma\} = [\sigma_x \quad \sigma_y \quad \sigma_z \quad \tau_{xy} \quad \tau_{yz} \quad \tau_{zx}]^{\mathrm{T}} \quad \{V\} = [u \quad v \quad w]^{\mathrm{T}}$$

By using geometrical equation of spatial question in elastic theory, we can get:

$$\{\varepsilon\} = \sum_{m=1}^{r}\sum_{n=1}^{s}[A]_{mn}\{\delta\}_{mn} = [A]\{\delta\} \tag{5-56}$$

where

$$[A] = [[A]_{11} \quad [A]_{12} \quad \cdots \quad [A]_{1s} \quad \cdots \quad [A]_{r1}[A]_{r2} \quad \cdots \quad [A]_{rs}] \tag{5-57}$$

$$[A]_{mn} = \begin{bmatrix} [A]_{mn}^1 \\ [A]_{mn}^2 \end{bmatrix} \tag{5-58}$$

$$[A]^1_{mn} = \text{diag}(\varphi_i X'_m X_n, \varphi_i Y_m Y'_n, \varphi'_i Z_m Z_n) \tag{5-59}$$

$$[A]^2_{nm} = \begin{bmatrix} \varphi_i X_m X'_n & \varphi_i Y'_m Y_n & 0 \\ 0 & \varphi'_i Y_m Y_n & \varphi_i Z_m Z'_n \\ \varphi'_i X_m X_n & 0 & \varphi_i Z'_m Z_n \end{bmatrix} \tag{5-60}$$

where: φ' —the first derivative of φ.

By using physical equation of spatial question in elastic theory, we can get:

$$\{\sigma\} = [R]\{\varepsilon\} = [R][A]\{\delta\} \tag{5-61}$$

In this equation, $[R]$ is elastic matrix as follows:

$$[R] = \text{diag}([R]_1, [R]_2) \tag{5-62}$$

$$[R]_1 = \begin{bmatrix} R_1 & R_2 & R_3 \\ & R_1 & R_3 \\ & & R_4 \end{bmatrix} \quad [R]_2 = \text{diag}(R_5, R_6, R_6) \tag{5-63}$$

For isotropic elastic body, R_i is:

$$R_1 = \frac{2(1-\mu)G}{1-2\mu}, R_2 = R_3 = \frac{R_1\mu}{1-\mu}; R_4 = R_5 = R_6 = G \tag{5-64}$$

Taking Eqs.(5-52), (5-56), and (5-61) into Eq. (5-30), we can get:

$$\Pi = \frac{1}{2}\{\delta\}^{\mathrm{T}}[G]\{\delta\} - [\delta]^{\mathrm{T}}\{f\} \tag{5-65}$$

where

$$[G] = [[G]_{mnpq}] \quad m, p = 1, 2, \cdots, r \quad n, q = 1, 2, \cdots, s \tag{5-66}$$

$$\{f\} = [\{f\}^{\mathrm{T}}_{11} \quad \{f\}^{\mathrm{T}}_{12} \quad \cdots \quad \{f\}^{\mathrm{T}}_{1s} \quad \cdots \quad \{f\}^{\mathrm{T}}_{r1} \quad \{f\}^{\mathrm{T}}_{r2} \quad \cdots \quad \{f\}^{\mathrm{T}}_{rs}]^{\mathrm{T}} \tag{5-67}$$

$$\{f\}_{mn} = \int_{\Omega} [N]^{\mathrm{T}}_{mn}\{q\} d\Omega \quad \{q\} = [q_x \quad q_y \quad q_z]^{\mathrm{T}} \tag{5-68}$$

According to variation principle:

$$[G]\{\delta\} = \{f\} \tag{5-69}$$

$$[G]_{mnpq} = [0] \quad m \neq p, n \neq q \tag{5-70}$$

Because X_m, Y_m, Z_m, and X_n, Y_n, Z_n are orthogonal functions, so:

$$[G]_{mnpq} = [0] \quad m \neq p, n \neq q$$

Therefore, Eqs.(5-65) and (5-69) can be altered into the following rs independent equations:

$$\Pi_{mn} = \frac{1}{2}\{\delta\}^{\mathrm{T}}_{mn}[G]_{mnmn}\{\delta\}_{mn} - \{\delta\}^{\mathrm{T}}_{mn}\{f\}_{mn} \tag{5-71}$$

$$[G]_{mnmn}\{\delta\}_{mn} = \{f\}_{mn} \quad m = 1, 2, \cdots, r; \quad n = 1, 2, \cdots, s \tag{5-72}$$

where

$$[G]_{mnmn} = [(S_{ik})]_{mnmn} \tag{5-73}$$

$$(S_{ik})_{mnmn} = \begin{bmatrix} S_{uu} & S_{uv} & S_{uw} \\ & S_{vv} & S_{vw} \\ & & S_{ww} \end{bmatrix} \tag{5-74}$$

$$\left.\begin{aligned} &S_{uu}=K_1F_{ik}+K_2C_{ik} \quad S_{uv}=K_3F_{ik} \\ &S_{uw}=K_4H_{ik}+K_5H_{ik}^{\mathrm{T}} \quad S_{vv}=K_6F_{ik}+K_7C_{ik} \\ &S_{vw}=K_8H_{ik}+K_9H_{ik}^{\mathrm{T}} \quad S_{ww}=K_{10}C_{ik}+K_{11}F_{ik} \end{aligned}\right\} \tag{5-75}$$

$$\left.\begin{aligned} &K_1=R_1C_{x1}F_{y1}+R_5F_{x1}C_{y1} \quad K_6=R_1F_{x2}C_{y2}+R_5C_{x2}F_{y2} \\ &K_2=R_6F_{x1}F_{y1} \quad K_7=R_6F_{x2}F_{y2} \\ &K_3=R_2H_{x1}L_y+R_5F_{x4}C_{y4} \quad K_8=R_3J_xH_{y1} \quad K_9=R_6J_xH_{y2} \\ &K_4=R_3T_xI_y \quad K_5=R_6H_{x2}I_y \quad K_{10}=R_4F_{x3}F_{y3} \\ &K_{11}=R_6(C_{x3}F_{x3}+F_{x3}C_{y3}) \end{aligned}\right\} \tag{5-76}$$

where: C_{ik},F_{ik},H_{ik} and H_{ik}^{T} are the elements of the ith row and kth column in matrix $[C_z]$, $[F_z]$, $[H_z]$ and $[H_z]^{\mathrm{T}}$, which have the same forms as Eq.(5-44). just as:

$$\left.\begin{aligned} &C_{x1}=\int_{-a}^{a}(X_m')^2\mathrm{d}x \quad F_{x1}=\int_{-a}^{a}(X_m')^2\mathrm{d}x \quad H_{x1}=\int_{-a}^{a}X_m'Y_m\mathrm{d}x \\ &C_{x2}=\int_{-a}^{a}(Y_m')^2\mathrm{d}x \quad F_{x2}=\int_{-a}^{a}(Y_m)^2\mathrm{d}x \quad F_{x4}=\int_{-a}^{a}X_mY_m\mathrm{d}x \\ &C_{x3}=\int_{-a}^{a}(Z_m')^2\mathrm{d}x \quad F_{x3}=\int_{-a}^{a}(Z_m)^2\mathrm{d}x \quad H_{x2}=\int_{-a}^{a}X_mZ_m'\mathrm{d}x \\ &T_x=\int_{-a}^{a}X_m'Z_m\mathrm{d}x \quad J_x=\int_{-a}^{a}Y_mZ_m\mathrm{d}x \end{aligned}\right\} \tag{5-77}$$

$$\left.\begin{aligned} &C_{y1}=\int_{-b}^{a}(X_n')^2\mathrm{d}y \quad F_{y1}=\int_{-b}^{b}(X_n)^2\mathrm{d}y \quad H_{y1}=\int_{-b}^{b}Y_n'Z_n\mathrm{d}y \\ &C_{y2}=\int_{-b}^{b}(Y_n')^2\mathrm{d}y \quad F_{y2}=\int_{-b}^{b}(Y_n)^2\mathrm{d}y \quad I_y=\int_{-b}^{b}X_nZ_n\mathrm{d}y \\ &C_{y3}=\int_{-b}^{b}(Z_n')^2\mathrm{d}y \quad F_{y3}=\int_{-b}^{b}(Z_n)^2\mathrm{d}y \quad L_y=\int_{-b}^{b}X_nY_n'\mathrm{d}y \\ &C_{y4}=\int_{-b}^{b}X_n'Y_n'\mathrm{d}y \quad H_{y2}=\int_{-b}^{b}Y_nZ_n'\mathrm{d}y \end{aligned}\right\} \tag{5-78}$$

$$\{f\}_{mn}=[\{f\}_0^{\mathrm{T}} \quad \{f\}_1^{\mathrm{T}} \quad \{f\}_2^{\mathrm{T}} \quad \cdots \quad \{f\}_N^{\mathrm{T}}]_m^{\mathrm{T}} \tag{5-79}$$

$$\{f\}_{imn}=[f_u \quad f_v \quad f_w]^{\mathrm{T}} \tag{5-80}$$

$$f_u=\int_\Omega \varphi_iX_mX_nq_x\mathrm{d}\Omega,\ f_v=\int_\Omega \varphi_iY_mY_nq_y\mathrm{d}\Omega \tag{5-81}$$

$$f_w=\int_\Omega \varphi_iZ_mZ_nq_z\mathrm{d}\Omega$$

3) Integral analysis. After established sub-domain stiffness matrix $[G]_{nn}$ and sub-domain load vector $\{q\}_{mn}$, the integral stiffness equation of subgrade, which is composed of $r\times s$ independent equations, can be built on the basis of displacement coordination relation among sub-domains, and be used to calculate subgrade displacement and stress.. Using spline sub-domain to analyze layering subgrade will get better precisions.

5.3.4 Settlement Calculation Method for Box Foundation of Super High-Rise Buildings Considering the Effect of Support Structures in Deep Foundation Pits

1. Up-down two segments combination method for settlement calculation of box foundation of super high-rise buildings

Given the effect of support structures in deep foundation pit, box foundation settlement is divided into two parts: the lateral-limitation compression of subgrade in the range of insert-into-subgrade support structure (up part), and the subgrade compression under the horizon of insert-subgrade depth of support structure (down part). Adding these two parts together to calculate settlement is called combination method for settlement calculation of box foundation of super high-rise buildings.

There are two assumptions in this method: the stiffness of box foundation of super high-rise buildings is infinity and the foundation is looked as an rigid foundation; the subgrade is an elastic, even and continuous body. The diagram and model (including up and down two parts) of settlement calculation of super high-rise buildings indicate that:

1) In the insert-into-subgrade depth D of support structure in deep foundation pit, the up part of subgrade is in the situation of lateral-limitation compression under the vertical loads.

2) Beneath the insert-into-subgrade depth horizon, the subgrade is in the natural compression situation. According to *Code* JGJ6-99 (*Technical code for box and raft foundation of high-rise building*), it is difficult to calculate the final settlement of box or raft foundations if considering the effect of support structure. Because this code regulated that the final settlement of box or raft foundations should be counted by compression modulus or by deformation modulus. When compression modulus is adopted, the layering-summation method with the modification of average additional stress coefficient should be used; when deformation modulus is concerned, the elastic theory method by considering total load as calculated pressure is applied to settlement calculation.

In the diagram shown in Fig. 5-9, basement outside wall is separated with support structure, the subgrade in the range of support structure insert-into-subgrade part has lateral-limitation effect, but not absolute lateral-limitation. The subgrade around foundation bottom will squeeze backfill subsoil which are in the part between basement outside walls and support structures after being compressed. Give the large bottom area of foundation, this kind of squeezed effect is very limited. Therefore this effect can be ignored and the lateral limitation effect of subgrade can be considered as complete in actual calculation In Fig. 5-10, basement outside walls and support structures are combined as integration. It is obvious that the subgrade in the range of the insert-into-subgrade part (up part) of support structure is in the complete lateral-limitation situation, just like the laboratory condition. So the two situations mentioned above are all considered as complete lateral-limitation forced state. Thus, the settlement of up part subgrade beneath box foundation is calculate only by using compression modulus, not by using deformation modulus and elastic modulus, which is different from the specification calculation method. In addition, the deformation of up part subgrade beneath box foundation consists of resilience recompression deformation and ordinary compression deformation.

Besides, the two forced states of subgrade (down part) under the insert-into-subgrade depth horizon of support structures in deep foundation pit, shown in Fig. 5-9 and 5-10, are basically similar and can be counted by the two methods introduced in code, that is, resilience recompression deformation calculation and ordinary subgrade deformation calculation. The deformation modulus can also be used to calculate the settlement of ground (down part) under the insert-into-subgrade depth horizon of support structures. Here up-down two segments combination method for settlement calculation of box foundation is introduced in details.

(1) deformation calculation of up part ground under box foundation — resilience recompression deformation plus lateral-limitation compression deformation. Assumed the insert-into-subgrade depth of support structures as *D*, the final settlement of up part ground under box or raft foundation of super-high building as S_u, whose resilience recompression and lateral-limitation compression are respectively S_{u1} and S_{u2}, the final settlement can be expressed as:

$$S_u = S_{u1} + S_{u2} \tag{5-82}$$

1) Calculation of resilience recompression deformation S_{u1} of up part subgrade under box foundation. Because of the subgrade resilience (including lumps) after digging pit, the recompression at foundation pit bottom will occur during construction, which is expressed as S_{u1} and is calculated as:

$$S_{u1} = \psi_c \sum_{i=1}^{n} \frac{P_c}{E_{ci}} (z_i \bar{a}_i - z_{i-1} \bar{a}_{i-1}) \tag{5-83}$$

where: ψ_c —Empirical coefficient of settlement calculation considering resilience effect. Beacure of lack of observation data, ψ_c=1 when S_c is equal to resilience; and ψ_c>1 when S_c is larger than resilience (according to the resilience-recompression curve);

P_c— Self-weight pressure of subgrade above the bottom surface of foundation pit. It can be calculated by deducting the fictional force from schematic diagram and the buoyancy should also be deducted if it is under the groundwater level;

E_{ci}— The resilience-recompression modulus;

n— The calculating layer number, the calculated depth could be 3—5m under the inserted depth of supporting structure and be double of inserted depth of supporting structure if there is groundwater;

$z_i, z_{i-1}, \bar{a}_i, \bar{a}_{i-1}$— The values should be taken according to the code (JGJ6-99).

2) The calculation of S_u which is confined compression deformation of the upper part of box foundation. Because the upper part of box foundation is not deep (the subgrade is good and homogeneous), the inserted depth of supporting structure is about 5m if the foundation pit is 20m. It can be calculated with the model of uniaxial compression deformation and also with the method of layer-wise summation. S_{u2} is calculated with the method of layer-wise summation as follows.

The calculating formula of final settlement S_{u2} in the inserted depth of supporting structure is as follows:

$$S_{u2} = \phi_r \sum_{i=1}^{n} \frac{p_0 - p_f - p_w}{E_{si}} (z_i \bar{a}_i - z_{i-1} \bar{a}_{i-1}) \tag{5-84}$$

where: ϕ_r— The empirical coefficient of settlement calculation of super high-rise building foundation. Presently there is only empirical coefficient when $\overline{E_s} \leqslant 20\text{MPa}$ defined in the code. For the box foundation of super high-rise building the empirical coefficient should be obtained from measured data and result analysis because $\overline{E_s}$ is much more than 20MPa . The empirical coefficient in the region of highly weathered granite is 0.2;

p_0— Additional stress in bed plate;

p_f— Sum of frictional resistance of peripheral ectotheca of bed plate and end frictional resistance in the inserted depth of supporting structure (the resistance of inserted end of supporting structure could be considered in Fig. 5-10);

p_w— Buoyancy of groundwater;

E_{si}— Compression modulus of subgrade of numberunder bed plate;

n and $z_i, z_{i-1}, \bar{a}_i, \bar{a}_{i-1}$— The values should be taken according to the code(JGJ6-99).

(2) The deformation calculation of lower part of box foundation—sum of resilience-recompression deformation and unconfined compression deformation. In Fig. 5-9 and Fig. 5-10, there is also resilience recompression deformation if the supporting structure inserts to the foundation (lower part) under the level surface of D. If the depth which supporting structure inserts to the subgrade is $<$10m or $>$5m and there is no groundwater the resilience recompression deformation could not be calculated; if the depth which supporting structure inserts to the subgrade is $>$10m or there is groundwater the resilience recompression

deformation could be calculated with the depth of 10m. The deformation of foundation is calculated with the method of layer-wise summation and also with the method of deformation modulus evaluation.

When there is no consideration of resilience recompression deformation, the deformation of lower part of box foundation is calculated with deformation modulus. Suppose that there is no confinement in this foundation. However, there is action of self-weight stress and friction and so there is action of confinement actually. The value calculated with the method of layer-wise summation approaches to the practical situation.

The final unconfined settlement of semi-infinite foundation which is under the level D of inserted depth of supporting structure can be calculated with the following formula:

$$S_0 = P_{k0} b\eta \sum_{i=1}^{n} \frac{\sigma_i - \sigma_{i-1}}{E_{0i}} \tag{5-85}$$

where: E_{0i}— Deformation modulus of the number i subgrade under the level D of inserted depth of supporting structure;

P_{k0}— In the combination of long term effect, the standard value of mean pressure which is in the level of D of inserted depth of supporting structure deducts the standard value of self-weight pressure of the foundation subgrade which is above the level D of inserted depth of supporting structure and buoyancy of groundwater.

The meanings of other symbols can be turned to the code (JGJ6-99). The settlement calculating depth of Z_n under the condition without confined compression can be expressed with the following formula:

$$Z_n = (Z_m + \xi b)\beta \tag{5-86}$$

where: Z_m— Empirical value. Z_m =11.6m while it is box foundation;

ε— Reduction coefficient, ε =0.42 while it is box foundation;

The values of Z_m and ε can be taken according to the code and had better not be less than the width of box foundation;

b— The width of box foundation's bed plate;

β— Adjustment coefficient. While the subgrade is sand β =0.6; while the subgrade is gravel β =0.3; while the subgrade is weathered granite β =0.4. In the code (JGJ6-99), only non-gravel subgrade is prescribed. That means the better the subgrade the less the calculating depth.

2. The simplified calculation method for settlement of box foundation of super high-rise building

(1) The simplified calculation method for homogeneous deformation of foundation. The

formula for settlement of rigid box foundation in elasticity mechanics is as follows:

$$S = \omega b P_0 \frac{1-\mu^2}{E} \tag{5-87}$$

where: S— The mean settlement;

b— The depth of box foundation;

P_0— The mean pressure of foundation's bed plate;

E— Elastic modulus;

μ— Poisson ratio of subgrade;

ω— Influence coefficient of settlement which can be obtained from the table. For example, while it is square foundation (rigid foundation) ω=0.88. With trial calculation of considered action of supporting structure ω=0.6—0.8 in highly weathered granite foundation.

Rough estimation for foundation settlement is convenient for simple and initial design of foundation.

The biggest defect of this method is the problem of the determination of E. E_s is compression modulus in experiment and elastic modulus is much higher than compression modulus. Elastic modulus will be correct through the cross-computation of data from plate loading test and settlement observation. For example, E of gravel is 40—56MPa and E of gravel is 40—56MPa.

(2) The method of layer-wise summation with linear deformation (improved Egorov method). Suppose that foundation soil is the continuous body with linear deformation. The method of layer-wise summation with linear deformation for box foundation settlement is as follows:

$$S = K b P_0 \sum_{i=1}^{n} \frac{1-\mu^2}{E_{0i}} (\omega_{zi} - \omega_{zi-1}) \tag{5-88}$$

where: K— Regional empirical coefficient. The result of computation is K=0.65—0.75;

E_{0i}— The deformation modulus of number i subgrade under the foundation; deformation modulus is almost as same as compression modulus;

ω_{zi}, ω_{zi-1}—The influence coefficient with depth to width ratio which is Z_i/b and Z_{i-1}/b according to the table.

The means of the other symbols are as same as that before.

This simplified method introduced deformation modulus and the deformation modulus is the stress-strain ratio under the unconfined condition. So there is error existing in the calculated result. Certainly the combination of uniaxial compression method and this method is more suitable for the reality.

(3) The simplified calculation for foundation settlement of uniaxial compression. The depth of subgrade which is under the box foundation's bed plate level of super high-rise buildings is not deep and so is the depth of subgrade which is above the level of the inserted depth of supporting structure. In a deep foundation pit the inserted depth of supporting structure is no more than 20m in soft soil subgrade and is no more than 10m in sand and weathered granite subgrade. Therefore the thickness of compressible layer is less than the half of box foundation width. The self-weight stress and additional stress both varies little through the thickness and there is no lateral deformation in the foundation. Therefore it can be considered to be uniaxial compression and the final settlement of this foundation is simplified as follows:

$$S_s = \frac{e_1 - e_2}{1 + e_1} H = K \frac{P_0}{E_s} H \tag{5-89}$$

where: K— Regional empirical coefficient;

S_s— The final uniaxial compression settlement of the subgrade which is above the level of inserted depth of supporting structure and under box foundation's bed plate;

e_1— Void ratio from the compression curve with the parameter of the mean self-weight stress σ_c (namely the initial pressure P_1) which is at level of the top and bottom surface of this layer subgrade;

e_2— Void ratio from the compression curve with the parameter of the sum of σ_c and mean additional stress σ_z (namely total pressure $P_z = \sigma_c + \sigma_z$);

E_s— Compression modulus of resilience-recompression;

P_0— Additional stress $\sigma_z = P_z - P_1$.

The calculated results may be larger than the actuality. The reason for this is that there is no consideration for the condition of three-dimensional stress and no accurate simulation for the resilience action of foundation pit bottom. Therefore there is empirical coefficient used for modification.

3. Comprehensive coefficient method of settlement calculation for box foundation of super high-rise buildings

This method is suitable for the foundation which is sandy subgrade, homogeneous foundation, not poor foundation and satisfies the elastic theory. Therefore the process is as follows: ① calculate foundation settlement with elasticity mechanics method; ② estimate a comprehensive coefficient after considering the influence of different settlement. This coefficient is like the regional empirical coefficient in *Code for design of building foundation*. Because the elasticity mechanics formula is simple the settlement will be calculated quickly and application in engineering is convenient. In addition, the calculated value will approach to measured value with the regional empirical coefficient set.

The formula for calculating box foundation settlement with method of elasticity mechanics is as follows:

$$S = KBP_a \frac{1-\mu^2}{E} \tag{5-90}$$

This formula is like the Formula (4-16), but the means differs.

where: B— The width of box foundation;

P_a— The total load on the building, namely calculating pressure (kPa);

E— Elastic modulus of subgrade;

μ— Poisson ratio of foundation;

K— Comprehensive coefficient.

$$K = \prod_{i=1}^{6} K_i \tag{5-91}$$

The coefficient value will be obtained after analysis of calculation and analogy. That is as follows:

K_1— Influence coefficient of inhomogeneity of foundation , K_1=0.6—0.8;

K_2— Influence coefficient of additional stress of foundation, K_2=0.75—0.85;

K_3— Influence coefficient of settlement depth of foundation, K_3=0.30—0.40;

K_4— Influence coefficient of resilience-recompression of foundation, K_4=0.65—0.75;

K_5— Influence coefficient of confinement of foundation pit's supporting structure, K_5=1.00—1.10;

K_6— Influence coefficient of ω in Formula (5-87), $K_6 = \omega$=0.88.

Therefore the comprehensive coefficient K of settlement is 0.10—0.20.

The comprehensive coefficients of different regions can be obtained with statistics and analysis through a great deal of settlement data. K which is 0.10—0.20 can be suitable for settlement calculation of box (raft) foundation of super high-rise buildings in the region of sandy soil or highly weathered granite. The comprehensive coefficient is also meaningful for scheme design and conceptual design. K of Qingdao is suggested to 0.1144.

4. Step layer-wise summation method of calculation for oblique box foundation settlement

The foundation of super high-rise buildings is generally layered and homogenous and every layer is level basically. Therefore the final deformation can be obtained from the sum of every layer deformation which can be calculated with the layer-wise summation method. The settlement calculating depth can be extended to the depth of geological exploration with computer. Some foundation layers is oblique and there will be big error if it is calculated as level layer (especially the characteristics of upper and nether is discrepant widely). When the oblique foundation is calculated with layer-wise summation method it can be divided to many steps longitudinal and the deformation can be calculated by steps longitudinally not transversally (Fig. 5-16). The highly weathered layer's bed plate is irregular. It is simple to calculate with method of finite element. Therefore the settlement calculation with the method of longitudinal step layer-wise summation is simple. This method is universally significant to be extended to settlement calculation for oblique box (raft) foundation (with layer-wise summation method).

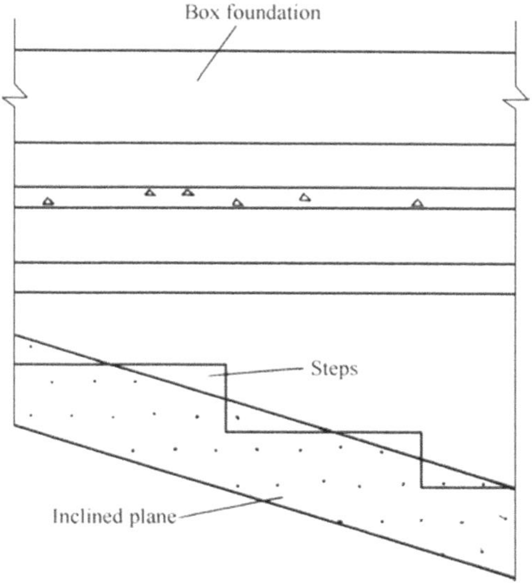

Fig. 5-16 Step layer-wise summation method for calculation of box foundation settlement

5. The entire structural settlement of box foundation of super high-rise buildings

The upper part of super high-rise buildings, foundation and subgrade work together. They can be regarded as an entire structure in settlement calculation with the method of finite element, boundary element, unbounded element. If the parameters are proper the error of the calculated results are within the limits. The results of preliminary study showed that the complicated boundary condition and nonlinear characteristics of foundation could be considered.

With the development of computer technology we can calculate the settlement with the above methods. The final settlement for super high-rise buildings should and must be calculated with method of finite element or other numerical methods. The whole results of different methods should be compared, analyzed, synthesized with the measured value. Therefore the estimated value of box foundation settlement can provide evidence for structure engineer's design. We can say that the estimated value of settlement conforms to reality. However it is difficult to judge which calculated value is more accurate because of no much measured value. At this time, it is better to compare the calculated value with finite element method with the value according to the code in order to determine the estimated value.

5.4 The Box Foundation Settlement Calculation of Qingdao BC Mansion with Finite Element Method

5.4.1 Project Introduction

Qingdao BC mansion is about 100 thousand m^2 in floor area for the whole building, 245.8 m high, 4 levels underground (the foundation pit is −19.5m) and with box foundation. Qingdao BC mansion is the highest building independently designed by Chinese person at that time, which is exhibited in Fig. 5-17(a), (b) and (c).

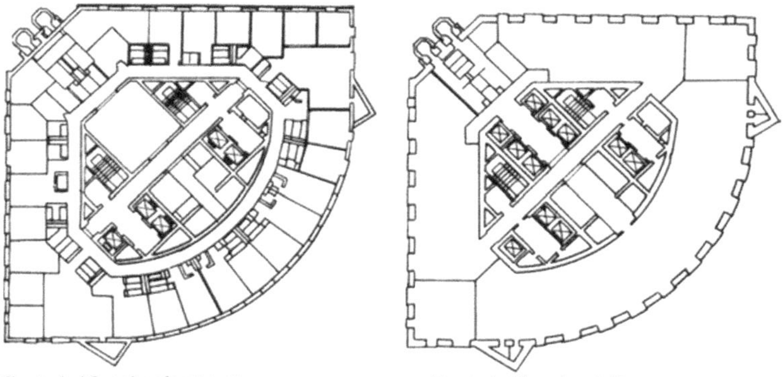

(a) The plane graph of Qingdao BC mansion

Fig. 5-17

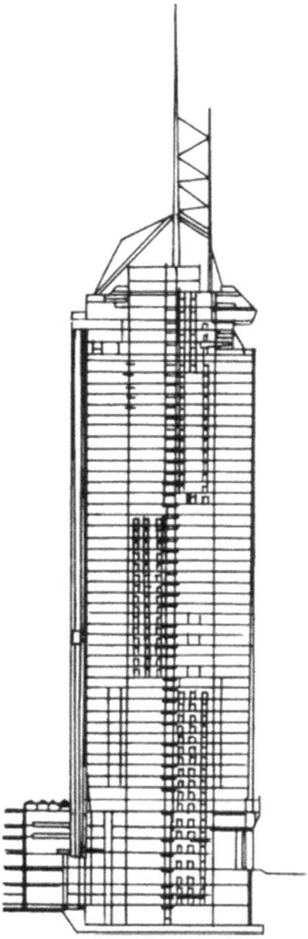

(b) Profile graph of Qingdao BC mansion

(c) The color graph of Qingdao BC mansion

Fig. 5-17(continued)

The engineering was considered to be safe with box foundation. However, afterwards the box foundation was applied to highly weathered granite subgrade through reiterated calculation and demonstration of more than half a year. It is also the highest one (H=245m) of super high-rise buildings which adopt box foundation. There are many experts attending the seminar including Academician SunJun and Doctor LiuGuobin from Tongji University; Academician HuangXiling and researcher LiuJinli from China Academy of Building Research. This project started construction at the end of 1993 and finished in June, 1996. The settlement difference of foundation is 36.98 mm, the inclination of the whole structure was 0.00076 (the measured result in 1996 was much less than 0.0015) and the sedimentation rate of the main building is 0.0096 mm/d (much less than 0.03 mm/d). Actually the foundation settlement is stable after the main building was completed. The fact that the whole foundation settlement is homogeneous proved that it was right and successful for Qingdao BC mansion to adopt box foundation on highly weathered granite subgrade.

5.4.2 The Geological Situations

According to the engineering geological report from China Institute of Geological Investigation & Survey and Qingdao Geological Investigation and Survey Research Institute, the geological situation of construction area is exhibited from upper to lower as follows:

1) Artificial filled subgrade: layer thickness is 0.70—2.8 m, the elevation of layer bottom is 4.28—2.84 m.

2) Silt: layer thickness is 0.00—1.3 m and the elevation of layer bottom is 2.31—3.38 m.Water content was 24.1% and bulk density is 19.5kN/m^3; void ratio is 0.71; spt blow count is 3.

3) Gravel sand: layer thickness is 3.00—6.40 m and the elevation of layer bottom is 0.00—3.44 m. The gravel sand, which is the main aquifer, is distributed in the whole area. It is organic polluted seriously, mixed with fine sand lens, strong permeability and rich water quantity.

4) Silt clay with organic matter: layer thickness is 0.5—3.10m and the elevation of layer bottom is −1.39—3.87m. Water content is 24.6% and bulk density is 19.6kN/m^3; $C = 0.01$ MPa ; $\phi = 7.5°$; spt blow count is3.2.

5) Silt clay: layer thickness is 0.8—2.8m and elevation of layer bottom is −2.85—6.37m. It is distributed around the whole area. Water content is 23.9% and bulk density is 19.8KN/m^3; $C = 0.49$ MPa ; $\phi = 9°$; spt blow count is 7.

6) gravel sand and gravel soil: layer thickness is 3.9—7.2m and the elevation of layer bottom is −8.26—11.42m. They are main aquifer, strong permeability, moderately rich in water quantity, widely distributed above the bedrock surface. The standard value of bearing capacity is 400kPa. They are natural bearing stratum of raft foundation of podium .

7) Highly weathered granite ground: layer thickness is 8.2—14.14m and the elevation of layer bottom is −16.68—20.68m. Water content is 18.3% and bulk density was 19.8KN/m^3. The standard value of bearing capacity is 2000—2500kPa. They are natural bearing stratum of main building foundation.

In addition, the site is 100 m away from the seashore and the groundwater basically is pore phreatic water, confined water and confined water of bedrock crack. The height of pressure water head is 7.28—4.54m. The direction of the area is to the south from north and northeast. The situation of construction area are exhibited as follows: the water quantity is medium; the water outflow from single well is $<$150m^3/d; the permeability coefficient K is 19.9m/d; the influence radius is 50—80m; the elevation of groundwater is 0.91—1.19m.

5.4.3 The Supporting Structure of Foundation Pit

Pile-anchor supporting structure is used in the foundation pit. The bored piles of $\phi 800$ were used as row piles. The pile is 24m long and plain concrete with the diameter of $\phi 400$. The distance of piles is 200mm. The inserted depth of pile is 3.5m to retain groundwater. There are three layers of pre-stressed anchor and the pile top is combined with ring beam. Steel is used at the end of pre-stressed anchor in every layer in order to make the supporting structure act as a whole.

5.4.4 The Finite Element Method in Settlement Calculation of Box Foundation of Qingdao BC Mansion

There are field load test in the foundation pit for convenience (the *P-s* curve of load test is in Fig. 5-20). The results of experiment are as follows: the deformation modulus E_0 of highly weathered granite subgrade is 50MPa; the deformation modulus E_0 of syenite porphyry is 80MPa; the standard value of bearing capacity f_k is 1000kPa. The result of final settlement with the general model of finite element method is 94mm. The contour distributions of stress tensor of σ_x, σ_y, σ_z, τ_{xy}, τ_{yz}, τ_{zx} are exhibited respectively in the Fig. 5-18(a)—(f). The contour distribution of settlement and local amplified contour distribution of settlement are exhibited in Fig. 5-19(a), (b). The settlement value which is calculated with elastic theory is 99.4mm. We can see that the value calculated with the finite element method is close to the reality. We could say the highly weathered granite subgrade is elastic-plastic body through the P-s curve and the residual deformation is 57%—62%. The *P-s* curve is line in loading and curve in unloading (opposite to the elastic-plastic characteristics of general subgrade). Therefore the highly weathered granite subgrade can't be considered to be purely elastic body (the elastic modulus of 4 points were 53.88MPa, 72.65MPa, 84.85MPa, 141.76MPa). Because of the experiment carried in the bottom of foundation pit, the bottom of foundation pit has resiled and the *P-s* curve contains the process of resilience-recompression.

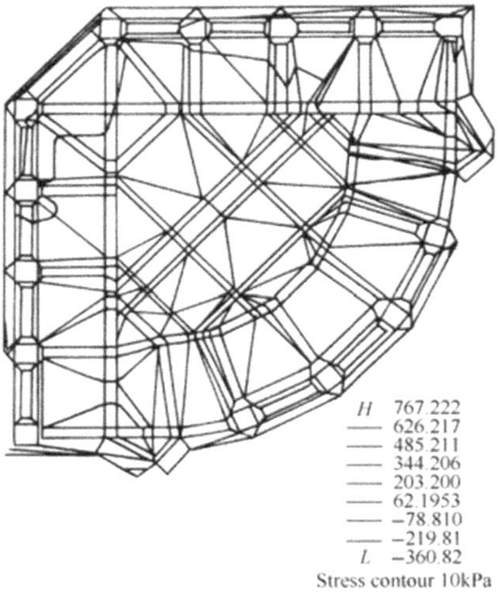

(a) Contour graph of calculating stress σ_x in the box foundation calculation of Qingdao BC mansion with the method of finite element

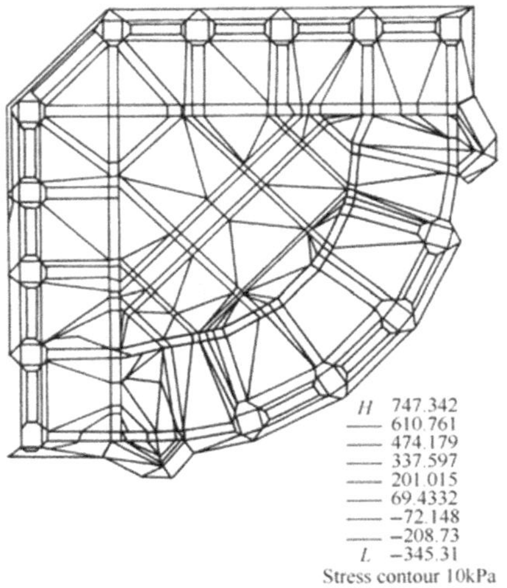

(b) Contour graph of calculating stress σ_y in the box foundation calculation of Qingdao BC mansion with the method of finite element

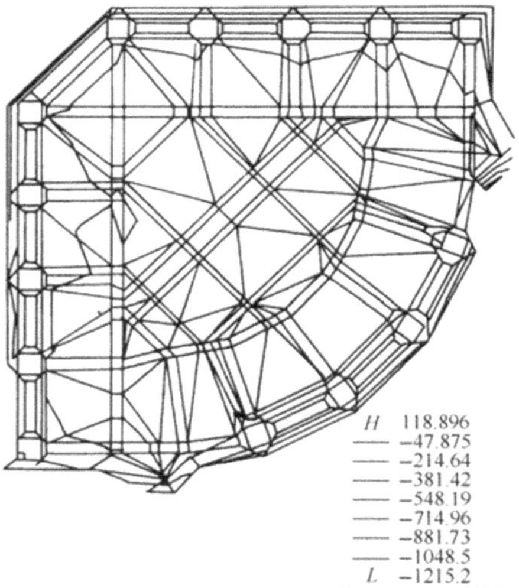

(c) Contour graph of calculating stress σ_z in the box foundation calculation of Qingdao BC mansion with the method of finite element

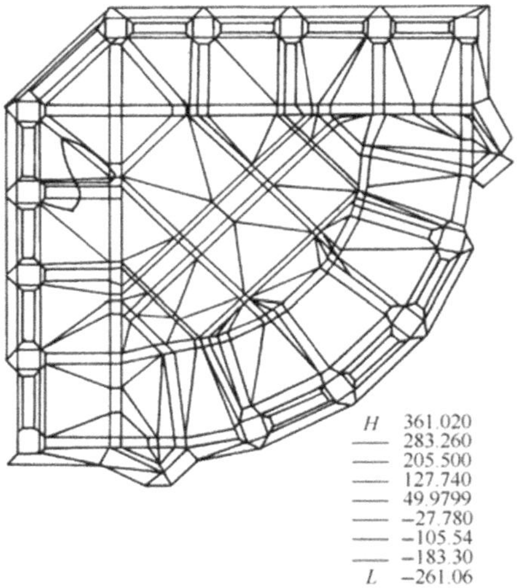

(d) Contour graph of calculating stress σ_{xy} in the box foundation calculation of Qingdao BC mansion with the method of finite element

Fig. 5-18

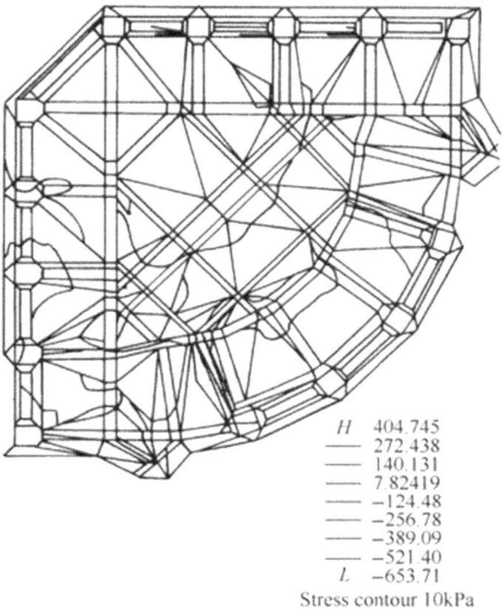

(e) Contour graph of calculating stress σ_{yz} in the box foundation calculation of Qingdao BC mansion with the method of finite element.

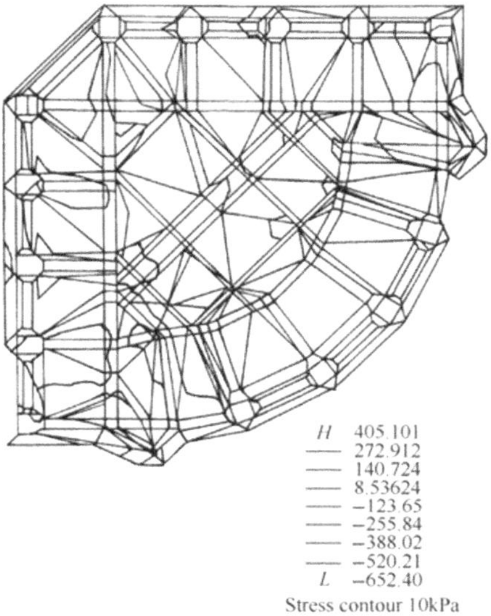

(f) Contour graph of calculating stress σ_{zx} in the box foundation calculation of Qingdao BC mansion with the method of finite element

Fig. 5-18(continued)

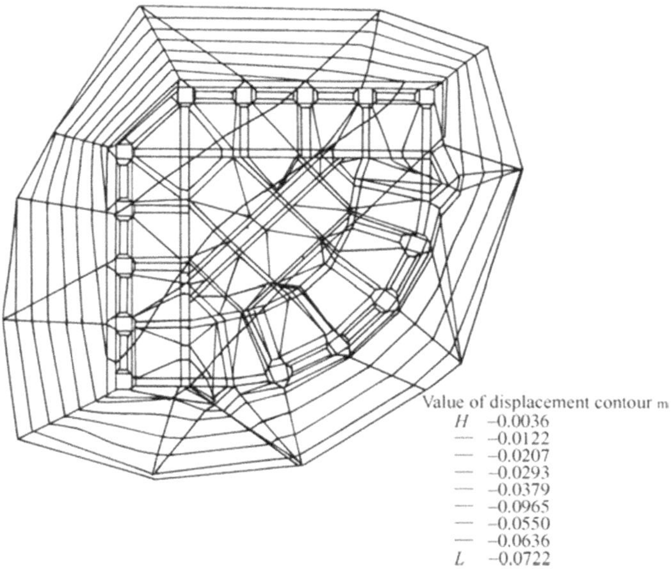

(a) The contour distribution graph of foundation settlement calculation ofQingdao BC mansion with finite element method

Fig. 5-19

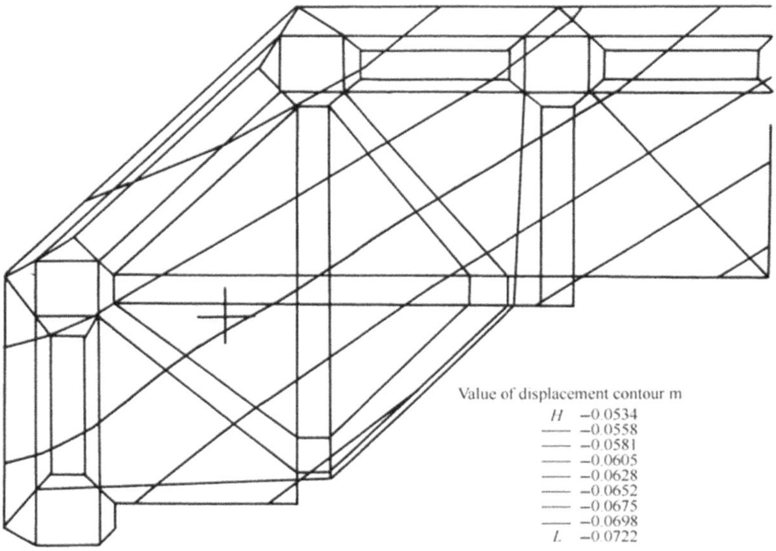

(b) Local amplified contour distribution graph of foundation settlement calculation of Qingdao BC mansion with finite element method

Fig. 5-19(continued)

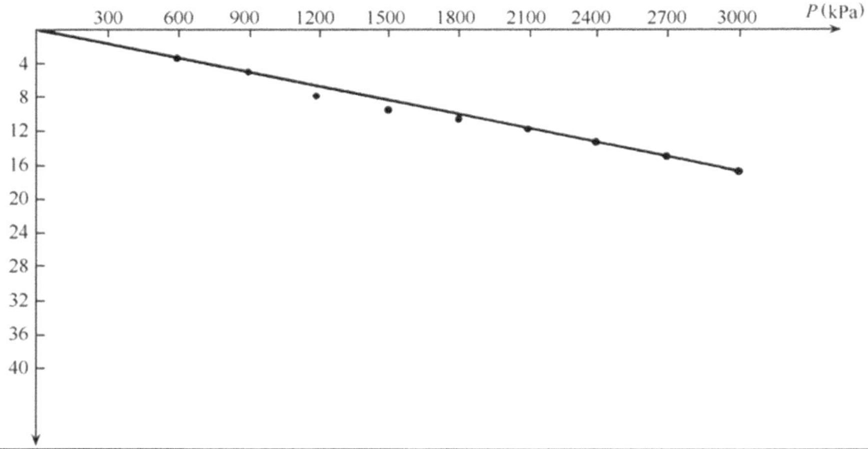

Unit load(MPa)	600	900	1200	1500	1800	2100	2400	2700	3000
Accumulative settlement(mm)	3.28	6.30	7.82	9.34	10.19	11.45	12.86	14.43	16.48
Duration(min)	40	80	70	90	60	50	50	50	50

Remark: point number: 4, elevation:-19.90m, lithology: normal porphyry (dike), diameter of bearing plate: 80cm.

(a) *P-s* curve namely result graph of load test

Fig. 5-20 *P-S* curve of load test

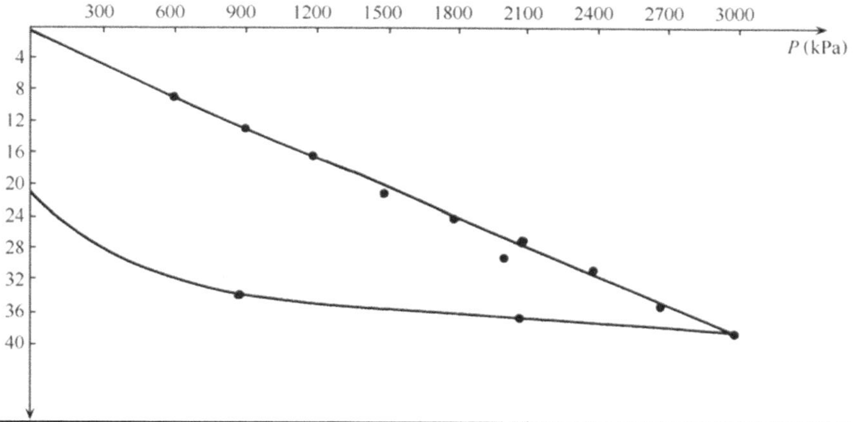

Unit load(MPa)	600	900	1200	1500	1800	2100	2400	2700	3000	2100	900	0
Accumulative settlement(mm)	8.63	12.84	17.42	20.95	23.93	26.90	34.84	38.24	36.31	35.29	33.82	20.40
Duration(min)	80	60	50	60	60	60	60	60	30	30	30	30

Remark: point number: 1, elevation:-19.90m, lithology: highly weathered granite, diameter of bearing plate: 80cm.

(b) *P-s* curve namely result graph of load test

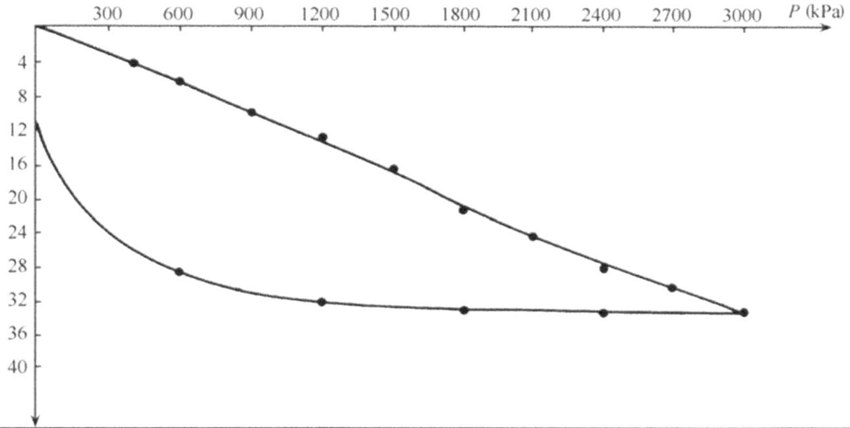

Unit load (MPa)	600	900	1200	1500	1800	2100	2400	2700	3000	2400	1800	1200	600	0
Accumulative settlement (mm)	6.40	10.30	13.56	17.33	22.24	25.44	29.41	31.58	34.64	34.26	33.85	32.41	28.90	11.84
Duration (min)	50	50	40	50	60	50	70	50	50	30	30	30	30	30

Remark: point number: 2, elevation:-19.00m, lithology: highly weathered granite, diameter of bearing plate: 80cm.

(c) *P-s* curve namely result graph of load test

Fig. 5-20 *P-S* curve of load test(continued)

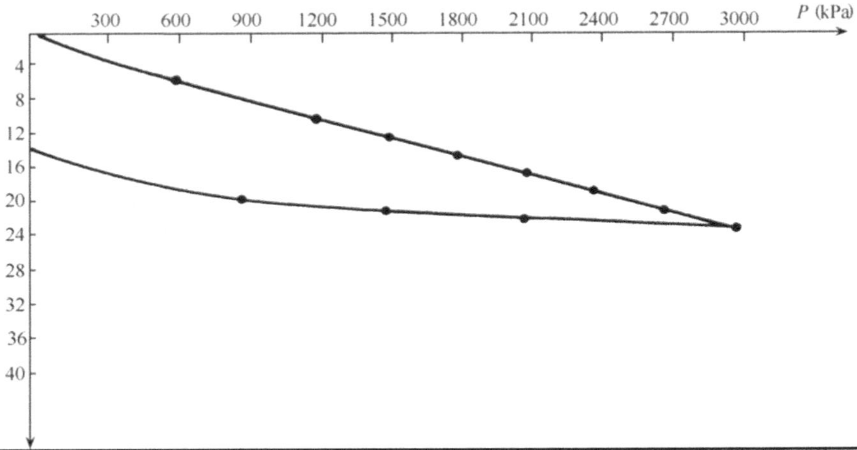

Unitload (MPa)	600	900	1200	1500	1800	2100	2400	2700	3000	2100	1500	900	0
Accumulative settlement (mm)	5.48	8.04	9.67	11.96	13.85	15.81	17.73	19.82	21.74	21.15	20.27	19.27	13.76
Duration (min)	30	50	80	40	80	50	50	60	50	30	30	30	30

Remark: point number: 3, elevation:-19.00m, lithology: normal porphyry (dike), diameter of bearing plate: 80cm.

(d) *P-s* curve namely result graph of load test

Fig. 5-20 *P-S* curve of load test(continued)

5.5 Calculation and Empirical Coefficient of Box Foundation Settlement of Qingdao BC Mansion with Consideration of Action of Supporting Structure

With consideration of action of supporting structure the settlement of box foundation should be calculated with the method of combination of the upper and the lower. That is as follows:

5.5.1 Calculation for Box Foundation Settlement with the Method of Uniaxial Compression in Upper Part and Layer-wise Summation in Lower Part

The upper part is under the bed plate of box foundation and above the level of inserted depth of supporting structure. Because of the totally confined action of supporting structure the settlement of the upper part with the method of uniaxial compression is as follows:

1) The settlement of point 10mm is 91.8mm.

2) The settlement of point 26mm is 91.8mm.

The lower part is under the level of inserted depth of supporting structure. The settlement of the lower part with the method of layer-wise summation is as follows:

1) The settlement of point 10 is 50.9mm.

2) The settlement of point 26 is 106.1mm.

Therefore the final settlements of the two points are the sum of that of the upper and lower part, namely:

1) The final settlement of point 10 is 142.7mm.

2) The final settlement of point 26 is 197.9mm.

5.5.2 Calculation of Box Foundation Settlement with the Method of Foundation Code in Upper Part and Box Foundation Code in Lower Part

The settlement of the upper part which is under the bed plate of box foundation with the method of layer-wise summation in *Code for design of building foundation* is as follows:

1) The settlement of point 10 is 34.0mm.

2) The settlement of point 26 is 34.0mm.

With the deformation modulus in *Code for design of box and raft foundation* of high-rise building, the settlement of the lower part which is under the level of inserted depth of supporting structure is as follows:

1) The settlement of point 10 is 63.6mm.

2) The settlement of point 26 is 62.6mm.

Therefore the final settlements of the two point are the sum of the upper and lower parts, namely:

1) The final settlement of point 10 is 97.6mm.

2) The final settlement of point 26 is 96.6mm.

This result approaches to the value which is calculated with the method of finite element.

5.5.3 Calculation for Box Foundation Settlement with the Method of Layer-Wise Summation of Both Parts in *Code for design of foundation*

The settlement under the box foundation is calculated with the method of layer-wise summation in *Code for design of building foundation*. There are 27points and the mean settlement is123.11mm. The mean settlement of point 10 is 109.8mm and mean settlement of point 26 is 172.5mm. Point 16 has the maximum of settlement and it is 303.9mm.

5.5.4 Calculation of the Settlement Empirical Coefficient ψ_s of Qingdao

1) If the settlement empirical coefficient of ψ_s is calculated with the expression that follows: ψ_s=the mean value of measured settlement /the maximum of calculated settlement, ψ_s=59.65/303.9=0.20.

2) If it is calculated with the mean value of calculated settlement, ψ_s=59.65/123.11=0.49.

3) If it is calculated with the final settlement (197.9mm) which is calculated with the point 26which has the maximum of settlement, ψ_s=59.65/197.9=0.30.

4) If it is calculated with the whole settlement (96.6mm) which is calculated with the point 26, ψ_s=59.65/96.6=0.62.

The results above show that the settlement empirical coefficient in highly weathered region of Qingdao is 0.2—0.6. According to the comparison of trial calculation with values of other projects the suggested value of ψ_s is 0.2.

5.5.5 Calculation for Box Foundation Settlement with the Author's Method of the Comprehensive Coefficient

The total load P of Qingdao BC mansion is 1565840KN. The area of foundation is 1480m^2 and width B of foundation is 38.47m. The calculating pressure is as follows:

$$Pa = P/B^2 = 1565840/1480 = 1058(\text{kN/m}^2)$$

$$E = 63.265 \text{ MPa}$$

$$\mu = 0.25$$

The total settlement of Qingdao BC mansion is as follows (the comprehensive coefficient is 0.1144):

$$S = KBPa\frac{1-\mu^2}{E}$$

$$=0.1144\times 38.47\times 105.8\times(1-0.25^2)/6326.5$$

$$=0.0608\text{m}$$

$$=60.8\text{mm}$$

This value approaches to the measured value well.

If the ψ_s is 0.2 the $S = 0.2 \times 0.531 = 0.1062\text{m} = 106.2\text{mm}$. This value approaches to the calculated value with the finite element method (the maximum of settlement with the finite element method is 94.00mm).

5.6 Measured Data of Box Foundation Settlement of Qingdao BC Mansion and Result Analysis

5.6.1 Measured data

The plan of Qingdao BC mansion is sector. There are 16 observation points in outer cylinder, 9 in inner cylinder and 2 in the middle of foundation. Because the foundation pit is deep (−19.5m), groundwater is rich and joined with seawater and dewatering is difficult, there is no measured resilience of foundation pit. The work of measuring foundation settlement didn't started until the main building constructed to ±0.00m. As showed in Fig. 5-21(a) the maximum of settlement is −2.58mm (point 25) and the minimum of settlement is 0.94mm (point 1). The graph of measured value of foundation settlement when the main building finished (June 22,1996) is exhibited in Fig. 5-21(b). The data is as follows: the maximum of settlement is 59.31mm (point 1); the minimum of settlement is −33.57mm (point 10); the maximum of sedimentation rate is 0.1533mm/d; the minimum of sedimentation rate is 0.0862mm/d. For comparison the measured value of foundation settlement after half a year of the finish of main building is exhibited in Fig. 5-22. Because of construction of project the building was completed one year after the main building was completed. After the load of decoration and installation was imposed on the building, the settlement of the main building had been stable and there was little settlement difference. There was settlement measured two or three years after the completion of the main building. The settlements of most points were stable and few were different (exhibited in Fig. 5-23 and Fig. 5-24). In Fig. 5-25, the settlement is totally stable. All the data conform to the design requirement which are exhibited as follows: the maximum of settlement is −74.27mm ; the minimum is -47.29mm.; the maximum of settlement difference is 26.98mm.

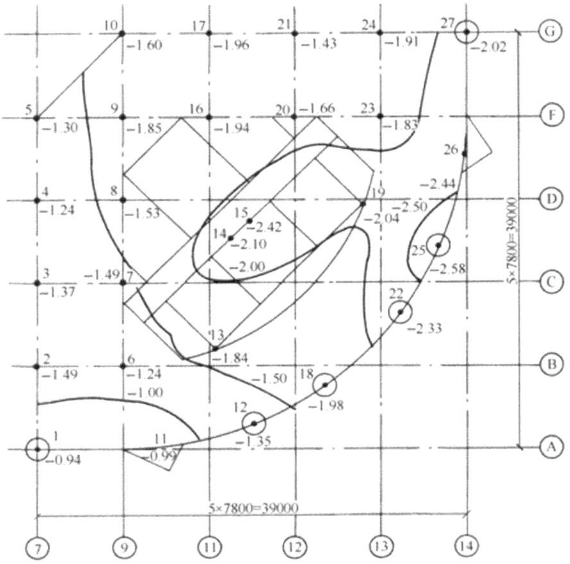

The maximum of settlement (point 26):-2.58mm, the minimum of settlement (point 10): −0.94mm

(a) The initial settlement when the main building constructed to ±0.00m (mm) (June 16,1995)

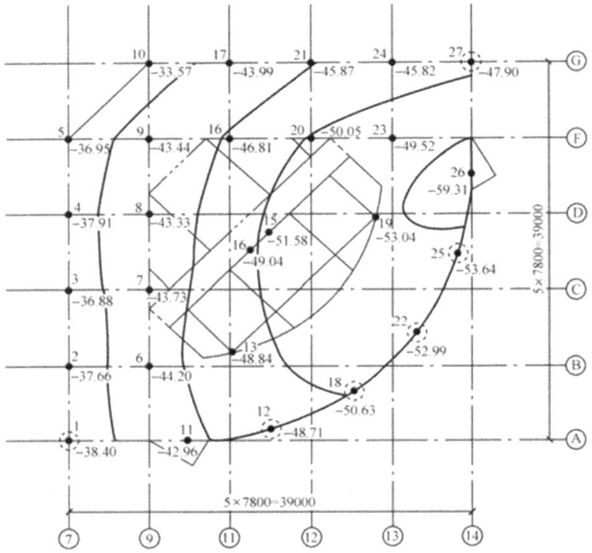

The maximum of settlement (point 26):−59.31mm, the minimum of settlement(point 10): −33.57mm;

The maximum of sedimentation rate (point26):0.1533mm/d, the minimum of sedimentation rate (point 10):0.0862mm/d

(b) The settlement opon completion of the main building (mm) (June 22, 1996)

Fig. 5-21 The settlement of the main building

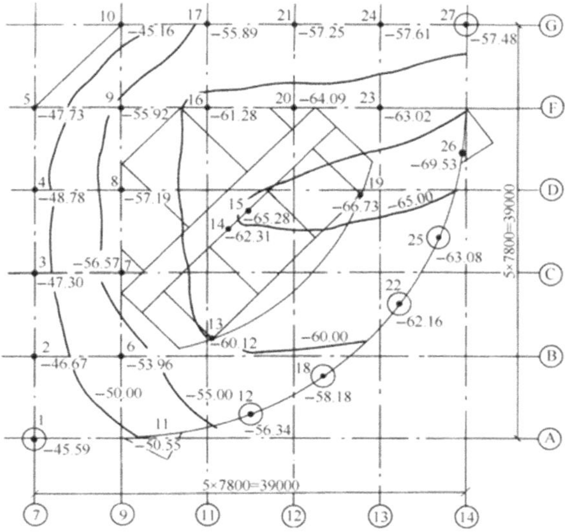

The maximum of settlement (point 26):−69.53mm, the minimum of settlement(point 10): -45.16mm;

The maximum of sedimentation rate (point26):0.121mm/d, the minimum of sedimentation rate (point 10):0.079mm/d

Fig. 5-22 he settlement 6 months after completion of the main building (mm) (Dec 16, 1996)

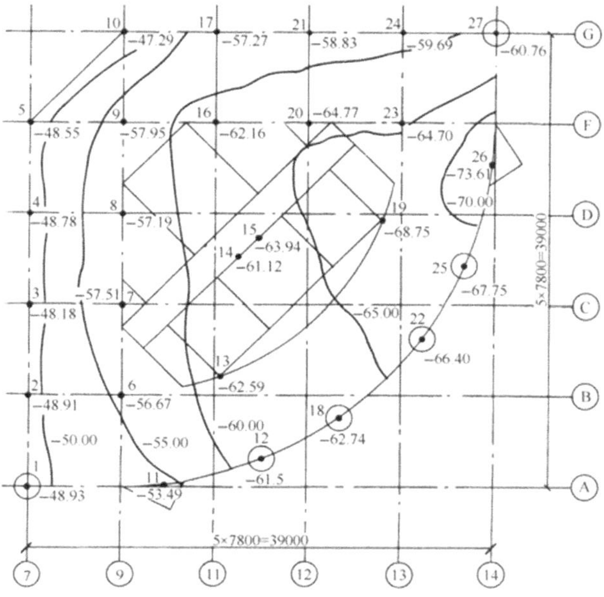

The maximum of settlement (point 26):−72.61mm, the minimum of settlement (point 10): −47.29mm;

The maximum of sedimentation rate (point26):0.096mm/d, the minimum of sedimentation rate (point 10):0.064mm/d

Fig. 5-23 The settlement one year after completion of the main building (mm) (July17, 1997)

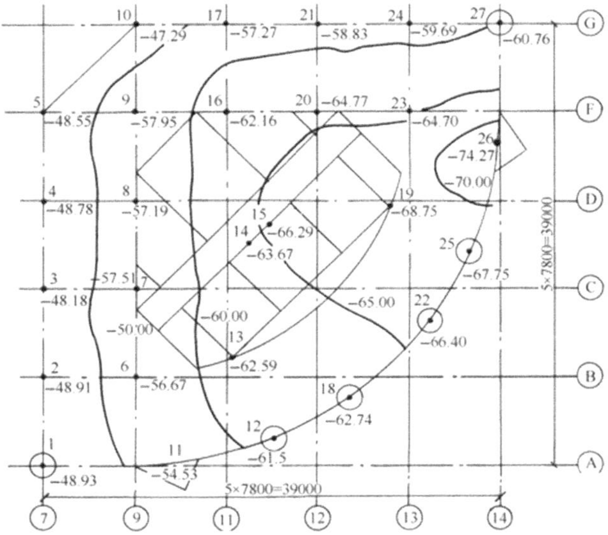

The maximum of settlement (point 26):−74.27mm, the minimum of settlement (point 10): −47.29mm;

The maximum of sedimentation rate (point26):0.097mm/d, the minimum of sedimentation rate (point 10):0.062mm/d

Fig. 5-24 The settlement two years after completion of the main building (mm) (August 11, 1998)

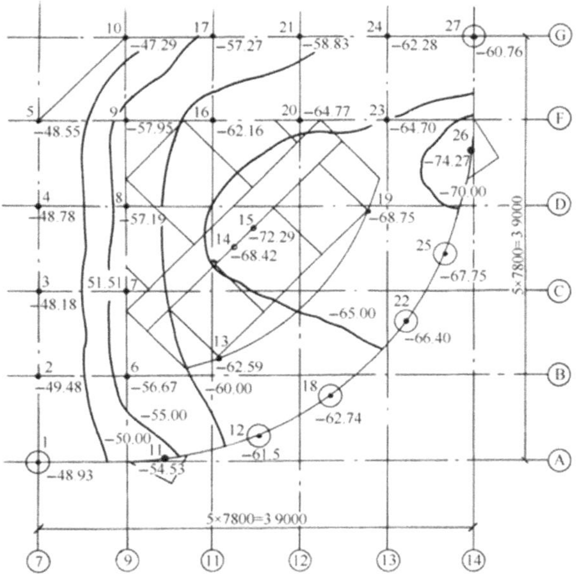

The maximum of settlement (point 26): −72.61mm, the minimum of settlement (point 10): −47.29mm;

The maximum of sedimentation rate (point26): 0.096mm/d, the minimum of sedimentation rate (point 10): 0.064mm/d

Fig. 5-25 The settlement three years after of completion of the main building (mm) (August 17, 1999)

In order to find out if the box foundation settlement was homogeneous or not, there were many times' observation after completion of the main building. Fig. 5-26 shows that the settlement difference from August 7, 1996 to Dec 16 1996 was 7.51mm and the mean sedimentation rate was 0.057mm/d which was close to being stable. Fig. 5-27 shows that settlement difference was 13.01mm and mean sedimentation rate was 0.033mm/d which had been stable already. Fig. 5-28 shows that the settlement difference increased little and the maximum of sedimentation rate (point 19) is 0.0202mm/d which had been stable already. Fig. 5-29 shows: the point of maximum of settlement difference changed to point 15(in the middle of foundation) and the value was 20.17mm; the mean settlement difference was 14.30mm which was 1.29mm bigger than that of the year of June 22, 1997; the mean sedimentation rate was 0.012mm/d. Compared with comparative settlement the settlement had been already stable 8 months after of the completion of the main building.

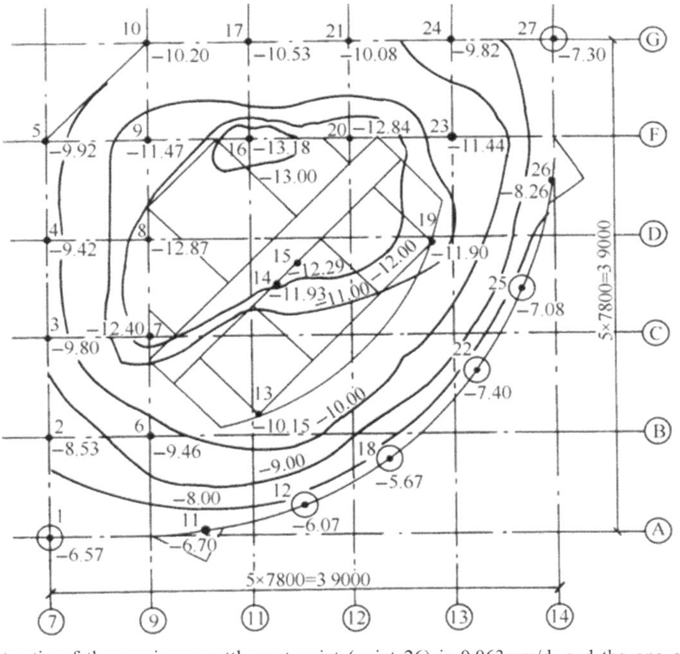

The settlement ratio of the maximum settlement point (point 26) is 0.063mm/d, and the one of the minimum settlement point (point 10) is 0.078mm/d. The biggest and smallest settlement differences at point 16 and point 18 are respectively 13.18mm and 5.67mm. The biggest settlement ratio (at point 16) is 0.1mm/d, and the smallest one (at point 18) is 0.04mm/d. The average settlement difference and settlement ratio of foundation are respectively 7.51mm and 0.057mm/d

Fig. 5-26 Settlement difference of the main tower of China Bank Mansion in Qingdao from 7th, 8, 1996 to 16th, 12, 1996

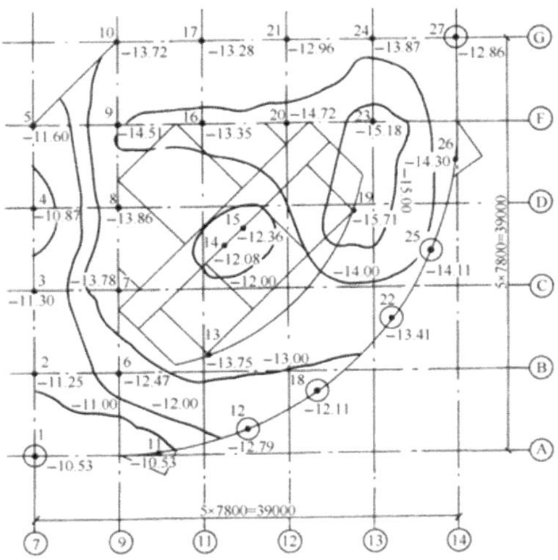

The settlement ratio of the maximum settlement point (point 26) is 0.037mm/d, and the one of the minimum settlement point (point 10) is 0.0352mm/d. The biggest and smallest settlement differences at point 19 and point 1 are respectively 15.71mm and 10.53mm. The biggest settlement ratio (at point 19) is 0.04mm/d, and the smallest one (at point 1) is 0.027mm/d. The average settlement difference and settlement ratio of foundation are respectively 13.01mm and 0.033mm/d

Fig. 5-27 Settlement difference of the main tower of China Bank Mansion in Qingdao from 22th ,6, 1996 to 17th ,7, 1997 after completion

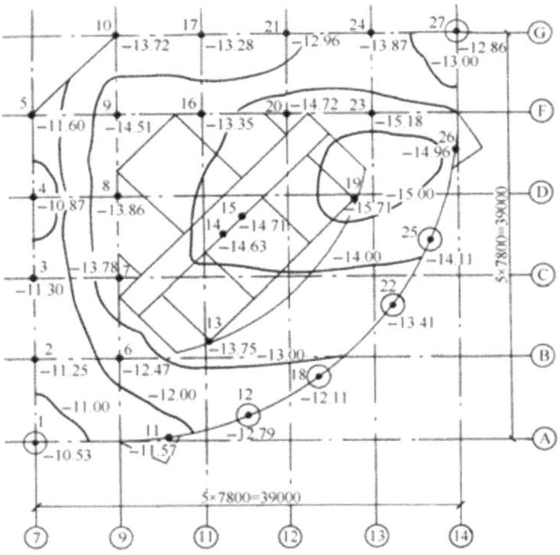

The settlement ratio of the maximum settlement point (point 26) is 0.019mm/d, and the one of the minimum settlement point (point 10) is 0.018mm/d. The biggest and smallest settlement differences at point 19 and point 1 are respectively 15.71mm and 10.53mm. The biggest settlement ratio (at point 19) is 0.0202mm/d, and the smallest one (at point 1) is 0.0135mm/d.

Fig. 5-28 Settlement difference of the main tower of China Bank Mansion in Qingdao from 22th ,6, 1996 to 11th ,8, 1998 after completion

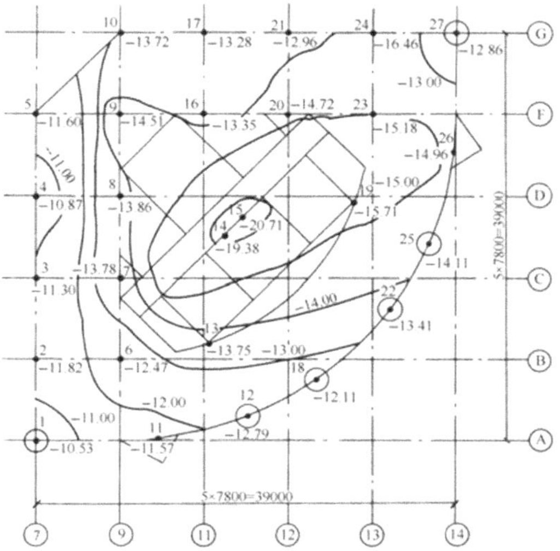

The biggest settlement ratio is 0.018mm/d, and the smallest one is 0.009mm/d. The biggest and smallest settlement differences at point 15 and point 1 are respectively 20.71mm and 10.53mm. The average settlement difference and settlement ratio of foundation are respectively 14.30mm and 0.012mm/d

Fig. 5-29 Settlement difference of the main tower of China Bank Mansion in Qingdao from 22th ,6, 1996 to 17th ,8, 1999 after completion

According to the value of settlement the settlement curve of 4 points in the foundation of main building is exhibited in Fig. 5-30. The settlement curves of point 26 (maximum of settlement) and point 10 (minimum of settlement) are amplified to Fig. 5-31. The sedimentation rate of the two points shows in Fig. 5-32 and Fig. 5-33. There is negative value in settlement as means that there is positive value in the comparative settlement. The reason may be the action of foundation and local upper load.

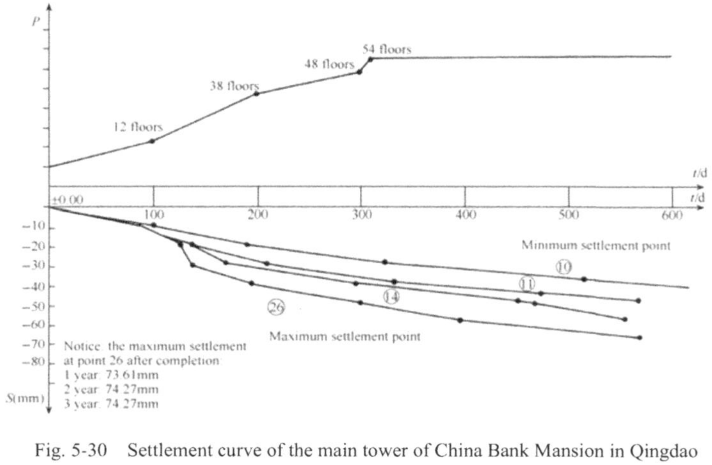

Fig. 5-30 Settlement curve of the main tower of China Bank Mansion in Qingdao

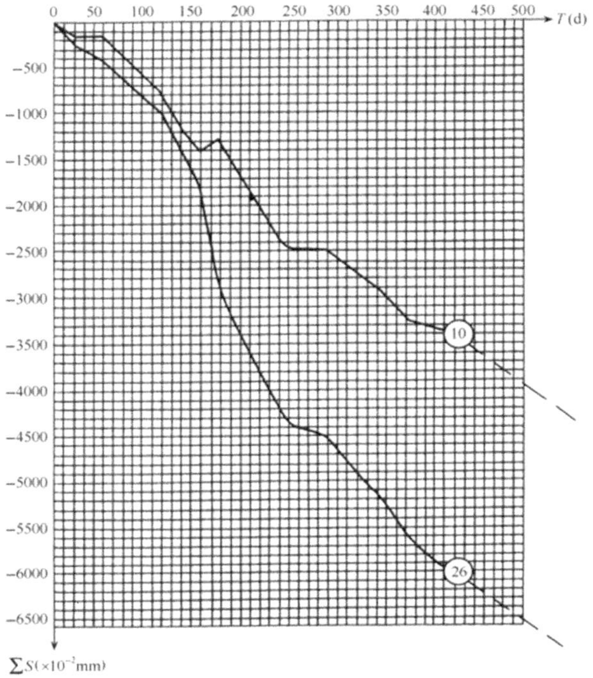

Fig. 5-31 Settlement curves of China Bank Mansion in Qingdao at point 10 and point 26 after completion

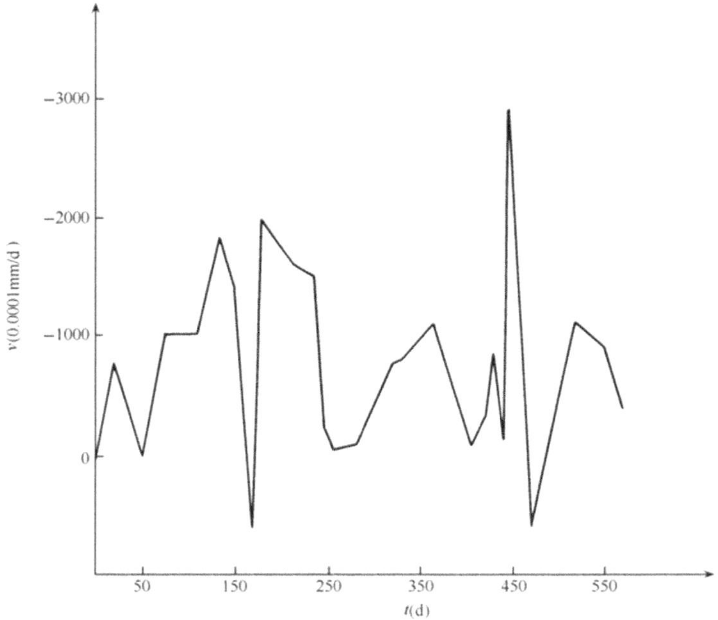

Fig. 5-32 Settlement ratio curve of China Bank Mansion in Qingdao at point 10 after completion

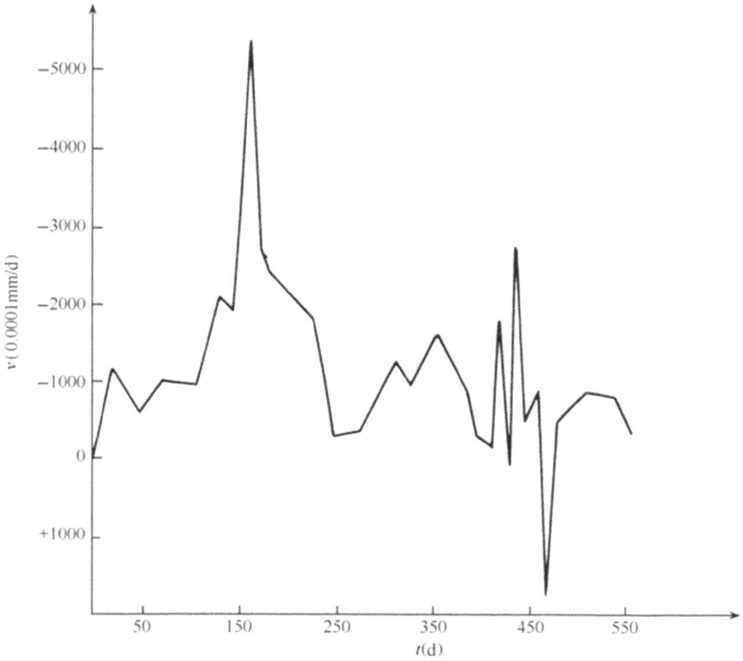

Fig. 5-33 Settlement ratio curve of China Bank Mansion in Qingdao at point 26 after completion

5.6.2 Observed Data Analysis

Some conclusions can be drawn from observed data mentioned above:

1) The settlement of the box foundation of China Bank Mansion in Qingdao is even and the inclination of the main tower is very small, which have already met the design demands.

2) The observed data shows that the settlement has been stable one year after of completion of the main tower. In the strong-weathered granite areas, the main settlement is initial settlement which accounts for over 95%, and the consolidated settlement is very small, about 5%.

5.6.3 Analysis of Observed and Calculated Results

1) The box foundation settlement calculated by elastic theory (−99.4mm) is rather close to the observed settlement (−74.27mm).

2) The maximum settlement calculated by layering-summation method is 303.9mm and 'the average observed settlement is 59.65mm. So the empirical coefficient $\psi_s' = 0.20$.

3) In the range of calculated depth $Z_n = (Z_m + \xi b)\beta$, the suggested value of adjustment coefficient β is 0.4.

4) The results from finite element method (−94mm) is very close to the results from elastic theory (-99.4mm).

5.7 Settlement Analysis of Rock Subgrade of Guangdong International Mansion

5.7.1 Project Introduction

Guangdong International Mansion lies in Huanshi Road in Guangzhou, which has 63 floors and is 200.15 meter high. Its total floor area is 177,500 square meters. This mansion is a super high-rise building (shown in Fig. 5-34 and Fig. 5-35), whose basement has 4 levels and foundation pit is 15.8 meters deep. Its foundation is box foundation on rock subgrade. This building's structural system is reinforced concrete tube in tube, whose external tube is 37m×35.1m and internal tube is 17m×23m. Guangdong International Mansion was the highest building at that time in China.

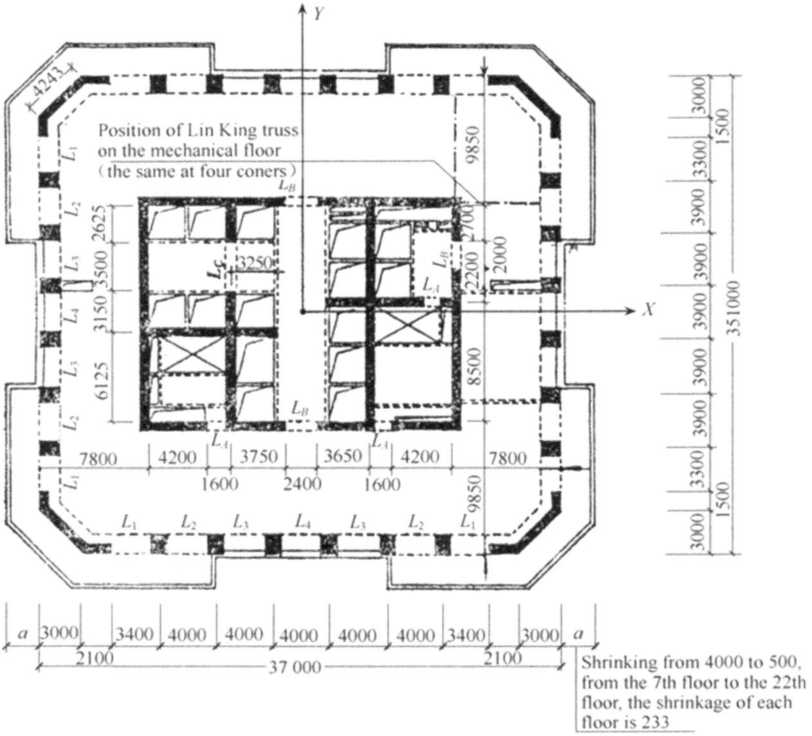

Fig. 5-34 Plane of the the main tower of Guangdong International Mansion

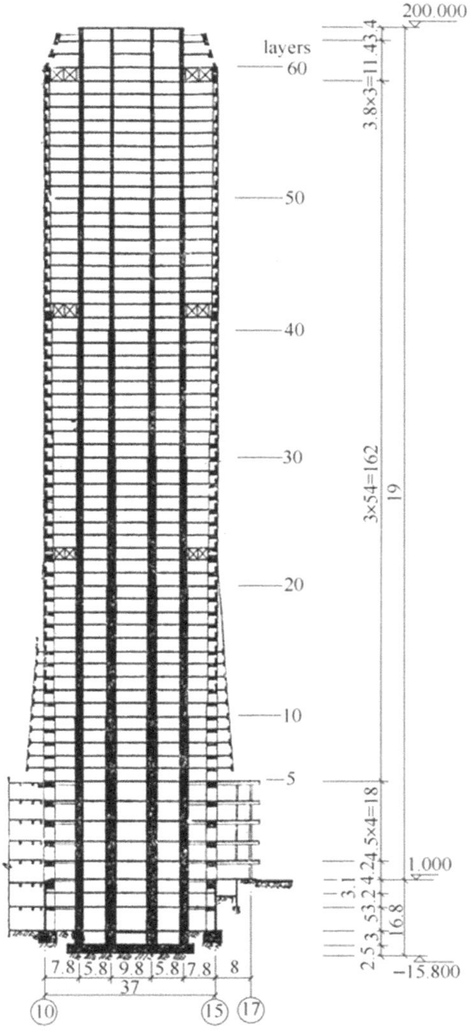

Fig. 5-35 Profile of the main tower of Guangdong International Mansion (unit in m)

5.7.2 Engineering Geological Conditions

1. Rock and soil subgrade

The residual subgrade is waxiness-hard-plastic medium compression subsoil, and its maximum allowable bearing capacity is 300kPa which cannot satisfy the requirement of constructing dormitory buildings and high-rise buildings, but can be used as the natural subgrade of the north podium (without basement). On the other hand, pile foundation should be applied for the north main tower (without basement) and hence the settlement joint should be set between podium and main tower.

The region about the north boundary (now the south part of the warehouse) of basement, which is constructed under 10.26 meter deep at the north foot of the little hill usually contains strong-weathered residual rock blocks, whose thickness is about 3—4m and distribution range extends more than 20 meters.

In terms of conglomerate, sandy conglomerate, and residual subgrade containing sandy conglomerate, sometimes they contain strong-weathered residual rock blocks, even not very popular but it might give rise to big damp during construction, even causes cracks of pile body or damage of pile tip, if precast pile or driving filling pile is adopted.

As far as medium sandstones and the residual subgrade containing sandy conglomerate (these kind of subgrade are called mild clay in site definition, and usually called light loam in geotechnical test) are concerned, the sand mass can be measured by sieving method. If the content of sandy conglomerate is from 50% to a little more than 80%, the subgrade is apt for disintegration after preserving water under the condition of non-lateral limitation. When the subgrade is found in the excavation slope under groundwater level, they are very inclined to lose stability because the seepage flow pressure (but most of the subgrade are sandwiches and don't distribute widely). Therefore, more attention should be paid to the stability of excavation slope during construction drainage, and it should be handled in time when lumps or cracks are found on the slope or at the slope foot.

Weathering zone: Most of weathering zones are strong-weathering and have very slight water, which are stable during excavation. Because of the less of thickness, it is not apt for pile foundation bearing stratum. On the other hand, there are difficulties in passing through, and even the design depth cannot be realized when using driving-pile foundation.

Fresh rock: Given the height and large gravity of the main tower, the fresh rock parts are taken as bedrocks without consideration of slightly-weathered parts. According to drilling zoning, the bedrock surface below the site is fluctuating, which is higher in the middle and lower in the north and east. The height fluctuation is more than 17m. For the middle and south parts in the site, it is necessary to dig 1—8 meters fresh rocks according to the elevation of the basement bottom. In the east part of the basement and the south boundary, the bedrock is lower than the basement bottom, so the covering residual subgrade above needs to be treated, especially for the east part of main tower where the thickness of residual soil is approximately 8m. The excavated part of bedrock can be directly used as platform for basement box foundation because embedding into bedrock is stable enough.

According to rock sample mechanical experiments, empirical statistics and the geological conditions, the suggested maximum value of allowable bearing capacity can be taken as 13MPa, which has already satisfied the bearing requirements of buildings completely.

2. Groundwater

Bedrock contains very slight water and residual subgrade is also weak aquifer, which result in small inflow of water during digging pits. However, there are still some water in the pit because the dewatering depth estimated according to the groundwater level needs to be about 10m considering the deep excavation of basement and large area of foundation pit.

In the dry season, the groundwater level is lower and therefore the pit drainage get less along with the prolonged dewatering time. It is good for the slope stability and so construction in winter is suggested.

3. Slope stability

Main focus is placed on residual subgrade. Based on observation data, the slope above the groundwater level can keep erect during construction and the slope angel can be 80 degree. However, the slope below groundwater level needs to be designed in accord with codes to meet the demand of allowable slope angle. Given the short construction period, the dewatering level will get decreasing along with excavation and too large seepage pressure will not occur, so the allowable slope angle can be appropriately enlarged and taken different angles in different parts of above and below groundwater level, referring to the dewatering construction experiences of other projects.

It is definitely that pit excavation area is larger than building bottom area. If the basement is firstly constructed, there are still some extended space in the north, west and east parts of the boundary and the drainage and safety zones can be set on the slope top. However, there are no space in the south of the pit which is adjoin closely to the enclosing walls and road. The traffic flow in the road will cause unfavorable influence to the slope stability. In the east part of the south boundary, the fresh bedrock is deeper about one meter than the basement bottom.

By estimating on the basis of the lowest groundwater level in winter (lower about one meter than drilling period), the depth of dewatering part of water-content residual subgrade is about 10—11m in the east of the basement, and is about 8—9 in the north, 6—9m in the west and 9—11m in the south.

5.7.3 Analysis of Foundation Settlement Observation

The foundation of main tower is placed on the fresh rock which is mainly composed of siltstones and whose allowable bearing capacity reaches 13MPa, far over the demand of design bearing capacity. Therefore, the external tube is designed a ring foundation with 4m width and 3m thickness. The internal tube is established on a foundation plate with 2.5m thickness. The buried depth of foundations of external and internal tubes is varying according to the different depth of basements. The foundations are connected with four huge rigid strips. The foundation depth of internal tube is about 16m, and the one of external tube is 13m. Below the strips, there are anchor rods: 32,L=5m @ 2000. The average contact pressure of the foundation bottom is 1.7MPa. The observed settlement is 7.21mm after about a year since the structure is completed, and the average settlement is 6.20mm. The maximum settlement difference between neighbor points is 3.03mm, which shows that the foundation settlement is very small and even. The observation points are shown in Fig. 5-36 and the specific settlement data is in the appendix.

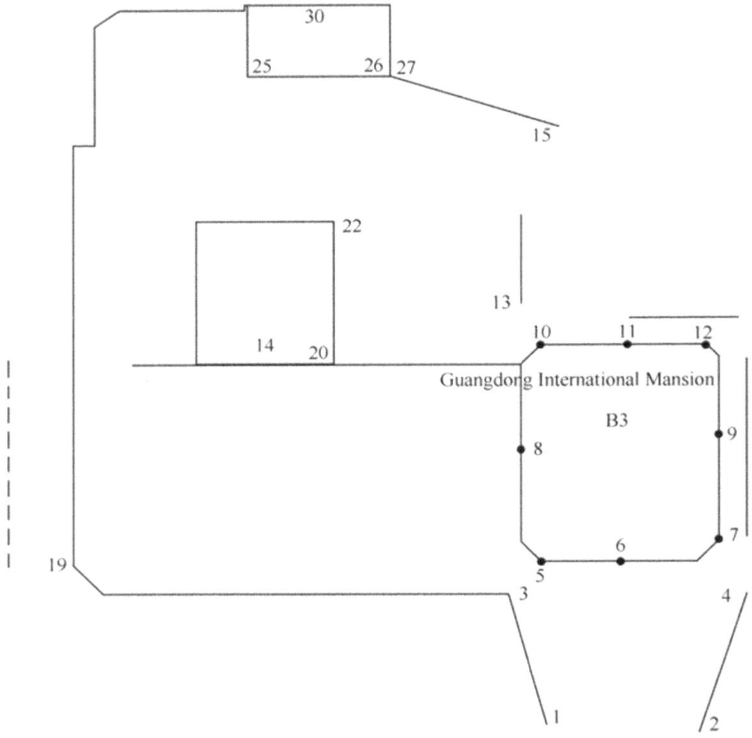

Fig. 5-36 Sketch of settlement observation points distribution of Guangdong International Mansion

Some conclusions are drawn from the analysis of settlement observation data of Guangdong International Mansion:

(1) When the bearing capacity of foundation on rock subgrade is higher, it is not necessary to calculate the settlement because the foundation settlement of super high-rise building is very small.

(2) The foundation of super high-rise buildings on rock subgrade should be counted as

rigid foundation when box foundation and thick plane are used, in order to coordinate the load of superstructure to make foundation settlement even.

(3) If the buried depth of super high-rise building on rock subgrade cannot satisfy the stability requirements, the anchor rods can be used to insure the stability of structure.

5.8 Chapter Summary

In this chapter, the compensation characteristics, groundwater buoyancy, and the relation between settlement and box foundation width are specifically introduced. Aiming at the stress and strain states and the resilience recompression after unloading of deep foundation pit, some settlement calculation methods in which the effect of support structures in foundation pit is not taken into account, are introduced, such as layering-summation method specified in the code, modified layering-summation method, Егоров method and Japanese method. At the same time, some calculation models and methods for box foundation settlement in which the effect of support structures in foundation pit is considered are firstly proposed, including up and down segmentation combination method, simplified calculation method, comprehensive coefficient calculation method, inkling subgrade step layering-summation method, integral structure calculation method. Using spline function to analyze layering subgrade shows prominent merits. In addition, the settlement observation data accumulated for 5 years of China Bank Mansion in Qingdao are listed in details. By using three different settlement calculation methods, like finite element method, the theoretical calculated values are very close to actual observations. After lots of trial calculation and comparison, we obtained the settlement empirical coefficient in the strong-weathered granite region ψ =0.2, and the depth adjustment coefficient for settlement calculation $\beta = 0.4$. Five conclusions are drawn from the analysis of actual observation of settlement:

(1) The settlement of box foundation in the strong-weathered granite regions is mainly composed of initial settlement and consolidation settlement, which can hardly be completely separated.

(2) The secondary consolidation settlement in the strong-weathered granite regions is not very obvious.

(3) After the completion of China Bank Mansion in Qingdao, its settlement has accounted for over 70% of the total settlement and gradually got stable. The settlement got completely stable in about 400 days upon completion of construction.

(4) The effect of support structures in deep foundation pit to box foundation settlement is obvious and cannot be ignored.

(5) The two empirical coefficients obtained above can be used in specification.

The settlement observation data of this project is very integrated, and its analyzed results are very important for further reference.

Appendix Settlement Observation data Table

Project Name: Guangdong International Mansion

Points ID Times and date			5	6	7	8	9	10	11	12
1th (4 layers)	21, 10, 1988	Elevation(mm)	—	20826.59	—	20826.88	20825.70	20826.39	20826.79	20828.07
		Settlement(mm)	—	—	—	—	—	—	—	—
		Total Settlement	—	—	—	—	—	—	—	—
2th (12 layers)	21, 10, 1988	Elevation(mm)	20253.42	20825.74	20817.90	20825.36	20823.45	20825.36	20825.15	20827.29
		Settlement(mm)	—	-0.85	—	-1.52	-2.25	-1.03	-1.64	-0.78
		Total Settlement	—	—	—	—	—	—	—	—
3th (20 layers)	21, 12, 1988	Elevation(mm)	20253.32	20824.11	20815.49	20824.09	20821.96	20824.08	20823.75	20826.00
		Settlement(mm)	-0.10	-1.63	-2.41	-1.27	-1.49	-1.28	-1.40	-1.29
		Total Settlement	-0.10	-2.48	-2.41	-2.79	-3.74	-2.31	-3.04	-2.07
4th (28 layers)	29, 03, 1989	Elevation(mm)	20251.11	20823.81	20813.85	20821.91	20822.20	20823.76	20823.25	20825.68
		Settlement(mm)	-2.13	-0.30	-1.64	-2.18	+0.24	-0.32	-0.50	-0.32
		Total Settlement	-2.23	-2.78	-4.05	-4.97	-3.50	-2.63	-3.54	-2.39
5th (38 layers)	16, 06, 1989	Elevation(mm)	—	20824.06	20815.94	20822.73	20820.76	20823.22	20822.80	20824.12
		Settlement(mm)	—	+0.25	+2.09	+0.82	-1.44	-0.54	-0.45	-1.546
		Total Settlement	—	-2.53	-1.96	-4.15	-4.94	-3.17	-3.99	-3.95
6th (49 layers)	15, 09, 1989	Elevation(mm)	20250.67	20822.10	20815.35	20822.55	20821.02	20822.76	20822.36	20824.06
		Settlement(mm)	+0.48	-1.96	-0.14	-1.54	+0.26	-0.46	-0.44	-0.06
		Total Settlement	-1.75	-4.49	-2.55	-4.33	-4.68	-3.63	-4.43	-4.01
7th (58 layers)	11, 11, 1989	Elevation(mm)	20252.27	20822.08	20815.28	20821.76	20821.40	20822.58	20822.32	20824.20
		Settlement(mm)	+0.60	-0.02	-0.07	-0.79	+0.38	-0.18	-0.04	+0.14
		Elevation(mm)	-1.15	-4.51	-2.62	-5.12	-4.30	-3.81	-4.47	-3.87
8th (63 layers)	21, 12, 1989	Elevation(mm)	20250.85	20820.55	20814.95	20820.05	20820.61	20820.55	20820.43	20822.20
		Settlement(mm)	-1.42	-1.53	-0.33	-1.71	-0.79	-2.03	-1.89	-2.00
		Elevation(mm)	-2.57	-6.64	-2.95	-6.83	-5.09	-5.84	-6.36	-5.87
9th Decor-ation	25, 04, 1990	Elevation(mm)	20250.47	20820.60	20812.87	20820.54	20818.90	20820.51	20820.13	20822.00
		Settlement(mm)	-0.38	+0.05	-2.08	+0.49	-1.71	-0.04	-0.30	-0.20
		Elevation(mm)	-2.95	-5.99	-5.03	-6.34	-6.80	-5.88	-6.66	-6.07
10th Decor-ation	17, 11, 1990	Elevation(mm)	20249.24	20820.06	20812.67	20819.67	20818.68	20820.54	20810.93	20821.37
		Settlement(mm)	-1.23	-0.54	-0.20	-0.87	-0.22	+0.03	-0.20	-0.63
		Total Settlement	-4.18	-6.53	-5.23	-7.21	-7.02	-5.85	-6.86	-6.70

References

Chen X.F. 1998. Computation and Measurement of Natural Ground Settlement of Tall Building, The Fifth International Conference on Tall Buildings, Hong Kong.

Chen X.F. 2005. Settlement Calculation Considering the Effect of Retaining and Protection of Deep Excavations for Box Foundation on Super Tall Building, Beijing: Construction Technology Magazine.

Chen X.F., Chen Wei. 2002. New Design Methods of Space Variable Stiffness Pile Groups Equal-Settlement, International Conference on Civil Engineering Innovation and Sustainable Development in the 21st Century, Beijing, China.

Chen X.F. 1999. The Highest Building Designed Ourselves in China——China Bank High-rise in Qingdao: Memoir of The First Academic Conference of China Association of Science and Technology, Beijing: China Science and Technology Press.

Cheung Y.K., Yeo M.F. 1979.A Practical Introduction to Finite Element Analysis, Oxford: Pergamon Press

Desai C. S. 1971. Nonlinear Analysis Using Spline Functions. J. Soil Mech. Found. Engg. Div., ASCE. Vo. 197 SM10

He G.Q., Chen X.F., Liu Daolan. 1990. Chinese Mansion, Beijing: New Era Press.

He G.Q., Chen X.F., Xu Z.J. 1994. Design and Construction of High-rise Building, Beijing: Science Press.

Huang X.L. 1993. Underground Structure and Foundation Pit Support of High-rise Buildings, Beijing: Aerospace Pre .

Qian L.H. 1983. A Number of Issues of Box-foundation Design for High-rise Building, Building Structure, No. 4.

Qian W.C., Ye K.Y. 1956. Elastic Mechanics, Beijing: Science Press.

Qin Rong. 1988. Spline Boundary Element Method, Nanning: Guangxi Science and Technology Press.

Qin Rong. 1999. Calculation Structure Non-linear Mechanics, Nanning: Guangxi Science and Technology Press

Shanghai Industrial Design Institute of Architecture. 1983. Design Discussion of Box-foundation for High-rise Building in Shanghai, Building Structure, No. 4.

Sun Jun, Wang B.J. 1998. Finite Element Analysis of Underground Structure, Shanghai: Tongji University Press

Winterkorn H.F. 1983. Handbook of Foundation Engineering, Beijing: China Building Industry Press

Zienkiewicz O.C. 1971. The Finite Element Method in Engineering Science, New York: McGraw-Hill.

Chapter 6 Research on Settlement Calculation Method of Super-Long Pile Foundation

For deep foundation of super high-rise building, pile box (raft) foundation is mostly adopt, and pile foundation is usually formed by super-long bored piles with large diameter, only a few super high-rise buildings are of super-long steel pipe pile (for example, for Jinmao Tower in Shanghai, steel pipe pile over 80m long is used. Generally, super-long drilled pile's diameter $d \geqslant$800mm, while pile length $l \geqslant$50m. At present, in the latest *Technical Code for Pile Foundations of Building* (JGJ94-94) of China, the vertical load capacity and other parameters of under water bored piles are determined by modifying prefabricated piles in *Code for Design of Foundation and Subgrade of Building* (GBJ7-89) combined with measured data of under water bored piles. In China, more and more super high-rise buildings have been built in soft subgrade area, such as Shanghai, Tianjin, Wuhan, Fuzhou, Shantou, Wenzhou, Wuxi, Nanjing, Zhengzhou, Xi'an and etc, and large number of super-long bored piles are used, and there is undergoing trend. After 100 years' application and research of bored piles, admittedly there have been much study on short pile, middle-long pile and long pile, and there have also been much data & material accumulated. But for super long pile, there have been reletively less study and test data. The reason is that it is difficult to form a pile and also difficult to reach the ultimate bearing capacity of pile in pile compression test for engineering. So it is very pressing and important to study the performance and settlement of super-long pile. In this chapter, settlement characteristics and engineering application of super-long pile are researched, and some suggestions and opinions about using super-long pile are put forward. Meanwhile, settlement calculation method of pile foundation is presented, which is derived from *Code for Design of Foundation and Subgrade of Building* (GB50007-2001).

6.1 Single Pile Settlement

Settlement of single pile is composed of pile body elastic compression deformation, pile side subgrade compression deformation, pile end subgrade compression deformation, pile end stab deformation. That is:

$$S = S_e + S_f + S_p + S_l \tag{6-1}$$

where: S_e—Single pile elastic compression deformation;

S_f —The compression deformation of under pile toe subgrade which is caused by side friction of pile which transfers to pile toe plane;

S_p —The compression deformation of under pile toe subgrade which is caused by pile end load;

S_t —The stab deformation which is produced by pile toe.

From Formulate (6-1), it can be seen that all the later three kinds of deformation mentioned above are deformation that takes place below the pile toe. As it is super-long pile, the bearing capacity of a single pile can't reach its ultimate state. When the load is small, the pile toe basically doesn't produce stab deformation. So this part of deformation doesn't exist under the normal circumstances. When the load is large, and the properties of bearing subgrade at pile toe is poor, stab deformation can't be neglected. The common calculation method of single pile doesn't divide the below-the-pile-toe deformation for calculation, the calculation method itself has taken into account the effect. In fact, it is unnecessary and also difficult to differentiate between the subgrade compressive deformation below the pile toe which is caused by side friction and by toe bearing.

Calculation methods of single pile settlement are usually used for settlement calculation of single super-long pile, which are elastic theory method, load transfer method, Shear displacement transfer method, shears displacement transfer method, finite element method, simplified method, empirical method and etc.

6.1.1 Single Pile Settlement Calculation by Elastic Theory Method

1. Mechanism analysis of settlement

This method is based on Mindlin solution to calculate the stress dispersion of pile, it idealized pile subgrade for elastic material in order to calculate the settlement of pile. Mindlin provides solution of the stress and elastic displacement of any position in homogeneous elastic semi-infinite body which were caused by applying vertical concentrated force at any point in elastic semi-infinite body. Provided the existing of pile doesn't affect the Mindlin's solution, to format the pile into several elements vertically, as Fig.6-1 shown, side friction of the number i element will cause the displacement of the subgrade around the number i element of the pile, so, it can be got by superposition all side friction of the n elements and the displacement of the element pile side subgrade which is caused by end-Friction of the number n element. The displacement formula of pile side subgrade is as follows:

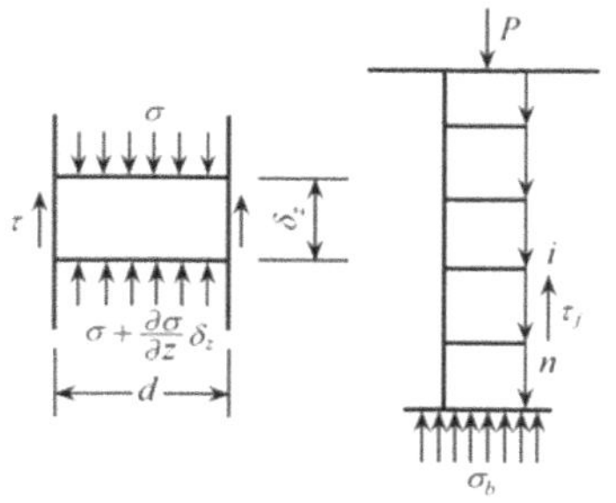

(a) Element of pile (b) Stress of pile

Fig. 6-1 Schematic diagram of subgrade sharing

$$\left.\begin{aligned}[s_i'] &= \frac{d}{E_s}\sum_{j=1}^{n} I_{ij}\tau_j + \frac{d}{E_s} I_{ib}\sigma_b \\ [s'] &= \frac{d}{E_s}[I_s]\{\tau\}\end{aligned}\right\} \tag{6-2}$$

d —Diameter of the pile;

E_s —Subgrade Elastic Modulus;

I_{ij} —The displacement coefficient of the number i element of pile side subgrade, when the shear stress of the number j element τ_i=1. The result is given by Mindlin integral equation;

I_{ib} —The displacement coefficient of the number i element of pile side subgrade, when the vertical stress of the pile end σ_b=1, The result is given by Mindlin integral equation;

$[s']$—The displacement vector of pile side subgrade. $\{s'\}=[s_1's_2'\cdots s_n's_b']^{\mathrm{T}}$;

$[I_s]$ —The displacement coefficient matrix of pile side subgrade;

$\{\tau\}$ —Shear stress of pile side and internal force vector of pile toe.

From the relationship between the micro segment's deformation of Hooker law and side friction, the displacement of pile body $\{S''\}$ can be got. Consider the deformation compatibility between the displacement of pile side subgrade and the displacement of pile body, that $\{S''\}=\{S'\}$, can get the distribution of pile, side friction along the length of the pile $\{\tau\}$, Replacing pby $\{S''\}$ or $\{S'\}$, will get the settlement of the pile.

2. Concrete calculation method

Poulos provides parameter solution of settlement calculation about single pile tip in homogeneous subgrade. That is:

$$S=\frac{P}{E_S L}I_P \tag{6-3}$$

where: S—The settlement of single pile tip;

P—Load on pile tip;

L—Length of pile;

I_p—Settlement coefficient. For semi special homogeneous subgrade, single pile settlement coefficient I_0 is set as $v_s = 0.5$, according to $\frac{L}{d}$ and pile stiffness K (refer to graph), for finite thickness subgrade layer, $I_p = I_0 R_h$, in that formula, R_h is correction coefficient when considering the thickness of homogeneous subgrade layer. Poisson's ratio of subgrade has less effect on settlement (usually less than 15%). If the effect of Poisson's ratio must be considered, settlement coefficient must be multiplied by a correction coefficient R_v which reflects the effect of the Poisson's ratio. (refer to graphs).

When pile is punctured into better bearing stratum, the settlement of pile tip can also be calculated according to the following formula. But it must consider correction coefficient of stiffness effect. Those are:

$$S = M_R \frac{PL}{E_P A_P}$$

$$M_R = \frac{\tau}{4} K \left(\frac{d}{L}\right)^2 I_P \tag{6-4}$$

where: I_P—Pile Elastic Modulus;

A_P—Cross sectional area of pile;

K—Stiffness of pile;

M_R—Settlement coefficient of single pile. (refer to graphs).

6.1.2 Load Transfer Method

The vertical pressure of the pile transfers to the subgrade though frictional resistance and toe resistance. If we can find the distribution function of side frictional resistance and toe resistance of the pile, then the settlement can be got. This method which calculates settlement of single pile according to side frictional resistance and toe resistance of the pile is called load transfer method. Meanwhile, the load transfer law of single pile can be analysed. This method was initially proposed by Seed and Reese in 1955, then got continuous development. This method takes the pile as columnar member which is composed of many elastic elements. Each element is related to subgrade by nonlinear spring, as shown in Fig.6-2. These springs express the relationship between side resistance (or toe resistance) and shear displacement (or pile tip displacement), this load transfer function is also called relationship function of $\tau - z$.

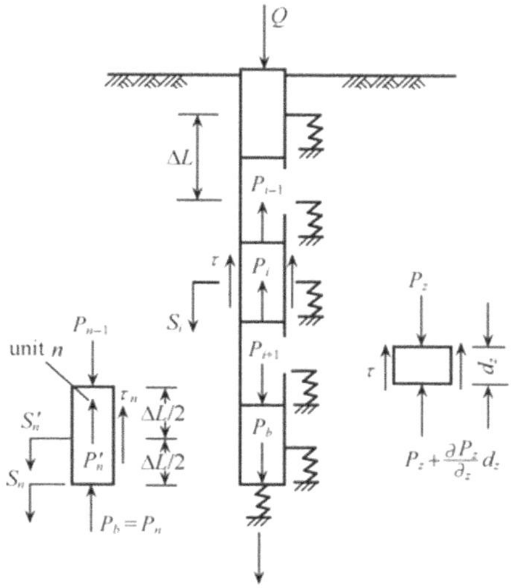

Fig. 6-2 Schematic diagram of load transfer method

The key of the load transfer method is that the research and determination of the load transfer function. Whether or not the transfer function is reasonable, is decisive for the right calculation analysis. According to the study of theory and test, domestic & foreign scholars put forward various transfer functions from different angles in the past decade, such as parabola, hyperbola, broken line and other several kinds of functions. These can be shown in Table 6-1.

Table 6-1 Load transfer function

Author	Side resistance transfer function	Remarks
Kezdi A(1957)	$\tau(z)=K\gamma z\tan\varphi\left[1-e^{\left(-\frac{R_s}{s_u-s}\right)}\right]$	K is side pressure coefficient , K is coefficient
佐藤悟(1965)	$s<s_u$， $\tau(z)=C_s S$； $S\geqslant S_u$， $\tau(z)$	S is relative displacement, C_s is coefficient
Gardner(1975)	$\tau(z)=A[S/(1/K+S/\tau_u)]$	K,A are experimental constants
Vijayvergia V.N.(1977)	$\tau(z)=\tau_{\max}(2\sqrt{S/S_u}-S/S_u)$	S_u is critical relative displacement of pile
Kraft L.M.(1981)	$\tau(z)=G_0 S/r_0/\ln[(r_m/r_0-\psi)]$ $\psi=\tau(z)R_f/\tau_{\max}$	G_0 is original shear modulus of subgrade r_0 is radius of pile. r_m is settlement influencing radius of pile R_f is fitting constants
Desai C.S., et al.(1987)	$\tau(z)=\dfrac{(K_0-K_f)S}{\left(1+\left\|\dfrac{(K_0-K_f)S}{P_f}\right\|^m\right)^{1/m}}+K_f S$	K_0 is initial spring stiffness K_f is final spring stiffness P_f is yield load m is curve index

When load transfer relation is measured through embedded instruments, load transfer function can be solved with displacement coordination method. This method discretes the pile into several elements first, and hypothesizes there is initial displacement value on pile toe, according to the deformation coordination relationship between axial direction deformation of pile body and deformation of pile side subgrade, the initial force distribution law along the pile, as well as the settlement of the pile piecewise upward can be obtained.

Because of complex geology and change of engineering, there are a lot of factors which affect load transfer function. There are different load transfer functions under different conditions, so it is difficult to find the functional relationship of $\tau - z$ which is consistent with the reality. Although it can be monitored by embedding instruments during engineering process, it is of limited effect. Functional relationship measured indoor is not so close to practical engineering. In addition, the load transfer method shows that the displacement of pile is only related to the friction where the pile is, regardless of effect of other elements. But these factors could influence calculation accuracy, which limitate the application of load transfer method.

6.1.3 Single Pile Settlement Calculation by Shear Displacement Method

Cooke conducted study on displacement of the subgrade around pile when the stress is relative low for the pile body. He put forth shear displacement transfer module in 1974, and apply it to calculate settlement of single pile. In this method, the displacement of pile relative to side subgrade is syntropic under working load, and there is no relative displacement between them. And with the increase of the distance to pile side, shear stress gradually diffuses and decreases, and the shear displacement is relatively small, displacement distribution surface in the shape of funnel is formed around the single pile. Pile settlement occurs resulting from shear strain of subgrade caused by transfer of pile side load in the subgrade.

There is a range for the pile side shear stress transfers in the subgrade. When the distance is great, from the pile heart $r_m = nr_0$ (Cooke thinks that n could be taken as 20), the shear stress is so little that it could be ignored. Under the effect of the shear stress, the shear strain of differential element is as follows:

$$r = \frac{\mathrm{d}S}{\mathrm{d}r} = \frac{\tau}{G_s} \tag{6-5}$$

where: S—Vertical displacement of single pile;

G_s—Shear modulus of subgrade;

τ—The stress which affects element, can be got from equilibrium condition

$$\tau = \tau_0 \frac{r_0}{r}$$

The settlement formula S_s of pile surface is as follows:

$$S_s = \int_{r_0}^{r_m} \frac{\tau_0 r_0}{G_s} \frac{dr}{r} = \frac{\tau_0 r_0}{G_s} \ln\left(\frac{r_m}{r_0}\right) \tag{6-6}$$

If the pile side friction is uniform distribution, such as pure friction pile, when $v_s = 0.5$, pile tip load $P_0 = 2\pi r_0 L \tau_0$, elastic modulus of subgrade $E_S = aG_s$, the pile tip settlement can be shown as Eq.(6-7).

$$S_0 = \frac{3}{2\pi} \frac{P_0}{LE_s} \ln\left(\frac{r_m}{r_0}\right) \tag{6-7}$$

where: r_0—Radius of pile;

G_s—Shear modulus of subgrade.

The shear displacement method doesn't consider the interaction among layers of subgrade, and doesn't consider the effect of toe resistance which exists practically. Therefore there is big error for short pile. However, for super-long pile, pile toe resistance doesn't play basically, so this method can be applied to calculate settlement of single pile. Randolph developed Cooke's method mentioned above, he considered the effect of toe resistance sharing load P_b, thus pile tip load P_0 is composed of side resistance P_s and toe resistance P_b, for rigid pile, the pile settlement is that:

$$S_0 = S_s = S_b = \frac{P_0}{G_s r_0 \left[\frac{2\pi L}{r_0 \ln\left(\frac{r_m}{r_0} + \frac{4}{(1-v_s)\eta}\right)}\right]} \tag{6-8}$$

where: η—The effect coefficient of pile subgrade, usually within the range of 0.8~1.0.

6.1.4 Single Pile Settlement Calculation by Simplified Method from *Code for Road and Bridge* of China

According to local specific geological condition and length of pile, style of pile, load and so on, we can get empirical formula to estimate settlement of single pile by statistical analysis of data of the field measurements. Because the limitation of engineering conditions, although empirical formula has limitation, it can't be used widely, it is very useful for local condition. It can estimate settlement of single pile exactly, and can make comparison and reference with other places.

When pile is presumed to take part in bearing pressure, the settlement of pile tip is composed of pile toe settlement S_b and compression amount of pile body S_s, and the side resistance and the toe resistance both have effect on S_b and S_s. There are different simplified calculation methods of single pile settlement based on different viewpoints. The following settlement calculation formula of single pile from railway bridge design specifications (TBJ2-85) and highway bridge and culvert foundation design specifications (JTJ024-85), can work as reference.

$$S = S_a + S_b = \Delta\frac{PL}{E_p A_p} + \frac{P}{C_0 A_0} \tag{6-9}$$

where: P —Vertical load of pile tip;

L —Length of pile;

E_p, A_p —Elastic modulus and pile section area respectively;

A_0 —Diffusion area from subgrade (or pile top) to pile toe plane with $\frac{\varphi}{4}$ angle;

Δ —Diffusion coefficient of pile side friction. For friction pile whose sinking style is driven or vibration, Δ can be taken as 2/3, while for the drill hole grouting friction pile, Δ can be taken as 1/2;

C_0 —Vertical foundation coefficient of pile toe subgrade. When the length of pile $L \leqslant$ 10m, $C_0 = 10\ m_0$, when L>10m, $C_0 = L\ m_0$, where m_0 is proportional coefficient which changes with the depth. It can be got from the table according to the category of the pile toe subgrade.

6.2 Settlement Calculation of Pile Group Foundation

The stress of super-long pile group foundation is greater than that of single pile because the load which lay impact on single pile will superpose each other when diffused in the subgrade. So the settlement of pile group foundation is bigger than that of single pile. The mechanical properties of this kind of pile group foundation are different from that of single pile. Study and measurement have shown that the following factors all have impact on the settlement of pile: pile spacing, style of pile, length of pile, pile diameter, pile formation technology (including whether or not grouting technology is adopted later on), contact between basement and subgrade, physical and mechanical properties of bearing subgrade and pressured subgrade. Until now, there has been no perfect calculation method for pile foundation settlement and super-long pile settlement. In China, solid foundation calculation method, pile foundation standard calculation method, elasticity calculation method are usually applied. These methods can be adopted to calculate the settlement of super-long pile.

6.2.1 Solid Foundation Calculation Method for Super-Long Pile Group Foundation

In fact, this method is equivalent pier method. It takes the pile as solid foundation, and then calculates the settlement according to shallow foundation. The key of this method is how to get the value of solid foundation area and buried depth. In China, the following ways are often used:

1. Boundary pile bounding method

It is based on the simulation that pile group solid foundation is bounded by edge piles in outer margin, and the basement is at the place where the pile tips are. It can be shown as Fig.6-3(a). The basement area is the range of bounded pile edge. The buried depth D equals the length of pile plus the buried depth of box (raft) foundation. Induced stress is calculated from end of pile.

2. According to diffusion method with $\frac{\bar{\varphi}}{4}$ *angle*

As shown in Figure 6-3(b), diffusing from the edge of side pile in $\frac{\bar{\varphi}}{4}$ angle downward to the pile toe plane forms the solid foundation area which is the area subject to diffusion. It can be calculated according to the following formula. And the buried depth is $L+D$.

$$F = A \times B = \left(a + 2L\tan\frac{\bar{\varphi}}{4}\right)\left(b + 2L\tan\frac{\bar{\varphi}}{4}\right) \tag{6-10}$$

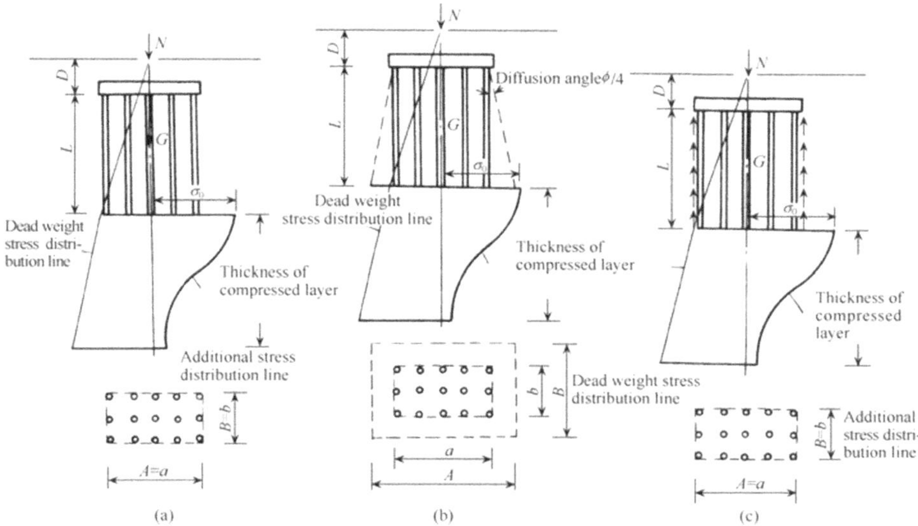

Fig. 6-3 Settlement calculation model of pile group foundation

where: *a, b*—The long side and short side of rectangular which is bounded by edge piles in outer margin;

A, B—The long side and short side of the basement of simulated solid foundation;

L—Length of pile;

D—The buried depth of box (raft) foundation;

$\bar{\varphi}$—Layer-thickness-weighted average internal friction angle of subgrade within the range of the pile length.

3. Side frictional resistance deduction method

As shown in Fig. 6-3(c), the part which is bounded by edge piles in outer margin of the range of pile length can be taken as deep foundation. Then the area of deep foundation is the area which is bounded by edge piles in outer margin. The calculation method is the same as the first method, except that side frictional resistance of deep foundation should be deducted from the basement pressure. The basement pressure P and the induced stress P_0 can be calculated as follows:

$$\left.\begin{aligned} &\mathrm{P}=[F+G-\sum_{i=1}^{n}2(A+B)l_i q_{si}]\div(A+B) \\ &\mathrm{P}_0=\mathrm{P}-\sigma_{cd} \end{aligned}\right\} \tag{6-11}$$

where: P, P_0—Basement reaction and basement induced stress of deep foundation respectively;

F—The load from the superstructures;

G—The dead weight of simulated deep foundation, can be taken in kN;

l_i—The thickness of the number i subgrade layer in the range of pile length;

q_{si}—The side friction resistance of the number i subgrade layer in the range of pile length;

σ_{cd}—The dead weight stress of the simulated deep foundation basement subgrade.

It obviousl that when calculating the settlement of pile group foundation with the first method and the second method, the friction resistance can be taken as zero for pressure of basement.

There are three kinds of methods in practical engineering when applying the above three methods to calculate final settlement. They are national foundation standard method, layer-wise summation method and Shanghai standard method.

(1) National foundation standard method

$$S_\infty=\psi_s S_i'=\psi_s\sum_{i=1}^{n}\frac{P_0}{E_{si}}(z_i\bar{a}_i-z_{i-1}a_{i-1}) \tag{6-12}$$

where: S_∞—The final settlement of foundation (mm);

z_i, z_{i-1}—The distance to the pile toe plane from the layer bottom and layer top respectively, of the number i subgrade layer which is under the pile toe;

$\bar{a}_i$, a_{i-1}—The coefficient of average induced stress of layer bottom , layer top of the number i subgrade layer which is under the pile toe (refer to attached list of specifications);

E_{si}—The compression modulus of the number i subgrade layer which is under the pile toe (MPa);

ψ_s—The regional empirical correction coefficient of settlement calculation. (refer to attached list of specification);

S_i'—Foundation deformation based on layer-wise summation method;

n—The number of the subgrade layer in the range of the calculated depth of foundation settlement. The calculated depth of settlement should meet requirement, it can be got according to $z_n = B(2.5 - 0.4\ln B)$, but must comply with the following formula

$$\Delta S_i' \leqslant 0.025\sum_{i=1}^{n}\Delta S_i'$$

where: $\Delta S_i'$—Calculated settlement of the number i subgrade layer within the calculation depth;

$\Delta S_n'$—Calculated settlement of the subgrade with the thickness of Δz from above the calculation depth. Δz can be got from the table in code.

(2) Layer-wise summation method

$$S_\infty = mS_c = m\sum_{i=1}^{n}\frac{\bar{\sigma}_{zi}}{E_{si}}H_i = m\sum_{i=1}^{n}\frac{e_{1i} - e_{2i}}{1 + e_{1i}}H_i \tag{6-13}$$

where: n—Delaminating number within compression layer which is under pile toe. The compression layer can be determined by $\sigma_z \leqslant (0.1 \sim 0.2)\sigma_c$ .when compression layer is soft soil layer, n can be 0.1, for other subgrade, n can be 0.2;

H_i—The depth of the ith layer of subgrade;

$\bar{\sigma}_{zi}$—Average additional stress of the ith layer of subgrade;

e_{1i}, e_{2i}—The void ratio corresponding to the compression curve respectively, of the average of dead weight of the ith layer of subgrade $\bar{\sigma}_{ci}$, and the sum of the average of dead weight $\bar{\sigma}_{ci}$ and the average induced stress $\bar{\sigma}_{zi}$, i.e. $\bar{\sigma}_{ci} + \bar{\sigma}_{zi}$;

E_{si}—The compression modulus corresponding to stress increment of the ith layer of subgrade. $E_{si} = \frac{1 + e_{1i}}{a_i} = \frac{1 + e_{1i}}{e_{1i} - e_{2i}}\bar{\sigma}_{zi}$, a_i is compression coefficient of corresponding stress increment of the ith layer of subgrade;

m—The empirical correction coefficient of settlement calculation when considering the effect of the factors such as side deformation of subgrade. m =1.0~1.4, smaller value for the condition when the load area is large and the load is small and even, bigger value for the condition when the load is big and partially distributed.

(3) Shanghai code method

$$S_{\infty} = \psi B p_0 \sum_{i=1}^{n} \frac{\delta_i - \delta_{i-1}}{E_{si}} = \psi \sum_{i=1}^{n} \frac{\sigma_{zi}}{E_{si}} H_i \tag{6-14}$$

where: B—The width of the basement of the solid foundation for simulation of pile group;

P_0 —The additional stress of the solid foundation;

δ_i —Settlement coefficient;

E_{si} —The compression modulus corresponding to the real range of stress;

σ_{zi} —The induced stress of the center of the ith layer below the pile end;

n —Delaminating number in the range of compression, the compression layer can be determined by $\sigma_z \leqslant 0.2\sigma_c$, and the depth of each layer is no larger than 0.4B;

ψ —The empirical coefficient of settlement calculation by Shanghai code method.

(4) Calculation illustration of equivalent pier method used in US and European countries, and its difference with Chinese method is to be introduced, so that comparison can be made.

1) Peck method: about the basement position of the simulation solid foundation. Provided there is compressive deformation of subgrade between piles, Peck suggests to lay the basement of the simulated solid foundation above the pile toe plane by the amount of L_c. If the pile is in the uniform clay layer, L_c can be taken as 1/3 of the pile length [Shown as Fig. 6-4(a)]; If the pile penetrates soft subgrade into hard bearing stratum, L_c can be taken as 1/3 of the penetrated depth into the bearing stratum by the pile toe [Shown as Fig. 6-4(b)].

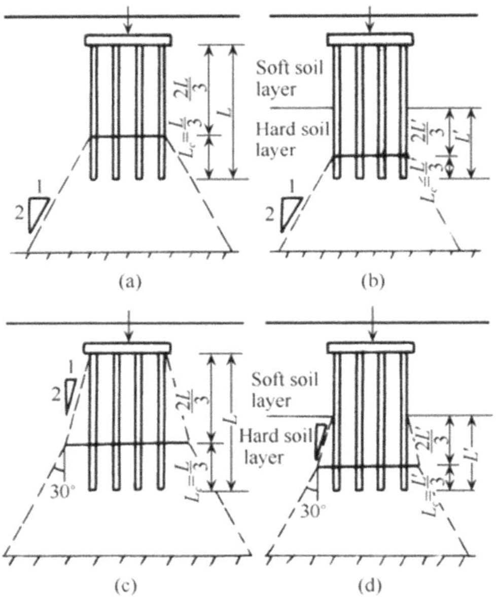

Fig. 6-4 Calculation illustration of equivalent pier method abroad

The suggestion of Pecks to move upward the simulation basement position is advisable in general. But the influencing factors involved are too simple in that their suggestion only considers the effect of subgrade profile, so it needs further study and improvement. The test result of the pile group settlement deformation show that to determine the position of the simulated basement is actually to estimate the proportion of the compressive deformation of subgrade to the total settlement of pile group. So the elevation amount of the simulation basement position is related to not only subgrade profile, but also subgrade type, pile spacing, pile length, load amount, pile formation technology and etc. When the whole pile is in uniform subgrde, the softer is the subgrde, the easier there is lateral extrusion, and the more the simulation basement position be lifted upward. Thus to some extend it is not reasonable to use the same method to treat the simulation basement position for uniform soft subgrde and uniform hard subgrde, and different elevation amount should be suitably chosen according to the softness degree of subgrde. When the bearing stratum is of hard subgrde and pile spacing is small (3d), the simulation basement position is close to pile end plan, and will the increase of pile spacing, the simulation basement position ascends. If the effect of pile body compression is neglected, the simulation basement position is identical to pile toe plane in the condition of long pile, and ascends with the decrease of pile length. When the loads of pile group is small, the simulation basement position is identical to pile end plane, and ascends with the increase of loads. The subgrade extrusion effect which occurres in the process of pile drivinge makes subgrade between piles and at pile toe become compact, thus prestress impact is aroused for residual compressive stress at the pile toe and residual tensile stress in the pile body, while pile formation technology of bored pile is not subject to this impact. This has led to the difference in deformation behavior of settlement between the two kinds of pile group. Available test results of pile group have shown that under the condition of less than or equal working load, the working behavior of bored pile group is more closed to solid foundation than bored pile group, so for bored pile, it is suitable to set relatively large value for L_c.

2) Tomlinson method : Tomlinson (1977) put forward another simplified method for diffusion effect of pile group peripheral side, i.e. diffusing downwards from the periphery of the pile group end with 1 ∶ 4 ratio of horizontal direction to vertical direction [shown as Fig 6-3(b)]. The correspondingly determined basement area of the simulation solid foundation is usually larger than the that associated with $\frac{\varphi}{4}$ diffusion angle.

To calculate the induced stress of subgrade, simplified method is mostly used abroad for downward diffusion of load from the edge of simulation solid foundation, which assumes oblique line with 1 ∶ 2 ratio of horizontal direction to vertical direction [shown as Fig. 6-4 (a), (b)] or with 30° degree [shown as Fig. 6-4 (c), (d)]. This method is suitable for pile foundation in clay subgrade. The result of the induced stress has little difference with that determined by Boussinesq. The depth of compression layer is usually the place where the induced stress of the subgrade is 1/10 of the induced stress of the basement, or smaller than the top of compression layer. It is very convenient to use the method which determines the load diffusion area by oblique line with the ratio of 1 : 2. Usually, the total induced load N_g at the elevation of the bottom plane of the pile-cap (N_g equals the total load of the upper structure above the elevation of the pile-cap bottom plane minus the effective weight of the overlaid subgrade) is directly taken as the total induced load of the simulation foundation basement. The induced stress σ_{zi} at the depth z_i (corresponding to the center point of a certain subgrade layer) where is below the simulation basement is:

$$\sigma_{zi} = \frac{N_g}{(B+z_i)(A+z_i)} \tag{6-15}$$

where : B and A —The width and length of the simulation foundation basement.

With the calculation result of induced stress by the models presented in Fig.6-4, settlement is calculated by layer-wise summation method. Some scholars think it represents the consolidation settlement of pile foundation, while some other scholars think that multiplication should be made by depth correction coefficient and earthiness correction coefficient before it represents the consolidation settlement of pile foundation, the depth correction coefficient depends on the ratio of equivalent width to buried depth of the simulation solid foundation, and the earthiness correction coefficient depends on the over-consolidation ratio of subgrade. It shows that there are difference of opinions among experts. In addition, according to the different deformation properties of subgrade, some scholars think that the settlement of the pile foundation is composed of consolidation deformation and instantaneous deformation. The former is calculated by compression modulus E_c of subgrade, and the latter is calculated by deformation modulus E_u under non-drainage condition. However, the value of E_u obtained from the stress-strain curve of no-drainage shear test indoor is reletively small. It often requires settlement observation of building prototype and data on subgrade test in door and in field to comprehensively figure out the empirical relationship between E_u and non-drainage shear strength C_u. But, even in the region with construction experience, it's difficult to establish reliable relationship between E_u and C_u, thus the settlement calculation method of pile foundation which considers consolidation deformation and instantaneous deformation is limitated in engineering application .

6.2.2 Method of Pile Foundation JGJ94-94

Technical Code for Pile Foundation of Building (JGJ94-94) adopts equivalent action layer-wise summation method to calculate pile foundation settlement, which is suitable for pile foundation whose distance of pile center is less than or equal to 6 times of pile diameter. In fact, it is also a kind of solid foundation method. This method doesn't consider the stress diffusion effect of pile foundation side. It takes the pile cap as acting on the pile toe plane directly, i.e, it takes the length and the width of solid foundation as equal to the length and the width of pile cap, and the additional stress which acts on the basement of solid foundation is as well taken as the additional stress of pile cap basement.

$$S = \psi \cdot \psi_e \cdot \sum_{j=1}^{n} p_{0j} \sum_{i=1}^{n} \frac{z_{ij} a_{ij} - z_{(i-1)j} a_{(i-1)j}}{E_{si}} \tag{6-16}$$

where: S —The final settlement of pile foundation (mm);

$S^{'}$ —The settlement of pile foundation which is calculated by layer-wise summation method (mm);

m—The block number of rectangular uniform loads corresponding to the calculation point for corner points method;

p_{0j} —The additional stress of long-term effect combination of the *j*th rectangular basement corresponding to the calculation point for corner points method;

n—The number of subgrade layer within the range of pile settlement calculation depth. The settlement calculation depth can be controlled by $\sigma_z = 0.2\sigma_c$, where $\sigma_z = \sum a_n p_{0j}$, while $a_j^{'}$ is the ratio of length to width of rectangle and the ratio of depth (refer to the code);

E_{si} —The compression modulus of the *i*th practical stress range below the solid foundation (MPa);

$z_{ij}, z_{(i-1)j}$ —The distance from the *j*th load of pile end plane to the basement of the *i*th subgrade layer, and to the *i*-1th subgrade layer;

$a_{ij}, a_{(i-1)j}$ —The average additional stress coefficient of load calculation point of the *j*th pile end plane to the basement of the *i*th subgrade layer, and to the *i*-1th subgrade layer;

ψ —The empirical coefficient of pile settlement calculation. For regions of non-soft subgrade or of soft subgrade with sound bearing stratum of pile end, it is taken as $\psi = 1$. For regions of soft subgrade (mainly refers to the region of Shanghai) without sound bearing stratum, the value of ψ can be detetmined as follows:

Pile length L<25m, $\psi = 1.7$

Pile length L>25m, $\psi = \dfrac{5.9L-20}{7L-100}$

ψ_e—The equivalent settlement coefficient of pile foundation. Because pile group settlement solution of Mindlin is more consistent with practice than the solution of Boussinesq, but the former is complx for calculation. So the code combines them to find the empirical relation, introducing the equivalent settlement coefficient of pile foundation. It can be determined as follows:

$$\psi_e = C_0 + \frac{n_b - 1}{C_1(n_b - 1) + C_2}$$

$$n_b = \sqrt{n \cdot B_c / L_c}$$

where: n_b—The number of pile laid along short side when piles are laid in rectangle. When piles are laid irregular, n_b can be calculated approximately according to the formula, if the calculation value is less than 1, take n_b=1;

L_c, B_c, n—The length, width and total pile number respectively of rectangular pile cap;

C_0, C_1, C_2—Parameters, which can be referred to in the code according to the ratio of pile center distance to pile diameter S_a/d, length to diameter L/d and foundation length to foundation width L_c/d_c. When the pile layout is irregular, S_a/d can be calculated approximately as following formula:

Circular pile

$$S_a / d = \sqrt{A_e} / \sqrt{n} \cdot d$$

Square pile

$$S_a / d = 0.886\sqrt{A_e} / \sqrt{n} \cdot b$$

where: A_e—The total area of pile cap;

b—The side length of square pile.

(1) The calculation formula of central point settlement of pile foundation is:

$$S = \psi \cdot \psi_e \cdot s' = 4\psi \cdot \psi_e \cdot P_0 \sum_{i=1}^{n} \frac{z_i a_i - z_{(i-1)} a_{(i-1)}}{E_{si}} \tag{6-17}$$

where: a_i, a_{i-1}—Can be referred to in tables of the code according to the ratio of length to width a/b of rectangle and the ratio of depth to width $\frac{z_i}{b} = \frac{2z_i}{B_c}, \frac{z_{i-1}}{b} = \frac{2z_{i-1}}{B}$

(2) The calculatin formula of the settlement at the angular point of rectangular pile group foundation is as follows:

$$S = \psi \cdot \psi_e \cdot s' = \psi \cdot \psi_e \cdot P_0 \sum_{i=1}^{n} \frac{z_i a_i - z_{(i-1)} a_{(i-1)}}{E_{si}} \tag{6-18}$$

where: a_i, a_{i-1} —Can be referred to in tables of the code according to the ratio of length to width a/b of rectangle and depth to width $\frac{z_i}{b}=\frac{2z_i}{B_c}, \frac{z_{i-1}}{b}=\frac{2z_{i-1}}{B}$. Other symbols are the same as previous.

6.2.3 Composite Method of Pile Foundation

The method of composite pile foundation is the theory based on the principle of co-working of pile, subgrade and foundation, it uses the Mindlin to solution the Geddes integral to analyse the stress of pile in the subgrade, and through superposition it is applied to analyse pile group settlement. The theory takes into account the fact that the basement slab shares part of the load.

1. Calculation of stress of subgrade by Geddes integral method

The Mindlin to solution provides the integral equation of stress and displacement of any point in semi-infinite elastic body when applying concentrated force at any point of the semi-infinite elastic uniform body. According to integral equation of Mindlin, and combined with bearing characteristics of pile, Geddes presents the expression of vertical stress of any point in the subgrade under conditions of applying concentrated force on the pile toe, side friction uniformly distributed along the length of pile, and side friction linearly increasing along the length of pile. The stress passed from foundation to subgrade is composed of pile toe resistance and pile side resistance. The stress induced by the total resistance of the pile end is:

$$\sigma_{zp}=P_p I_p / l^2 \tag{6-19}$$

The stress induced by total friction of pile side can be calculated as follows:

(1) Side resistance distributed in rectangular:

$$\sigma_{zs}=P_s^g I_s^g / l^2$$

(2) Side resistance distributed in equilateral triangle:

$$\sigma_{zs}=P_s^s I_s^s / l^2$$

So the vertical induced stress of pile is:

$$\sigma_z=\sigma_{zp}+\sigma_{zs} \tag{6-20}$$

where: σ_{zp} , σ_{zs} —The vertical induced stress induced by pile toe resistance and pile side resistance respectively;

P_p, P_s —The total resistance of pile toe and pile side respectively. P_s^g , P_s^s is the total side friction of rectangular distribution and equilateral triangle distribution respectively;

l —The embedded depth of pile;

I_p, I_s—Tthe vertical stress coefficient induced by concentrated force of pile toe and side friction of pile respectively. I_p can be calculated as the following formula. For side friction distributed in rectangle, I_s can be calculated according to the formula I_s^g, for side friction distributed in equilateral triangle, I_s can be calculated according to the formula I_s^s:

$$I_p = \frac{1}{8\pi(1-\mu)}\left[\frac{-(1-2\mu)(m-1)}{A^3} + \frac{(1-2\mu)(m-1)}{B^3} - \frac{3(m-1)^3}{A^5} - \frac{3(3-4\mu)m(m+1)^2 - 3(m+1)(5m-1)}{B^5} - \frac{30m(m+1)^3}{B^7}\right]$$

$$I_s^g = \frac{1}{8\pi(1-\mu)}\left[\frac{-(2-\mu)}{A} + \frac{2(2-\mu)+2(1-2\mu)\left(\dfrac{m^2}{n^2}+\dfrac{m}{n^2}\right)}{B} - \frac{(1-2\mu)^2\left(\dfrac{m}{n}\right)^2}{F} + \frac{n}{A^3} + \frac{4m^2-4(1+\mu)\left(\dfrac{m}{n}\right)^2 m^2}{F^3} + \frac{4m(1+\mu)(m+1)\left(\dfrac{m}{n}+\dfrac{1}{n}\right)^2 - (4m^2+n^2)}{B^3} + \frac{6m^2\left(\dfrac{m^4-n^4}{n^2}\right)}{F^5} + \frac{6m\left(mn^2-\dfrac{1}{n^2}(m+1)^5\right)}{B^5}\right] \tag{6-21}$$

$$I_s^s = \frac{1}{4\pi(1\text{-}\mu)}\left[\frac{-2(2-\mu)}{A} + \frac{2(2-\mu)(4m+1)-2(1-2\mu)\left(\dfrac{m}{n}\right)^2(m+1)}{B} + \frac{2(1-2\mu)\dfrac{m^3}{n^2}-8(2-\mu)m}{F} + \frac{4\mu n^2 m+4m^3-15n^2 m-2(5+2\mu)\left(\dfrac{m}{n}\right)^2(m+1)^3+(m+1)^3}{B^3} + \frac{mn^2+(m-1)^3}{A^3} + \frac{2(7-2\mu)mn^2-6m^3+2(5+2\mu)\left(\dfrac{m}{n}\right)^2 m^3}{F^3} + \frac{6mn^2(n^2-m^2)+12\left(\dfrac{m}{n}\right)^2(m+1)^5}{B^5} - \frac{12\left(\dfrac{m}{n}\right)^2 m^5+6mn^2(n^2-m^2)}{F^5} - 2(2-\mu)\log e\left(\frac{A+m-1}{F+m}\cdot\frac{B+m+1}{F+m}\right)\right] \tag{6-22}$$

$$A^2 = [n^2+(m-1)^2]$$
$$B^2 = [n^2+(m+1)^2]$$

where: $F^2 = n^2 + m^2$;

$m = z/l$;

$n = r / l$;

μ —The Poisson ratio of subgrade;

r —The horizontal distance from calculation point to pile-axis line;

z —The vertical distance from calculation point to the ground surface. According to the above formula, when r =0, i.e. the position of vertical line of the pile center $n = 0$, the vertical stress will appear to be discontinuous. In order to avoid this situation, usually it is set as $n = 0.002$ instead of $n = 0$.

For the trapezoidal distribution situation of side friction with linearly increase along the pile depth, superposition could be done for side friction with rectangular distribution and equilateral triangle distribution. That is:

$$\sigma_{zs} = P_s^g I_s^g / l^2 + P_s^s I_s^s / l^2 \tag{6-23}$$

For the distribution situation of trapezoidal or inverse triangle of side friction with linear decrease along the pile depth, superposition could be done for side friction of rectangular distribution minus that of equilateral triangle distribution, and vertical stress is induced. That is:

$$\sigma_{zs} = P_s^g I_s^g / l^2 - P_s^s I_s^s / l^2 \tag{6-24}$$

As mentioned above, distribution of pile side friction along the pile depth is of the following types: rectangle, equilateral triangle, positive trapezoid, inverse trapezoid, inverse triangle and etc. When i the ratio of the pile toe load P_p to the pile tip load P is available as α ($\alpha = P_p / P$), the ratio of the total side friction to the pile tip load P is $1-\alpha$. Presumely the ratio of the total friction distributed in rectangle along the pile length to the load of pile tip is β ($\beta = P_s^g / P$), and the ratio of the total friction distributed in triangle along the pile length to the load of pile tip is $1-\alpha-\beta$, thus the vertical stress σ_z which is induced by the load of single pile in the subgrade can be calculated as follows:

1) For friction distributed in rectangle, the formula is

$$\sigma_z = [\alpha I_p + (1-\alpha) I_s^g] \frac{P}{l^2}$$

2) For friction distributed in triangle, the formula is

$$\sigma_z = [\alpha I_p + (1-\alpha) I_s^s] \frac{P}{l^2}$$

3) For friction distributed in positive trapezoid, the formula is

$$\sigma_z = [\alpha I_p + \beta I_s^g + (1-\alpha-\beta) I_s^s] \frac{P}{l^2}$$

4) For friction distributed in inverse trapezoid or inverse triangle, the formula is

$$\sigma_z = [\alpha I_p + \beta I_s^g - (1-\alpha-\beta) I_s^s] \frac{P}{l^2}$$

The unified expression of the above four formulas is as follows

$$\sigma_z = [\alpha I_p + \xi \beta I_s^g - \eta(1-\alpha-\beta) I_s^s] \frac{P}{l^2} \tag{6-25}$$

where: ξ —The coefficient of friction distribution in rectangle. For equilateral triangle distribution, the value is 0, for distribution in rectangle, positive trapezoid, inverse trapezoid or inverse triangle, the value is 1;

η —The coefficient of friction distribution in inverse triangle. For distribution in equilateral triangle and positive trapezoid, the value is 1, for distribution in rectangle, the value is 0, for distribution in inverse triangle, the value is −1.

Formula (6-25) is just for the vertical stress induced by load of single pile in the subgrade. For pile group, superposition principle could be applied for calculation.

$$\sigma_z = \sum_{i=1}^{n} \sigma_{zi} \tag{6-26}$$

where: n—The number of piles;

2. Calculation of settlement of pile group and determination of reasonable pile number by Dualistic Simultaneous Equations method.

Suppose the pressure on the basement of foundation is uniformly distributed, and each pile bears the same amount of load Q, then the induced stress q of the foundation basement is:

$$q = \frac{N+G-nQ}{F-nF_1} - \sigma_{cd} \tag{6-27}$$

where: n —The number of piles;

F—The area of foundation basement;

σ_{cd} —The geostatic stress of the foundation basement subgrade;

F_1 —The sectional area of single pile;

N—The load transferred from the superstructure;

G—The weight of the foundation and the subgrade overlaid.

With consideration of the coaction of all the piles, the settlement of a pile tip point A is S_A, and the settlement of a point B of subgrade in-between piles which is close to the foundation basement is S_B. The values of them can be calculated as follows:

$$\left.\begin{aligned} S_A &= \Delta_{AS} q + \delta_{AP}(Q + \gamma_G F_1 l) = \Delta_{AS}\left(\frac{N+G-nQ}{F-nF_1} - \sigma_{cd}\right) + \delta_{AP}(Q + \gamma_G F_1 l) \\ S_B &= \Delta_{BS} q + \delta_{BP}(Q + \gamma_G F_1 l) = \Delta_{BS}\left(\frac{N+G-nQ}{F-nF_1} - \sigma_{cd}\right) + \delta_{BP}(Q + \gamma_G F_1 l) \end{aligned}\right\} \tag{6-28}$$

where: r_G —The weight of unit volume of pile body;

l —The length of pile;

Q—The actual load of a single pile. $Q \leqslant P_u$, P_u is the ultimate bearing capacity of a single pile;

Δ_{AS}, Δ_{BS}—The respective settlement of point A and B when the foundation basement bears unit pressure;

δ_{AP}, δ_{BP}—The respective settlement of point A and B when each pile bears unit load. They are:

$$\delta_{AP} = \int_0^l \frac{P(z)}{E_P} \mathrm{d}z + \sum_{i=K_1+1}^{K} \sum_{j=1}^{n} \int_{z_{bi}}^{z_{ai}} [\alpha I_P(i,j) + \xi \beta I_s^g(i,j) + \eta(1-\alpha-\beta) I_s^s(i,j)] / E_{si} \cdot \mathrm{d}z$$

$$S_{BP} = \sum_{i=1}^{K} \sum_{j=1}^{n} \int_{z_{bi}}^{z_{ai}} [\alpha I_P(i,j) + \xi \beta I_s^g(i,j) + \eta(1-\alpha-\beta) I_s^s(i,j)] / E_{si} \cdot \mathrm{d}z$$

$$\Delta_{AS} = \sum_{i=K_l+1}^{K} \int_{z_{bi}}^{z_{ai}} \alpha'(z) / E_{si} \cdot \mathrm{d}z$$

$$\Delta_{BS} = \sum_{i=1}^{K} \int_{z_{bi}}^{z_{ai}} \alpha'(z) / E_{si} \cdot \mathrm{d}z$$

where: $P(z)$—The axial force of pile at the depth of z;

E_p, E_{si}—The anti-elastic modulus, and compression modulus of the ith subgrade layer respectively;

K_l—The number of subgrade layers within the pile length;

z_{bi}, z_{ui}—The distances to the basement of pile cap respectively from the top and the basement of the ith subgrade layer;

$\alpha'(z)$—The coefficient of additional stress at the depth of z. It can be got with corner-points method based on the superposition principle, and together by referring to the table or calculation.

According to coaction principle of pile and subgrade, presumely the settlement of pile tip is equal to the settlement of subgrade between adjacent piles. For a practical engineering project, the loads of superstructure is available, and when the number of piles, pile diameter, pile length and pile spacing are determined, the above two formulas could be simultaneously soluted to get the settlement S and the pile tip load Q. The ratio of load sharing between pile and subgrade could be further determined. This is the Dualistic Simultaneous Equations method for settlement calculation of pile group.

As is seen from the above, integral is required by this method to calculate settlement. And the calculation and integral of vertical stress coefficient such as I_p, I_s^g, I_s^s are especially of heavy mathematical work. And now there are relevant tables for referrence.

For a specific engineering case, the important relation between number of piles and settlement can be obtained according to the above formula under the condition that pile length and pile diameter are constant. So, there exits the issue of reasonable number of piles n_b for a particular engineering case. Research and test have shown that when the number of piles exceeds n_b, it is of no remarkable effect in reducing settlement, and sometimes even unfavorable situation might happen. For the single pile, if the settlement is composed of the subgrade compression below the pile toe and the elastic compression of pile body. i.e.:

$$\left.\begin{aligned} S_P &= \int_l^H \sigma_z / E_s \mathrm{d}z + \int_0^l \frac{\sigma(z)}{E_P}\mathrm{d}z \\ S_P &= \sum_{i=K_l+1}^{K} \int_{z_{bi}}^{z_{ai}} \frac{\sigma_z}{E_{si}}\mathrm{d}z + \frac{(P_P + \lambda P_s)l}{f_1 e_p} \end{aligned}\right\} \tag{6-29}$$

where: H—The depth of compression layer.

λ—Shape coefficient of pile side friction relating to distribution with depth.

3. Simplified method

The calculation method of pile settlement presented by the above Dualistic Simultaneous Equations is calculation couducted under the condition of knowing piles' layout and etc. When the major effect of pile foundation is for reducing settlement of building, the spacing of pile foundation is larger than that of normal pile foundation and the amount of piles allocated is much smaller. The area of the total pile toe only accounts for a small part of the area of foundation cap, and the stress superposition between the piles is small. In order to simplify calculation, the item of nF_1 in the formula is omitted, and δ_{AP} is substituted by unit settlement δ_p induced by unit load of single pile, and the settlement of point B δ_{BP} when all piles bear unit load at the same time is approximately taken as 0, thus the simplified dualistic simultaneous equations is as follows:

$$\left.\begin{aligned} S_A &= \Delta_{AS}\left(\frac{N+G-nQ}{F} - \sigma_{cd}\right) + \delta_p(Q + \lambda_G F_1 l) \\ S_B &= \Delta_{BS}\left(\frac{N+G-nQ}{F} - \sigma_{cd}\right) \\ \delta_{AP} &= \sum_{i=K_1+1}^{K} \int_{z_{bi}}^{z_{ai}} [\alpha I_p + \beta I_s^g - (1-\alpha-\beta) I_s^s(i,j)] \frac{1}{l^2 E_{si}}\mathrm{d}z + \frac{(P+\lambda P_s)l}{F_1 E_p} \end{aligned}\right\} \tag{6-30}$$

Calculation has shown that the thickness of subgrade layer which affects the settlement of pile toe under unit load is no bigger than 0.1 times of pile length. When the Poisson ratio of subgrade is taken as 0.4, for reinforced concrete friction pile, the calculation formula of δ_p is as follows:

(1) For friction distributed in triangle, the formula is

$$\delta_p = \frac{204.165\alpha + 20141}{lE_s}$$

where: E_s is average compression modulus of bearing stratum in the range of 0.1 times of pile length below the pile tip.

(2) For friction distributed in inverse triangle, the formula is

$$\delta_p = \frac{206.221\alpha + 0.085}{lE_s}$$

(3) For friction distributed in rectangle, the formula is

$$\delta_p = \frac{205.108\alpha + 10198}{lE_s}$$

In the same way, it is taken as $S_A = S_B = S$. For a specific engineering case, pile length, pile diameter and foundation area can be determined according to comprehensive analysis. When the number of piles is available and the pile spacing is determined, settlement can be obtained conveniently through calculation with the formula. If settlement is fixed, the number of piles can also be obtained directly with the formula.

Calculation has shown that there is deviation with the simplified method, usually within 10%～20%. And the simplified method can be seen as a simple and practical method.

6.3 Empirical and Simplified Method of Settlement Calculation of Single Pile

6.3.1 Empirical Method

Frank (1985) summarized the experience of engineering practice of single pile, and presented the empirical relation between typical value of single pile settlement S and pile diameter d under specific geological condition and design loads:

For driven pile: $S = 0.9\%d$ (The average relation)
$S = (0.8 \sim 1.2)\%\ d$ (The range of change)

For bored pile: $S = 0.6\%d$ (The average relation)
$S = (0.3 \sim 1.0)\%\ d$ (The range of change)

Briaud and Tucker (1988) made statistical analysis of test data of 98 single piles, among which there are 64 concrete square piles, 27 H steel piles and 7 bored piles. The average value of pile length is 12.2 m, the average pile diameter is 38.1 m. The subgrade condition is hard clay, medium-dense sand and layered soil. The average value of non drainage shear strength of clay is 144 kPa, the average value of standard penetration degree of sand is 43. Thus, there comes the relation between pile tip settlement and pile diameter associated with 0.5 times the ultimate load when the probability is 95%. That is

$$S = d \times 1.25\%$$

When the pile tip load is less than 1/3 of the ultimate load, if there is no soft subgrade layer under the pile toe, Meyerhof suggested to use the following formula to estimate the settlement of single pile.

$$S = \frac{d_b}{30F} \tag{6-31}$$

where: d_b—The diameter of pile toe;

F—The safety coefficient.

6.3.2 Simplified Method

When the pile bears vertical working load, the settlement of single pile S is composed of compression of pile body and settlement of pile toe. That is

$$S = S_S + S_b$$

If the pile side friction and the pile toe resistance are consider respectively, S can be expressed as follows:

$$S = S_{SS} + S_{Sb}$$

$$S = S_{bS} + S_{bb}$$

where: S_{SS}—The compression of pile body which is induced by pile side friction;

S_{Sb}—The compression of pile body which is induced by pile toe resistance;

S_{bS}—The settlement of pile toe resulting from subgrade compression which is induced by transferring of pile side load to below the pile toe plane;

S_{bb}—The settlement of pile toe resulting from subgrade compression which is induced by pile toe load.

If the ratio of pile toe load P_b to pile tip load P is α, the pile side load P_s equals to $(1-\alpha)P$. When the pile tip flushes with ground surface, the expression of S_S is as follows:

$$S_s = \frac{\Delta(1-\alpha)PL}{E_pA_p} + \frac{\alpha PL}{E_pA_p} = [\Delta + \alpha(1-\Delta)]\frac{PL}{E_pA_p} = \xi\frac{PL}{E_pA_p} \tag{6-32}$$

where: $\xi = \Delta + \alpha(1-\Delta)$;

L—The length of pile;

E_p, A_p—The elastic modulus and sectional area of pile body;

Δ—The distribution coefficient of pile side friction. The value of Δ depends on the distribution of side friction along the pile body. If the friction is uniformly distributed, Δ=1/2, if is distributed in triangle, Δ=2/3;

ξ—The comprehensive coefficient of pile body compression.

Base on the above formula, for there is difference in considering composition and approaches of single pile settlement, various kinds of simplified methods of settlement calculation of single pile are to be presented.

(1) Das method. Here the method in literature (Das,1984) is cited.

The determination of S_S :

$$S_s = S_{ss} + S_{sb} = \varDelta \frac{P_s L}{E_p A_p} + \frac{P_b L}{E_p A_p} \tag{6-33}$$

The determination of S_{bb} :

Calculation method similar to calculating settlement of shallow foundation is applied to determine the settlement S_{bb} which is induced by pile end load P_b :

$$S_{bb} = \frac{\sigma_b d}{E_s}(1-\mu_s^2)I_b \tag{6-34}$$

where: d —The diameter or width of pile;

σ_b —The load in unit area at the pile toe. That is $\sigma_b = P_b / A_b$;

E_s, μ_s —The elastic modulus and Poisson ratio of subgrade. If there is no empirical value, they can be referred to in Table 6-2;

I_b —The influence coefficient. It can be set as 0.88.

Table 6-2 Elastic parameters of various types of subgrade

soil types	Elastic modulus E_s		Poisson ratio μ_s
	MN/m^2	Ib/in^2	
Loose sand	10.365—24.15	1500—3500	0.20—0.40
Medium-dense sand	17.25—27.60	2500—4000	0.25—0.40
Silty sand	34.50—55.20	5000—8000	0.30—0.45
Sand and gravel	10.35—17.25	1500—2500	0.20—0.40
Soft clay	69.00—172.50	10000—25000	0.15—0.35
General clay	2.07—5.18	300—750	
Hard clay	5.18—10.35	750—1500	0.15—0.35
	10.36—24.15	1500—3000	

Vesic puts forward a semi-empirical formula for estimating S_{bb} , that is

$$S_{bb} = \frac{P_b C_b}{d \sigma_{bu}} \tag{6-35}$$

where: σ_{bu} —The ultimate resistance of pile toe;

C_b —The empirical coefficient, the representative value of C_b for various types of subgrade are listed in Table 6-3.

Table 6-3 Determination of representative value of C_b

Soil types	Driven pile	Bored pile
Sand (close-grained to loose)	0.02—0.04	0.09—0.18
Clay (hard to soft)	0.02—0.03	0.03—0.06
Silty soil (close-grained to loose)	0.03—0.05	0.09—0.12

The determination of S_{bS}:

The settlement S_{bS} which is induced by pile side load P_s can be calculated according to the expression similar to Formula (6-34), that is:

$$S_{bs}=\left(\frac{P_s}{VL}\right)\frac{d}{E_s}(1-\mu_s^2)I_s \tag{6-36}$$

where: V and l —The circumference and length of pile;

I_s—The influence coefficient, which can be got by the following empirical relation.

Vesic also put forward a empirical relation similar to the above formula to estimate S_{bS}. That is:

$$S_{bs}=\frac{P_S C_S}{L\sigma_{bu}} \tag{6-37}$$

where

$$C_S=\left(0.93+0.16\sqrt{\frac{L}{d}}\right)C_b$$

In the formula, the value of C_b can be got by referring to Table 6-3.

(2) Ting method (1982). Base on the simplified analysis, Randolph and Worth (1978) presented the relation formula of S_b/S, which is the ratio of settlement of pile toe S_b to settlement of pile tip S. That is:

$$\frac{S_b}{S}=\frac{1}{\cosh \mu L} \tag{6-38}$$

where

$$\mu L=\sqrt{\frac{8}{\delta\lambda}\frac{L}{d}}$$

$$\xi=\ln\left[5.0(1-\gamma_s)\frac{L}{d}\right]S$$

$$\lambda=\frac{E_P}{G_s}$$

where: G_s is the shear modulus of subgrade, other symbols are of the same meaning as previous.

Considering $S = S_s + S_b$, the above formula can be expressed as follows:

$$S = S_s \frac{1}{\left(1-\frac{S_b}{S}\right)} = S_s \frac{\cosh \mu L}{\cosh \mu L - 1} \tag{6-39}$$

If the compression of pile body which is induced by pile toe resistance is neglected, the formula can be expressed as follows:

$$S = S_{ss} \cdot \beta \tag{6-40}$$

where:

$$\beta = \frac{\cosh \mu L}{\cosh \mu L - 1}$$

Ting suggested to use the above formula to estimate the settlement of single pile, where S_{ss} can be determined as follows:

$$S_{ss} = \Delta \frac{PL}{E_p A_p} = \left(\frac{1}{3} \cdots \frac{1}{2}\right) \frac{PL}{E_p A_p} \tag{6-41}$$

Hereby are some notes: ① The value of Δ in the above formula is relatively small, because the safety coefficient adopted abroad for pile design (usually about 3) is bigger than that of in China, and the value of Δ decreases with reduction of load. ② It is more reasonable to use Formula (6-39) than to use the Ting Formula to estimate the settlement of single pile, but the problem of the amount of pile toe load needs to be solved.

6.4 Calculation of Final Settlement of Pile Foundation in GB50007-2002

(1) In *Code for Design of Foundation & Subgrade of Building* (GB50007-2002), calculation of the final settlement of pile foundation is as:

$$S = \psi_p \sum_{j=1}^{m} \sum_{i=1}^{n} \frac{\sigma_{j,i} \Delta H_{j,i}}{E_{sj,j}} \tag{6-42}$$

where: S—The calculated final settlement of pile foundation (mm);

m—The total number of subgrade layers within the range of compression stratum under the pile toe plane;

$E_{sj,j}$ —The compression modulus of the ith hierarchy of the jth subgrade layer under the pile toe plane in the range from geostatic stress to geostatic stress plus induced stress;

n_i —The calculation hierarchy number of the jth subgrade layer which is under the pile toe plane;

$\Delta H_{j,i}$ —The thickness of the ith hierarchy of the jth subgrade layer which is under the pile toe plane (m);

$\sigma_{j,i}$ —The vertical stress of the ith hierarchy of the jth subgrade layer which is under the pile toe plane. It can be calculated according to Mindlin stress formula or Boussinesq stress formula;

ψ_p —The empirical coefficient of settlement calculation of pile foundation. For different regions, it should be determined according to statistical comparison of measured data of local engineering practice.

(2) When method of solid deep foundation is used to calculate the final settlement of pile group, the formula of single-axial compression layer-wise summation method of Boussinesq stress formula is applied. In the formula, the additional stress should be that at the pile toe plane. The support area of the solid foundation could be determined according to Fig. 6-5.

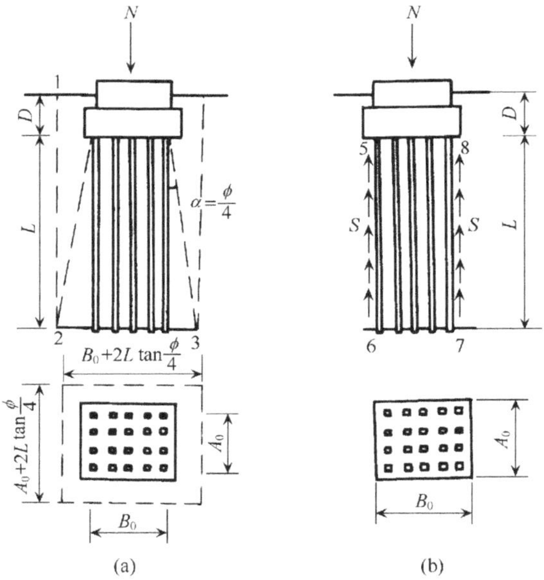

Fig.6-5 Illustration of basement area of deep solid foundation

The empirical coefficient ψ_p of pile settlement calculation of solid deep foundation should be determined according to regional observation data of pile foundation settlement and experience & statistics. The value of ψ_p can be set according to Table 6-4 when condition is not available.

Table 6-4 Empirical coefficient of pile settlement calculation of solid deep foundation

E_s(MPa)	$E_s<15$	$15\leqslant E_s<30$	$30\leqslant E_s<40$
ψ_p	0.5	0.4	0.3

(3) When calculating vertical induced stress of a certain point in the subgrade by Mindlin stress formula, the induced stress of each pile at this point could be superposed one by one. The formula is as follows:

$$\sigma_{j,i}=\sum_{K=1}^{K}(\sigma_{zP,K}+\sigma_{zS,K}) \tag{6-43}$$

In Fig.6-6, Q is the induced load of a single pile which is under the quasi-permanent combined action of vertical load. It is composed of pile toe resistance Q_p and pile side friction Q_S. And $Q_p=\alpha Q$, α is the ratio of pile toe resistance. The pile toe resistance is presumely concentrated force, and presumely the pile side friction has two kinds of distribution forms, which are uniform distribution and linear growth distribution along the pile body, the value being βQ and $(1-\alpha-\beta)Q$ respectively.

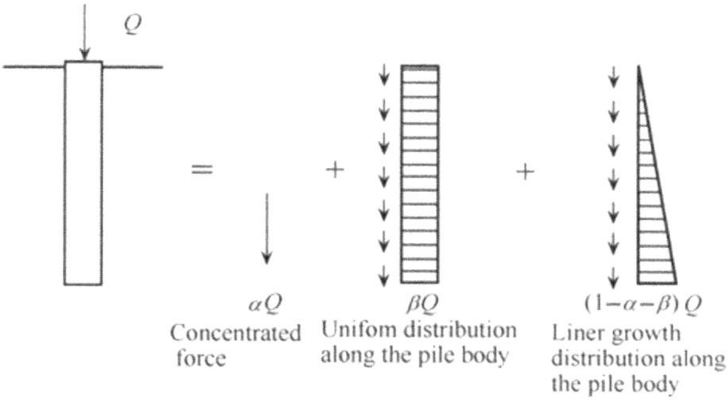

Fig.6-6 Illustration of load sharing of single pile

The stress of the kth pile which is induced by the pile toe resistance at the depth is:

$$\sigma_{zP,K}=\frac{\alpha Q}{L^2}I_{s2,k} \tag{6-44}$$

The stress of the kth pile which is induced by the pile side friction at the depth is:

$$\sigma_{zs,k}=\frac{Q}{L^2}[\beta I_{s1,k}+(1-\alpha-\beta)I_{s2,k}] \tag{6-45}$$

For general friction pile, presumely all the pile side friction is distributed with linear growth along the pile body (i.e. this method hardly affect the calculation result), then the above formula could be simplified as follows:

$$\sigma_{zs,k} = \frac{Q}{L^2}(1-\alpha)I_{s2,k} \tag{6-46}$$

where: L—The length of pile (m);

Q—The induced load of a single pile which is under the quasi-permanent combined action of vertical load;

I_p, I_{s1}, I_{s2}—The stress influence coefficient, which could be obtained by integral of Mindlin stress formula.

The concentrated force on the pile tip is

$$I_p = \frac{1}{8\pi(1-\mu)}\left[\frac{(1-2\mu)(m-1)}{A^3} - \frac{(1-2\mu)(m-1)}{B^3} + \frac{3(m-1)^3}{A^5} + \frac{3(3-4\mu)m(m+1)^2 - 3(m+1)(5m-1)}{B^5} + \frac{30m(m+1)^3}{B^7}\right] \tag{6-47}$$

For pile side friction uniformly distributed along the pile body, I_{s1} can be expressed as follows

$$I_{s1} = \frac{1}{8\pi(1-\mu)}\left[\frac{2(2-\mu)}{A} - \frac{2(1-2\mu)(m^3/n^2 + n^2/m^2)}{B} + \frac{2(1-2\mu)(m/n)^2}{F} - \frac{n^3}{A^5} - \frac{4m^2 - 4(1+\mu)(m/n)^2 m^2}{F^3} + \frac{4m(1+\mu)(m+1)(m/n+1/n)^2 - (4m^2+n^2)}{B^3} + \frac{6m^2(m^4+n^2)}{B^3} - \frac{6m[mn^2 - (m+1)^5/n^2]}{B^5}\right] \tag{6-48}$$

For pile side friction distributed with linear growth along the pile body, I_{s2} can be expressed as follows

$$I_{s2} = \frac{1}{4\pi(1-\mu)}\left[\frac{2(2-\mu)}{A} - \frac{2(1-2\mu)(4m+1) - 2(1-2\mu)(1+m)m^2/n^2}{B} - \frac{2(1-2\mu)m^3/n^2 - 8(2-\mu)m}{F} - \frac{mn^2 + (m-1)^3}{A^3} - \frac{4\mu n^2 m + 4m^3 - 15n^2 m - 2(5+2\mu)(m/n)^2(m+1)^3}{F^3} - \frac{2(7-2\mu)mn^2 - 6m^3 + 2(5+2\mu)(m/n)^2 m^3}{F^3} - \frac{6mn^2(n^4-m^4) + 12(m/n)^2(m+1)^5}{B^5} + \frac{12(m/n)^2 m^5 + 6mn^2(n^2-m^2)}{F^5} + 2(2-\mu)\ln\left(\frac{A+m-1}{F+m} \times \frac{B+m+1}{F+m}\right)\right] \tag{6-49}$$

where: $A^2 = \left[n^2 + (m-1)^2\right], B^2 = \left[n^2 + (m+1)^2\right], F^2 = n^2 + m^2, n = r/L, m = z/L;$

μ—The Poisson ratio of subgrade;

r—The horizontal distance from the calculation point to pile body axis;

z—The vertical distance from the stress-calculation point to the foundation basement.

Thus the calculation formula of settlement of single-axial compression layer-wise summation method is obtained as follows:

$$S = \psi_m \frac{Q}{L^2} \sum_{j=1}^{m} \sum_{i=1}^{K} \frac{\Delta H_{j,i}}{E_{sj,i}} \sum_{k=1}^{K} \left[\alpha I_{p,k} + (1-\alpha) I_{s2,k} \right] \tag{6-50}$$

When adopting Mindlin stress formula to calculate the final settlement of pile foundation, the pile toe resistance ratio which is under the quasi-permanent combined action of vertical load, and the empirical coefficient of settlement calculation of pile foundation should be statistically determined by measured data of local engineering cases.

6.5 Allowable Deformation of Pile Foundation

Deformation of pile includes settlement amount, settlement difference, inclination and partial inclination. Inclination refers to the ratio of settlement difference of two endpoints by their distance in the inclination direction of the pile foundation of building. Partial inclination refers to the ratio of settlement difference of two points of pile foundation to their distance, the two points being in a certain length range of the beneath-wall strip pile cap in the vertical direction. Foundation deformation is caused by factors of uneven thickness and properties of subgrade, the difference in load, complex shape of building and etc. For super high-rise building and high-rise structure, foundation deformation is controlled by inclination.

Technical code for pile foundation of building (JGJ94-94) specifies that:
When $200m < H_g < 250m$, the allowable deformation value is 150mm.

Code for design of foundation & subgrade of buildings (JG-50007-2002) specifies that:
When $200m < H_g < 250m$, the allowable deformation value is 200mm.

6.6 Study on Characteristics and Settlement of Super-Long Bored Pile

Bored pile could be classified into long pile and short pile according to length ratio. It is usually discriminated by the follow formula:

$$\alpha = \frac{L}{\lambda} \tag{6-51}$$

where

$$\lambda = \sqrt[4]{\frac{4EI}{BK_n}}$$

in the above formula: L—The length of pile;

λ—The characteristics length of pile;

E—The vertical elastic modulus of pile;

I—The moment of inertia of pile section;

B—The width of pile;

K_n—The subgrade coefficient in horizontal direction of subgrade.

When $\alpha > 3$, it is a long pile, and when $\alpha = 15 \sim 30$, it is a short pile. Usually, when $10\text{m} < L < 30\text{m}$, it is a middle long pile, when $30\text{m} < L < 50\text{m}$, it is a long pile, and when $L > 50\text{m}$, it is a super-long pile. In the case of the 360 piles in Shanghai, long piles whose length-diameter ratio (*L*/*D*) is 60—80 account for most of the piles used, and super-long piles whose length-diameter ratio (*L*/*D*) is bigger than 80 account for 14%. It indicates that the application of long pile or super-long pile is increaing with the development of high-rise building or super high-rise building.

At present, although there have been much theoretical research and data of super-long bored pile (single pile and pile group), which could be used for the study on super-long bored pile, for the difficulty in pile test, the scarcity of test data and the technology development of post grouting bored pile, the mechanics behavior of super-long bored pile hasn't been fully understood. Now the mechanics behavior of super-long bored pile can be got only through data analysis of pile test of a few engineering projects:

1) Super-long bored pile is of friction pile in the regions of soft subgrade such as Shanghai and etc. The pile toe resistance measured is very small, usually being no more than 15% of the ultimate load of the pile tip. It has been indicated through test data of 8 piles in Shanghai (length-diameter ratio of piles being 83, pile length being 76m, pile diameter being 850mm, and length-diameter ratio of piles being 89, pile length being 58m, pile diameter being 700mm) and 3 piles in Tianjin that when the length-diameter ratio of pile is 34 (pile length being 50.5m, pile diameter being 1.5m), the pile toe resistance accounts for 12% of the pile side friction, and when the length-diameter ratio of pile is 40 (pile length being 60.5m, pile diameter being 1.5m), the pile toe resistance accounts for 14% of the pile side friction, and when the length-diameter ratio of pile is 55 (pile length being 54.4m, pile diameter being 1.0m), the pile toe resistance accounts for less than 1% of the pile side friction. The pile toe resistance of 2 bored piles in Fuzhou whose diameter is 1200mm and length is 62m accounts for about 10% of the pile side friction. This means that the side friction of the upper part of pile could almost be completely exerted, while the side friction of the lower part of pile has not been fully exerted, and the pile toe resistance has been exerted even worse.

2) The pile tip settlement of super-long bored pile is far more less than the allowable settlement specified by the code. The ratios of pile tip settlement to pile diameter are all less than 0.05. When the 8 bored pile in Shanghai reached the ultimate load that is required by design, the measured pile tip settlement of each was less than 50mm. Among them, for the bored pile of 58m long, the settlement of pile tip was measured to be 12.2—46.77mm; and for the bored pile of 76m long, the settlement of pile tip was measured to be 30.23—47.39mm. Obviously, the pile tip settlement of these 8 super-long test piles is mainly induced by elastic deformation of pile body. The measured results of super high-rise buildings in Shanghai and Tianjin have indicated that the settlement is usually 20—100mm.

3) Super-long bored pile can remarkably reduce settlement, and the vertical induced stress of pile basement decreases remarkably.

4) For settlement calculation of super-long pile group foundation with the method of simulation solid foundation, as the induced stress of the subgrade layer below the pile basement is remarkably large through calculation by the Boussinesq formula, the calculation value of the settlement of super-long pile group foundation is remarkably large as well.

5) The *Q*-*s* curves of 3 super-long test piles in Tianjin are as Fig. 6-7, and the geologic section map, the axial force distribution map and side friction distribution map are as Fig. 6-8, the curves are shown as Fig. 6-9. The parameters and the measured data of these 3 super-long test piles are shown in Table 6-5.

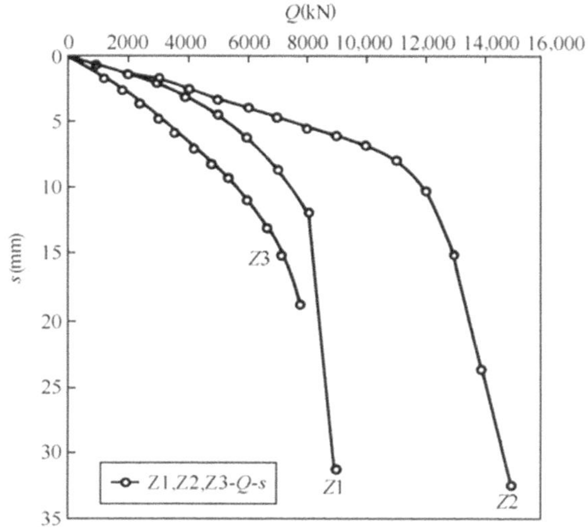

Fig.6-7 Q-s curve

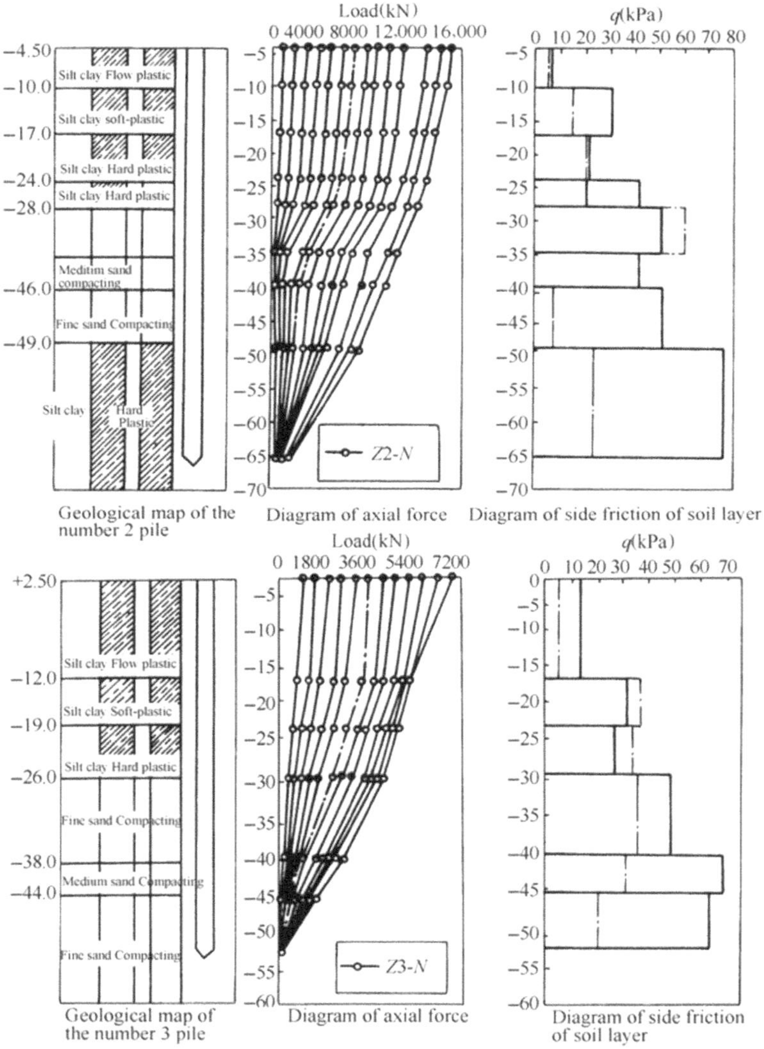

Fig.6-8 Geological map, axial force map and side friction distribution map

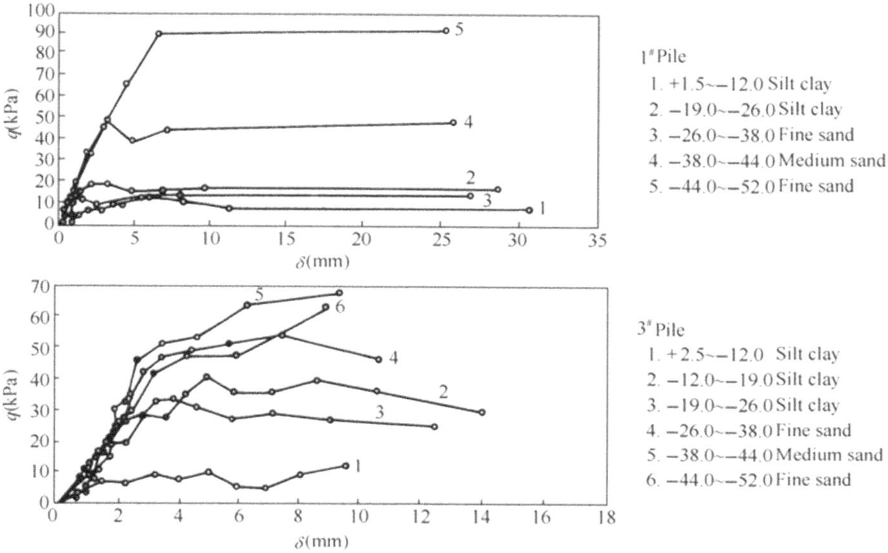

Fig.6-9 $\delta - q_s$ curve

Table 6-5 Parameters and results of super-long test pile

Number of pile	The number 1 pile L=50.5m, D=1.5m, L/D=34		The number 2 pile L=60.5m, D=1.5m, L/D=40		The number 3 pile L=54.5m, D=1.0m, L/D=55	
	Q_u	Q_a	Q_u	Q_a	Q_u	Q_a
Bearing capacity/kN	8000	4000	15000	7500	8500	4250
Pile end settlement/mm	11.89	3.24	32.30	5.30		7.09
Side friction/kN	7120	3707	13141	6780		4213
Pile end resistant/kN	880	293	1869	750		37

Notes: Q_u is allowable bearing capacity, Q_a is the ultimate bearing capacity.

The above measured data show that for the topic of super-long bored pile, besides that the mechanism of excersion of side friction and pile toe resistance has been far from complete understanding, the settlement calculation method of super-long pile group requirs further discussion. Statistics of a large amout of pile test data have indicated that the corresponding settlement of super-long bored pile under working load is usually only a few millimeters. On General condition, the relative displacement of pile to subgrade would be bigger than 5mm for the pile side friction to be fully exerted. As for clay or silt clay, the pile-subgrade relative displacement needs to be 5—10mm, and for sand, it needs to be about 10mm. (the research results of foreign scholars are all bigger than the above displacement).

6) Mechanics behavior and settlement of post grouting super-long bored pile. Super-long bored pile is mainly used in deep foundation of signifcant buildings like super high-rise

building, high-rise structure and etc, the cost of each pile is high, and it requires that settlement be decreased while bearing capacity be increased. So the technology of post-grouting bored pile has developed fast, plenty of grouting techniques and engineering methods have been put forth. (Schnitter, Brudk, D.A firstly applied pressed grouting technology on the toe of bored pile of a bridge in 1961.) The application of super-long bored pile is also gradually increasing in the area of soft subgrade. With this kind of post-grouting bored pile, not only the bearing capacity is increased (by as much as over 20%), but also the difficult problems of hole-bottom sediment and hole-wall relaxation during the construction process of bored pile are solved. Thus the pile settlement is remarkably reduced. The generally law is as follows:

① For super-long pile to which jointly grouting technology of pile side and pile toe is applied (see Table 6-5), the load associated with the pile tip settlement $S_u = 0.05 — 0.08D$ (D is diameter of pile) is the ultimate load Q_u, the load associated with the tip settlement of a single pile $S_u = 0.07 — 0.016D$ is the standard value of bearing capacity of a single pile R_k.

② For super-long pile with pressed pile toe grouting, the load associated with the pile tip settlement $S_u = 0.05 — 0.08D$ (D is diameter of pile) is the ultimate load Q_u, while the load associated with $S_u = 0.006 — 0.014D$ is the standard load R_k. These pile-test data and analysis are of great referable significance for bearing capacity and settlement of pile foundation.

The bearing capacity of super-long pile with pile toe grouting can increase over 20% (some as much as 80%) compared with that of no grouting one. Whileas the settlement of pile tip decreases greatly, basically the elastic compression deformation of the super-long pile (as Fig.6-7 and Fig.6-8).

Case 1:

The parameters of 3 non-grouting piles:

1# pile: $\phi 750, l = 49.6$m (sediment 50mm)

2# pile: $\phi 1000, l = 68.0$m (sediment 30mm)

3# pile: $\phi 750, l = 66.7$m (sediment 20mm)

The parameters of 3 toe-grouting piles:

4# pile: $\phi 750, l = 49.8$m (sediment 340mm)

5# pile: $\phi 750, l = 49.4$m (sediment 340mm)

6# pile: $\phi 1000, l = 66.1$m (sediment 460mm)

From Fig.6-10, it could be seen that after grouting of pile toe, the bearing capacity of the pile increase, whileas the settlement of pile tip decreases greatly.

Case 2:

The parameters of 2 non-grouting piles:

1# pile: $\phi 1200, l = 54$m (scree bearing stratum)

3# pile: $\phi 1000, l = 68.0$m (sediment 30mm)

The parameters of 2 toe-grouting piles:

2# pile: $\phi 1200, l = 54\text{m}$ (scree bearing stratum)

4# pile: $\phi 1000, l = 66.1\text{m}$ (sediment 460mm)

From Fig.6-11, it could be seen that for piles with basically equal diameter and length, the bearing capacity of the pile is increased by more than 80%, and the settlement of pile tip is all very small, being only about 20 mm.

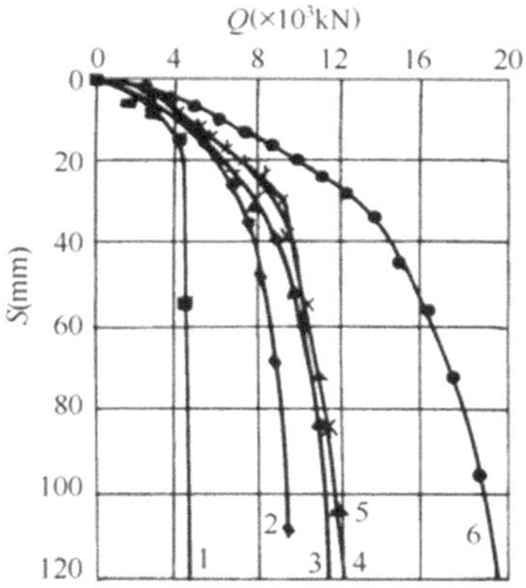

Fig.6-10 *Q-S* curve of non-grouting & toegrouting super-long pile for comparison

Notes: non-grouting for1#, 2#, 3#, toe-grouting for 4#, 5#, 6#

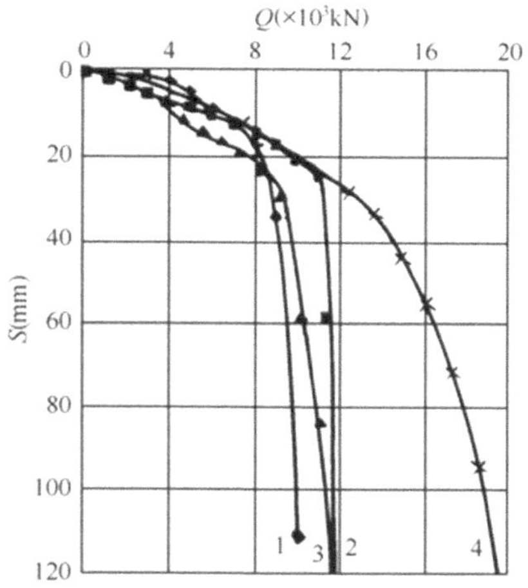

Fig.6-11 *Q-S* curve of non-grouting & toegrouting super-long pile for comparison

Notes: non-grouting for1#, 3#, toe-grouting for 2#, 4#

6.7 Research on Force Mechanism of Pile Group under Vertical Load

The original research on the working mechanism of the pile group mainly includes model test (Cambefort, 1953, Whitaker, 1957, Kezdi, 1957, 1958, Kerisel, 1967, Vesic, 1968). According to the outcome of the model test, an empirical method was put forward, which evaluated or estimated the bearing capacity and settlement of pile group by efficiency coefficient of pile group and ratio of settlement. In the 1960's, H.G. Poulos and others conducted theoretical research on the settlement of pile group, and applied elastic theoretical method and considered the interaction between piles to calculate the settlement of pile group. China's study on the pile group started from the late 1950's, and has had great development in terms of intensity and extensity, and has surpassed foreigners in the fields of research on model test and etc. The major research work done in China includes large in-field test on pile group on a large scale, testing research on load transfer law and settlement deformation of pile foundation of high-rise building, and analysis on the coaction mechanism of pile group-pile cap(raft, box)-subgrade. And a lot of achievements have been made, such as the design principle and calculation method of *pile foundation with reduced settlement* and etc.

6.7.1 Load Transfer Behavior of Pile Group

Load transfer of pile group is much more complicated than that of single pile. According to field test, pile test and finite element analysis, the characteristics of behavior could be generalized as follows:

1. Route of load transfer

The load of pile foundation of high-rise building is transferred to the subgrade through the two routes of pile body and pile cap basement. The transfer routes under the long term impact of load is related to various factors, such as the compression of subgrade around pile, the stiffness of bearing stratum, stress history and load condition. When the settlement of pile tip (pile cap) is smaller than the settlement of subgrade under the basement of pile cap, the subgrade breaks away from the pile cap, and the load all transfers to the subgrade through the pile. If the load makes the pile produce enough pierced deformation, even the subgrade around pile is soft, the basement of pile cap would still keep contact with the subgrade and transfer the load. For toe bearing pile foundation, because the bearing stratum is hard, the settlement of pile tip is just pile depth and elastic compression of bearing stratum, the load would all be transferred through pile. So, the load transfer and work behavior of each pile of toe bearing pile group are almost the same as those of single pile, the bearing capacity of pile group is superposed by bearing capacity of each single pile, and the settlement is equal to that of a single pile.

2. Analysis of subgrade stress of pile group

The subgrade of pile group foundation includes the subsoil between piles, the subsoil within a range out of pile group and the subsoil under the pile-toe of pile group which has impact on its bearing capacity and deformation. Stress in the subgrade of pile group is composed of geostatic stress, induced stress and subsoil stress.

Construction stress refers to the compression stress and the super-hydraulic pressure of pore water which are induced by the process of sinkage of compaction pile. The compression stress will dissipate with the loose of the subsoil, and the pore water pressure will disappear with consolidation process. The construction stress is temporary, however it has effect on the work behavior of pile group in that the dissipation of pore pressure greatly increases the effective stress, thus increases the bearing capacity of pile, but the consolidation subsidence of subgrade between piles detaches the basement of pile cap, and brings about negative friction to the piles.

Induced stress arouses from the contact stress of the basement of pile cap, pile side friction and the compression force of pile basement. When the spacing between piles is 3~4d, the stress superposes to each other, so that the stress of under-pile-basement subgrade within around-pile subgrade all becomes much bigger than that of single pile, and both the depth of effect and the thickness of compressed layer increase duplicatedly, thus resulting in lower bearing capacity and bigger settlement.

Geddes calculated the subgrade stress of single pile and pile group according to the stress distribution solution got by Mindlin. The general law of the subgrade stress of pile group is as follows:

1) The stress of pile end plane of pile group is divided into tow parts: the stress of the field between piles is formed by superposition under the effect of pile side friction. When the pile length and pile distance are constant, its value will increase with the increase of number of piles. The pile basement stress of pile group is formed by superposition of the between-piles stress mentioned above and the basement stress of each single pile.

2) The effect depth of pile group is much more than that of single pile. The bigger the plane size of the pile group is, the larger the effect depth is, and the slower the stress convergences with the depth.

3) The stress condition of the subgrade between piles is complex. There is small induced tensile stress around single pile; there is usually no tensile stress in the subgrade between the piles of pile group.

4) The effect width of pile group is bigger than that of single pile. The bigger the pile number is, the bigger the effect width is, i.e. the bigger the diffusion angle is (the angle between the vertical direction and the line connecting the tip of lateral side of pile boundary and the point on the pile toe plane whose additional stress is equal to 0.1 times of its geostatic stress).

3. The ratio of pile side friction to pile end resistance

Because of the effect of the pile superposition, the vertical stress of the pile end toe plane of the pile group is bigger than that of single pile obviously. So, the unit end resistance of every pile of the pile group is bigger than that of single pile too. In addition, because of the decreasing of the friction, the ratio of the toe resistance to the total load of pile tip is bigger than that of single pile. The shorter the pile is, the obviously the situation is. For the super-long pile group, the total load transfers to the pile group end plane directly through the super-long pile. It provides a evidence to the calculation of the solid-foundation.

6.7.2 Deformation Analysis of Pile Group Foundation

The deformation of the friction pile group foundation is mainly the settlement of pile group, the compression of the subgrade between piles and the deformation of the subgrade under pile. The relation among them is complex, and is associated with time and space effect.

1. The deformation law of friction pile group is as follows:

1) On the condition of the same pile spacing, the number of the piles is the decisive factor that lays impact on the deformation characteristics of pile group foundation. When the number of piles is small, the settlement of the pile group foundation is mainly the compression of the subgrade between piles. For super-long pile group foundation of super high-rise buildings, the settlement is mainly the compression of the subgrade under pile.

2) For pile spacing of 3—4*d*, the major compression section of the subgrade gradually moves downward as the number of piles increases.

3) When the pile spacing increases, the ratio of the subgrade compression between piles increases remarkably. When pile spacing is 6~8d. The major compression layer will transfer from subgrade layer under pile to subgrade layer between piles.

For appraisal of the work performance of pile group, two parameters are usually used, as *pile group efficiency coefficient* and *settlement ratio*.

2. Toe-bearing friction pile group

Because the bearing stratum of pile end is hard, yet it is not bedrock or density gravel, under normal design-load, there isn't any great stab deformation in the pile toe subgrade; the settlement of pile group is mainly compression deformation of the subgrade under pile. If the subgrade between piles is of soft or under-consolidated status, there could still be compression and consolidate, thus detaches the basement of pile-cap, but the deformation wont be reflected by the settlement of pile group. Only when the service load is close to the ulimate load, there would be stab deformation in the pile toe subgrade, and the subgrade between piles is compressed correspondingly, thus the settlement of pile group foundation includes the compression deformation of the subgrade between piles and the deformation of the subgrade under pile.

6.8 Chapter Summary

In this chapter, elaboration is conducted on settlement caculation methods of single pile and pile group, especially the calculation method of pile foundation settlement of the new national code. The basic characteristics of super-long pile are researched in detail. Analysis is done on the test data (Q-*s* curve) of pile compression of over 40 super-long piles provided by Shen Baohan and etc. The following important conclusions have been drawn:

1) Super-long pile has outstanding advantages in controlling settlement.

2) For large-diameter bored pile, it is suitable to apply post-grouting technology in order to solve the problems of pile end sediment and hole-wall relaxation.

3) Research should be done on mechanics of super-depth subsoil to promote the research on settlement calculation.

References

Banerjee P. K., Davis T. G. 1977. Analysis of Pile Groups Embedded in Gibson Soil. Proc. 9th Int. Conf. Soil Mech. Fdn. Engng., Tokyo.

Cooke R. W., Price G. and Tarr K. 1982.Jacked Piles in London Clay. Interaction and Group Behavior under Working Conditions, Geotechnique,Vol. 30

Canadian Geotechnical Society. 1985. Canadian Foundation Engineering Manual, 2nd Edition.

Janbu N.1996. Static Bearing Capacity of Friction Piles, Proc J.L. 6thEurope, Conference on SMFE, Vol.2.

Liu J.L. 1990. Design and Calculation of Pile Foundation, Beijing: China Building Industry Press.

Poulos H. G., Davis E.H. 1980. Pile Fundation Analysis and Design, New York: Wiley.

Shi P.D., Gao D.Z., Gui Y.K. 2000. Handbook of Foundation Engineering fort High-rise Building, Beijing: China Building Industry Press.

Wang Z.H., Chen X.F., Zhuang Y.J. 1999. Application of Long Large-diameter Pile in the Soft Soil in Wuxi, Construction Technology, No.9.

Yang Min, et al., 1997. Solving of Single Pile Settlement by Geddes Stress Factor Formula, Shanghai: Tongji University Press.

Appendix Comparison among super-long piles: pile end grouting, pile side and pile-end joint grouting, and non grouting

Location of pile-test	Numbering of pile-test	Pile diameter d(mm)	Pile length L(mm)	Soil layer of pile-end	Soil layer of pile side	Grouting weight(concrete) pile-end/pile side(kg)	Q_u		S_u (mm)	$V(m^3)$	Q_u/V		Q_{vc}	S_a (mm)
							Value (kN)	comparison (%)			value(kN/m^3)	comparison (%)	(kN · m^3/kg)	
Wuhan	W5-2	1000	56.32	gravel	clay, sand dip gravel	4000/6000	30192	100	66.40	44.21	683	100	(0.10)	9.20
	W5-4	1000	56.33	gravel		4000/3000	32560	108	64.07	44.22	736	108	(0.11)	9.75
	W8-3	900	52.10	gravel	silt clay, gravle	2500/0	20700		74.00	33.13	625		0.25	5.50
	W8-4	900	53.70	gravel		2500/0	18200		66.95	34.15	533		0.21	3.21
Shanghai	SK95	850	70.80	silt lay	silt caly, sandy silt	0/0	10400		50.71	40.16	259			16.85
	SK163	850	70.80	silt sand		0/0	10400		50.96	40.16	259			15.45
Wenzhou	WT-3	750	66.70	gravel	miscellaneous fill, clay, silt clay	0/0	7480	81	35.07	29.50	254	148		7.36
	WT-2	1000	68.00			0/0	9200	100	29.32	53.40	172	100		11.04
	WT-6	1000	66.10			1800/0	16400	178	60.00	51.90	316	184	0.18	15.10
Wuhan	W5-1	1000	56.35	gravel	clay, sand dip gravel	2100/2100	29896		57.83	44.23	676		(0.16)	10.20
	W5-3	1000	56.35			2200/2100	30192		62.46	44.23	683		(0.16)	10.10
	W8-1	900	51.60		silt clay, gravel	2500/0	19600		74.18	32.81	591		0.24	6.59
	W8-2	900	51.00			2500/0	21400		64.83	32.43	660		0.26	6.95
Leqing	ZLG-1	1200	54.00	gravel	cultivation soil, silt, silt clay, gravel	0/0	9000	100	34.07	61.04	147	100		3.50
	ZLG-4	1200	54.00			2750/0	11600	129	58.91	61.04	190	129	0.07	8.40
	ZLG-3	1200	54.00			2750/0	11400	127	58.91	61.04	187	127	0.07	9.80
	ZLG-2	1200	60.00			0/0	8000		34.80	67.82	118	80		4.71
Wenling	ZWS-4	800	54.00	gravel		0/0	6600	100	42.41	27.13	243	100		5.59
	ZWS-3	800	54.00	sand		750/0	10200	155	48.89	27.13	376	155	0.50	8.66
Shanghai	SJ-112	800	70.00	fine sand	fill, silt clay, fine sand	0/0	8400	100	26.28	35.17	239	100		10.50
	SJ-116	800	70.00			500/0	1000	119	39.57	35.17	284	119	0.57	14.05
	SJ-114	800	70.00			600/500	1200	143	38.37	35.17	341	143	(0.31)	12.99

continued

Location of pile-test	Numbering of pile-test	Pile diameter d(mm)	Pile length L(mm)	Soil layer of pile-end	Soil layer of pile side	Grouting weight(concrete) pile-end/pile side(kg)	Q_u		S_u (mm)	V(m^3)	Q_u/V		Q_{vc}	S_a (mm)
							Value (kN)	comparison (%)			value(kN/m^3)	comparison (%)	(kN・m^3/kg)	
Tianjin	TG-11	800	65.00	fine sand	fill, silt, silt clay, clay, fine sand	0/0	8000	100	56.46	32.66	245	100		4.76
	TG-6	800	65.00			300/0	1100	138	71.98	32,66	337	138	1.12	9.80
	TM-2	1000	69.00	silty sand	fill, silt clay, silty sand	0/0	20800	100	55.00	54.17	384	100		13.17
	TM-3	1000	70.00	silt		600/0	23750	114	59.33	54.95	432	113	0.72	13.60
	TH-8	800	56.00	silty sand	clay, silty sand	0/0	11000	100	59.50	28.13	391	100		8.30
	TH-9	800	56.00			0/0	1000	100	57.40	28.13	355	100		8.32
	TH-7	800	56.00			500/0	1400	133	55.83	28.13	498	133	1.00	13.80
	TH-10	800	56.00			500/0	1500	143	59.98	28.13	533	143	1.07	15.20
	TGH-8	800	61.50	silt clay	clay, silty sand	0/0	13750	100	45.86	30.90	445	109		14.20
	TGH-15	800	61.50			0/0	15000	109	42.93	30.90	486	109		14.13
	TGH-20	800	61.50			700/0	17500	127	51.73	30.90	566	127	0.81	16.21
	TGH-3	800	61.50			700/0	17500	127	50.67	30.90	566	127	0.81	16.32
Fuzhou	FL-4	800	66.00	gravle clay	miscellaneous fill, clay,gravel,gravel, silt,gravel dip silt	0/0	7000	100	57.02	33.16	211	100		13.40
	FL-1	800	66.05			1500/0	1300	186	63.92	33.18	392	186	0.26	12.40
	FL-3	800	66.35			1800/0	14000	200	51.66	33.33	420	199	0.23	9.80
	FL-5	800	66.18			1700/0	14000	200	61.24	33.25	421	200	0.23	10.67
	FM-1	1200	75.00		miscellaneous fill, silt, silty and, mid- ium coarse sand, intermediary weath- ered granite inclu- sion, strong weath- ered granite	0/0	24000		63.96	84.78	283	100		19.80
	FM-2	1200	51.90			0/0	24000		57.59	58.67	416	145		16.20
	FM-3	1200	52.40			0/0	20000		55.50	59.23	338	119		20.70
	FM-1A	1200	57.00			2500/0	32000		58.78	64.43	497	176	0.20	13.10
	FM-3A	1200	70.50			2500/0	30000		66.39	79.69	377	133	0.15	14.77

Notes: d—The diameter of pile(mm), L—The length of pile, m, V—The volume of pile(m^3), Q_u—The ultimate vertical compression bearing capacity of single pile determined by S-log$Q$ method (kN), Q_u/V—The ultimate bearing capacity per cubic meter (abbreviated as ultimate unilateral bearing capacity)(kN/m^3); S_u—The settlement of pile-end associated with Q_u, mm; S_a— The settlement of pile-end associated with Q_u/2(mm).

Chapter 7 New Design Method for Space-Varying Rigidity Pile Group with Equal Settlement

At present the design method of high-rise building and super high-rise building is based on static equilibrium method. The settlement of foundation should be checked according to the code after the quantity of super-long piles is determined. If theoretical value of settlement has satisfied the design requirement, the design is completed. In *Calculation and Study of Settlement of High-rise Building's Super-long Pile-box (Raft) Foundation*, semi-theory and semi-experience solid pier and elastic mechanics are mainly used to calculate the sedimentation value of pile groups. Domestic and foreign experts and code compilation commonly pay attention to the first method, for the method proposed by H.G. Poulis is difficult to get accurate calculation parameters. Otherwise for the settlement calculation of super-long pile-box (raft) foundation (>50m), the value get by theoretical calculation is much higher, even up to ten times of the observed settlement date (for example, for a super long bored pile which is 52.2m long and has piled raft foundation, sedimentation value is 24.5mm, which is got by theoretical calculation based on Shanghai codes, but the measured settlements is 6.9mm and the sedimentation rate is 0.013mm/d before it tended to be stable. Sedimentation value is 22.4mm for another piled-raft foundation which is 59.00m long, but the measured settlements is 2.93mm and the sedimentation rate is 0.0096mm/d before it tended to be stable). The reason for the large error lies in that the composite stiffness of foundation and shoring structures of foundation pit are not considered. According to the distribution of foundation stress, foundation stress and strain analysis, the composite stiffness of foundation play decisive role in foundation settlement, a new design method can be got for pile group with space-varying rigidity and equal settlement. The brief introduction is as follows.

7.1 General Rules and Application Reason of Analyzed and Measured Data of Pile Group

1. The relationship between subgrade compressive depth and foundation width

According to elastic mechanics, distribution depth of induced stresses in foundation increases with the increase of foundation width, so the calculation depth of settlement also increases with foundation width. According to the actual statistic data in Fig. 7-1, the ratio of settlement to foundation width keeps constant when the foundation width is more than

40m, and the depth of deformation decreases to only 1/3 when the foundation width is more than 5m. In the graph 7-2, the measured value of deformation range on the loading soft soil subgrade is about 20% of the Mindlin solution. The actual effect is a little smaller than the calculated value based on elastic mechanics.

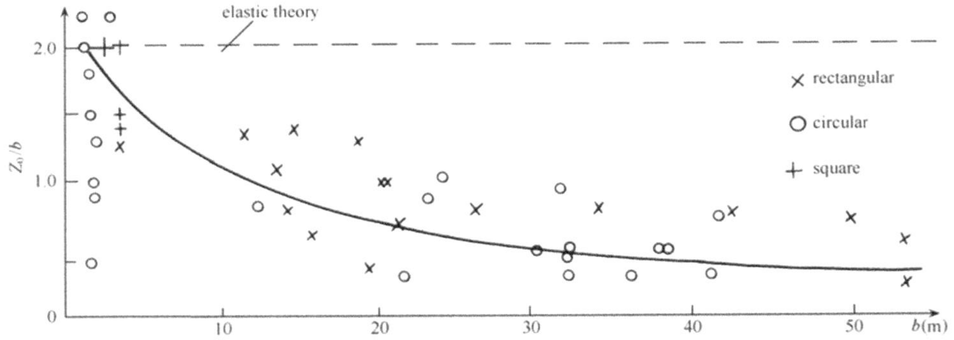

Fig. 7-1 Relationship between measured depth of settlement deformation Z_0 and foundation width b

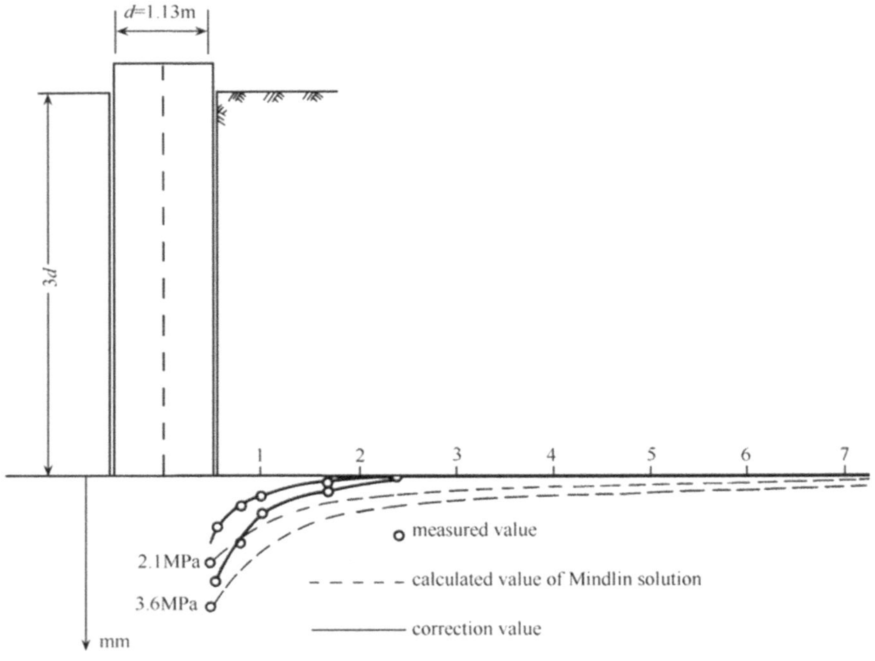

Fig. 7-2 defoarmations of subgrade around foundation in soft subgrade

2. Deformation range of pile side subgrade

The results of finite element calculation and measured results show that the deformation range of pile side subgrade approximately is 3—8*d*, 4—6*d* is usually used (compression modu-lus is 8MPa). So, the deformation range of pile side subgrade increases with the increase of compression modulus of subgrade.

3. The Influence of pile spacing on side resistance and deformations (graph7-4)

Site exploration numerical analysis show that the interaction between piles are very small (counts about 10%). When the pile spacing is 6*d* (in silt, *d*=330mm, pile spacing is 8—23d, double piles test, elastic coefficient of interaction between piles is 1/2—1/8 of the value from elastic mechanics, and increases with the increase of pile spacing), the influence coefficient of pile spacing is 0.05, it can give guidance for pile layout in pile group foundation.

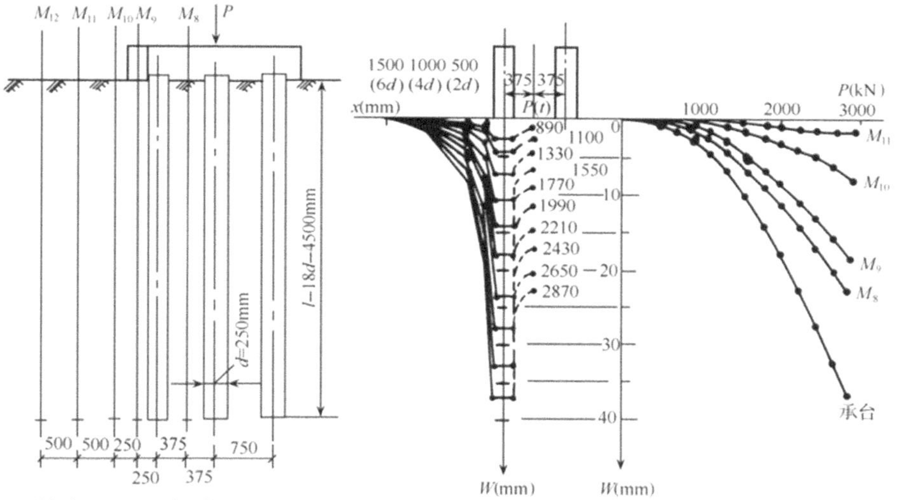

(a) Displacement mark points (GS) (b) Displacement of pile side subgrade and pile (c) Load-displacement

Fig. 7-3 Deformation of pile side subgrade in silt

4. The load distribution on group pile tip

In pile-box (raft) foundation, load distribution on group pile tip is changing along with the gradual formation of superstructure rigidity. After the construction of 8～10 superstructure floors, higher structural stiffness makes little contributions to the global stiffness of foundation, so foundation stiffness of super high-rise building can be made sufficiently large to approach rigidity. The load distribution on group piles tip is as the following table:

item	corner pile	side pile	inside pile
calculated value	Q_c/Q=2.10—3.00	Q_b/Q=1.15—0.50	Q_i=0.05—0.35
measured value	1.32—1.50	1.05—1.42	0.40—0.86

Note: Q_c,Q_b,Q_i are calculating loads based on elastic mechanics and measured load of pile tip respectively; Q is the average loads of pile tip.

From above, it is known that the measured loads of inside pile is obviously higher than that of calculated one based on elastic mechanics, otherwise the measured loads of corner pile is obviously higher than that of calculated value based on elastic mechanics and it is about 50% of calculated value. The above results are from general high buildings which are less than 31 floors. For the tube structural system in super high-rise building, as lack of measured data, the load distribution of pile tip is only based on theoretical calculation. Because the plate of deep foundation for high-rise building is rather thick and the structural stiffness of basement is large,it can be simplified to uniform load and line load of inner & outer tube to calculaote the loads of pile tip. Generally line load of inner cylinder is much larger than that of outer cylinder, as is the case for Jinmao Tower in shanghai, the line load of inner cylinder is 85,000kN/m, the line load of outer cylinder is 10500kN/m, the average load is 1950kN/m^2.

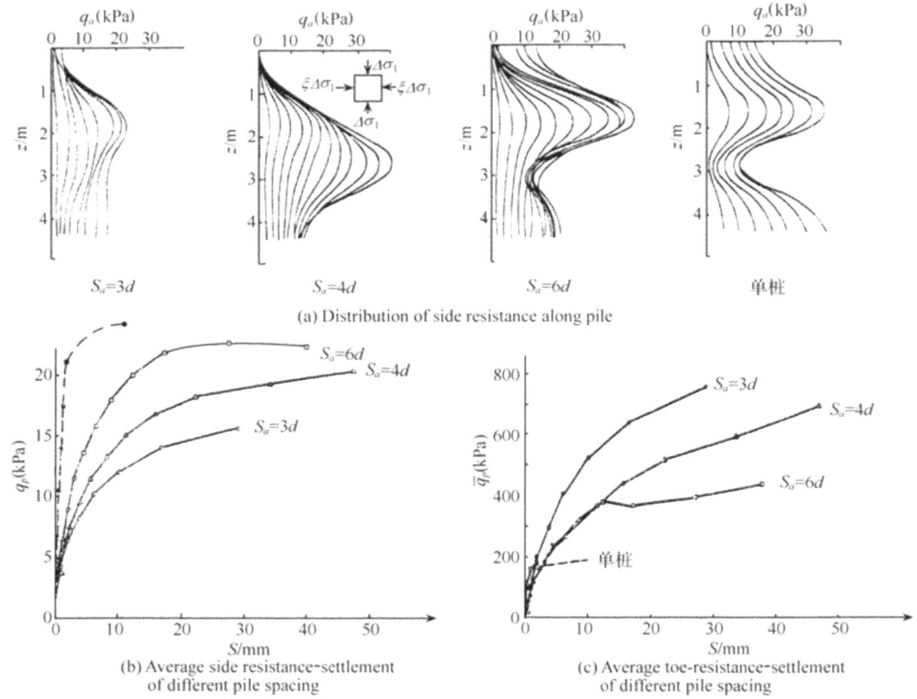

Fig. 7-4 Effects of pile spacing on side resistance and deformation

5. Stress distribution of pile group foundation

The stress in pile group foundation includes geostatic stress, induced stress and construction stress.Ceddes calculates the stress in single pile and pile group based on Mindlin solution, and compares the stress distribution of pile group with Boussinesq solution. As can be seen in Fig. 7-5—7-7.

In the case of pile type, pile diameter, pile length and geological conditions are all consistent, the stress distribution of pile group foundation in graph is: ①inter-pile stress increases with the increase of pile numbers. ②the influencing depth of pile group increases with the increase of pile numbers. ③the stress superposition of pile group is not only displayed in pile's lateral friction, but also the vertical stress of pile group bottom plane is obviously larger than that of single pile andunit toe resistance of each pile of pile group is also larger than that of single pile, so toe resistance of super-long pile group plays a leading role. Pile group foundation can be regarded as an integral base.

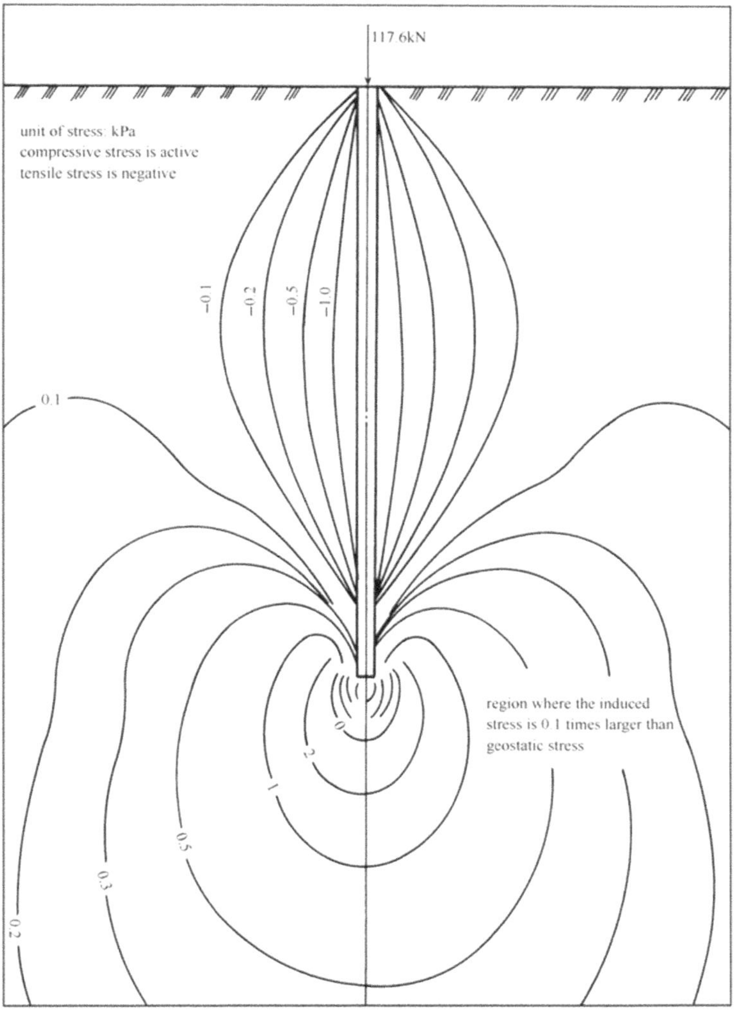

Fig. 7-5 Stress contour graph of the subgrade around single pile

6. The consistency of calculated value and measured results of principal vertical stress components (σ_z) in foundation settlement

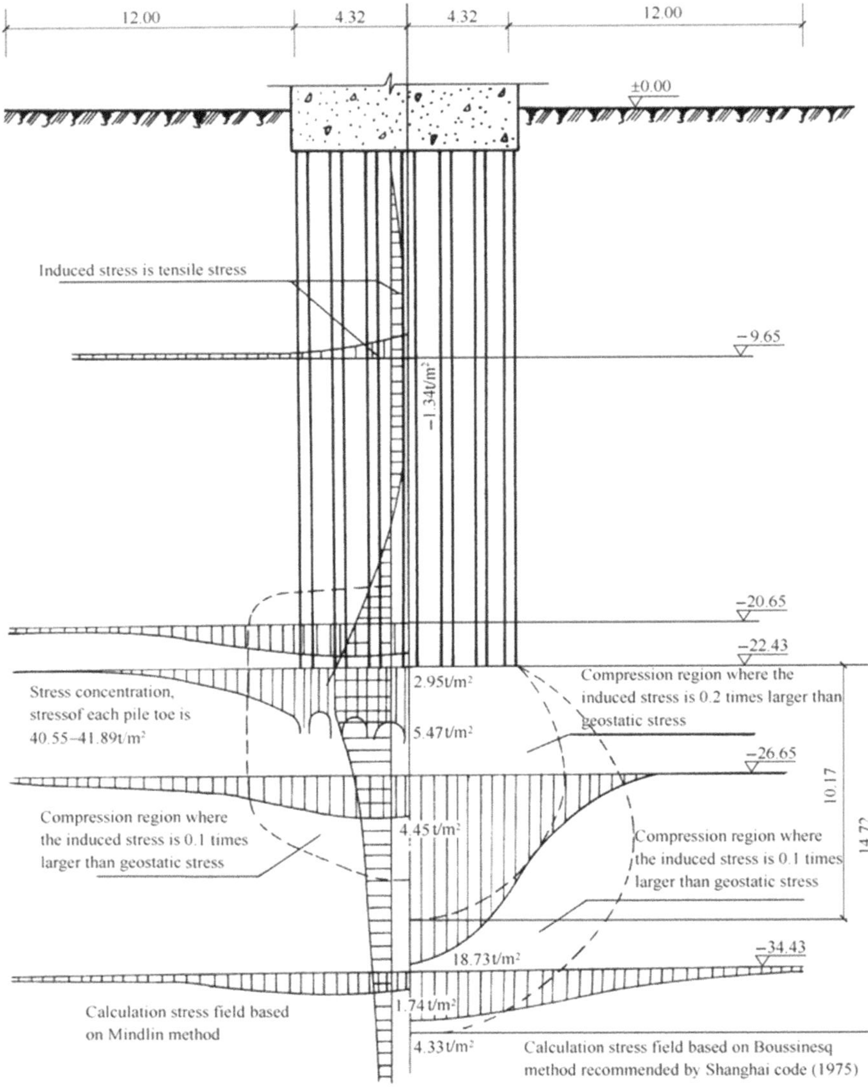

Fig. 7-6 Stress Field Distribution of Pile Group Foundation (7×7piles)

In the plane problem of stress distribution of foundation, stress distribution of subgrade under strip even loads is shown in Fig. 7-7. When the foundation is uniform and continuous and is in linear variation stage, the calculated value based on elastic mechanics and measured results are basically identical, no matter it is contact pressure in foundation base or stress distribution of subgrade. Influencing scope of vertical stress (σ_z) is as deep as 6 times of foundation width. Influencing scope and lateral expansion of (σ_z) mainly occurs in shallow layer (1.5 times of foundation width), shear deformation also mainly occurs in shallow layer. So vertical stress is the major factor of causing foundation settlement.

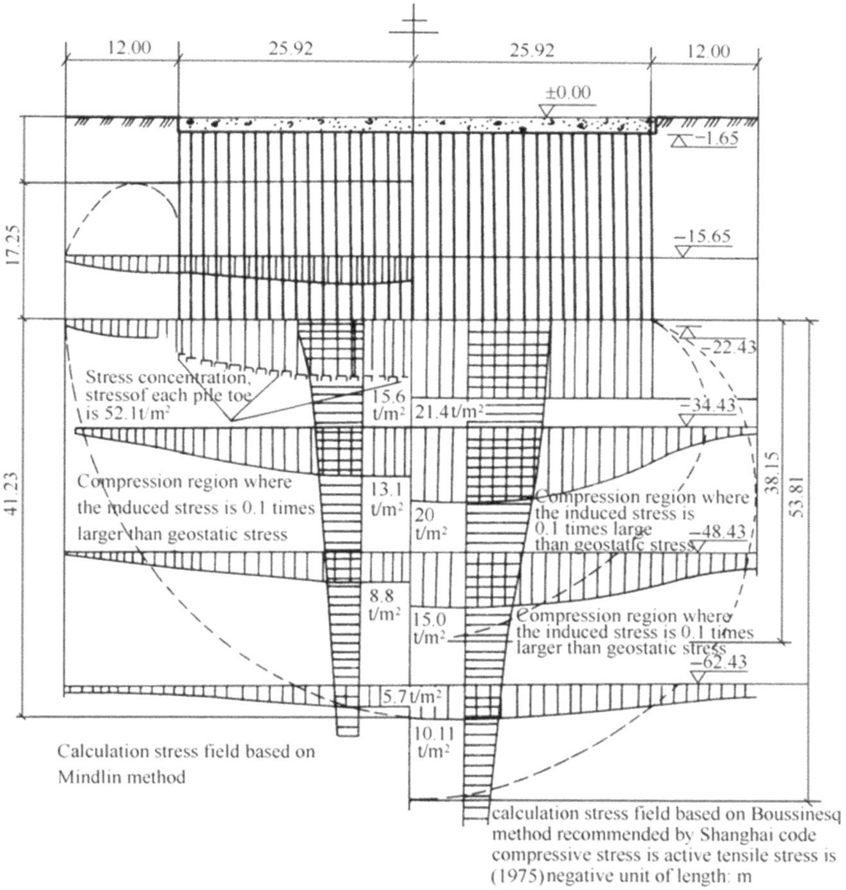

Fig. 7-7 Stress field distribution of pile group foundation (37×37 piles)

7. Pile group effect

Pile group effect mainly depends on the geometric parameters of pile group, such as pile length, pile diameter, pile spacing, besides geological conditions, pile formation technology, upper structure system and foundation design. In fact, it depends on pile-subgrade composite stiffness.

8. When the load is undertaken by piles in cooperation with subgrade, the advantage of short pile is to bear load, the advantage of long pile is to control settlement.

In graph 7-8, the relationship between pile number and settlement shows that long pile is good at controlling settlement, while short pile is good at bearing load but is poor in controlling settlement. So optimized combination of long pile and short pile can form space-varying rigidity pile group.

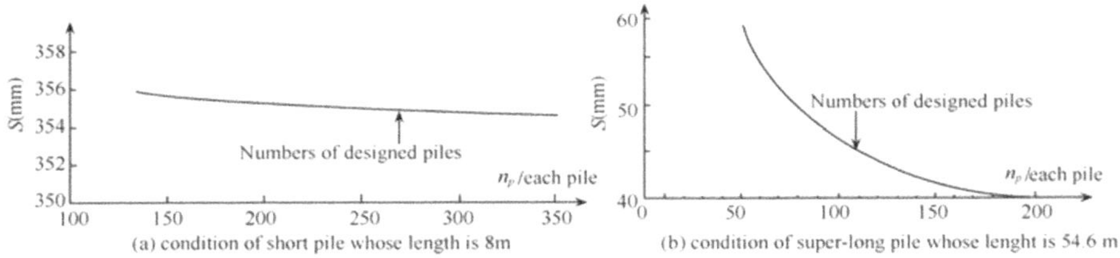

Fig. 7-8 Relationship between pile number and settlement

The content shown above is the theoretical and practical basis of the new method for designing space-varying rigidity and equal settlement pile group.

7.2 The Development of Pile Group Foundation Design Method

At present, the design methods of pile group foundation are almost following the procedure specified by codes, such as the selection of bearing stratum, determination of pile type and pile length, bearing capacity of single pile, pile number and determination of the thickness of raft foundation (design of box foundation) and so on. Settlement analysis of pile group should be performed to make it reach the design requirements under the condition that load bearing should be satisfied. Using the above method to design piles, the piles all have the same length and bearing stratum at pile toes is on the same horizontal level. If the bearing stratum is not a horizontal plane, the value difference on pile length should be strictly stipulated. Experts of foundation engineering has been attempting to seek new design methods of pile foundation for a long time, as high cost, construction difficulty and great risk is associated with pile foundation

1. sparse pile foundation —— design method of pile-subgrade interaction

The design method on pile-subgrade interaction bearing the loads is used when the pile-foundation-box-raft foundation interaction is studied overseas (such as Burland, Broms and De Mello have studied the above method). In this way, the bearing capacity of natural foundation can be exerted, and the bearing capacity of natural foundation can be improved by using a few of pile foundation (even short pile). This design method is called method of sparse pile foundation. The project which was designed based on the above theory is the box-raft foundation of exhibition mansion of Frankfurt in Germany, as following graph 7-9. It is a typical sparse pile foundation on pile-subgrade interaction. In order to explain it, brief introduction of the project is given as follows.

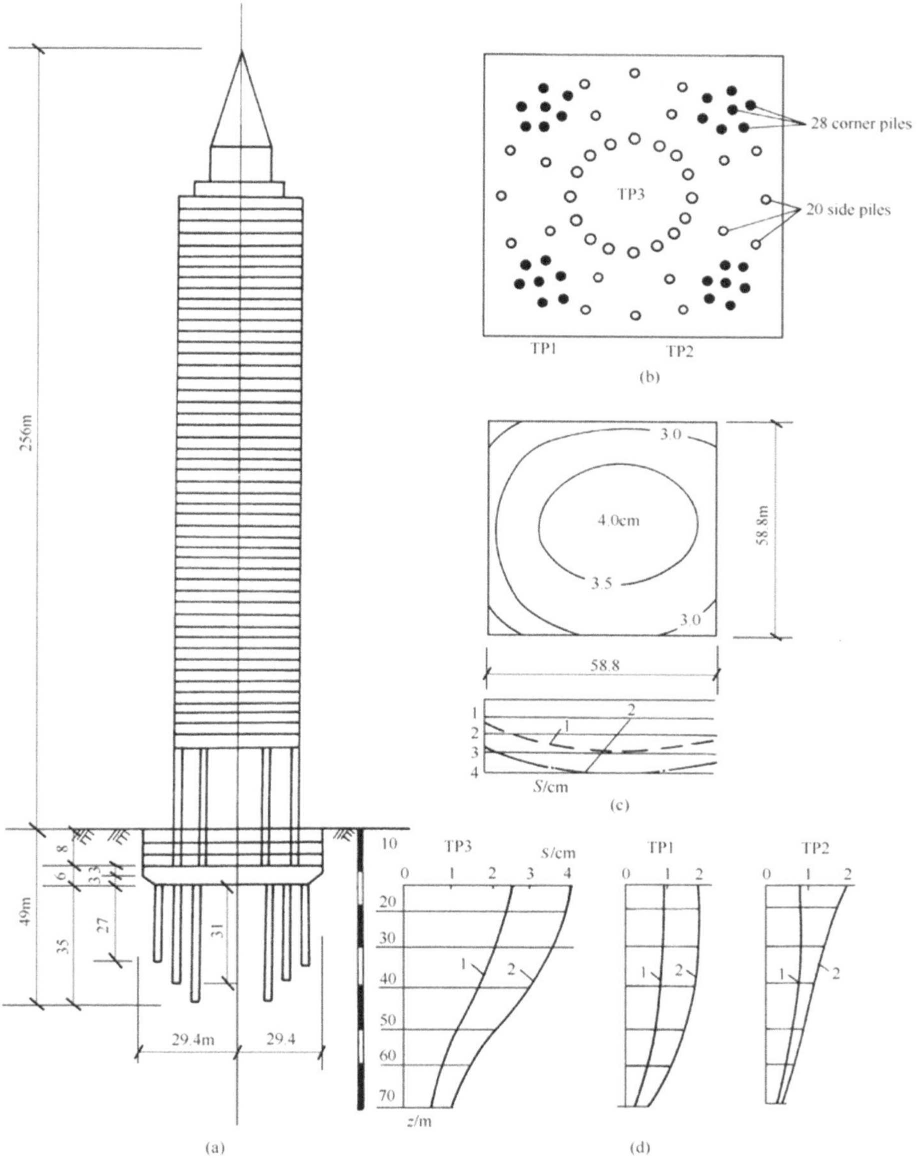

Fig. 7-9 Infrastructure and measured results of sedimentation of exhibition mansion in Frankfurt , in Germany

The building is of tube-in-tube structure, it is the highest building in Europe, and 256m high above ground , 56 floors totally. The building uses box-raft foundation, the piles are friction piles and the foundation is supported by clay of 3 century tertiary . The buried depth of thick raft (the central is 6m, peripheral areas is 3m) is 14m, and three-level basement is adopted. Sparse pile foundation is boldly adopted in the design, 67% of the loads are supposed to be supported by subgrade of raft bottom, and the rest 33% are supported by piles. 64 unequal-length bored piles whose diameter is ϕ 1300 is approximately in circular arrangement. There are 28 piles in four corners, 20 side piles which are 30.9m long, and 16 piles in inner loop which are 34.9m long. The design idea is that piles are arranged according to the idea that interior stiffness is stronger than exterior in order to achieve that the bottom plate of raft foundation could support smaller bending moment. The total weight of the building is 1880MN, and the effective load Q is 1700MN. Curve 1and curve 2 of layered settlement data measured in field in graph 7-8 correspond to 0.3Q and 0.5Q when the applied load is Q. The measured settlement of bottom plate of raft foundation is a basin form curve, as seen in graph 7-8. When half of the building has been constructed ,the settlement in the center of raft foundation is 4.0cm, differential settlement between center and margin is 1.5cm and the deflection ratio is 2.55×10^{-4} . All the indexes described above are the same as those upon completion of foundation. Foundation Inclination is about 1.53×10^{-5} . As it has been considered that piles and subgrade work together to the support the loads, that is to say, 67% of the loads are supposed to be supported by subgrade of raft bottom, and the rest 33% are supported by piles, sedimentation value. SO got by theoretical calculation is 15cm and just 50% that of raft foundation, that is to say, 1/2 of the sedimentation is minified by the 64 piles. Measured results show that the proportion of load supported by the subgrade of raft bottom is less than predicted value. Meanwhile, we can see that theoretical values of settlement of piled raft foundation (150mm) are much larger than measured results.

Table 7-1 Proportion of loads seperately supported by pile and subgrade and statistics of measured settlement

item	original design			measured results
applied load Q_t (MN)	1700	510	850	1105
Q_t/Q (%)	100	30	50	65
pile foundation Q_p (MN)	576	310	600	830
P (MN)	8.84	4.84	9.38	12.97
Q_p/Q (%)	33	61	71	75
subgrade under raft Q_p (MN)	1133	about 200	about 250	about 275
P (kPa)	327.7	59.3	74.1	81.5
Q_s/Q (%)	67	39	29	25
sediment value s_0 (cm)	15	3	4	—
s_0/S_s (%)	100	20	27	—

2. CM composite foundation

This composite foundation method is proposed by Xinglin Shan in Hainan Province and has been applied in several projects. Its design idea still is increasing foundation bearing capacity, combination of cement mixing short piles with plain concrete long piles can not only increase foundation bearing capacity but also decrease foundation settlement. But this composite foundation method has fundamental difference with pile foundation design method, it is limited by material and equipments, building height and engineering application.

3. Design method of sparse pile proposed by Shaoming Huang

This method is based on foundation stress formula of single pile load proposed by Geddes. He generalized the Mindlin formula of elastic mechanics and get the above formula. Vertical induced stress in foundation is solved after consideration of the stress superposition of pile group. The settlement is calculated by layer-wise summation method. In this way, the deficiency of settlement calculation based on pier foundation of pile group is overcome and the influencing factors of settlement calculation such as pile number, pile spacing, irregular pile layout and uneven load distribution in pile foundation can be easily considered. When this method is used for settlement calculation of pile foundation in order to reduce settlement, the relationship between external load and each ultimate bearing capacity of single pile can be divided into two conditions: ①when external load is less than the ultimate bearing capacity of each pile ($P<P_a$), settlement of pile foundation can be directly calculated based on the above method. ②when external load is larger than the ultimate bearing capacity of each pile ($P>P_a$), pile group in pile foundation always support P, bearing platform support the rest ($P-P_a$), the calculation method of foundation vertical stress is the same as that of natural foundation. The foundation vertical stress is the sum of vertical stress produced by the two loads, and then pile foundation settlement can be calculated based on layer-wise summation method. On this basis, principle and steps of pile foundation design that can reduce settlement are proposed.

4. Calculation method of pile foundation design considering settlement control proposed by Yangmin and software of Qimingxing

At present, design theories of pile foundation are all based on that all the upper loads are supported by piles. No matter the foundation is in good or poor condition, subgrade among piles is supposed to directly undertake no loads. The piles in sparse pile foundation are all friction pile, the upper loads are supported by pile and subgrade together, piles can be laid more sparse, and pile amount is less than that used in traditional design while settlement can be satisfied. In addition, natural foundation can meet the upper loads but cannot meet the foundation settlement. In order to decrease subsidence, some friction pile, which is called settlement-reduction pile can be properly laid. The purpose of the above two cases are both reducing displacement and controlling settlement, and then complete design method and computer software can be summarized (Tongji Qimingxing). The application to multistory building and sub-high-rise building has tended to be mature.

There is two critical research results in the above method, that is

(1) The calculation method of pile-box (raft) foundation of high-rise buildings

According to magnitude of external load, settlement calculation can be performed by the following steps:

1) When the loads is smaller than overall shear resistances (*T*) which is distributed in effective pile length along depth direction of length and width periphery of pile-box(raft) foundation, induced stress should be calculated from the bottom of pile-box(raft) foundation, Boussinesq or Mindlin can be used to calculate the induced stress. Final settlement of pile-box (raft) foundation can be divided into two parts: pile compression and subgrade compression blow pile toe. Method of material mechanics can be used to calculate the pile compression, and layer-wise summation method can be used to calculate the subgrade compression blow pile toe.

2) When the loads is larger than overall shear resistances (*T*) which is distributed in effective pile length along depth direction of length and width periphery of pile-box(raft) foundation, modified model of physical deep foundation can be used, induced stress should be calculated from pile tip, final settlement of pile-box(raft) foundation can be divided into two parts: pile compression and subgrade compression blow pile tip, the calculation method is basically the same as above.

(2) Relation curve between pile number and settlement

The foundational settlement corresponding to different pile numbers can be calculated based on the principle that pile and subgrade bear loading together, thus the nonlinear relation between pile number and settlement can be got. When quantity of pile is less, increasing pile number can significantly decrease settlement. But when the quantity of pile reaches some extent, the increased pile number can not significantly decrease settlement. This shows that in some condition economical and reasonable pile number can be determined in order to control settlement. This is the basis of optimum design.

5. The method of adjusting superstructure stiffness, foundation stiffness and pile foundation stiffness proposed by Jinli Liu

The variable rigidity design method proposed by Jinli Liu means that: interaction method can be used to calculate the isoline of foundation settlement, and to adjust stiffness to make the differential settlement reach the minimum. The adjusting stiffness in the method means adjusting superstructure stiffness, foundation stiffness and pile foundation stiffness, and has been applied to projects.

The foundation treatment method proposed by Jinmin Zai, in which man-made adjusted foundation stiffness, is applied to a 9-story building. Its thought is the foundation treatment design in which pile and subgrade undertake load together, resistance on the pile tip and subgrade base are adjusted.

During the revision of *national building foundation design code*, pile foundation design based on settlement control is insisted.

7.3 Scheme and New Method for Pile Group Design Considering the Space-Varying Rigidity with Equal Settlement

Enlightenments to be got from design method of foundation treatment and pile foundation, and law of pile group stress and settlement regularity, which have been discussed above, are as follows:

1) For all the friction pile, pile-subgrade interaction and undertaking upper loads together should be considered, whatever form it belongs to.

2) Long pile or super-long pile has significant effects on reducing foundation settlement, the advantage of short or middle long pile is undertaking loads yet has little effects on reducing foundation settlement.

3) The effects of reducing foundation settlement increases with the increase of pile length.

4) Compared with large diameter pile, the concrete of per cubic meter of small diameter pile undertakes larger loads.

5) Mindlin and Boussinesq solution are used to calculate induced stress.

These laws have been confirmed by theoretical research and measured data.

When designing piles, the ultimate bearing capacity of pile is hard to be reached if static equilibrium principle is used in considering safety factor. Actually, since the bearing capacity of subgrade was made little use of, and the bearing capacity of piles was made full use of, the potentiality of design carrying capacity is very great. So, the design consideration of space-varying rigidity with equal settlement not only has theoretical basis, but also has great technical and economic benefits. It is feasible to be used in engineering design.

7.3.1 Design Condition of Space-Varying Rigidity Pile Group Foundation

Design conditions of space-varying rigidity pile group foundation considering equal settlement is proposed as follows:

1) Assume that foundation soft clay is continuum body.

2) The height of super high-rise building is commonly higher than 200m, at least 50 floors,

the depth of the basement burial also exceeds 10m. Stiffness of basement is great because of the requirements of earthquake resistance, wind resistance and civil aerial defense requirement. For the stiffness of superstructure has little effect on foundation settlement when the height exceeds 8~10 floors, the effects of stiffness of superstructure can be neglected.

3) Pile and subgrade work together to undertake the loads and the bearing capacity of subgrade should be fully utilized.

4) All the pile foundation are assumed friction piles and should be designed according to current codes, bearing capacity of pile group should meet the design requirements.

7.3.2 Design Theory of Space-Varying Rigidity Pile Group Foundation with Equal Settlement

After engineering practices and long term exploration by domestic and foreign experts, besides the above important enlightenments are got, pile group effect (effectiveness factor of pile group and settlement ratio) mainly depends on geometric features of pile itself, that is installation mode of foundation slab, pile length, pile diameter and ratio of cap width and pile length, installation mode of piles and pile amount, certainly, it also depends on physical mechanics properties of subgrade of pile side and pile tip, statumn character of subgrade and formation technology (displacement pile or non-displacement pile). The latter (except formation technology) is natural conditions which is hard to be changed. According to engineering requirements, optimum combination of the former can be completely achieved under the condition that bearing capacity demands is met, and traditional design method can be broken. Traditional design method has two remarkable characteristics:

1) Pile group supports all the loads.

2) Pile layout is designed to be equal length, equal diameter and equal interval.

The first principle of traditional design method discussed above has been broken, now, pile and subgrade work together to support the loads, such as settlement control design, sparse pile design , pile reduction design, and so on. The second principle of traditional design method has not yet been broken. The several design methods discussed above all originate from the idea that pile and subgrade work together to support loads, but not originate from stress-strain relationship of pile group. Taking into account the composite stiffness of pile and subgrade and making full use of properties of pile group can drive pile group foundation reach the comprehensive effects which mean high carrying capacity, less settlement or equal settlement, low cost and short construction period. It is the design principle of space-varying rigidity pile group foundation with equal settlement. According to the analysis above, the theory of space-varying rigidity pile group can be illustrated concretely as follows:

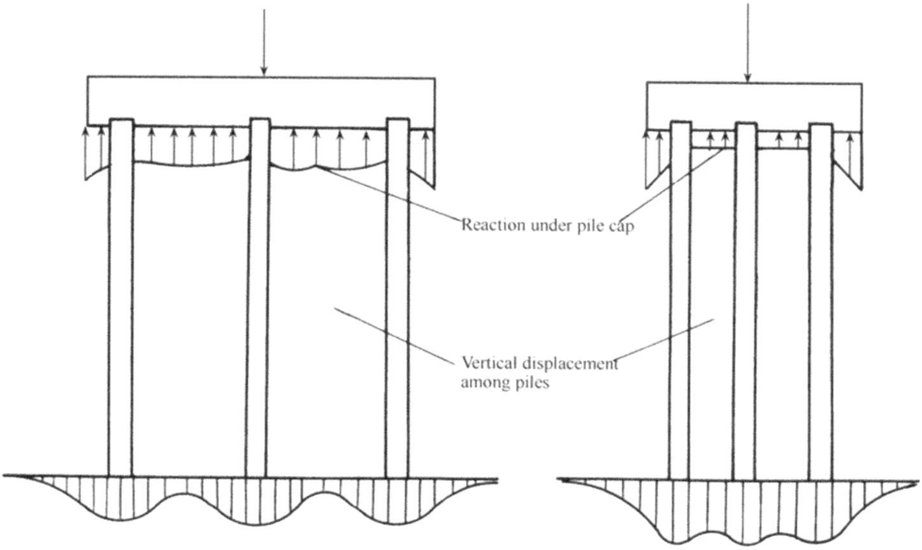

(a) Vertical displacement of foundation of piles which have the same pile length but big and small pile spacing (3 piles)

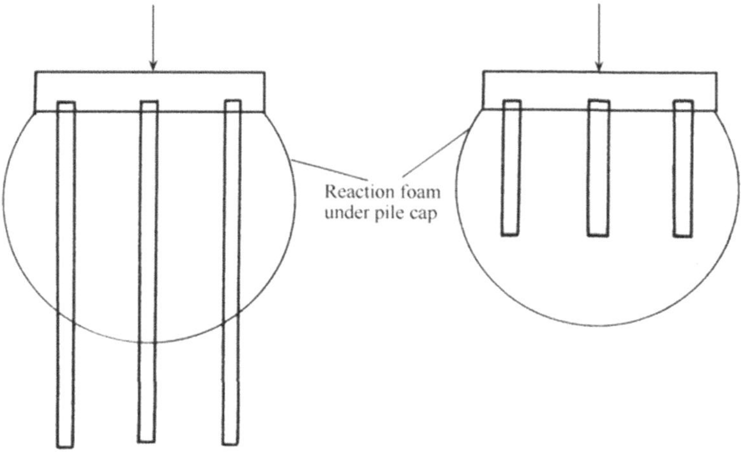

(b) Reaction foam of foundation of piles which have the same pile spacing but different pile length

Fig. 7-10 Vertical displacement of foundation piles which have the same pile length different pile spacing and reaction distribution of foundation piles which have the same pile spacing but different pile length

1) Static equilibrium principle of pile group foundation can ensure the bearing capacity of pile group foundation.

2) For pile group foundation, the proportion of loads supported respectively by pile and subgrade is based on the principle of pile-subgrade interaction, not based on artificial separation.

3) Pile group foundation should meet the basic principle and hypothesis of elastic mechanics and the general law of stress-strain relationship, for example, use Boussinesq and Mindlin method to calculate induced stress.

4) Fully exert the work ability advantage of long pile and short pile respectively, the advantage of long pile is settlement control and the advantage of short pile is load bearing. The optimum combination of long pile and short pile can reach the purpose of high carrying capacity and equal settlement. The finite element calculation results of strain and deformation of long pile are as shown in Figs. 7-11~7-13. Single pile settlement is obvious inversely proportional to pile length.

5) According to general vertical stress and deformation distribution law of foundation under rigid plate or pile group foundation, that is, the stress is gradually decreasing with gradually far away from the basement, and the strain is also gradually decreasing, so is the 'foundation stiffness' (not the stiffness of foundation itself). Conversely, 'foundation stiffness' is gradually increasing. Taking the pile group foundation as a united whole, the composite stiffness foundation of space-varying rigidity pile group is formed.

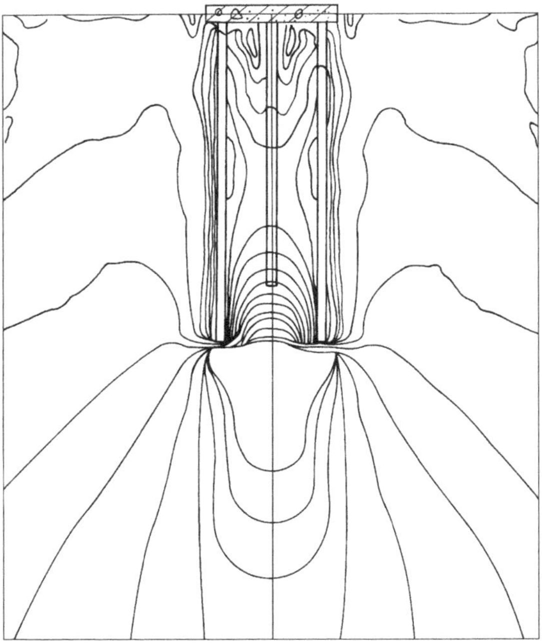

Fig. 7-11 Vertical stress distribution of long-short pile foundation with variable stiffness (finite element plane problem)

The five items discussed above are the theoretical basis of space-varying rigidity pile group.

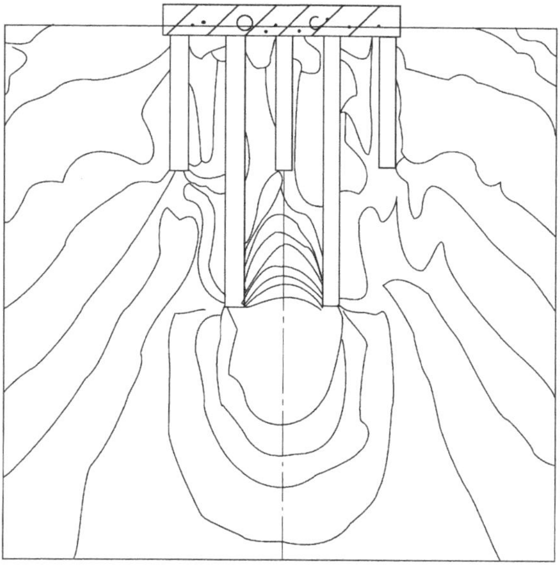

Fig. 7-12 Vertical stress distribution of long-short pile foundation with variable stiffness (5piles)

7.3.3 Design Method of Space-Varying Rigidity Pile Group with Equal Settlement

If design method of space-varying rigidity pile group is used to design the pile foundations of multi-storey buildings and relative tall buildings, foundation treatment method can be used. According to the foundation treatment method above, cushion should be laid under the foundation slab, if the design of space-varying rigidity pile group is based on engineering conditions, design scheme of long-short pile, rigid-soft piles and different diameter pile could all be used. According to the design and construction experiences, for convenience and feasibility, the scheme of cement short pile and long concrete pile is generally better.

The design method of space-varying rigidity group piles with equal settlement has fundamental difference with the method discussed above and it is more complex, its design procedures are:

1) The choice of pile type and pile formation technology.

2) The scheme study of pile layout in plane, initially define the pile layout scheme in plane.

3) The scheme study of space-varying rigidity pile, initially define the scheme of spatial long-short pile.

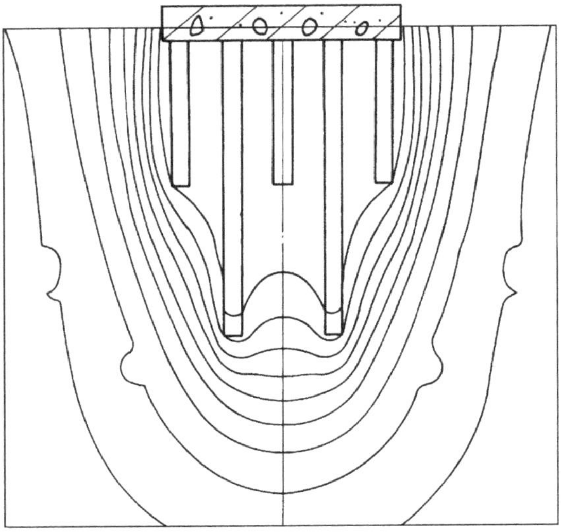

Fig. 7-13 Vertical deformation distribution of long-short pile foundation with variable stiffness (finite element results)

4) Calculate bearing capacity based on codes, make the total reaction of pile meet the bearing requirement (including safety factor).

5) According to reaction on the pile head and settlement of piles, revise the scheme of pile layout in plane and space-varying rigidity pile group and repeat several times, control the settlement difference of pile tips in a certain range (equal settlement), control the total settlement of pile foundation within the allowable range. During the first design, some empirical, simplified and reliable methods can be used to calculate and analyse, after determining the scheme of pile layout in plane and space-varying rigidity pile group, computer software can be choose to perform some analysis. As the purpose of this paper is mainly to study foundation deformation, so the basic steps of design method and design process have to be simply introduced.

7.3.4 Design Scheme of Space-Varying Rigidity Pile Group with Equal Settlement

According to the design method and structure system discussed above, the preliminary design scheme for common space-varying rigidity pile group is given here to be referred to for practical design. The design schemes below is classified according to the height of multi-story building or super high-rise building and the structural systems. There are many design conditions of practical project. Scheme of long-short pile, scheme of rigid-soften piles and scheme of different diameter pile could all be chosen; the scheme of two or three section space-varying rigidity group piles could also be used. In a word, the scheme must be combined with engineering practice and meet all the engineering practice discussed above.

1. Design scheme of variable stiffness pile foundation for foundation treatment of pure frame relative high-rise building and multi-storey building

Pure frame relative high-rise building and multi-storey building generally include buildings no more than 12 floors. Concrete pile (precast pile or bored pile) can be adopted for long pile and cement mixing pile can be adopted for short pile. Long pile is laid under each column and short pile is laid according to carrying capacity demands.This pile foundation is called variable stiffness pile foundation of foundation treatment (Fig. 7-14). Certainly the design methods of reducing-settlement pile and settlement control discussed above can also be adopted. If it is multi-storey building, cement mixing pile may be enough to meet the bearing capacity and settlement requirement. If design requirements can not be satisfied, the scheme of large diameter long pile combined with small diameter short pile can be adopted (Fig. 7-15).

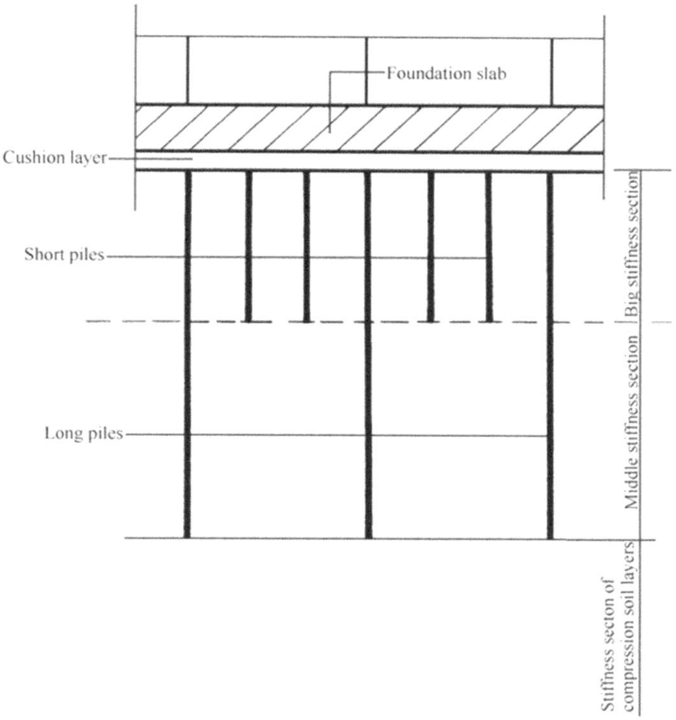

Fig. 7-14 Variable stiffness pile foundation of foundation treatment for relative high-rise building and multi-story building

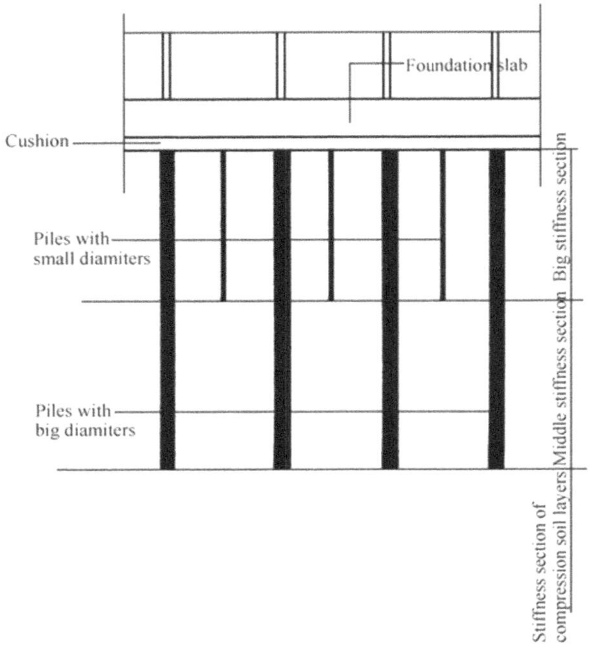

Fig. 7-15 Variable stiffness pile foundation of foundation treatment for relative high-rise building and multi-story building

2. Design scheme of variable stiffness pile group foundation of foundation treatment for pure frame middle-high building

The pure frame middle-high building is generally no more than 80m in height (its height is just 90m in special conditions), and the height is about 60m in seismic region. There is elevator in each of this kind of buildings, and elevator tube is a favorable factor for seismic resistance. In this case, long pile must be laid under the wall of elevator tube, 1—2 piles can be laid under columns, short piles are laid in other section wherever needed according to calculation. Short pile can be cement mixing pile, or can be bored pile (Fig. 7-17).

3. Design scheme of variable stiffness pile group foundation for frame-shear wall or shear wall high-rise buildings

The height of reinforced concrete frame-shear wall structure or shear wall structure is about 130m in earthquake nonresistive region. The height of shear wall structures in Beijing is generally no more than 100m, and box foundation is mostly adopted. For shear wall structures on soft soil area, pile-box(raft) foundation is commonly adopted, the traditional method is laying dense long piles.

For high-rise building with the above structure systems, the scheme of variable stiffness pile group foundation should be determined after comparing with several schemes according to planar structural loads and superstructure loads. Generally, more than two long piles are laid under the frame column, middle long piles which have the same diameter as long piles are laid around the above columns (Fig. 7-18), the length of long-short pile is difficult to determined, several trial calculation must be done in order to choose the optimal plan. The arrangement principle of pile under shear wall structure is that long pile is laid based on the equivalent loads of columns, and short piles with the same diameter are laid among the long piles (Fig. 7-19).

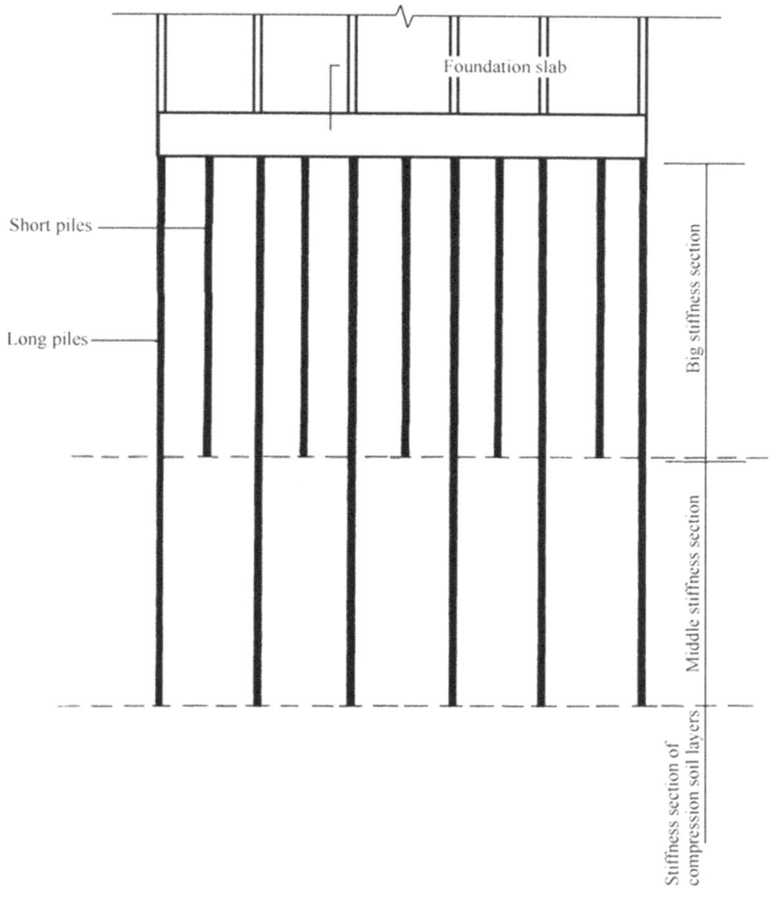

Fig. 7-16 Variable stiffness pile foundation of middle-high building

4. Design scheme of variable stiffness pile group foundation for super high-rise building with tube-in-tube structure system

The variable stiffness pile foundation of Exhibition Mansion in Frankfurt, Germany has been discussed above. The building has larger load in center and smaller load in outer cylinder. It has good foundation which can support 67% of loads, the rest 33% are supported by pile foundation. The inner cylinder is restricted by its location, only long pile can be laid under it, so the variable stiffness pile foundation is formed, whose piles in inner cylinder are longer than those in outer cylinder. In essence, this variable stiffness pile-raft foundation is sparse pile foundation, pile and subgrade supporting loads together is not the design of space-varying stiffness pile group proposed by this paper. According to calculation, the calculated settlement is 30cm, after 64 piles are laid, (16 piles in inner cylinder with the length of 34.9m, 20 piles in side pile with the length of 30.9m, 28 piles in four corners with the length of 26.9m, there is no remarkable difference between lengths of long piles and short piles) , the calculated settlement reduces to 15cm. Besides, the pile length in pile-raft foundation of Double-tower Mansion in Malaysia, the pile length in central areas is longer than other piles, it is due to geological structure, not due to the design of variable stiffness pile group.

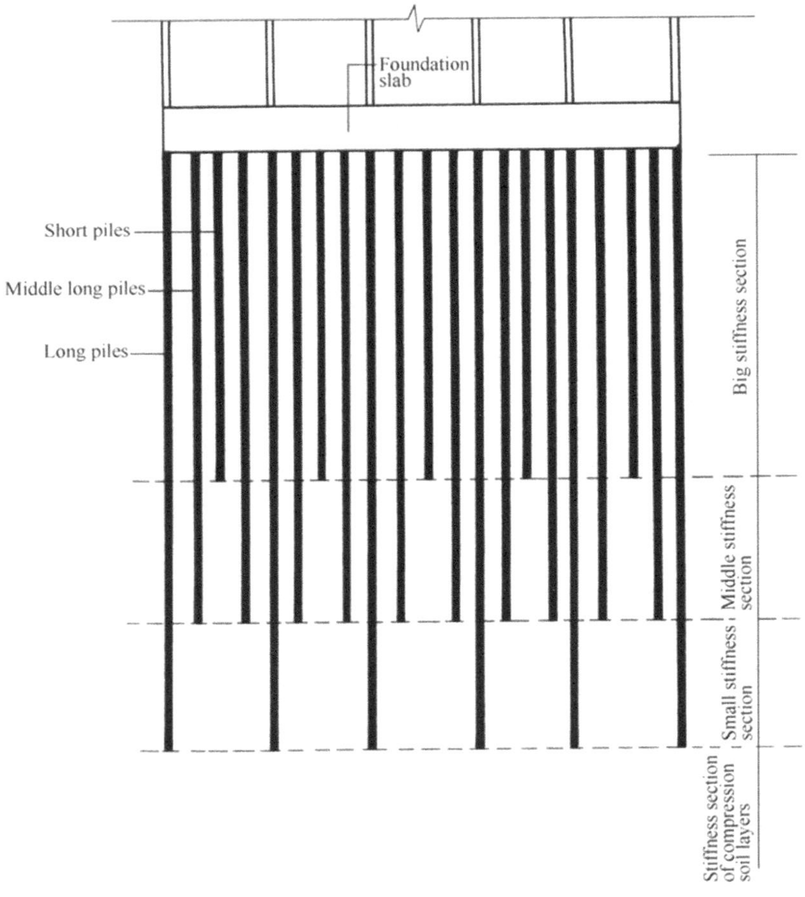

Fig. 7-17 Variable stiffness pile foundation of middle-high building

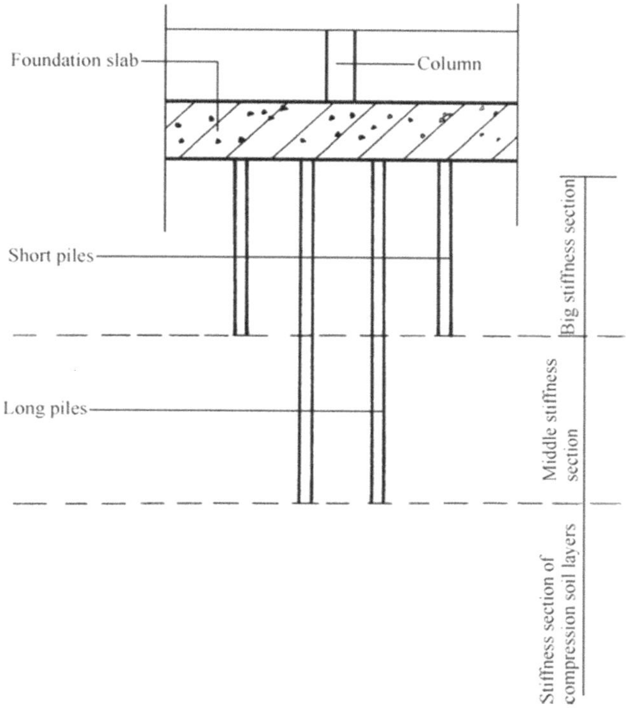

Fig. 7-18 Variable stiffness pile foundation under column (2 piles)

Super high-rise building with tube-in-tube structure generally has regular plane and simple facade. Force transfer is clear. In pile-box (raft) foundation, it is line load in inner cylinder, and uniform load is rare. When pile foundation plane is laid, besides considering the plane characteristics, generally it is laid along the inner and outer cylinder, so the variable stiffness pile group is composed (Fig. 7-20). There is no long pile in inner cylinder because the line load of inner cylinder is large and pile is different to be laid; generally there is space to lay piles in outer cylinder, so the piles which are not in equal length can be laid, the piles lengths of pile group are the same based on conventional design.

In the pile-box(raft) foundation of super high-rise building with tube-in-tube structure system, long and short piles can be laid as septal quincunx.

The design scheme of variable stiffness pile group foundation for the four structure systems above can work as design reference. Several trial calculation and optimization treatment are needed during practical design, final scheme can be determined based on the principle of *bearing, settlement and cost*.

The design method of variable stiffness pile group with equal settlement is proposed by the author in 1997 and subjected to the ovation of engineering circle. Problems are only proposed at that time, subsequently some research is done under the instruction of the tutor, Xueyuan Hou, and now the method is becoming mature. It is the historic breakthrough of pile foundation design. The method is not only theoretical advance, reliable technique but also has tremendous technical and economic benefit. According to the amount of pile every year, billions of money can be saved if design method of variable stiffness pile group considering equal settlement is used.

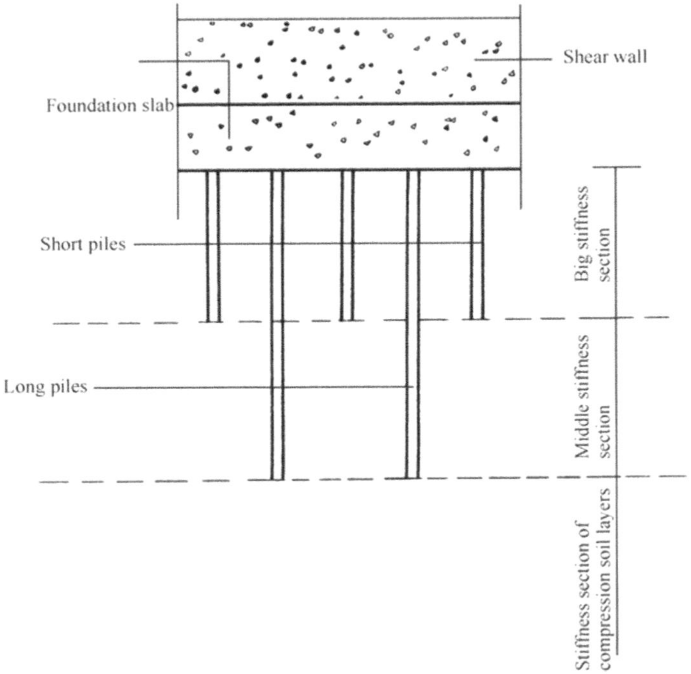

Fig. 7-19 Variable stiffnesspile foundation under shear wall

7.4 Settlement Calculation of Space-Varying Rigidity Pile Group

The Settlement calculation of space-varying rigidity pile group is very complex, besides finite element method and spline function method, layer-wise summation method can be used in engineering application because it is easy and feasible. The critical of settlement calculation is pile-subgrade interaction, the 'composite modulus' of pile and subgrade calculation is the critical of pile-subgrade interaction. Preliminary study has been done there and it can be a reference for engineering design.

7.4.1 The Calculation Using Layer-Wise Summation Method in Codes

In Fig. 7-20, settlement of space-varying rigidity pile group is calculated using layer-wise summation method in codes, the total settlement of it is:

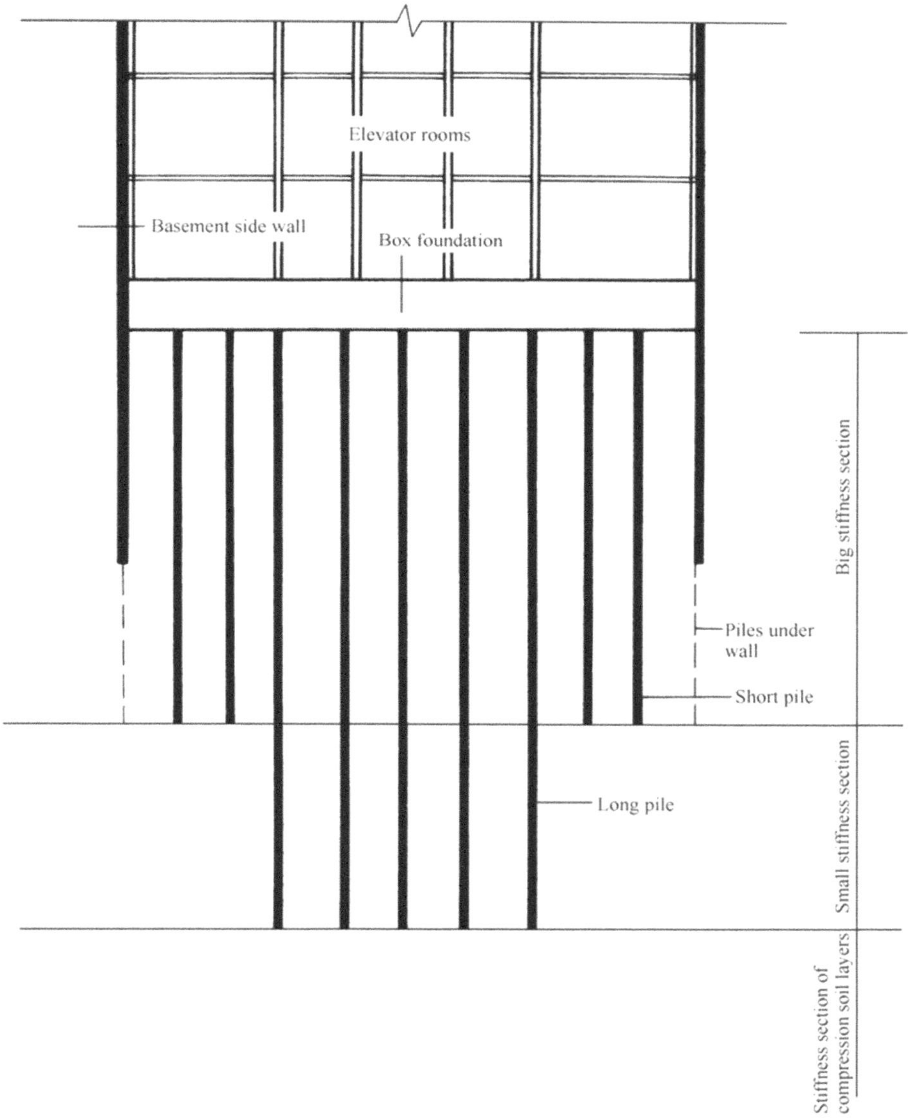

Fig. 7-20 Variable stiffness pile foundation of super high-rise building with tube-in-tube structure system

$$s = s_1 + s_2 + s_3 + s_4 \tag{7-1}$$

where: s_1 — the settlement of pile subgrade within shoring structure of deep foundation pit, refer chapter 5;

s_2 — the settlement of short pile subgrade under shoring structure of deep foundation pit;

s_3 — the settlement of long pile subgrade under short piles;

s_4 — the settlement of subgrade layer under long piles after deformation.

According to the calculation program in codes considering the safety factor, it is not difficult to obtain the total settlement of space-varying rigidity pile group.

7.4.2 The Calculation of 'Composite Stiffness' of Pile-Subgrade

The complexity of "composite stiffness" calculation of pile-subgrade is due to the nonlinearity, heterogeneity and inelasticity of subgrade. when treating the composite foundation, this kind of 'composite stiffness' of pile-subgrade is called 'complex stiffness' or 'equivalent stiffness'.

Substantially, the composite modulus of foundation is calculated. It is impossible to clearly calculate the composite modulus of foundation according to the theory. But it can be estimated according to measurement and project experience. If theoretical calculation (based on elastic theory) is used, the problem must be simplified in order to give convenience to engineering application.

1. Basic assumption

In the analysis on structural body of pile and subgrade, the pile and subgrade are dispersed into finite element respectively. Coordination of displacement of pile element and subgrade element need to be conducted in order to analyze the pile-subgrade interaction and stress features. The other analysis method is pile-subgrade ascontinuum model, it is similar to the combination of steel bar and concrete—reinforced concrete material. In this way, the stress features of pile-subgrade can be easily analysed. Certainly, for settlement calculation, foundation has the very complex problems of secondary consolidation and consolidation, subgrade is three-phase discrete body (water, air and solid, microstructure is more complex, there is no constitutive model to simulate the nonlinearity, heterogeneity and discontinuity of subgrade. Especially the study of mechanics of super deep subgrade has just started, and a lot of properties and physical and mechanical characteristics of super deep subgrade are not clear. So in the study of settlement calculation, the discrete body of binding foundation is simplified as follows:

(1) The hypothesis of continuum model of pile-subgrade foundation

In Fig. 7-21, the pile is square pile ($2l_x \times 2l_y$), pile spacing is $2L_x \times 2L_y$, the vertical height of pile-subgrade element is $2L_z$,comparatively speaking, the dimension of pile is usually 1/3—1/20 of pile spacing, $2L_z$ can be taken as small as possible.

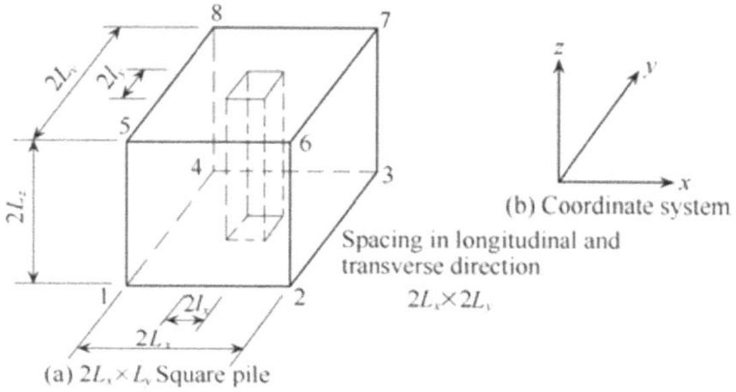

Fig. 7-21 Continuum element of pile-subgrade foundation

In this pile-subgrade element, it is assumed a continuum structure, and the six surface of element are still plane after distortion, the stresses of each plane are assumed to be uniform (reduced stress), the pile-subgrade internal element is continuous, so it is easy to analyze using finite element method after discrete element is assumed to be continuum structure.

(2) The hypothesis of constant strain

According to different modification hypothesis internal element, different reduced elastic modulus can be got, the simplest method is constant strain assumption. Complex properties of pile-subgrade foundation can be simulated if elements are as many as possible.

(3) The hypothesis of constant percolation gradient

After the element is assumed to be continuous, the seepage coefficient of the six surface of it is assumed constants, the seepage coefficient of three directions are also constants, the equivalent seepage coefficient can be got based on Sandhn-Wlison functional and finite element scheme or variational principle of Laplace transformation form, that is :

$$K_{ei} = nK_{pi} + (1 - n) K_{si} \qquad (i = x, y, z) \tag{7-2}$$

where: n—pile rate of pile-subgrade foundation;

K_{pi}—seepage coefficient of pile in x,y,z direction;

K_{si}—seepage coefficient of subgrade in x,y,z direction.

The three hypothesises above make the complex pile-subgrade-structure simple. Certainly, in the finite element calculation, pile and subgrade can also be subdivided into element respectively, according to displacement coordination of pile and subgrade (assuming there is no slippage between pile and subgrade), the formulistic of finite element calculation can be got based on variational principle.

2. The calculation of "composite modulus" of pile-subgrade

During the compound foundation treatment, concrete long pile and deep mixing subgrade short pile can be adopted, after applied in construction, Weilu Jin proposes the conception and expression of combination modulus, later on, Yaonan Gong and Dingyi Xie, etc, all studied the problems of composite modulus of composite foundation and get some achievements. National regulation gives the compression modulus of composite subgrade, that is:

$$E_{sp} = [1 + m(n-1)]E_s \tag{7-3}$$

where: m—replacement ratio (or pile rate);

n— pile-subgrade stress ratio;

E_s—compression modulus of subgrade among piles.

If settlement is calculated based on composite foundation method, its composite modulus is:

$$E_c = mE_p + (1-m)E_s \tag{7-4}$$

where: m—replacement ratio (or pile rate);

E_p—compression modulus of pile;

E_s—compression modulus of subgrade among piles.

According to the hypothesis of continuum model of pile-subgrade, the distortion internal pile-subgrade element is also assumed constant, so the "composite modulus" or "combination modulus" of pile-subgrade element can be got based on the elastic theory. The general stress-strain relationship is

$$\{\sigma\} = \{E\}\{\varepsilon\} \tag{7-5}$$

where: $\{E\}$— elastic matrices, if it is isotropic.

$$\{E\} = \begin{pmatrix} \Theta + \frac{4}{3}\Psi & \Theta - \frac{2}{3}\Psi & \Theta - \frac{2}{3}\Psi & 0 & 0 & 0 \\ \Theta - \frac{2}{3}\Psi & \Theta + \frac{4}{3}\Psi & \Theta - \frac{2}{3}\Psi & 0 & 0 & 0 \\ \Theta - \frac{2}{3}\Psi & \Theta - \frac{2}{3}\Psi & \Theta + \frac{4}{3}\Psi & 0 & 0 & 0 \\ 0 & 0 & 0 & \Psi & 0 & 0 \\ 0 & 0 & 0 & 0 & \Psi & 0 \\ 0 & 0 & 0 & 0 & & \Psi \end{pmatrix} \tag{7-6}$$

If it is anisotropic in (x, y, z) directions

$$\{E\}=\begin{pmatrix} E_{11} & E_{12} & E_{13} & 0 & 0 & 0 \\ E_{12} & E_{22} & E_{23} & 0 & 0 & 0 \\ E_{13} & E_{23} & E_{33} & 0 & 0 & 0 \\ 0 & 0 & 0 & G_1 & 0 & 0 \\ 0 & 0 & 0 & 0 & G_2 & 0 \\ 0 & 0 & 0 & 0 & & G_3 \end{pmatrix} \tag{7-7}$$

The strain energy density of Formula (7-6) is

$$\begin{aligned} A &= \frac{1}{2}\varepsilon^T\sigma = \frac{1}{2}\varepsilon^T E\varepsilon \\ &= \frac{1}{2}\left(\Theta - \frac{2}{3}\Psi\right)(\varepsilon_x+\varepsilon_y+\varepsilon_z)^2 + \Psi(\varepsilon_x^2+\varepsilon_y^2+\varepsilon_z^2) \\ &\quad + \frac{1}{2}\Psi(\gamma_{yz}^2+\gamma_{zx}^2+\gamma_{xy}^2) \end{aligned} \tag{7-8}$$

where: E—abbreviated matrices.

The strain energy density of Formula (7-7) is

$$\begin{aligned} A &= \frac{1}{2}\varepsilon^T\sigma = \frac{1}{2}\varepsilon^T E\varepsilon \\ &= \frac{1}{2}(E_{11}\varepsilon_x^2 + E_{22}\varepsilon_y^2 + E_{33}\varepsilon_z^2 + G_1\gamma_{yz}^2 + G_2\gamma_{zx}^2 + G_3\gamma_{xy}^2) \\ &\quad + (E_{12}\varepsilon_x\varepsilon_y + E_{13}\varepsilon_x\varepsilon_z + E_{23}\varepsilon_y\varepsilon_z) \end{aligned} \tag{7-9}$$

Based on the assumption of constant strain, respectively calculate strain energyof pile U_p, strain energy of subgrade, total strain energy $U = U_p + U$ and combination strain energy. $U = U_p + U_s$ Subscript p, s represents pile and subgrade respectively. As the strain of element is constant, so:

$$\begin{aligned} U_p &= \int_{V_p} A_p \mathrm{d}V = A_p \int_{V_p} \mathrm{d}V = A_p V_p \\ &= \frac{V_p}{2}\left[\left(\Theta_p - \frac{2}{3}\Psi_p\right)(\varepsilon_x+\varepsilon_y+\varepsilon_z)^2 + 2\Psi_p(\varepsilon_x^2+\varepsilon_y^2+\varepsilon_z^2) + \Psi_p(\gamma_{yz}^2+\gamma_{zz}^2+\gamma_{xy}^2)\right] \end{aligned} \tag{7-10}$$

$$\begin{aligned} U_s &= \int_{V_s} A_s \mathrm{d}V = A_s \int_{V_s} \mathrm{d}V = A_s V_s \\ &= \frac{V_s}{2}\left[\left(\Theta_s - \frac{2}{3}\Psi_s\right)(\varepsilon_x+\varepsilon_y+\varepsilon_z)^2 + 2\Psi_s(\varepsilon_x^2+\varepsilon_y^2+\varepsilon_z^2) + \Psi_s(\gamma_{yz}^2+\gamma_{yx}^2+\gamma_{xy}^2)\right] \end{aligned} \tag{7-11}$$

If the pile rate of foundation is m, the total area of pile and subgrade is $V = V_s + V_p$ that is

$$\frac{V_p}{V} = \frac{4l_x l_y}{4L_x L_y} = m\text{,}\quad \frac{V_s}{V} = 1 - m \tag{7-12}$$

The total strain energy U is

$$U = U_p + U_s$$
$$= \frac{V}{2}\left\{\left[m\left(\Theta_p - \frac{2}{3}\Psi_p\right) + (1-m)\left(\Theta_s - \frac{2}{3}\Psi_s\right)\right](\varepsilon_x + \varepsilon_y + \varepsilon_z)^2\right.$$
$$+ 2\left[m\Psi_p + (1-m)\Psi_s\right](\varepsilon_x^2 + \varepsilon_y^2 + \varepsilon_z^2)$$
$$\left. + \left[m\Psi_p + (1-m)\Psi_s\right](\gamma_{yz}^2 + \gamma_{zx}^2 + \gamma_{xy}^2)\right\} \tag{7-13}$$

The combination strain energy U_c got based on Formula (7-80) is

$$U_c = \int_V A_c \mathrm{d}V = A_c \int_V \mathrm{d}V = A_c V$$
$$= \frac{V}{2}[E_{11}\varepsilon_x^2 + E_{22}\varepsilon_y^2 + E_{33}\varepsilon_z^2 + 2E_{12}\varepsilon_x\varepsilon_y$$
$$+ 2E_{13}\varepsilon_x\varepsilon_z + 2E_{23}\varepsilon_y\varepsilon_z + G_1\gamma_{yz}^2 + G_2\gamma_{zx}^2 + G_3\gamma_{zy}^2] \tag{7-14}$$

assume $\varepsilon_x, \varepsilon_y, \varepsilon_z, \gamma_{yz}, \gamma_{zx}, \gamma_{xy}$ independent variable, the variation of $U - U_c$ is

$$\delta(U - U_c) = 0 \tag{7-15}$$

Make the multiplicator of $\delta\varepsilon_x, \delta\varepsilon_y, \delta\varepsilon_z, \delta\gamma_{yz}, \delta\gamma_{zx}, \delta\gamma_{xy}$ to be zero, the six equations follows can be got:

$$\left[m\left(\Theta_p + \frac{4}{3}\Psi_p\right) + (1-m)\left(\Theta_s + \frac{4}{3}\Psi_s\right) - E_{11}\right]\varepsilon_x$$
$$+ \left[m\left(\Theta_p - \frac{2}{3}\Psi_p\right) + (1-m)\left(\Theta_s - \frac{2}{3}\Psi_s\right) - E_{12}\right]\varepsilon_y$$
$$+ \left[m\left(\Theta_p - \frac{2}{3}\Psi_p\right) + (1-m)\left(\Theta_s - \frac{2}{3}\Psi_s\right) - E_{13}\right]\varepsilon_z = 0 \tag{7-16}$$

$$\left[m\left(\Theta_p - \frac{2}{3}\Psi_p\right) + (1-m)\left(\Theta_s - \frac{2}{3}\Psi_s\right) - E_{12}\right]\varepsilon_x$$
$$+ \left[m\left(\Theta_p + \frac{4}{3}\Psi_p\right) + (1-m)\left(\Theta_s + \frac{4}{3}\Psi_s\right) - E_{22}\right]\varepsilon_y$$
$$+ \left[m\left(\Theta_p - \frac{2}{3}\Psi_p\right) + (1-m)\left(\Theta_s - \frac{2}{3}\Psi_s\right) - E_{23}\right]\varepsilon_z = 0 \tag{7-17}$$

$$\left[m\left(\Theta_p - \frac{2}{3}\Psi_p\right) + (1-m)\left(\Theta_s - \frac{2}{3}\Psi_s\right) - E_{13}\right]\varepsilon_x$$
$$+ \left[m\left(\Theta_p - \frac{2}{3}\Psi_p\right) + (1-m)\left(\Theta_s - \frac{2}{3}\Psi_s\right) - E_{23}\right]\varepsilon_y$$
$$+ \left[m\left(\Theta_p + \frac{4}{3}\Psi_p\right) + (1-m)\left(\Theta_s + \frac{4}{3}\Psi_s\right) - E_{33}\right]\varepsilon_z = 0 \tag{7-18}$$

$$\left[m\Psi_p + (1-m)\Psi_s - G_1\right]\gamma_{yz} = 0 \tag{7-19}$$

$$\left[m\Psi_p + (1-m)\Psi_s - G_2\right]\gamma_{zx} = 0 \tag{7-20}$$

$$\left[m\Psi_p + (1-m)\Psi_s - G_3\right]\gamma_{xy} = 0 \tag{7-21}$$

During converting the elastic modulus, no matter what value the strain $\varepsilon_x, \varepsilon_y, \varepsilon_z, \gamma_{yz}, \gamma_{zx}, \gamma_{xy}$ is, each of the six equations above holds, so the multiplicator of each strain is zero, so the followed elastic coefficient can be got:

$$E_{11} = E_{22} = E_{33} = m\left(\Theta_p + \frac{4}{3}\Psi_p\right) + (1-m)\left(\Theta_s + \frac{4}{3}\Psi_s\right) \tag{7-22}$$

$$E_{12} = E_{13} = E_{23} = m\left(\Theta_p - \frac{2}{3}\Psi_p\right) + (1-m)\left(\Theta_s - \frac{2}{3}\Psi_s\right)$$

$$G_1 = G_2 = G_3 = m\Psi_p + (1-m)\Psi_s \tag{7-23}$$

The relationship above expressed by matrices is：

$$E_c = mE_p + (1-m)E_s \tag{7-24}$$

That is to say that combination elastic matrix E_c can be got according to elastic matrix of pile E_p, elastic matrix of subgrade E_s and pile rate. The E_c in the formula above is the "composite modulus" of pile-subgrade. It is consistent with "composite modulus".

Internal stress and strain may be arbitrarily distributed in spatial element of pile-subgrade, the assumption of constant strain and constant percolation gradient is the simplest and reasonable. Certainly, further study on internal element can be done.

7.5 Chapter Summary

The author proposes the new design method of space-varying rigidity group piles with equal settlement according to the properties of super-long pile, force transfer law of side friction of short pile, pile group effect and the study of Mindlin problems of applied load in semi-infinite body. This method has been successfully used in engineering. This chapter gives its design principle, design method and design scheme, and the method of settlement calculation, especially the calculation of composite modulus of pile-subgrade foundation.

References

Chen X.F., Chen Wei. 2002. New Design Methods of Space Variable Stiffness Pile Groups Equal-Settlement, International Conference on Civil Engineering Innovation and Sustainable Development in the 21st Century, Beijing, China.

Chen X.F. 1999. the Highest Building Designed Independently by Chinese——China Bank Tower in Qingdao: Memoir of the First Academic Conference of China Association of Science & Technology, Beijing: China Science and Technology Press.

Liu J.L., Chi L.Q. 2000. Calculation Model of Pile-soil Deformation and Design of Variable Stiffness Leveling, Journal of Geotechnical Engineering.

Liu J.L., Huang Qiang, Li Hua, Hu W.L., Li Xiong, et al., 1990. Research of the Working Situation and Deformation of Group Piles Foundation in Soft Subgrade, Research Report of Architecture Science by the Ministry of Construction.

Jin W.L. 1993. Practical Soil Mechanics and the Actual Measurement of Subgrade Treatment, Beijing: China Railway Press.

Chapter 8 Settlement Analysis and Case Study of Diaphragm Wall and Friction Pile-Box (Raft) Foundation on Super High-Rise Building

The calculative theory of settlement and analysis of measured settlement for pile-box (raft) foundation of general high-rise buildings and middle high-rise buildings have got rich achievement. Some research results of Chinese experts have reached internationally advanced level, such as Professor Xihong Zhao, Professor Jianguo Dong, Professor Yang Min, Professor Zhu Baili, Professor Hong Yukang and Professor Chen Zhuchang of Tongji University; Academician Huan Xiling, Researcher Liu Jinli and Huang Qiang of China Academy of Architectural Engineering; Academician Zhou Jing of Railway Institute of Science and Technology; Academician Shen Zhujiang of Water Conservancy Institute of Nanjing; Chief Engineer of Civil Design Institute of Shanghai: Huang Shaolou. But the interaction between diaphragm wall and friction pile-box (raft) foundation and the settlement analysis concerning the interaction haven't been considered in these results. Furthermore, a large number of these super high-rise buildings are lesser then 100m in height. There is little study result for super high-rise buildings higher than 150m. So far, there are only 12 super high-rise buildings exceeding 200m, 3 buildings exceeding 300m, and only one building exceeding 400m (It is Jinmao Tower, which is 395m in fact, not beyond 400m). So it could be said that the action of diaphragm wall is not involved in the analysis of foundation settlement of these super high-rise buildings. In addition, because of various reasons, the measured settlement data and analysis of these super high-rise buildings is scarce. So the settlement data of engineering case is very valuable, not only at present but also in the future. In this chapter, there is no discussion on various calculation methods or calculation cases, and emphasis is laid on the analysis of effect of diaphragm wall on settlement calculation, study is conducted on the settlement calculation principle and method of friction pile-box (raft) foundation, and then study and analysis is conducted on measured settlement data of Senmao Tower and Jinmao Tower of Shanghai, which can get useful result for further settlement study.

In soft subgrade, supporting structure of deep foundation pit is usually diaphragm continuous retaining wall, because of deep foundation and more than three-level basements for super high-rise buildings. There are two kinds of relationship between this diaphragm wall and the exterior wall of basement: ① when diaphragm wall is only for supporting structure, it has lateral limit and constraint on basement wall and pile group foundation under the box (raft) foundation (Fig. 8-1); ② Diaphragm wall is for not only supporting structure, but also acts as basement exterior wall, that is two wall in one. This kind of wall is very deep (Fig. 8-2), and usually has the same depth as foundation pit. In this case, diaphragm retaining wall and basement wall are combined into one, which has lateral limitation and anti-settlement effects on pile group foundation under the box (raft) foundation. In the past, the calculated value is different from the test value, and the gap could even be very large. One of the reasons is failing to taking into account the effect of diaphragm wall.

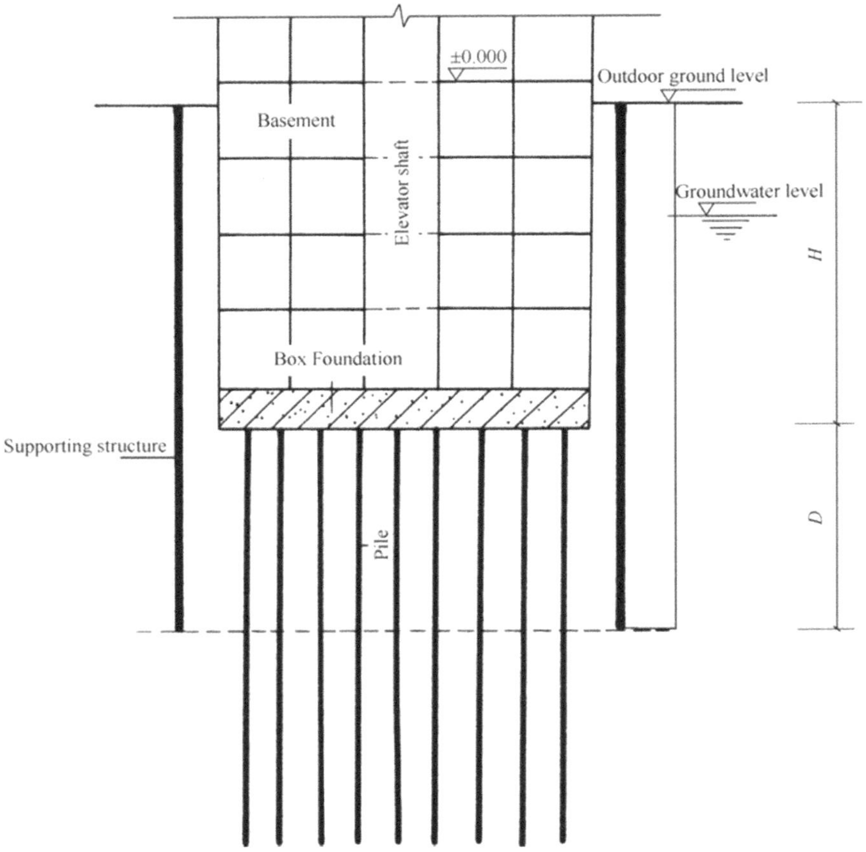

Fig. 8-1 The calculation diagram of super high-rise building pile-box foundation with separated underground wall and basement wall

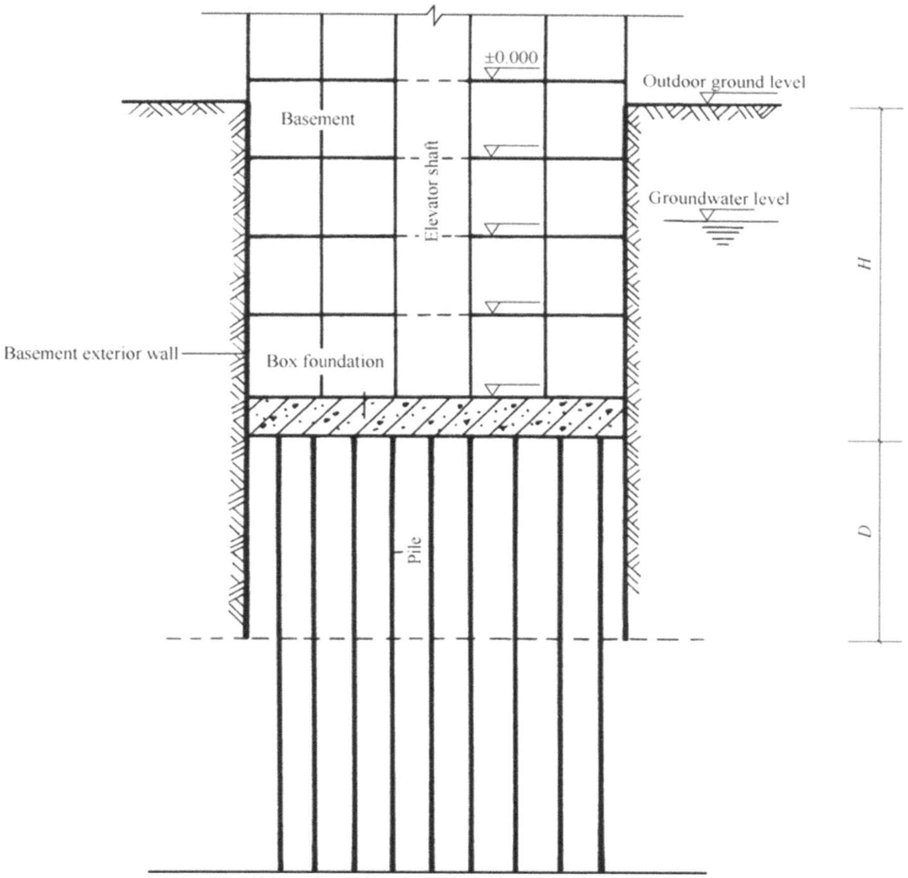

Fig. 8-2 Calculation diagram of super high-rise building pile-box foundation with one wall for two

8.1 Settlement Calculation Methods of Pile-Box (Raft) Foundation with Diaphragm Wall only as Retaining Structure for Deep Foundation Pit

As shown in the calculation diagram of Fig.8-1, when the effects of diaphragm wall and supporting structure on the settlement of pile-box foundation are taken into account, the computation of settlement will be divided into two parts.① The part of subgrade piercing depth (*D*) of diaphragm retaining wall; in this part, the compression modulus from side-limit consolidation test is used to be the deformation parameter; and the settlement of this part is computed by layer-wise summation method; meanwhile, the effects of the friction of basement exterior wall and the buoyancy of groundwater are considered. ② The part under the fist part; in this part, the settlement of pile foundation can be calculated by the method shown in the code for foundation.

The sum of the settlement computed by these two methods is just the theoretical value of the pile-box foundation settlement. The relative formulas are not shown here.

8.2 Settlement Calculation Methods of Pile-Box (Raft) Foundation with Diaphragm Wall as Retaining Structure and Basement Exterior Wall

As shown in the calculation diagram of fig. 8-2, pile-box foundation settlement can be computed by the method shown in section 8-1. ① The part of subgrade piercing depth (*D*) of diaphragm retaining wall; the settlement of this part is computed by layer-wise summation method; but the effects of the friction of basement exterior wall, the friction of both side of the diaphragm wall and the buoyancy of groundwater are all considered. ② The part under the fist part; in this part, the settlement of pile foundation can be calculated by the method shown in the code for foundation. If finite element method mentioned above is used in both situations, it is better to adopt substructure method of finite element method (FEM).

8.3 Settlement Calculation by Substructure Method of FEM with Effect of Diaphragm Wall on Pile-Box (Raft) Foundation

In considering the effect of diaphragm wall on the pile-box (raft) foundation, linear equations of the settlement computation are of high order, which often exceeds the current computer's memory capacity, because of the large number of elements. At this time, the whole structure is to be divided into several parts for analysis. However, it is practical to analysis the integral structure including superstructure, foundation and subgrade, rather than two or three separated terms. Many scholars have used the substructure method of FEM to analyse the interaction between superstructure and foundation, such as Academician Zhu Bofang, Professor Qin Rong, Professor Yang Min and Professor Zhao Xihong, beginning the fist use by M.J.Haddadin in 1971. Here a brief account of the principle and application of the substructure method are given.

The superstructure is often divided into several substructures (take the same standard floors as one substructure). We can also take each floor as one substructure, each level of basement as one substructure bottom plate and bottom plate as thick plate. The substructures are connected on the common boundary. Firstly each substructure analysed and the additional internal freedoms could be eliminated with static condensation method, and then the integral structure can be analysed. Then only the freedoms on the contacting boundary and the common boundary of the adjacent substructures are to be considered. In this way the computation is much easier. In addition, substructures could be integrated into a big substructure for multi-level substructure analysis. Static condensation of the substructure internal freedoms and coordinate transformation are two difficulties of substructure analysis of FEM. So they are demonstrated specially in the following section.

1) Static condensation method of the substructure internal freedoms. After partitioning the whole structure into several substructures and numbering their crunodes, the stiffness matrix, node displacement and node load can be shown in the following equation.

$$\begin{bmatrix} K_{bb} & K_{bi} \\ K_{ib} & K_{ii} \end{bmatrix} \begin{Bmatrix} \delta_b \\ \delta_i \end{Bmatrix} = \begin{Bmatrix} P_b \\ P_i \end{Bmatrix} \tag{8-1}$$

where: $\{\delta_b\}$ —the displacement vector of the substructure interface and constrained surface (constrained surface is also a kind of interface, which is the interface between structure and foundation);

$\{\delta_i\}$ — the displacement vector of the node in the substructure interior and unconstrained surface.

From Eq. (8-1), $\{\delta_i\}$ is given by

$$\{\delta_i\} = [K_{ii}]^{-1}(\{P_i\} - [K_{ib}]\{\delta_b\}) \tag{8-2}$$

Take Eq. (8-2) into (8-1), condensed equation is given by

$$[K_b^*]\{\delta_b\} = \{P_b^*\} \tag{8-3}$$

$$\left.\begin{aligned} [K_b^*] &= [K_{bb}] - [K_{bi}][K_{ii}]^{-1}[K_{ib}] \\ \{P_b^*\} &= \{P_b\} - [K_{bi}][K_{ii}]^{-1}\{P_i\} \end{aligned}\right\} \tag{8-4}$$

After eliminating the internal freedoms of substructure by the static condensation method, there only exists the freedom of interface $\{\delta_b\}$.

During the condensation process, if all the nodes of the interface are taken in one section to number, it is very difficult to get the minimal bandwidth of the stiffness matrix. When the number of the nodes is not very large, there will be no difficulty; but if the number is very large, the computer memory must be expanded, and then we can take the interface nodes and internal nodes into several sections respectively. For example, both can be collected in two sections, then the displacement vector is given by

$$\{\delta\} = \left[\delta_b^{(1)} \delta_i^{(1)} \delta_b^{(2)} \delta_i^{(2)}\right]^{\mathrm{T}}$$

And then the internal freedoms $\{\delta_{\mathrm{i}}^{(1)}\}$ and $\{\delta_{\mathrm{i}}^{(2)}\}$ is eliminated by the static condensation method.

2) Coordinate transformation. If the substructures of the fist level have the same shapes and sizes but different directions, they will have the same element stiffness matrix in the local coordinate system (x, y), and only one time of calculation is needed. But node displacement, node load and element stiffness matrix all need one coordinate transformation from the local coordinat to the global coordinate system, which is given by

$$\bar{\delta}_b = [\lambda]^{\mathrm{T}} \{\delta_b\} \tag{8-5}$$

$$\bar{P}_b = [\lambda]^{\mathrm{T}} \{P_b^*\} \tag{8-6}$$

$$\bar{K}_b = [\lambda]^{\mathrm{T}} \{K_b^*\} \{\lambda\} \tag{8-7}$$

$$[\lambda] = \begin{bmatrix} L & 0 & \cdots & 0 \\ 0 & L & \cdots & 0 \\ \vdots & \vdots & \vdots & \vdots \\ 0 & 0 & \cdots & L \end{bmatrix} \tag{8-8}$$

$$[L] = \begin{bmatrix} \cos(x,X) & \cos(x,Y) \\ \cos(y,X) & \cos(y,Y) \end{bmatrix} \tag{8-9}$$

where: $\{\bar{\delta}_b\}$, $\{\bar{P}_b\}$ and $\{\bar{K}_b\}$ —the related quantities in the global coordinate system;

$\{\delta_{\mathrm{b}}\}$, P_b^* and $[K_b^*]$ —the related quantities in the local coordinate system; (*x*, *X*),(*x*, *Y*), (*y*, *X*) and (*y*, *Y*) are the angles between axes *X*, *Y* and axes *x*, *y*. Counter-clockwise is positive.

In addition, although the high-rise building has asymmetrical structure, it can also be divided into substructures with the same shape and load condition, and then only one substructure is to be analysed. The computation can be simplified by certain transforms.

8.4 The Interaction among Superstructure, Foundation and Subgrade of Super High-Rise Building

The interaction analysis among superstructure, foundation and subgrade of super high-rise building is very complicated. Tongji University, Chinese Academy of Science, Qin Rong and others have made some breakthrough achievement. In this section, the use of the spline subdomain method for analysis of interaction is mainly introduced. From computation, it is shown that this method is simple and of high precision.

8.4.1 Calculation Diagram

The analysis of super high-rise building contains three sections, superstructure, foundation and subgrade. The superstructure of super high-rise buildings always uses frame-tube structure and tube-in-tube structure. Foundation could vary in form, and there are raft foundation, box foundation and pile foundation. At present, homogeneous elastic subgrade is widely used because of the complexity of subgrade. But in fact, the subgrade is heterogeneity, inelastic and nonlinear. The following models can be used in certain situations, ① homogeneous elastic subgrade model; ② layered elastic subgrade model; ③ homogeneous elastic-plastic subgrade model; ④ layered elastic-plastic subgrade model; ⑤ heterogeneity elastic, elastic-plastic subgrade model.

In this section, set of equations of superstructure, foundation and subgrade will be established by the spline subdomain method. And then they will be coupled and solved by the coordinative relationship of the interface.

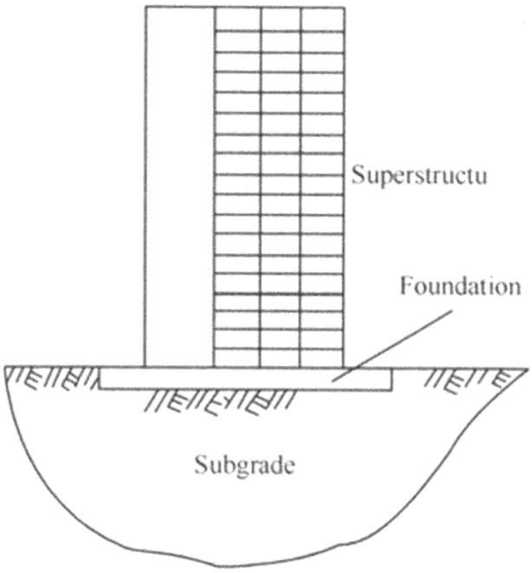

Fig. 8-3 Coupling system of the structure of super high-rise building

8.4.2 Establishment of Stiffness Equation of Superstructure

When the stiffness equation of superstructure is established by spline subdomain method, it will be divided into several sections, and each section is called one subdomain. Fistly the subdomains is analyzed, and then the whole structure is analyzed to establish the stiffness equation.

1. Choose the displacement functions of the subdomain

If the subdomain is a frame, the displacement functions is given by

$$\left.\begin{aligned} u&=[\varphi]\{u\}_0+\sum_{m=1}^{r}[\varphi]\{u\}_m X_m(y)\\ v&=[\varphi]\{v\}_0+\sum_{m=1}^{r}[\varphi]\{v\}_m Y_m(y)\\ w&=[\varphi]\{w\}_0+\sum_{m=1}^{r}[\varphi]\{w\}_m Z_m(y)\\ \theta_z&=[\varphi]\{\theta_z\}_0+\sum_{m=1}^{r}[\varphi]\{\theta_z\}_m Z_m^*(y)\\ \theta_y&=[\varphi]\{\theta_y\}_0+\sum_{m=1}^{r}[\varphi]\{\theta_y\}_m Y_m^*(y)\\ \theta_x&=[\varphi]\{\theta_x\}_0+\sum_{m=1}^{r}[\varphi]\{\theta_x\}_m X_m^*(y) \end{aligned}\right\} \tag{8-10}$$

where: u、v and w are the displacement components of the x, y and $z$directions; θ_x , θ_y and θ_z are the angles round X axis, Y axis and Z axis; X_m , Y_m , Z_m and X^*_m , Y^*_m , Z^*_m are plate strip functions and orthogonal functions.

$$\left.\begin{aligned} [\varphi]&=[\varphi_0\quad \varphi_1\quad \varphi_2\quad \cdots\quad \varphi_N]^{\mathrm{T}}\\ \{A\}&=[A_0\quad A_1\quad A_2\quad \cdots\quad A_N]^{\mathrm{T}} \end{aligned}\right\} \tag{8-11}$$

where:A= u, v, w, θ_x , θ_y , θ_z — the basis functions which are composed of cubic b-spline functions;

$\{\theta_x\}$, $\{\theta_x\}$ and $\{\theta_x\}$ — the displacement vectors of the superstructure-foundation junction;

$\{\theta_x\}_0$, $\{\theta_x\}_0$ and $\{\theta_x\}_0$ —the angle vectors of superstructure- foundation junction.

If the subdomain is a continuum structure (including opening structure), the displacement functions can be given by the fist three equations of the formula(8-10). For others, displacement functions can be derived by Formula (8-10).

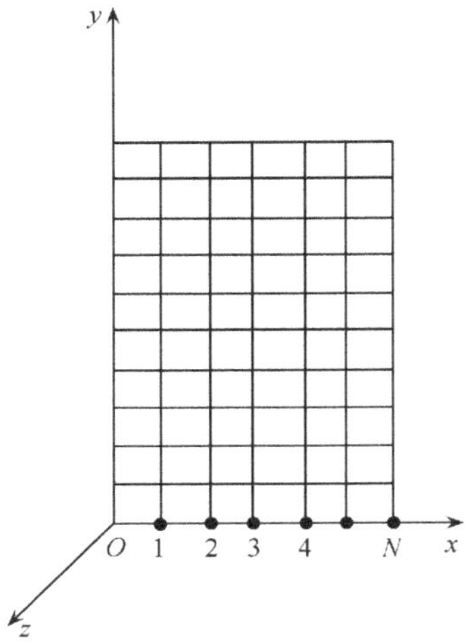

Fig. 8-4 Spline frame subdomain

2. Subdomain analysis

The superstructure is composed of several substructures, which are called subdomains, including frames, shear-wall, frame-shear wall, frame-tube and tube-in-tube structures. Certain parts, which are closely related with each other, can be taken as one subdomain. The most basic subdomains are frames, shear-walls, independent bars and connection beams, which can form various mixing subdomains. The basic subdomains can be established by spline finite element method. The spline discrete total potential energy functionals of the k-th sbudomain is given by

$$\Pi_k = \frac{1}{2}\{\delta\}_k^{\mathrm{T}}[G]_k\{\delta\}_k - \{\delta\}_k^{\mathrm{T}}\{f\}_k \tag{8-12}$$

where: $[G]_k$ and $\{f\}_k$ — the stiffness matrix and load vector of the k-th spline subdomain;

$\{\delta\}_k$ — the displacement vector of the k-th spline subdomain.

3. Global analysis

After the spline discrete total potential energy functions of the spline subdomains are established, the spline discrete total potential energy functions of the entire superstructure is given by

$$\Pi = \sum_{k=1}^{K}\Pi_k \tag{8-13}$$

Take Eq.(8-12) into Eq.(8-13), it will be given by

$$\Pi = \frac{1}{2}\{\delta\}_A^{\mathrm{T}}[G]_A\{\delta\}_A - \{\delta\}_A^{\mathrm{T}}\{f\}_A \tag{8-14}$$

The stiffness equation of the superstructure by variational principle is given by

$$[G]_A\{\delta\}_A = \{f\}_A \tag{8-15}$$

where: $[G]_A$, $\{\delta\}_A$ and $\{f\}_A$ — the stiffness matrix, displacement vector and load vector of the superstructure.

$$[G]_A = \sum_{k=1}^{K}[G]_k \{f\}_A = \sum_{k=1}^{K}\{f\}_k \tag{8-16}$$

When the stiffness matrix $[G]_A$ and the displacement vector $\{\delta\}_A$ are given by Eq.(8-16), chain additions can be done directly. And there is no need for expansion. So the number of the unknown quantity in Eq.(8-15) is small.

8.4.3 Establishment of Rigidity Equation of Foundation

Different stiffness equations should be established in different conditions, because of the variety of the foundations. They are given by

$$[G]_B\{\delta\}_B = \{f\}_B \tag{8-17}$$

where: the $[G]_B$, $\{\delta\}_B$ and $\{f\}_B$ are the stiffness matrix, displacement vector and load vector of the foundation.

8.4.4 Establishment of Stiffness Equation of Subgrade

Because of the complexity of the subgrade, it can be analyzed by the spline subdomain method. Different methods can be used to establish the stiffness equation for different subgrade calculation models.

1. The displacement function

A subgrade model for any complex condition is given in Fig. 8-5. It is to be analyzed as space problem, the displacement function of this subgrade is given by

$$\left.\begin{aligned} u&=\sum_{m=1}^{r}\sum_{n=1}^{s}[\varphi]\{u\}_{mn}X_m(x)X_n(y) \quad v=\sum_{m=1}^{r}\sum_{n=1}^{s}[\varphi]\{v\}_{mn}Y_m(x)Y_n(y) \\ w&=\sum_{m=1}^{r}\sum_{n=1}^{s}[\varphi]\{w\}_{mn}Z_m(x)Z_z(y) \end{aligned}\right\} \tag{8-18}$$

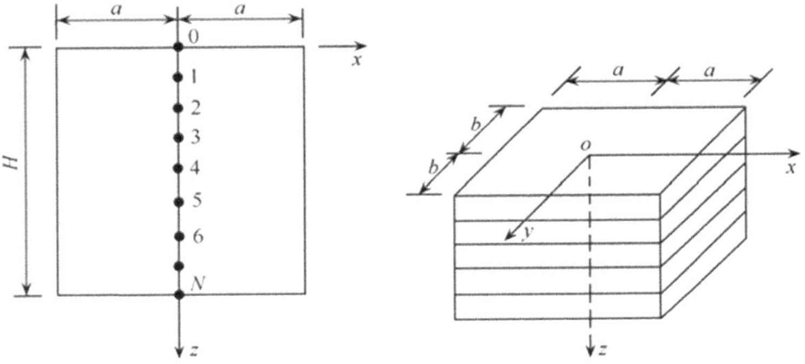

Fig. 8-5 Computation model of subgrade

where: X_m , Y_m , Z_m and X_n , Y_n , Z_n in the type of orthogonal function are given by

$$[\varphi]=[\varphi_0 \quad \varphi_1 \quad \varphi_2 \quad \cdots \quad \varphi_N]$$

$$[A]_{mn}=[A_0 \quad A_1 \quad A_2 \quad \cdots \quad A_N]_{mn}^{\mathrm{T}}$$

where: u, v, w; $\phi_i(z)$ are the basis functions which are composed of cubic b-spline functions. From Eq.(8-9), it is given by

$$V=\sum_{m=1}^{r}\sum_{n=1}^{s}[N]_{mn}\{\delta\}_{mn}=[N]\{\delta\}_e \tag{8-19}$$

where

$$\begin{aligned} &[N]=\left[[N]_{11} \quad [N]_{12} \quad \cdots \quad [N]_{1s} \quad \cdots \quad [N]_{r1} \quad [N]_{r2} \quad \cdots \quad [N]_{rs}\right] \\ &[N]_{mn}=\left[\varphi_i[\Gamma]_{mn}\right] \quad [\Gamma]_{mn}=\mathrm{diag}(X_{mn},Y_{mn},Z_{mn}) \end{aligned}$$

$$X_{mn}=X_mX_n \quad Y_{mn}=Y_mY_n \quad Z_{mn}=Z_mZ_n \tag{8-20}$$

$$\begin{aligned} &\{\delta\}_e=\left[\{\delta\}_{11}^{\mathrm{T}} \quad \{\delta\}_{12}^{\mathrm{T}} \quad \cdots \quad \{\delta\}_{1s}^{\mathrm{T}} \quad \cdots \quad \{\delta\}_{r1}^{\mathrm{T}} \quad \{\delta\}_{r2} \quad \cdots \quad \{\delta\}_{rs}^{\mathrm{T}}\right]^{\mathrm{T}} \\ &\{\delta\}_{mn}=\left[\{\delta\}_0^{\mathrm{T}} \quad \{\delta\}_1^{\mathrm{T}} \quad \{\delta\}_2^{\mathrm{T}} \quad \cdots \quad \{\delta\}_N^{\mathrm{T}}\right]_{mn}^{\mathrm{T}} \end{aligned}$$

$$\{\delta\}_{imn}=[u_i \quad v_i \quad w_i]_{mn}^{\mathrm{T}} \quad i=0,1,2,\cdots,N \tag{8-21}$$

2. Constitutive relation

Taking the viscoplasticity deformation into account, the stress-strain relationship of the subgrade model is given by

$$\sigma = [R]\varepsilon - \sigma_0 \tag{8-22}$$

where: $[R]$—the elastic matrix of the subgrade; ε and σ are the strain vector and stress vector, which are given by

$$\varepsilon = \begin{bmatrix} \varepsilon_x & \varepsilon_y & \varepsilon_z & \gamma_{xy} & \gamma_{yz} & \gamma_{zx} \end{bmatrix}^{\mathrm{T}}$$

$$\sigma = \begin{bmatrix} \sigma_x & \sigma_y & \sigma_z & \tau_{xy} & \tau_{yz} & \tau_{zx} \end{bmatrix}^{\mathrm{T}}$$

σ_0—the stress vector by viscoplasticity deformation of the subgrade, which is given by

$$\sigma_0 = [R]\varepsilon^{vp} \tag{8-23}$$

where: ε^{vp}—the viscoplasticity strain vector, the increment of which is given by

$$\Delta\varepsilon^{vp} = \varepsilon^{vp}\Delta t \tag{8-24}$$

where: Δt is the time-step;

ε^{vp}—the viscoplasticity strain vector, which is given by

$$\varepsilon^{vp} = \gamma < \Phi(F) > \frac{\partial F}{\partial \sigma} \tag{8-25}$$

where: γ—the flow parameter; F is the yield function or loading function, which is given by

$$F = F(\sigma, k) - A = 0 \tag{8-26}$$

$< \Phi(F) >$ is given by

$$< \Phi(F) > = \begin{cases} 0 & F \leqslant 0 \\ \Phi(F) & F > 0 \end{cases} \tag{8-27}$$

The forms of $\Phi(F)$ are various, the common form is given by

$$\Phi(F) = (F/A)^n \tag{8-28}$$

In fact, we always take n=1. And the increment of viscoplasticity stress vector is given by

$$\Delta\sigma_0 = [R]\Delta\varepsilon^{vp} \tag{8-29}$$

The strain vector of the subgrade is given by

$$\varepsilon = \sum_{m=1}^{r}\sum_{n=1}^{s}[A]_{mn}\{\delta\}_{mn} = [A]\{\delta\}_e \tag{8-30}$$

where

$$\left.\begin{aligned} &[A] = \begin{bmatrix}[A]_{11} & [A]_{12} & \cdots & [A]_{1s} & \cdots & [A]_{r1} & [A]_{r2} & \cdots & [A]_{rs}\end{bmatrix} \\ &[A]_{mn} = \begin{bmatrix}([A]_{mn}^{1})^{\mathrm{T}} & ([A]_{mn}^{2})^{\mathrm{T}}\end{bmatrix} \\ &[A]'_{mn} = \mathrm{diag}(\varphi_i X'_m X_n, \varphi_i Y_m Y'_n, \varphi'_i Z_m Z_n) \\ &[A]_{mn}^{2} = \begin{bmatrix} \varphi_i X_m X'_n & \varphi_i Y' Y_m & 0 \\ 0 & \varphi'_1 Y_m Y_n & \varphi_1 Z_m Z'_n \\ \varphi'_1 X_m X_n & 0 & \varphi_i Z'_m Z_n \end{bmatrix} \end{aligned}\right\} \tag{8-31}$$

where: φ'—the fist order derivative of t.

Taking Eq.(8-30) into Eq.(8-22), get

$$\sigma = [R][A]\{\delta\}_e - \sigma_0 \tag{8-32}$$

3. Analysis of subgrade

Dividing the whole subgrade into grids shown as Fig. 8-6, the total potential energy functional of each element is given by

$$\Pi_e = \frac{1}{2} V_e^{\mathrm{T}} [k]_e V_e - V_e^{\mathrm{T}} \{f\}_e - \int_e \varepsilon^{\mathrm{T}} \sigma_0 \mathrm{d}\Omega \tag{8-33}$$

where: $[k]_e$ and $\{f\}_e$ are the stiffness matrix and load vector of the hexahedral element, and it is the same as elastic state which is shown in FEM of elastic mechanics.

For each hexahedral element,

$$V_e = [N]_e \{\delta\}_c \tag{8-34}$$

where

$$\left.\begin{aligned} V_e &= \begin{bmatrix} V_A^{\mathrm{T}} & V_B^{\mathrm{T}} & V_C^{\mathrm{T}} & V_D^{\mathrm{T}} & V_E^{\mathrm{T}} & V_F^{\mathrm{T}} & V_G^{\mathrm{T}} & V_H^{\mathrm{T}} \end{bmatrix}^{\mathrm{T}} \\ [N]_e &= \begin{bmatrix} [N]_A^{\mathrm{T}} & [N]_B^{\mathrm{T}} & [N]_C^{\mathrm{T}} & [N]_D^{\mathrm{T}} & [N]_E^{\mathrm{T}} & [N]_F^{\mathrm{T}} & [N]_G^{\mathrm{T}} & \left[[N]_H^{\mathrm{T}}\right]^{\mathrm{T}} \end{bmatrix} \end{aligned}\right\} \tag{8-35}$$

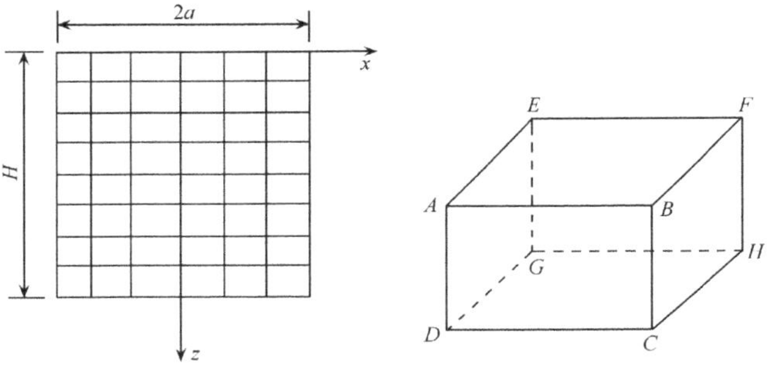

Fig. 8-6 Grids dividing of subgrade

Taking Eq.(8-30)and Eq.(8-34) into Eq.(8-33), get

$$\Pi_e = \frac{1}{2} \{\delta\}_c^{\mathrm{T}} [G]_e \{\delta\}_e - \{\delta\}_c^{\mathrm{T}} (\{f_N\}_e + \{f^p\}_e) \tag{8-36}$$

where

$$[G]_e = [N]_e^{\mathrm{T}} [k]_e [N]_e \quad \{f_N\}_e = [N]_e^{\mathrm{T}} \{f\}_e \tag{8-37}$$

$$\{f^p\}_e = \left[\{f^p\}_{11} \quad \{f^p\}_{12} \quad \cdots \quad \{f^p\}_{1s} \quad \cdots \quad \{f^p\}_{r1} \quad \{f^p\}_{r2} \quad \cdots \quad \{f^p\}_{rs} \right]^{\mathrm{T}} \tag{8-38}$$

where

$$\{f^p\}_{mn} = \int_e [A]_{mn}^{\mathrm{T}} \sigma_0 \mathrm{d}\Omega \tag{8-39}$$

The total potential energy functional of the whole subgrade is given by

$$\Pi = \sum_{e=1}^{M} \Pi_e \tag{8-40}$$

Taking Eq.(8-36) into Eq.(8-40), get

$$\Pi = \frac{1}{2} \{\delta\}_C^{\mathrm{T}} [G]_C \{\delta\}_C - \{\delta\}_C^{\mathrm{T}} (\{f\}_C + \{f^p\}_C) \tag{8-41}$$

where

$$[G]_C = \sum_{e=1}^{M} [G]_e \quad \{f\}_C = \sum_{e=1}^{M} \{f_N\} \tag{8-42}$$

$$\{f^P\}_C = \sum_{e=1}^{M} \{f^P\}_e = \int_{\Omega} [A]^{\mathrm{T}} \sigma_0 \mathrm{d}\Omega \tag{8-43}$$

The stiffness equation of the subgrade can be got by variational principle.

$$[G]_C \{\delta\}_C = \{f\}_C + \{f^P\}_C \tag{8-44}$$

where $[G]_C$ and $\{f\}_C$—the stiffness matrix and load vector of the subgrade, which are the same as elastic state; $\{f^P\}_C$ is the addition load vector of plastic deformation or viscoplasticity deformation.

If $\{f^P\}_C = \{0\}$, Eq.(8-44) is the same as elastic subgrade stiffness equation. When $\sigma_0 = 0$, $\{f^P\}_C = \{0\}$. If there is underground hole in the subgrade, we can take element stiffness matrix, load vector and addition load vector of this part as 0. So Eq.(8-44) applies to any situation.

From the above, although the subgrade is divided into grids by FEM, the number of the unknown quantity has no relation to the grids because of the conversion by the cubic b-spline functions. It is only related to the nodes of b-spline functions along Z direction and mn, so the number of the unknown quantity is very small. In addition, there is no need to expand Eq.(8-42) and Eq.(8-43), and plus can just be done directly, which is very easy.

8.4.5 Establishment of Total Stiffness Equation of Coupling System

After establishing the stiffness equation of the superstructure, foundation and subgrade, the total stiffness equation of the coupling system can be established by the coordinative relationship of their interface. The separation of Eq.(8-15), Eq.(8-17) and Eq.(8-44) by contact points and noncontact points there is given by

$$\begin{pmatrix} G_{11} & G_{12} \\ G_{21} & G_{22} \end{pmatrix}_A \begin{Bmatrix} \delta_1 \\ \delta_2 \end{Bmatrix}_A = \begin{Bmatrix} f_1 \\ f_2 \end{Bmatrix}_A + \begin{Bmatrix} 0 \\ 0 \end{Bmatrix}_A \tag{8-45}$$

$$\begin{pmatrix} G_{11} & G_{12} & G_{13} \\ G_{21} & G_{22} & G_{23} \\ G_{31} & G_{32} & G_{33} \end{pmatrix}_B \begin{Bmatrix} \delta_1 \\ \delta_2 \\ \delta_3 \end{Bmatrix}_B = \begin{Bmatrix} f_1 \\ f_2 \\ f_3 \end{Bmatrix}_B + \begin{Bmatrix} 0 \\ 0 \\ 0 \end{Bmatrix}_B \tag{8-46}$$

$$\begin{bmatrix} G_{11} & G_{12} \\ G_{21} & G_{22} \end{bmatrix}_C \begin{Bmatrix} \delta_1 \\ \delta_2 \end{Bmatrix}_C = \begin{Bmatrix} f_1 \\ f_2 \end{Bmatrix}_C + \begin{Bmatrix} f_1^P \\ f_2^P \end{Bmatrix}_C \tag{8-47}$$

where: δ_{2A}, δ_{1B}, δ_{3B} and δ_{1C} — the contact interface points displacement vectors of the superstructure, foundation and subgrade;

f_{2A}, f_{1B}, f_{3B} and f_{1C} — the contact interface points load vectors of the three. And they all accord with the following condition.

$$\left.\begin{matrix} \delta_{2A} = \delta_{1B} & f_{2A} = -f_{1B} & \text{at } \Gamma_1 \\ \delta_{3B} = \delta_{1C} & f_{3B} = -f_{1C} & \text{at } \Gamma_2 \end{matrix}\right\} \tag{8-48}$$

Eq.(8-45), Eq.(8-46) and Eq.(8-47) can be coupled by the above condition Eq. (8-48). And a total stiffness equation of the coupling system is given by

$$[G]\{\delta\}=\{f\}+\{f^{p}\} \tag{8-49}$$

By Eq.(8-48), we can solve the interaction problem of structure-foundation-subgrade coupling system and subgrade settlement for high-rise building.

8.5 Analysis of the Pile-Subgrade Interaction

For the deep foundation of the super high-rise building, the pile-subgrade interaction is the most basic problem. (eg. Single pile) Many experts have been involved in this problem, especially Professor Poulos. In the following, the pile-subgrade interaction is analyzed by the spline subdomain method.

8.5.1 Interaction Analysis Method of Lateral Loaded Pile and Subgrade

Fig. 8-7 is the computation model of the lateral load pile and subgrade. If the pile is very long, it can be taken as the interaction between one-dimensional beam and semi-infinite subgrade for analysis (as Fig. 8-7). Also, it can be taken as the interaction between one-dimensional beam and finite subgrade for analysis (as Fig. 8-8).

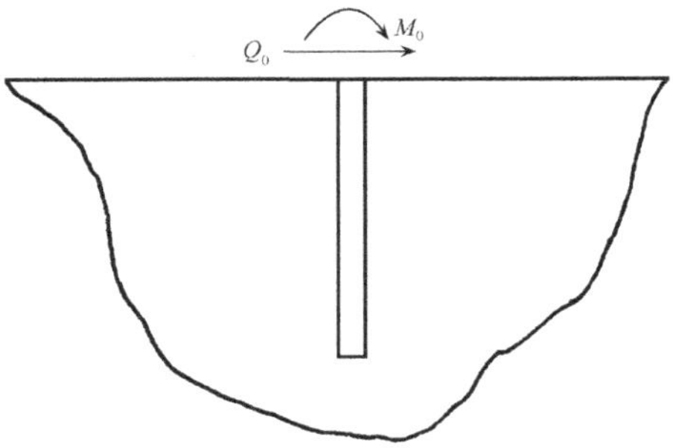

Fig. 8-7 Interaction between lateral load pile and semi-infinite subgrade

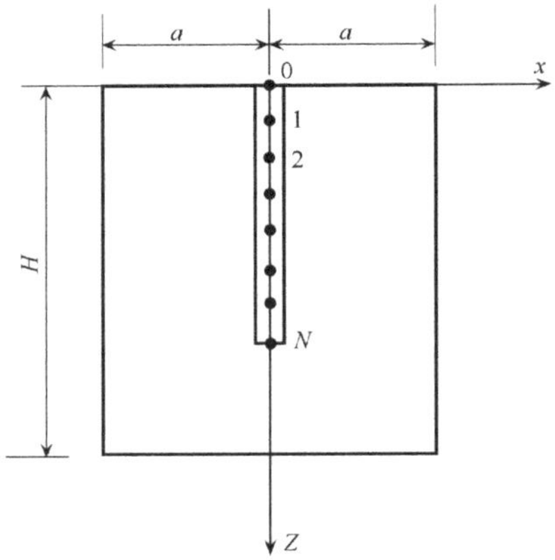

Fig. 8-8 The Interaction of the pile and subgrade

1. Analysis method of pile

1) Displacement function.

By spline partitions, the displacement function of the pile is given by

$$u=[\Phi]\{a\} \quad \theta=[\Phi]\{b\} \tag{8-50}$$

where

$$[\Phi]=[\Phi_0 \quad \Phi_1 \quad \Phi_2 \quad \ldots \quad \Phi_N]$$
$$\{a\}=[u_0 \quad a_1 \quad \ldots \quad a_{N-1} \quad u_N]^{\mathrm{T}}$$
$$\{b\}=[\theta_0 \quad b_1 \quad \ldots \quad b_{N-1} \quad \theta_N]^{\mathrm{T}}$$

where: u and θ —the displacement and rotation angle of the pile;

From the above,

$$V=[N]\{A\} \tag{8-51}$$

where

$$\left.\begin{aligned} &[N]=[N_0 \quad N_1 \quad N_2 \quad \ldots \quad N_N] \quad \{A\}=[A_0^{\mathrm{T}} \quad A_1^{\mathrm{T}} \quad A_2^{\mathrm{T}} \quad \cdots \quad A_N^{\mathrm{T}}]^{\mathrm{T}} \\ &V=[u \quad \theta]^{\mathrm{T}} \quad A_i=[u_i \quad \theta_i]^{\mathrm{T}} \quad i=0,N \\ &A_i=[a_i \quad b_i]^{\mathrm{T}} \quad i=1,2,\cdots,N-1 \\ &N_i=\mathrm{diag}(\Phi_i,\Phi_i) \quad i=0,1,2,\cdots,N \end{aligned}\right\} \tag{8-52}$$

where: $\Phi_i(z)$ —the basic function, which can be composed of one or cubic b-spline functions, and can also be composed of Lagrange interpolation functions or other interpolation functions. If

$$\Phi_i(z_k)=\delta_{ik} \tag{8-53}$$

then $a=u$, $b=\theta$ for Eq.(8-50).

2) Stiffness equation of the pile.

When the pile is divided into N elements, the node displacement vector of element AB (shown in Fig. 8-9) is given by

$$\{A\}_e=[N]_e\{A\} \tag{8-54}$$

where

$$\{V\}_e=[\{V\}_A^{\mathrm{T}} \quad \{V\}_B^{\mathrm{T}}]^{\mathrm{T}} \quad [N]_e=[[N]_A^{\mathrm{T}} \quad [N]_B^{\mathrm{T}}]^{\mathrm{T}} \tag{8-55}$$

The stiffness vector will be got by spline subdomain method.

$$[G]\{A\}=\{f\}-\{R\} \tag{8-56}$$

where

$$[G]=\sum_{e=1}^{M}[N]_e^{\mathrm{T}}[k]_e\{N\}_e \tag{8-57}$$

$$\{f\}=[\{f\}_0^{\mathrm{T}} \quad \{0\}_1^{\mathrm{T}} \quad \{0\}_2^{\mathrm{T}} \quad \cdots \quad \{0\}_N^{\mathrm{T}}]^{\mathrm{T}} \quad \{f\}_0=[Q_0 \quad M_0]^{\mathrm{T}} \tag{8-58}$$

where: $[k]_e$ —the element stiffness matrix of the pile (the axial force is ignored); the model in Fig.8-9 is the element of the pile;

$[N]_A$ and $[N]_B$ —$[N]$ of node A and node B;

$\{R\}$—the subgrade reaction force on the pile.

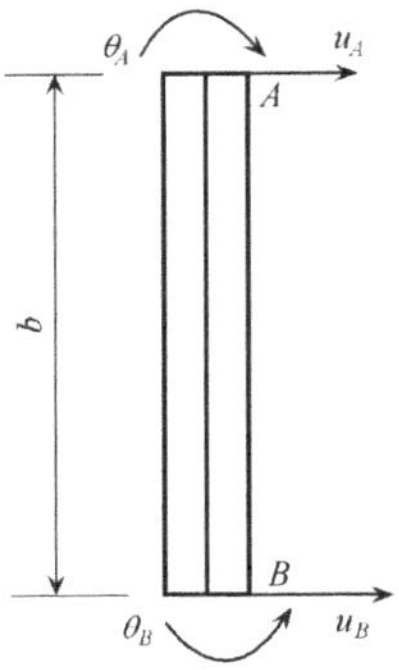

Fig. 8-9 the beam element

2. Analysis method of subgrade

1) Displacement function.The displacement function of the subgrade can be given by

$$\left.\begin{aligned} u &= \sum_{m=1}^{r}\sum_{n=1}^{s}[\Phi]\{u\}_{mn}X_m(x)X_n(y) \\ v &= \sum_{m=1}^{r}\sum_{n=1}^{s}[\Phi]\{v\}_{mn}Y_m(x)Y_n(y) \\ w &= \sum_{m=1}^{r}\sum_{n=1}^{s}[\Phi]\{w\}_{mn}Z_m(x)Z_n(y) \end{aligned}\right\} \tag{8-59}$$

where

$$[\Phi]=[\Phi_0 \quad \Phi_1 \quad \Phi_2 \quad \cdots \quad \Phi_N] \quad \{A\}_{mn}=[A_0 \quad A_1 \quad A_2 \quad \cdots \quad A_N]_{mn}^{\mathrm{T}}$$

where: A=u, v, w. $\Phi_i(z)$ is the basic function, which can be composed of one or cubic bspline functions, and can also be composed of by Lagrange interpolation functions or other interpolation functions. If $\Phi_i(z)$ accords with the condition shown in Eq.(8-53), the Eq.(8-59) will turn to the equations that follow.

$$\left.\begin{aligned} &u_i = \sum_{m=1}^{r}\sum_{n=1}^{s}u_{imn}X_m(x)X_n(y) \quad v_i = \sum_{m=1}^{r}\sum_{n=1}^{s}v_{imn}Y_m(x)Y_n(y) \\ &w_i = \sum_{m=1}^{r}\sum_{n=1}^{s}w_{imn}Z_m(x)Z_n(y) \end{aligned}\right\} \tag{8-60}$$

where: u_i, v_i and w_i — the displacement boundary of $z=z_i$;

X_m, Y_m, Z_m, X_n, Y_n and Z_n — the known functions chosen by the boundary condition. From Eq.(8-60), get

$$V_i=[N_i]\{\delta\} \tag{8-61}$$

where

$$V_i=[u_i \quad v_i \quad w_i]^{\mathrm{T}} \quad [N_i]=[[0]_0 \quad \cdots \quad [N]_i \quad [0]_{i+1} \quad \cdots \quad [0]_N] \tag{8-62}$$

$$[N]_i = [[N]_{11} \ \ [N]_{12} \ \cdots [N]_{1s} \cdots [N]_{r1} \ \ [n]_{r2} \cdots [N]_{rs}]$$
$$\{\delta\} = [\{\delta\}_0^{\mathrm{T}} \ \ \{\delta\}_1^{\mathrm{T}} \ \cdots \ \{\delta\}_Z^{\mathrm{T}}]^{\mathrm{T}}$$
$$\{\delta\}_i = [\{\delta\}_{11}^{\mathrm{T}} \{\delta\}_{12}^{\mathrm{T}} \cdots \{\delta\}_{1s}^{\mathrm{T}} \cdots \{\delta\}_{r1}^{\mathrm{T}} \{\delta\}_{r2}^{\mathrm{T}} \cdots \{\delta\}_{rs}^{\mathrm{T}}] \quad i = 0,1,\cdots,N$$
$$[N]_{mn} = \mathrm{diag}(X_m X_n, Y_m Y_n, Z_m Z_n) \quad \{\delta\}_{mn} = [u_{imn} \ \ v_{imn} \ \ w_{imn}]^{\mathrm{T}}$$

2) Basic equation. If the subgrade is divided into grids including finite and infinite elements (shown in Fig. 8-10), the nodes displacement vector of each element is given by

$$\{V\}_e = [N]_e \{\delta\} \tag{8-63}$$

where

$$[N]_e = [[N]_A^{\mathrm{T}} \ \ [N]_B^{\mathrm{T}} \ \cdots \ [N]_H^{\mathrm{T}}]^{\mathrm{T}} \quad \{V\}_e = [\{V\}_A^{\mathrm{T}} \ \ \{V\}_B^{\mathrm{T}} \cdots [V]_H^{\mathrm{T}}]^{\mathrm{T}}$$

By the spline subdomain method, the nonlinear stiffness equation of the subgrade can be got, which is given by

$$[G]\{\delta\} = \{F\} + \{F^P\} \tag{8-64}$$

where

$$[G] = \sum_{e=1}^{M} [N]_e^{\mathrm{T}} [k]_e [N]_e \quad \{F\} = \sum_{e=1}^{M} [N]_e^{\mathrm{T}} \{f\}_e, \{F^P\} = \sum_{e=1}^{M} [N]_e^{\mathrm{T}} \{f_e^0\} \tag{8-65}$$

where: $[k]_e$ and $\{f\}_e$—the stiffness matrix and load vector of the element;

$\{f^P\}_e$—the additional load vector caused by the plastic deformation and residual deformation, which is given by

$$\{f^P\}_e = \int_{\Omega e} [B]_e^{\mathrm{T}} \sigma_0 \mathrm{d}\Omega \tag{8-66}$$

where $[B]_e$ is the element strain matrix under local coordinate system. If $\{f^P\}_e$=0, the Eq.(8-64) will turn to the stiffness matrix of elastic body. If $\sigma_0 = 0$, $\{f^P\}_e = 0$.

For equation (8-65), we can do direct adding. And there is no need to do expansion. In equation (8-64), the number of the unknown value has no relation with grids dividing, but it depends on the nodes of B-spline function in direction z and mn; if X_m, Y_m, Z_m, X_n, Y_n and Z_n are the finite element plate strip functions, *m*=*n*=1. The displacement vector and stress vector of any point in the subgrade are given by

$$V = [N][N]_e \{\delta\} \quad \sigma = [D][B]_e \{N\}_e \{\delta\} - \sigma_0 \tag{8-67}$$

where: [*N*] is the element shape function matrix under the local coordinate system.

3. Analysis method of the pile-subgrade l interaction

Eq.(8-64) can turn to the following Eq.(8-68).

$$\begin{bmatrix} G_{11} & G_{12} \\ G_{21} & G_{22} \end{bmatrix} \begin{Bmatrix} \delta_1 \\ \delta_2 \end{Bmatrix} = \begin{Bmatrix} F_1 \\ F_2 \end{Bmatrix} + \begin{Bmatrix} F_1^P \\ F_2^P \end{Bmatrix} \tag{8-68}$$

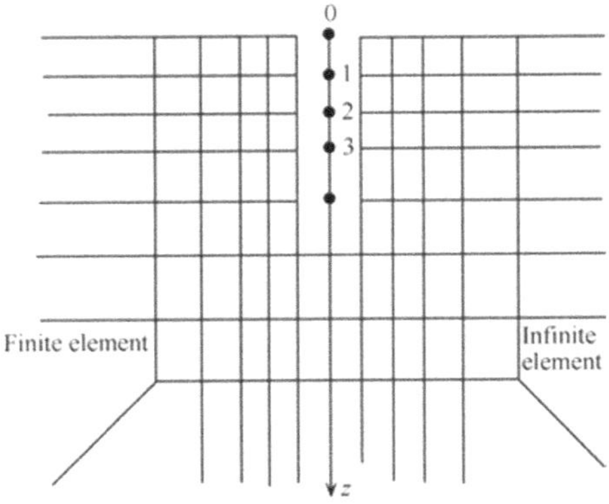

Fig. 8-10 Grids of subgrade

where: $\{\delta_1\}$ $\{F_1\}$ and $\{F_1^P\}$ are the displacement vector, load vector and additional mass vector of the nodes in the subgrade-pile interface; $\{\delta_2\}$ $\{F_2\}$ and $\{F_2^P\}$ are the displacement vector, load vector and additional mass vector of the other nodes. And from the above, it can be got

$$[G_s]\{\delta_1\}=\{F_1\}+\{F_1^P\}-[C_s](\{F_2\}+\{F_2^P\}) \tag{8-69}$$

$$\{\delta_2\}=[G_{22}]^{-1}(\{F_2\}+\{F_2^P\})-[G_{22}]^{-1}[G_{21}]\{\delta_1\} \tag{8-70}$$

where

$$[G_s]=[G_{11}]-[G_{12}][G_{22}]^{-1}[G_{21}] \qquad [C_s]=[G_{12}][G_{22}]^{-1} \tag{8-71}$$

$$\left.\begin{aligned}\{\delta_1\}&=[u_0v_0w_0u_1v_1w_1\cdots u_Nv_Nw_N]^{\mathrm{T}}\\ \{F_1\}&=[R_0H_0P_0R_1H_1P_1\cdots R_NH_NP_N]^{\mathrm{T}}\end{aligned}\right\} \tag{8-72}$$

If the dead weight is neglected, $\{F_2\}$ =0. If the deformation compatibility condition of the pile and the subgrade is taken into account, $v_i=w_i=0$. From the above, it can be got

$$[G_{sH}]\{u\}=\{F_{1H}\}+[a]\{F_1^P\}-[C_{sH}]\{F_2^P\} \tag{8-73}$$

where

$$\{u\}=[u_0 \quad u_1 \quad u_2 \quad \cdots \quad u_N]^{\mathrm{T}} \quad \{F_{1H}\}=[R_0 \quad R_1 \quad R_2 \quad \cdots R_N]^{\mathrm{T}}=[a]\{F_1\} \tag{8-74}$$

$$[a]=\mathrm{diag}([\gamma],[\gamma],\cdots,[\gamma]) \quad [\gamma]=[1 \quad 0 \quad 0] \tag{8-75}$$

If the pile and the subgrade are assumed to be compatible along horizontal direction, Eq.(8-63) turns into:

$$[G_{sH}{}^{A}]\{V\}=\{R\}+\{f^P\} \tag{8-76}$$

where

$$\left.\begin{aligned}&\{V\}=[u_0 \quad \theta_0 \quad u_1 \quad \theta_1 \quad \cdots \quad u_N \quad \theta_N]^{\mathrm{T}}\\ &\{R\}=[R_0 \quad 0 \quad R_1 \quad 0 \quad \cdots \quad R_N \quad 0]^{\mathrm{T}}\\ &\{f^P\}=[\beta]([a]\{F_1^P\}-[C_{sH}]\{F_2^P\}) \quad [\beta]=\mathrm{diag}(1,0,1,0,\cdots,1,0)\end{aligned}\right\} \tag{8-77}$$

From the above, the relation can be got $\{V\}$ and $\{A\}$.

$$\{V\}=[N^*]\{A\} \tag{8-78}$$

Taking the Eq.(8-78) into Eq.(8-76), the following equation can be got.

$$[G^*]\{A\} = \{R\} + \{f^P\} \tag{8-79}$$

where

$$[G^*] = [G_{sh}^A][N^*] \quad [N^*] = [[N(Z_0)]^T \quad [N(Z_1)]^T \quad \cdots [N(Z_N)]^T]^T$$

$[N(z_i)]$ can be got from Eq.(8-52). Doing cooperative solving of Eq.(8-56) and Eq.(8-79), the following equation can be got.

$$([G]+[G^*])\{A\} = \{f\} + \{f^P\} \tag{8-80}$$

And it is the nonlinear stiffness equation for interaction analysis of the laterally loaded pile and subgrade. The value of $\{A\}$ can also be got by the iterative method. Then the displacement and internal force of the pile and the displacement and stress of the subgrade can be got.

8.5.2 Interaction Analysis Method of Axial Load Pile and Subgrade

Fig. 8-12 is the calculation diagram of the axial load pile and subgrade interaction. It is an axisymmetric problem.

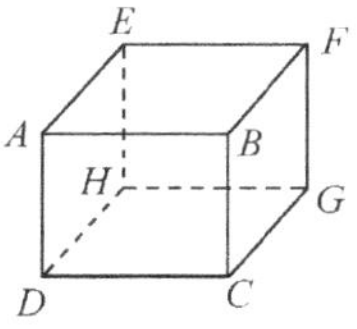

Fig. 8-11 The finite element

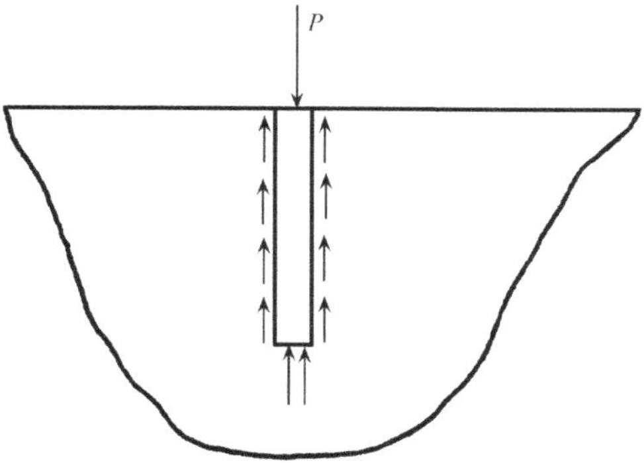

Fig. 8-12 The interaction of the axial load pile and infinite subgrade

1. Analysis method of the pile

In engineering applications, the stiffness of the pile is much higher than that of the subgrade. So the radial deformation is small. And then, the pile can be taken as axial rod for analysis. Let displacement function be

$$w = [\Phi]\{c\} \tag{8-81}$$

where

$$\{c\} = [w_0 \quad c_1 \quad c_2 \quad \cdots \quad c_{N-1} \quad w_N]^T$$

If the pile is divided into N elements, the node displacement vector of the AB element is given by

$$\{V\}_e = [N]_e\{c\} \tag{8-82}$$

where

$$\{V\}_e = [w_A \quad w_B]^{\mathrm{T}} \quad [N]_e = [[\Phi]_A^{\mathrm{T}} \quad [\Phi]_B^{\mathrm{T}}]^{\mathrm{T}} \tag{8-83}$$

The stiffness function of the pile can be got by QR method.

$$[G]\{c\} = \{f\} - \{R\} \tag{8-84}$$

where

$$[G] = \sum_{e=1}^{N}[N]_e^{\mathrm{T}}[k]_e[N]_e \quad \{f\} = [P \quad 0 \quad 0\cdots 0]^{\mathrm{T}} \tag{8-85}$$

where: $[k]_e$ — the element (axial rod element) stiffness matrix of the pile;

$\{R\}$ — the load vector of the friction of subgrade-pile interface and versa dint in approach end.

2. Analysis method of the subgrade

The subgrade around the pile is an axisymmetric problem. It can be taken as a two-dimensional problem for analysis. Its displacement function is:

$$u = \sum_{m=1}^{s}[\Phi]\{u\}_m X_m(r) \quad w = \sum_{m=1}^{s}[\Phi]\{w\}_m Z_m(r) \tag{8-86}$$

If $\Phi_i(z)$ satisfies the condition of Eq.(8-86), it can be got that

$$u_i = \sum_{m=1}^{s} u_{im} X_m(r) \quad w_i = \sum_{m=1}^{s} w_{im} Z_m(r) \tag{8-87}$$

We can get the following equation from the above.

$$\{V\}_i = [N]_i\{\delta\} \tag{8-88}$$

If the subgrade is divided into grids, the node displacement vector of every element (shown in Fig.8-13) can be given by

$$\{V\}_e = [N]_e\{\delta\} \tag{8-89}$$

Fig. 8-13 The two-dimensional element

The nonlinear stiffness matrix of the subgrade can be got by the spline subdomain method.

$$[G]\{\delta\} = \{F\} + \{F^P\} \tag{8-90}$$

3. Analysis method of the pile-subgrade interaction

From Eq.(8-90), it can be got

$$[G_s]\{\delta_1\}=\{F_1\}+\{F_1^P\}-[G_s]\{F_2^P\} \tag{8-91}$$

where

$$\{\delta_1\}=[u_0 \quad w_0 \quad u_1 \quad w_1 \cdots u_N \quad w_N \quad u_{N1} \quad w_{N1}]^{\mathrm{T}}$$
$$\{F_1\}=[H_0 \quad R_0 \quad H_1 \quad R_1 \quad \cdots \quad H_N \quad R_N \quad H_{N1} \quad R_{N1}]^{\mathrm{T}}$$

where the N node is on the symmetric axis (and also on the bearing surface of the pile tip). Because of the tiff assumption of the pile bearing surface of the subgrade, the equation $\omega_N=\omega_{N1}$ can be got. The pile and the subgrade are assumed deformation compatible, so $u_i=0$. From the above, the following equation can be got.

$$\{G_{sV}\}\{w\}=[F_{1V}]+[a]\{F_1^P\}-[G_{sV}]\{F_2^P\} \tag{8-92}$$

where

$$\{w\}=[w_0 \quad w_1 \quad w_2 \quad \cdots \quad w_N]^{\mathrm{T}}$$
$$\{a\}=\mathrm{diag}([\gamma],[\gamma],\cdots,[\gamma]);[\gamma]=[0 \quad 1] \tag{8-93}$$

From the above, it can be known that there is a kind relationship between $\{w\}$ and $\{c\}$.

$$\{w\}=[N^*]\{c\} \tag{8-94}$$

Taking Eq.(8-94) into Eq.(8-92), Eq.(8-92) is turned into the following equation

$$[G^*]\{c\}=\{R\}+\{f^P\} \tag{8-95}$$

where

$$\left.\begin{aligned}&[G^*]=[G_{sV}][[\Phi(Z_0)]^{\mathrm{T}} \quad [\Phi(z_1)]^{\mathrm{T}} \cdots \quad [\Phi(z_N)]^{\mathrm{T}}]^{\mathrm{T}}\\&\{R\}=\{R_{1V}\};\{f^P\}=[a]\{F_1^P\}-[C_{sV}]\{F_2^P\}\end{aligned}\right\} \tag{8-96}$$

where: $[\Phi(z_i)]$ can be got from $[\Phi]$ in Eq.(8-81). By combined solution of Eq.(8-84) and Eq. (8-95), it can be got

$$([G]+[G^*])\{c\}=\{f\}+\{f^P\}$$

For nonlinear stiffness matrix of the axial load, this is the interaction between pile and subgrade. By iterative method the value of $\{c\}$ can be got from Eq.(8-96). After that, the displacements and internal forces of the pile and subgrade can be got.

From the above, it can be known:

1) This method is an effective one for analysis of interaction between the pile and subgrade, whatever the subgrade is elastic or inelastic, uniform or non uniform. Moreover, it is an easy method.

2) The element stiffness matrix in the subgrade stiffness equation includes the infinite element stiffness matrix.

3) By considering the nonlinear deformation, the calculation results and the measured

results can be made similar.

4) From the calculation results, it can be seen that this method is not only easy but also accurate. So it can meet the accuracy demand of engineering application.

8.6 Analysis of the Pile-Pile Interaction

In the deep foundation of the super high-rise buildings, pile-pile interaction is a three-dimensional space method of the pile group. If finite element method is used, there will be too many nodes and elements to be calculated by small memory computer. But splines subdomain method will be easier and of higher accuracy.

8.6.1 Single Pile Analysis

1. Displacement function

Fig. 8-14 is number ***k*** pile of the pile group. If the pile is long enough, it can be taken as the interaction between one dimensional structure and semi-infinite space foundation. If the pile is divided arbitrarily, its displacement function will be

$$\left.\begin{aligned} &u=[\Phi]\{u\} \quad v=[\Phi]\{v\} \quad w=[\Phi]\{w\} \\ &\theta_x=[\Phi']\{v\} \quad \theta_y=[\Phi']\{u\} \quad \theta_z=R[\Phi](\cos\theta\{v\}-\sin\theta\{u\}) \end{aligned}\right\} \tag{8-97}$$

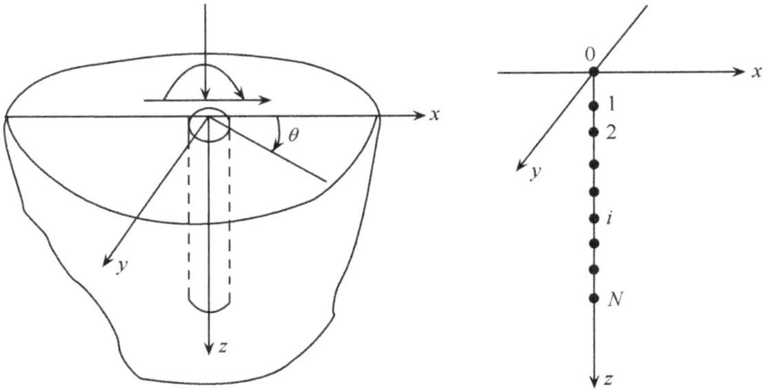

Fig. 8-14 Latoraction of pile and semi-infinate foundation and discrete rate

where

$$\{a\}=[a_0 \quad a_0' \quad a_1 \quad a_2 \cdots a_N \quad a_N']^{\mathrm{T}}$$

$$[\Phi]=[\Phi_0 \quad \psi_0 \quad \Phi_1 \quad \Phi_2 \cdots \Phi_N \quad \psi_N]$$

where: a=u, v, w; Φ_i and ψ_i — the basic functions composed of one or cubic b-spline functions;

u, v and w are the displacements of x, y or z direction;

θ_x, θ_y and θ_z —the rotation angles round x, y or z axis;

R —the external radius of the pile;

θ —the central angle and clockwise direction is the right direction. From the above, it can be got that

$$V=[N]\{A\}_k \tag{8-98}$$

where

$$\left.\begin{array}{l} V=[u\ v\ w\ \theta_x\ \theta_y\ \theta_z]^{\mathrm{T}}\quad A_i=[u_i\ v_i\ w_i]^{\mathrm{T}}\quad B_i=[u_i' v_i' w_i']^{\mathrm{T}} \\ \{A\}=[A_0^{\mathrm{T}} B_0^{\mathrm{T}} A_1^{\mathrm{T}} A_2^{\mathrm{T}} \cdots A_N^{\mathrm{T}} B_N^{\mathrm{T}}]_k^{\mathrm{T}}\quad [N]=[N_0\ M_0\ N_1\ N_2 \cdots N_N M_N] \\ N_i=\begin{bmatrix} \Phi_i & 0 & 0 \\ 0 & \Phi_i & 0 \\ 0 & 0 & \Phi_i \\ 0 & \Phi_i' & 0 \\ \Phi_i' & 0 & 0 \\ \alpha_1 & \alpha_2 & 0 \end{bmatrix}\quad M_i=\begin{bmatrix} \psi_i & 0 & 0 \\ 0 & \psi_i & 0 \\ 0 & 0 & \psi_i \\ 0 & \psi_i' & 0 \\ \psi_i' & 0 & 0 \\ \alpha_3 & \alpha_4 & 0 \end{bmatrix} \end{array}\right\} \tag{8-99}$$

where

$$\alpha_1=-R\Phi_i\sin\theta\quad \alpha_2=R\Phi_i\cos\theta\quad \alpha_3=-R\psi_i\sin\theta\quad \alpha_4=R\psi_i\cos\theta \tag{8-100}$$

2. Stiffness Function of Pile

If the pile is divided into N sections, the nodes displacement vectors of any section AB will be

$$\{V\}_e=[N]_e\{A\}_k \tag{8-101}$$

where

$$\{V\}_e=[\{V\}_A^{\mathrm{T}}\ \ \{V\}_B^{\mathrm{T}}]^{\mathrm{T}}\quad [N]_e=[[N]_A^{\mathrm{T}}\ \ [N]_B^{\mathrm{T}}]^{\mathrm{T}} \tag{8-102}$$

The stiffness function of the pile can be got by splines subdomain method.

$$[G]_k\{A\}_k=\{f\}_k-\{R\}_k \tag{8-103}$$

where

$$[G]_k=\sum_{e=1}^{N}[N]_e^{\mathrm{T}}[k]_e[N]_e\quad \{f\}_k=\sum_{e=1}^{N}[N]_e^{\mathrm{T}}\{f\}_e \tag{8-104}$$

In the above functions, k_e and $\{f\}_e$ are the element stiffness matrix and load vector of the pile. $[N]_A$ and $[N]_B$ are the $[N]$ value of A and B node. $[R]_k$ is the subgrade reaction vector to the pile. Function (8-104) can be added directly and there is no need to expand every value before addition. So, for pile group, there will be

$$[G]\{A\}=\{f\}-\{R\} \tag{8-105}$$

where

$$\left.\begin{array}{l} [G]=\mathrm{diag}([G]_1,[G_2],\cdots,[G]_n)\quad \{f\}=[\{f\}_1^{\mathrm{T}}\ \ \{f\}_2^{\mathrm{T}}\cdots\{f\}_n^{\mathrm{T}}]^{\mathrm{T}} \\ \{A\}=[\{A\}_1^{\mathrm{T}}\ \ \{A\}_2^{\mathrm{T}}\cdots\{A\}_n^{\mathrm{T}}]^{\mathrm{T}}\quad \{R\}=[\{R\}_1^{\mathrm{T}}\ \ \{R\}_2^{\mathrm{T}}\cdots\{R\}_n^{\mathrm{T}}]^{\mathrm{T}} \end{array}\right\} \tag{8-106}$$

8.6.2 Foundation Analysis

Fig. 8-15 shows the interaction between the pile group and semi-infinite foundation. For this case, the foundation can be analyzed by semi-infinite method or finite method.

1. Displacement function

The displacement function of the total foundation can be taken as the following form:

$$u_i=\sum_{m=1}^{r}\sum_{m=1}^{s}u_{imn}X_m(x)X_n(y) \quad v_i=\sum_{m=1}^{r}\sum_{m=1}^{s}v_{imn}Y_m(x)Y_n(y)$$

$$w_i=\sum_{m=1}^{r}\sum_{m=1}^{s}w_{imn}Z_m(x)Z_n(y) \tag{8-107}$$

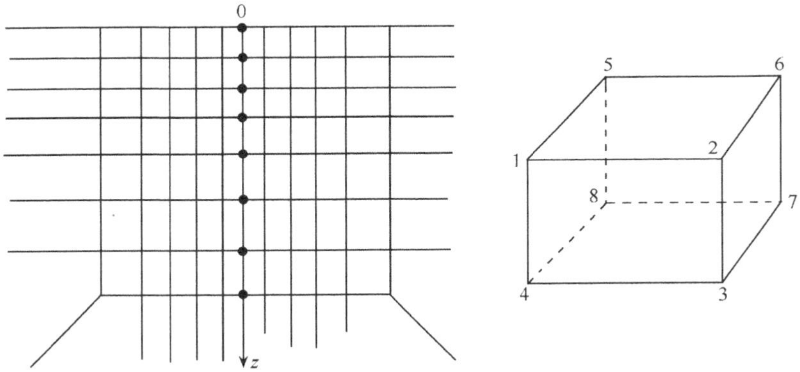

Fig. 8-15 The grids and the elements of foundation

where: u_i, v_i and w_i — the displacement functions of $z=z_i$ level;

X_m, Y_m, Z_m and X_n, Y_n, Z_n — the known functions got by the boundary conditions.

From the function (8-107), it can be got:

$$V_i=[N_i]\{\delta\} \tag{8-108}$$

2. Foundation stiffness function

If the foundation is divided into grids shown in Fig. 8-15, the nodes displacement vectors will be

$$\{V_e\}=[N]_e\{\delta\} \tag{8-109}$$

where

$$[N]_e=[\{V\}_1^{\mathrm{T}} \quad \{V\}_2^{\mathrm{T}}\cdots\{V\}_8^{\mathrm{T}}]^{\mathrm{T}};[N]_e=[[N]_1^{\mathrm{T}} \quad [N]_2^{\mathrm{T}}\cdots[N]_8^{\mathrm{T}}]^{\mathrm{T}} \tag{8-110}$$

The following stiffness function can be got by splines subdomain method.

$$[K]\{\delta_S\}=\{F_S\} \tag{8-111}$$

where

$$[K]=\sum_{e=1}^{M}[N]_e^{\mathrm{T}}[k]_e[N]_e;[F_s]=\sum_{e=1}^{M}[N]_e^{\mathrm{T}}\{f\}_e \tag{8-112}$$

In this function, $[k]_e$ and $\{f\}_e$ are the stiffness function and load vector of the foundation. Function (8-112) can be added directly and there is no need to expand every value before addition. Function (8-111) can turn into

$$\begin{bmatrix} K_{11} & K_{12} & K_{13} \\ K_{21} & K_{22} & K_{23} \\ K_{31} & K_{32} & K_{33} \end{bmatrix} \begin{Bmatrix} \delta_{ii} \\ \delta_{ji} \\ \delta_{si} \end{Bmatrix} = \begin{Bmatrix} F_i \\ F_{ji} \\ F_{si} \end{Bmatrix} \tag{8-113}$$

where δ_{ii} and F_i — the displacement vectors and load vectors of the subgrade nodes on the i-th pile interface; δ_{ji} and F_{ji} — the displacement vectors and load vectors of the subgrade nodes in the direction of the j-th pile axis;

δ_{si} and F_{si} —the displacement vectors and load vectors of the other subgrade nodes. If the i-th pile is assumed to be loaded in the form of single pile and only the nodes on the pile-subgrade interface are considered, it will be got $F_{ji}=F_{si}$ =0. So the following function can be got by eliminating δ_{si}.

$$\begin{bmatrix} K_{11}^* & K_{12}^* \\ K_{21}^* & K_{22}^* \end{bmatrix} \begin{Bmatrix} \delta_{ii} \\ \delta_{ji} \end{Bmatrix} = \begin{Bmatrix} F_i \\ 0 \end{Bmatrix} \tag{8-114}$$

where

$$\left.\begin{matrix} K_{11}^* = K_{11} - K_{13}K_{33}^{-1}K_{31} & K_{12}^* = K_{12} - K_{31}K_{33}^{-1}K_{32} \\ K_{21}^* = K_{21} - K_{23}K_{33}^{-1}K_{31} & K_{22}^* = K_{22} - K_{23}K_{33}^{-1}K_{32} \end{matrix}\right\} \tag{8-115}$$

From Eq.(8-114) the following equations can be got.

$$K_{ii}\delta_{ii} = F_i \quad K_{ji}\delta_{ji} = F_i \tag{8-116}$$

where

$$K_{ii} = K_{11}^* - K_{12}^*(K_{22}^*)^{-1}K_{21}^* \quad K_{ji} = K_{12}^* - K_{11}^*(K_{21}^*)^{-1}K_{22}^* \tag{8-117}$$

The nodes displacement vectors on the interface of the subgrade and the i-th pile can be got.

$$\delta_i = \sum_{j=1}^{n} d_{ij}F_j \quad i = 1,2,\cdots,n \tag{8-118}$$

Where n is the number of the piles. Therefore, the nodes displacement vectors on the interface of the subgrade and the i-th pile is not only influenced by the i-th pile, but also influenced by other piles. For the pile group, the following equation can be got

$$\{\delta\} = [d]\{F\} \tag{8-119}$$

where

$$\left.\begin{matrix} \{\delta\} = [\delta_1 \quad \delta_2 \cdots \delta_n]^{\mathrm{T}} \quad \{F\} = [F_1 \quad F_2 \quad \cdots \quad F_n]^{\mathrm{T}} \\ [d] = [d_{ij}] \quad d_{ij} = d_{ji} \quad d_{ij} = K_{ij}^{-1} \end{matrix}\right\} \tag{8-120}$$

From Eq.(8-119), the following equation can be got.

$$[G^*]\{\delta\}=\{F\} \tag{8-121}$$

where

$$[G^*]=[d]^{-1} \tag{8-122}$$

8.6.3 Pile-Pile Interaction

Taking the coordination function of the pile and influenced into account, it can be got

$$\{\delta\}=\{A\} \quad \{R\}=\{F\} \tag{8-123}$$

Taking Eq.(8-123) into Eq.(8-105) and Eq.(8-121), it can be got

$$([G]+[G^*])\{\delta\}=\{f\} \tag{8-124}$$

The displacement vectors of every pile can be calculated by Eq.(8-124). In the piles group, they are interacted.

8.6.4 A Example

Professor Cooke conducted field model test for pile group on the London Clay, and showed the difference between the test result and the result given by Poulos who used the elastic integration method (Fig. 8-16). From the figure, the result given by Poulos who used the elastic integration method is much higher than the test result. But the calculation result by splines subdomain method is close to the test result. In the figure, D is the diameter of the pile; S is the pile spacing; α is the coefficient of the pile-pile interaction.

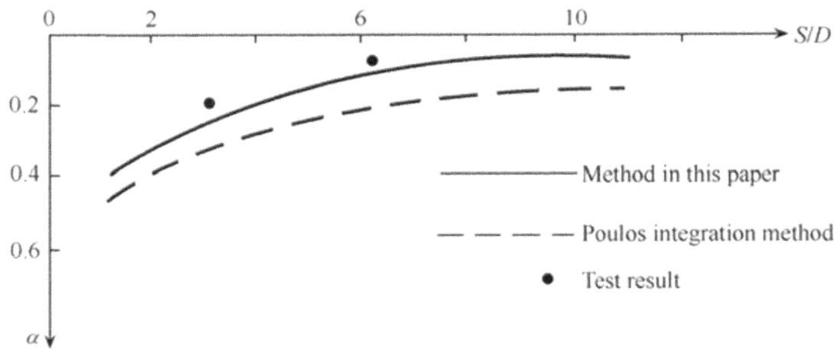

Fig. 8-16 The Comparison between calculation result and test resule

The analysis method of the pile-pile interaction in this paper is not only easy but also accurate. Therefore it is useful.

8.7 Settlement Measured Values and Analysis Results of Pile-Raft Foundation of Senmao Tower in Shanghai

8.7.1 The General Engineering Situation

Senmao Tower in Shanghai was designed by JV and constructed by Tengtan of Japnese. Its gross floor area is 113,000 m^2. And it is 202m high with 46 aboveground floors and 4 underground levels (shown in Fig. 8-17 and Fig. 8-18). It used 8,000t steel with reinforced concrete for inner-tube and steel-reinforced concrete for outside-tube. Its plane and façade are shown in Fig. 8-19 and Fig.8-20. The thickness of the diaphragm wall is 1m, the depth is 30m and the circumference is 330m. Inner supporting structure was used in the underground foundation pit. Using the basement floor for transverse support and making a trestle in the middle of the foundation pit, the foundation was constructed by half-inverted construction method. The heights of the four basements are 4.55m, 4.4m, 3.25m and 3.2m. The foundation slab is thick plate (the plane dimension is 91.00m×66.65m). The thickness of the main building bottom plate is 3.05m and the thicknesses of the podium bottom plate are 1.85m,2.0m and 2.85m. The buried depth of the internal bube bottom plate is -21.4m. There are 831 steel pipe piles for the pile-raft foundation. And the diameter of the piles is 609.4mm.

Fig. 8-17 Picture of Senmao Tower in shanghai after completion

8.7.2 The Engineering Geological Situation

The subgrade of the construction site is Quatemary shock layer formed by the shock from the estuary and the seashore. The following is the subgrade-layer distribution.

1) layer: about 1.30m deep, miscellaneous fill.

2) layer: about 1.30m deep, silty clay, rigid upper layer and soft lower layer.

3) layer: about 4.4m deep, muddy clay, containing mica, including multi-layers silty sand.

4) layer: about 11.2m deep, muddy clay, containing mica and organic matter, including a little gonidial layer silty soil, homogeneous soil.

5) layer: about 6.0m deep, silty clay, containing calcareous concretion and humus, homogeneous soil, $N_{63.5} = 6.5$.

6) layer: about 4.3m deep, silty clay, containing ferric oxide and kaolin, compact structure, $N_{63.5} = 15$.

7) −1 layer: about 7.0m deep, mineral silty soil, containing ferric oxide and mica, dominated by silty soil granules, including a little silty sand and clay, $N_{63.5} = 32$.

8) −2 layer: about 33.0m deep, silty fine sand, mainly containing quartz, feldspar and mica, homogeneous soil, $N_{63.5} > 50$.

Groundwater table is 0.7—1.2m. So it has no corrosive effect to the concrete.

The bearing stratum of the steel pipe pile is the 7) −2 layer.

The physical and mechanical properties of the subgrade layers are shown in Table 8-1.

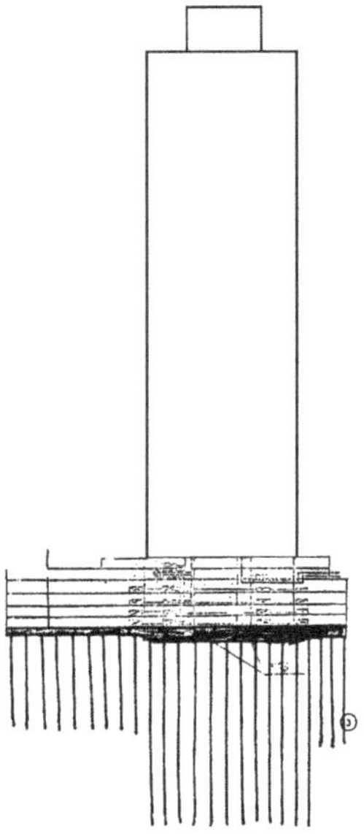

Fig. 8-18 Sectional drawing of Senmao Tower in shanghai

Table 8-1 Physical and Mechanical Comprehensive Index of Subgrade Layer

No.	Names	T	W (%)	e	$a_{0.1-0.2}$ (MPa^{-1})	$E_{0.1-0.2}$ (MPa)	c (kg/cm^2)	ψ(°)	$N_{63.5}$ (beat)	$Q_c(F_s)$ (MPa)
①-1	fill	1.3								
①-s2	backfilled	0								
②	Silty clay	1.3	32	0.92			13	14.9	3.8	0.83
③	Muddy silty clay	4.4	38.4	1.17	0.64	3.34	8	14.5	3	0.90
④	Muddy clay	11.2	49.2	1.39			10	7.2	1.3	0.48
⑤	Silty clay	6	33.1	0.95			9	15.8	6.3	0.97
⑥	Silty clay	4.3	23.2	0.68			40	13.6	15.4	2.56
⑦-1	Sandy silt	7	32	0.90	0.14	13.21	2	24.6	32.3	12.36
⑦-2	Fine sand	33.5	27	0.80	0.12	15.13	0	25.6	>50	24.64
⑦-3	Silty sand including silty clay	12	29.9	0.84	0.14	12.94	2	25.8	>50	17.40
⑨-1	Coarse sand including silty clay	8	30.2	0.87	0.17	10.59	0		>50	
⑨-2	Fine sand	22.7	22.7	0.69	0.12	14.64	0	26.5	>50	
⑨-3	Silty sand including silty clay								>50	

No.: Subgrade layers serial numbers; Name: Subgrade layers names; T: thicknesses of subgrade layers; W: water content; E: viod ratio; $a_{0.1-0.2}$: Compressibility; $E_{0.1-0.2}$: Compression modulus;c: Cohesion;ψ: internal friction angle; $N_{63.5}$: SPT count; $Q_c(F_s)$: CPT.

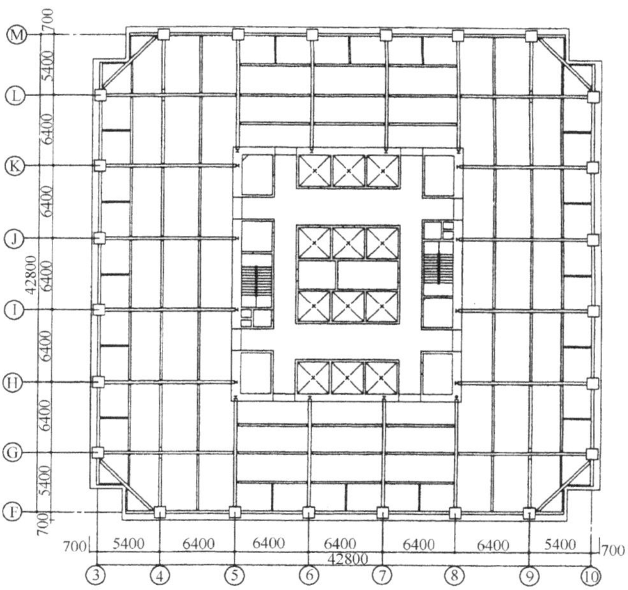

Fig. 8-19 Structural planar graph of the standard floor

8.7.3 Measured Settlement Values and Analysis Result of the Foundation of Senmao Tower in Shanghai

1. The foundation settlement test data.

Senmao Tower in Shanghai was designed by JV, signed general contract by Tengtan and Dalin construction enterprises of Japnese and constructed by a third company of SBC. The settlement test data are shown in Fig. 8-21, Fig. 8-22, Fig. 8-23, Fig. 8-24 and Fig. 8-25. The settlement curves of the four points (tow points at iner-tube and two points at outer tube) are shown in picture 8-27.

Foundation pit resilience: not the maximum resilience value. The maximum value in the figure is +11.00mm. And the minimum value is +6.00mm.

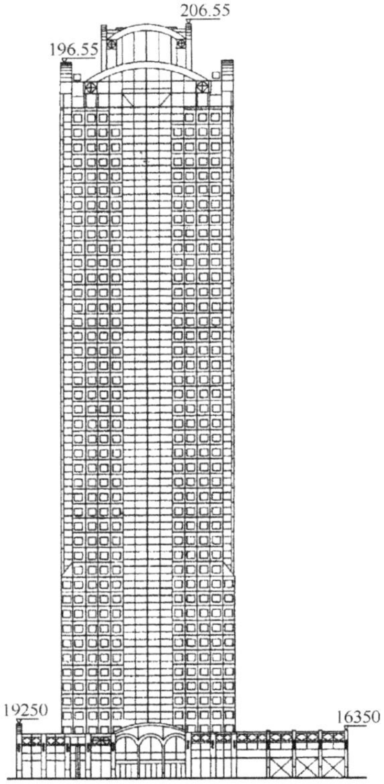

Fig. 8-20 Elevation drawing

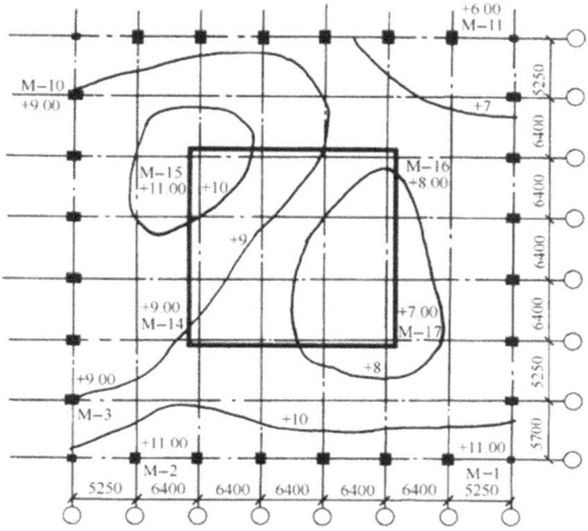

Fig. 8-21 Initially measured values for settlement of senmao tower in shanghai (May 19, 1996)

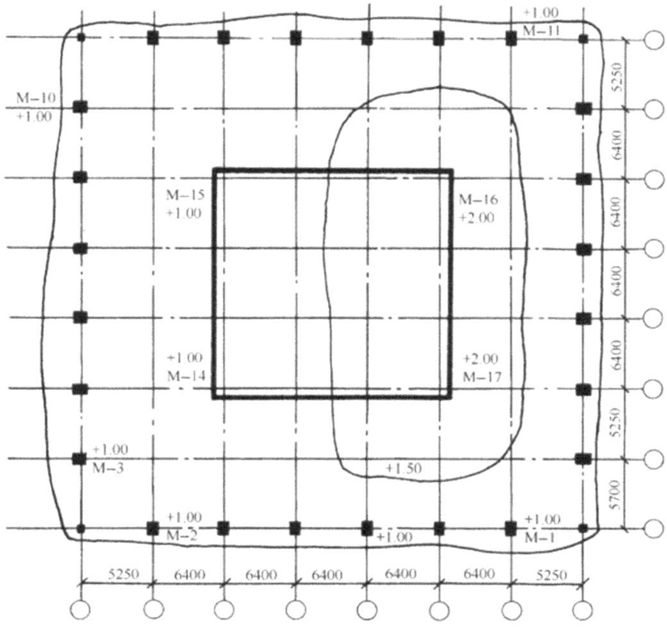

Fig. 8-22 Measured values for Settlement of senmao tower in shanghai (August 24, 1996)

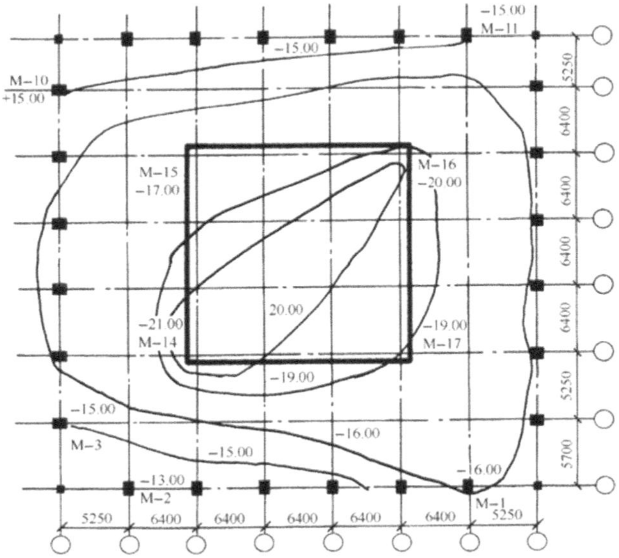

Fig. 8-23 Measured settlement value of senmao tower in shanghai
(after 24 floors were completed) (November 6, 1996)
Inner-tube: the maximum settlement is −21.00mm and the minimum settlement is −17.00mm.
Outer-tube: the maximum settlement is −15mm and the minimum settlement is −13mm

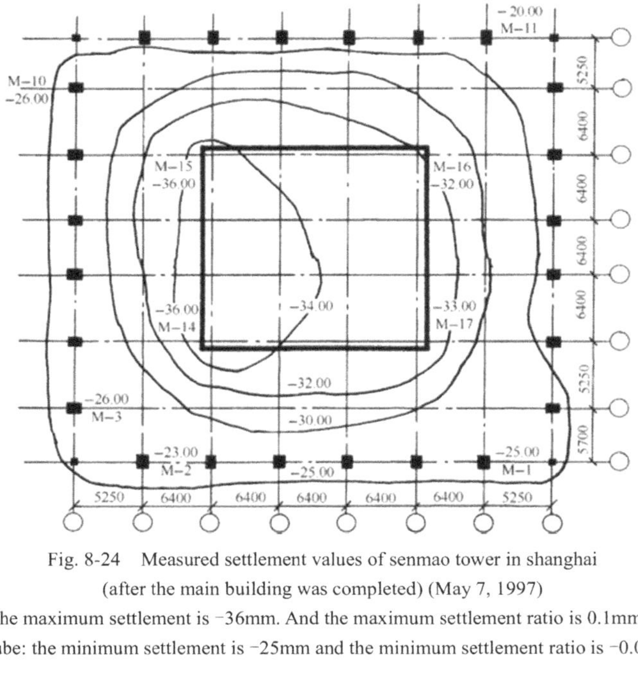

Fig. 8-24 Measured settlement values of senmao tower in shanghai
(after the main building was completed) (May 7, 1997)
The maximum settlement is −36mm. And the maximum settlement ratio is 0.1mm/d
Outer-tube: the minimum settlement is −25mm and the minimum settlement ratio is −0.069mm/d

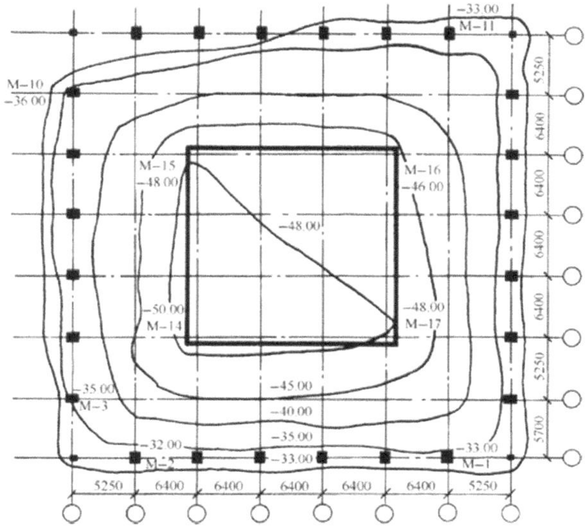

Fig. 8-25 Measured settlement values of senmao tower in shanghai
(six months later after completion of the main building) (November 8, 1997)
Inner-tube: the maximum settlement is −50mm and the minimum settlement is −46mm.
Outer-tube: the maximum settlement is −36mm and the minimum settlement is −32mm

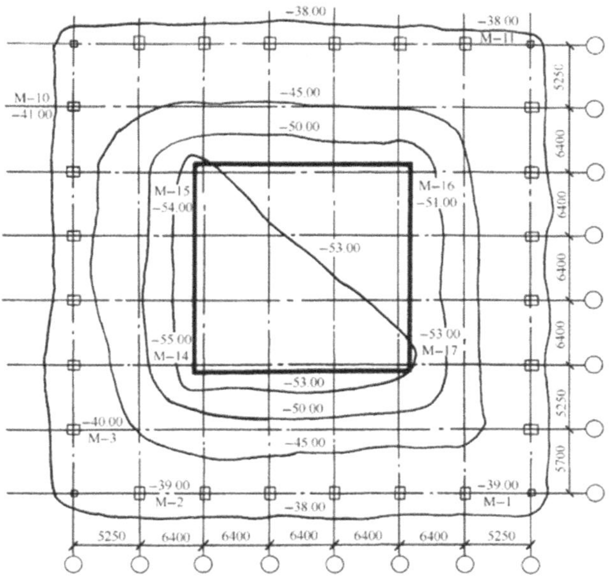

Fig. 8-26 Measured settlement values of senmao tower in shanghai
(nine months after completion of the main building) (February 5, 1998)
The maximum settlement is −55mm. And the maximum settlement ratio is 0.0416mm/d.
Outer-tube: the minimum settlement is −40mm and the minimum settlement ratio is −0.0416mm/d

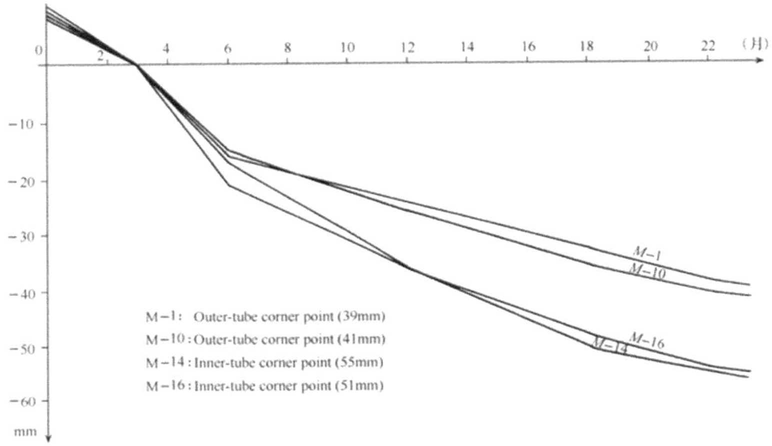

Fig. 8-27 Settlement measured curves of senmao tower in shanghai (May 3, 1996—February 5, 1998)

2. Analysis Result of the Measured Settlement Values

From the measured settlement values, it can be known that there is small settlement for the pile-raft foundation (with super-long steel pipe pile). Nine months later after finishing the main building, the maximum settlement is −55mm and the minimum settlement is −41mm. The settlement difference between inner-tube and outer-tube is −17mm. And the settlement differences between the four corners of the inner-tube and between the four corners of the outer tube are 4mm and 3mm. So the settlement of the whole foundation which includs podium is uniform. And the tilting value of the building meets the design requirements. By comparing the trial calculation and the measurement, the following preliminary conclusions can be got.

1) For super-long pile-craft foundation (pile is longer than 50m), the settlement calculation value is larger than the measured value, because the lateral influence of diaphragm wall and the restriction of the podium pile foundation are not taken into account.

2) One side of the main building overlap with the podium and the other three sides are in the podium. So one side of the main building has lateral influence from the diaphragm wall and the other three sides have restriction from the podium pile foundation. It can reduce the settlement of the main building.

3) The calculation result and measured result of the settlement of the super-long steel pipe piles group are all small than those of single pile. (Super long steel pipe pile is driven into the subgrade.)

4) When the settlement is calculated by deep massive foundation method, the least piles problem must be taken into account for super-long pile-box (raft) foundation. If the number of

the piles for the foundation is less than the critical number, other method is need to be used to calculate the settlement.

5) For super high-rise building (H>200m), not only the total settlement (for example in 100mm) needs to be controlled, but also the settlement difference needs to be controlled.

6) For super high-rise building with tube-in-tube structure, the load on the bottom plate should be calculated by linear loads of inner-tube and outer-tube.

8.8 Measured Settlement Values and Analysis of Jinmao Tower in Shanghai

8.8.1 The General Engineering Situation

Jinmao Tower in Shanghai is 420.5m high in total and 395m for the actual structure. And it's section drawing and plan are shown in Fig. 8-28, Fig. 8-30 and Fig. 8-30. It has 88 above-ground

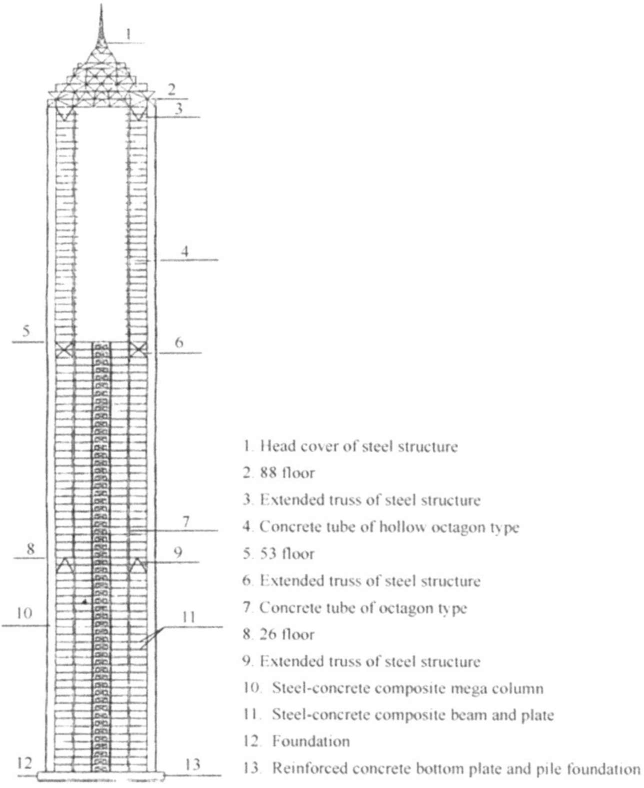

Fig. 8-28 Section drawing of the main building structure

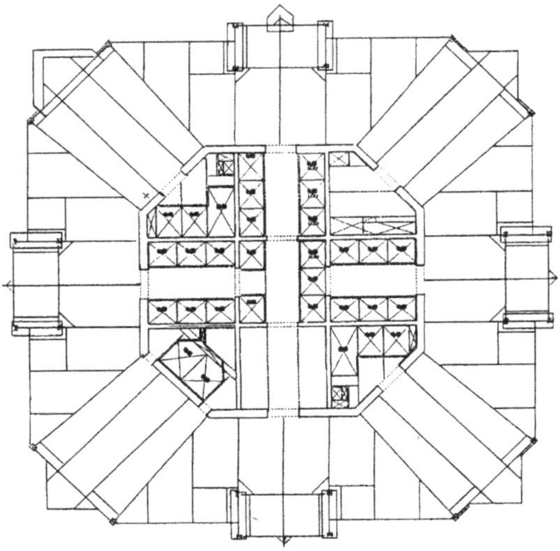

Fig. 8-29 Plan of the standard floor of office building

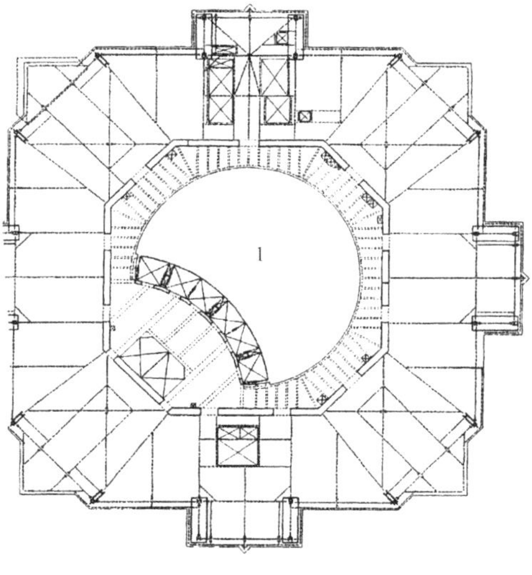

Fig. 8-30 Plan of the standard floor of hotel

floors and 3 under-ground levels. The foundation pit is −19.65m deep and supported by diaphragm wall. The diaphragm wall acts not only as supporting structure, but also as exterior wall of load-bearing basement (one wall for two uses). And the diaphragm is 1.00m thick, 36m deep and 568.4m long for its circumference. The building uses super-long pile-craft foundation. And there are two sizes of $\phi 914$ and $\phi 609$ for the 1061 pieces of steel pipe piles which are 80m long. The bottom plate of the foundation is 4m thick. The main building is in the podium.

So there is not only lateral influence from the diaphragm wall, but also restriction from the podium pile groups.

8.8.2 The Engineering Geological Situation

From the drilling geological report, the composition of subgrade layers is shown in Table 8-2 and the physical and mechanical properties are shown in Table 8-3.

Table 8-2 Composition and Description of the Subgrade Layers

Geological age	No.	Name and description of subgrade layer	Thickness(m)	Elevation of the layer head
Holocene Q4	①	Fill, variegation, slightly wet, clay containing a little impurity	0.8—1.4	3.6—4.0
	②	Silty clay, brownish yellow, very wet, plastic ~ soft-plastic	1.7—3.4	2.5—3.1
	③	Muddy silty clay, grey, saturated, soft-plastic~ flow-plastic, including a thin-layer of silty sand	3.5—4.5	-0.34— -1.39
	④	Muddy silty clay, grey, saturated, soft-plastic~ flow-plastic, containing a little of organic matter, including a thin-layer of silty sand	9.2—10.8	-4.02— -2.94
	⑤	Silty clay, grey, saturated, containing a lot of organic matter, including a thin-layer of silty sand	6.1—10.1	-13.90— -12.64
Early-Pleistocene Q3	⑥	Silty clay, dark green, very wet, hard-plastic~ plastic, containing a little of organic matter, including a thin-layer of silty sand	2.3—5.0	-23.80— -19.23
	⑦-1	Silty clay, grass yellow, saturated	4.8—8.5	-26.10— -23.85
	⑦-2	Fine silty sand, grass yellow~ grey, saturated, containing a little of organic matter	24.5—35.2	-32.58— -30.42
	⑧	Sandy silt, grey, saturated, containing a thin-layer of silty clay and a thin-layer of silty sand	3.0—11.0	-67.31— -57.11
	⑨-1	Sandy silt, grey, saturated, containing a little of fine sand and clay	3.0—6.0	-71.81— -63.42
	⑨-2	Fine sand, grey, saturated, including medium-coarse sand, containing a little of organic matter	46.0—48.0	-75.49— -66.42
Mid-Pleistocene Q2	⑩	Silty clay, battleship blue, very wet, dark-plastic~plastic, including a thin-layer of fine sand	7.5	-119.85— -119.07

8.8.3 Determination of the Pile Load Bearing Stratum

Estimation shows that the gravity load of the whole building transferred to the bearing sheet of the pile foundation is about 3,000,000kN. If the area is calculated as the projected area of the core tube structure, the mean pressure of the bearing sheet will be up to 2060kN/m^2. If the area is calculated as the projected area of the periphery structure, such as the mega columns and elephant columns, the mean pressure will almost reach 1075Kn /m^2. Jinmao Tower is 420.5m high and its aspect ratio is about 8：1. So, too large settlement difference in any direction will be unfavorable to the building's verticality. Moreover, the core tube and the periphery mega columns are connected by three extended steel truss, for which the vertical stiffness is relatively weak, therefore too large settlement difference between core tube and mega columns will be unfavorable to the normal work of the extended steel trusses, which are the main components of the lateral resistant system.

By the above characteristics of the main building's superstructure, some requirements for the pile foundation's bearing capacity and settlement control are provided. Such as, the allowable bearing of single pile should be 7500kN, and the final settlement of the pile foundation should be no more than 100mm. The measured result and engineering experience show that there is regular relation between the average settlement and the relative deformation of the pile foundation. So, it is feasible to control the relative deformation by the method of controlling the average settlement.

By the requirements provided in the designing, the allowable bearing of single pile and final settlement of the pile foundation are analyzed for different bearing layers. And the results are shown in Table 8-4 and Table 8-5. The analyzed results show that only ⑨-2 layer can meet the both requirements and it also can avoid the secondary consolidation settlement caused by the compression deformation of the ⑧ and ⑨-1 layers. Comprehensive consideration of bearing and settlement, the pile load bearing stratum of the main building should be ⑨-2 layer.

Table 8-4 Prediction of the allowable bearing of single pile

Elevation of pile tip(m)	Pile type	Specification(mm)	Bearing layer and deep of run -in	Allowable bearing of single pile(kN)
-43	Prefab square piles	500×500×25000	Layer ⑦-2, 7m	2000—250000
	Steel pipe pile	φ 914×25000	Layer ⑦-2, 7m	4000—4500
-51	Steel pipe pile	φ 914×37000	Layer ⑦-2, 19m	6050*
	Bored pile	φ 1000×37000	Layer ⑦-2, 19m	5600*
	Bored pile	φ 1250×37000	Layer ⑦-2, 19m	7050*
-75	Steel pipe pile	φ 914×61000	Layer ⑨-2, 2m	7250—9550*
	Bored pile	φ 1000×61000	Layer ⑨-2, 2m	9050*
	Bored pile	φ 1250×61000	Layer ⑨-2, 2m	11500*

*means the experience prediction value according to DBJ08-11-89.

Table 8-5 Prediction of final settlement of pile foundation

Elevation of pile tip/m	Bearing layer of the pile tip	Prediction settlement
-43	⑦-2	100—150*
-51	⑦-2	160*
-75	⑨-2	50—110*

*means the experience prediction value according to DBJ08-11-89.

8.8.4 Pile Testing Result and Analysis

1) Fig. 8-31 shows the relation between penetration resistance and depth of test piles ST-1 and ST-2. It shows that the general construction scheme of the pile driving test is reasonable. And the whole process of the pile driving is correct and it is possible to penetrate layer ⑦-2.

2) When the pile driving was finished, the pile follower (18m long) was pulled out smoothly by the vibrator. So it is reasonable to drive pile by pile follower method. In addition, ascending height of subgrade core for test pile and anchor pile are measured during the process of driving the pile. When the pile driving was finished, the height of the subgrade core would up to 80%~85% of the length of pile. So steel pipe pile of Φ914mm is basically not the displacement pile and its squeezing action to the surround subgrade is not obvious.

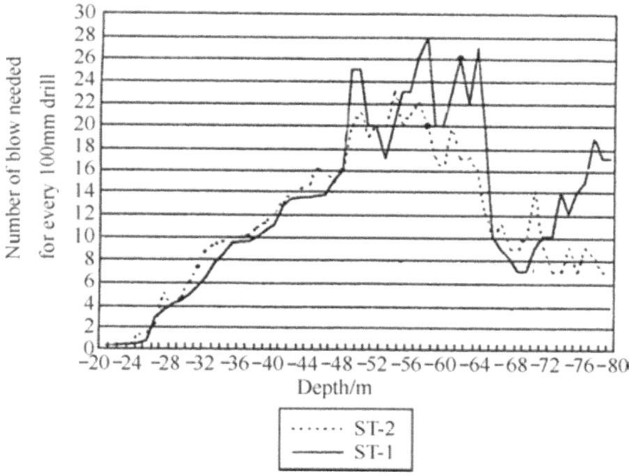

Fig. 8-31 Varying with depth of the penetration resistance in the process of the test Pile driving

3) Picture 8-32 shows the relationship between load and settlement of test pile ST-1 and ST-2 during the vertical static load test. Picture 8-33 shows the axial pressures of the test piles with different loads in the vertical static load test. With the test result according to ASTM, ultimate bearing capacity of single pile can be calculated by Davission method. Ultimate bearing capacity of ST-1 is 15,300kN and ultimate bearing capacity of ST-2 is 16800kN. If the safety factor is 2, the allowable bearing of ST-1 will be 7650kN and the allowable bearing of ST-2 will be 8400kN.

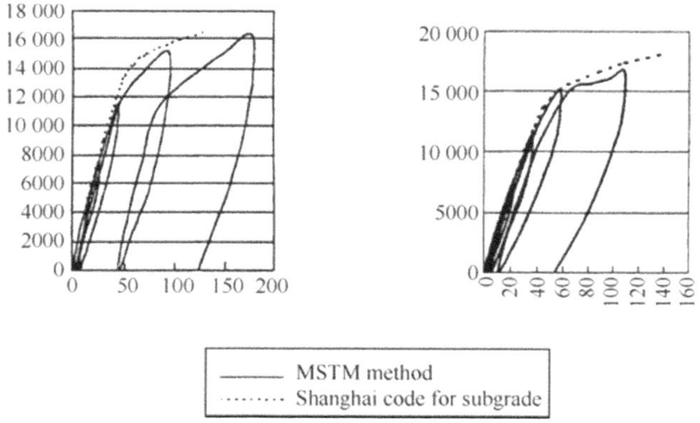

Fig. 8-32 Test piles load-settlement graph

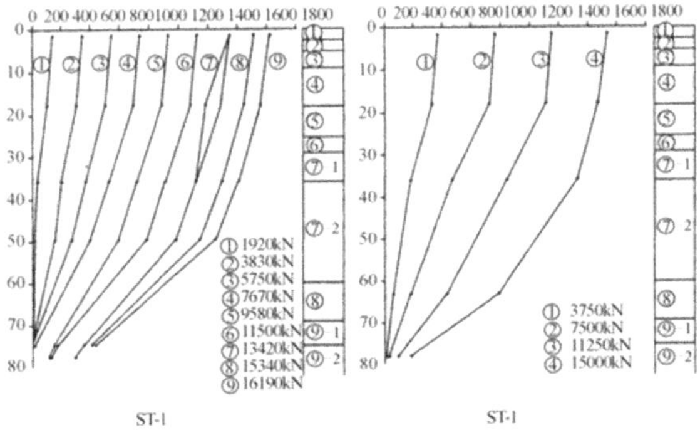

Fig. 8-33 Axial pressures distribution graph of the test piles

Because the pile top is at 17—18m under the ground, so the pile's lateral friction along 17—18m under the ground should be deducted. By the axial pressures shown in Picture 8-33, we can calculate the pile's lateral friction that ST-1 is 7085kN and ST-2 is 7980kN. These allowable bearing values are rather close to the designing allowable bearing 7500kN. But ST-2 is a little bigger and ST-1 is a little smaller, so the final pile end elevation is −79m instead of −75m.

8.8.5 Measured Settlement

The measured settlement of Jinmao Building is relatively uniform. And its value is 82mm which is quite close to the calculation value 85.2mm. By the foundation type and the analysis of measured value, conclusion can be drawn: the settlement of the foundation is mainly caused by the compression of the steel pipe pile and the subgrade under the pile foundation; the compression of the subgrade among piles is very small, so it can be neglected.

8.9 Chapter Summary

This chapter shows how to calculate the settlement of pile-box (raft) foundation by finite element method when deep foundation pit supporting structure is taken into account. And the interaction of superstructure-foundation-subgrade is analyzed by splines subdomain method, which shows the advantages of the method.

By the analysis of measured settlement of Senmao Tower, Jinmao Tower and other high-rise buildings in Shanghai, two important results are got:

1) For super high-rise buildings in Shanghai with super long piles (L >50m), the

foundation settlement is generally in the range of 60mm—100mm, which is relatively uniform. And settlement calculation by the methods in code is larger than the measured settlement.

2) Such small settlement for super high-rise buildings in Shanghai is challenging for the deep massive foundation method to calculate settlement. For the buildings like Jinmao Tower with more than 80m's 'super deep massive foundation', the settlement calculated by whole structure analysis method is more close to actual value.

References

Hans Ludwing Jessberger, Hou X.Y. 1991. Super Structure-Foundation-Subsoil Interaction Analysis.

Deng A.F. 1993. A New Analysis Method of the Interaction of Upper-structure, Raft Foundation and Subsoil, Nanjing: Hehai University Press.

Feng G.D., Liu Z.D., et al. 1986. Computing Model Discussion of Pile-cap Interaction under Vertical Load, Memoir of the Fourth National Soil Mechanics and Foundation Engineering Academic Conference, Beijing: China Building Industry Press.

Hu K.G. 1999. Global Analysis Calculation and Design Method Research of the Foundation and Subgrade of High-rise Building. Doctoral Dissertation of Southeast University.

Li G.H., Zhou S.H. 1991. Experimental Investigation of Vertical Bearing Capacity of Diaphragm Wall.

Ma Z.Z. 2000. New Method Research of Subgrade-foundation Interaction Calculation Analysis. Doctoral Dissertation of Tongji University.

Ni X.H. 1990. Digital Analysis of the Interaction of Raft Foundation, Pile Foundation and Subgrade. Doctoral Dissertation of Tongji University.

Poulos H. G. 1997. Comparison of Some Methods for Analysis of Piled rafts, Porc, 14th, CONF, SMFE.

Qin Rong. 1999. Calculation Structure Non-linear Mechanics, Nanning: Guangxi Science and Technology

Yang Min, Wang S.J. 1998. Interaction Analysis of Pile-raft Foundation Considering the Limit Overload, Journal of Geotechnical Engineering.

Zhao X.H., et al. 1999. Shanghai, Design Theory of High-rise Building Pile-raft and Pile-box Foundation, Shanghai: Tongji University Press.

Table 8-3 General Physical and Mechanical Properties of the Suberade Layers

Geological age	No.	Layer's name	Water content $W(\%)$	Density ρ_0 (g/cm^3)	Specific gravity (Void aratio)	e_0 (Void aratio)	Plasticity index	Shear test $C,\ \varphi$ (kPa)(°)	Triaxial text (Compression index) $C_u,\ \varphi_u$ (kPa)(°)	Triaxial text (Compression index) $C_{cu},\ \varphi_{cu}$ (kPa)(°)	Triaxial text (Compression index) $C',\ \varphi'$ (kPa)(°)	Compression modulus (MPa)	Compression modulus (MPa)	Super-consolidation radio (Prophase concretion pressure) P_c (kPa)	Super-consolidation radio G_c	Super-consolidation radio (Rebound index) G_s	Super-consolidation radio OCR	Super-consolidation radio P_0	Standard penetration S_n (kPa)	Standard penetration $N_{0.5}$	CPT (Geostationary system of the pressure measurement) QF_s (MPa)	Permeability coefficient K_vK_H (cm/s)	Consolidometer K_{20}(cm/s)
Holocene Q4	①	Fill												Compression index		cross-intensity							
	②	Silty clay	35.3	1.85	2.73	1.00	15.4	1215.0	540	5216.2	2231.4	0.580	3.59					0.48	54.2	2.0	0.59 0.02	5.11×10^{-5}	
	③	Muddy silty clay	39.6	1.81	2.72	1.11	13.1	815.6	450	3215.9	1530.0	0.632	3.66					0.54	48.9	2.0	0.66 0.01	2.81×10^{-6} 1.77×10^{-4}	
	④	Muddy clay	49.0	1.73	2.74	1.37	19.6	109.8	320	616.0	627.0	0.842	3.06					0.61	32.2	<1	0.45 0.01	2.47×10^{-7} 1.68×10^{-6}	
	⑤	Powder clay	34.4	1.85	2.73	0.93	14.4	95.3	650	5022.0	3330.0	0.343	5.99	288	0.293	0.040	1.54	0.55	45.9	5.0	0.84 0.02	2.49×10^{-5} 1.33×10^{-7}	2.06×10^{-7}
	⑥	Powder clay	23.0	2.01	2.72	0.67	14.5	3614.9	620	5319.0	3100.0	0.179	9.83	526	0.176	0.020	2.47			20.0	18.3 0.05		3.56×10^{-8}
	⑦-1	Sandy silt	31.2	1.86	2.70	0.91	13.0	322.9	1860			0.167	12.20		0.484	0.030				34.7	11.60 0.11		
	⑦-2	Fine silty	25.9	1.89	2.68	0.80		260.5				0.112	16.44							>50	23.26 0.16		
	⑧	Sandy silt	32.1	1.89	2.70	0.93	10.9	423.5	3730			0.199	10.27	721	0.209	0.020	1.16			>50	14.46 0.19		
	⑨-1	Sandy silt	28.9	1.89	2.70	0.84	12.5	270.5				0.147	12.69	741	0.225	0.020	1.18			>50	12.6 0.23		
		Fine sand with medium-coarse sand	24.1	1.96	2.69	0.71	11.3	922.0				0.177	16.00							>50	21.55 0.15		
Mid-Pleistocene Q_2	⑩	Powder clay	25.7	2.00	2.72	0.72	13.2	1223.0							0.270	0.020	1.29			>50			

Chapter 9 Settlement Analysis and Case Study on Rock Foundation and Combined Diaphragm Wall-end-Bearing Pile-Box (Raft) Foundation

In the igneous rock area of China, such as Qingdao, Shenzhen, etc, rock is mostly granite or granites gneiss, and the eluvium usually formed from slightly weathered granite is very thin, it is about 20—40m. The pile foundation engineering is always designed as one pile under one column, and most of the piles are designed to be manual hole digging pile with large diameter. During the design calculation, the side friction of the large diameter pile is usually neglected, only the bearing capacity is taken into account, when the settlement is analyzed. It is difficult to account for the effect of the retaining structure of the deep foundation, such as diaphragm wall, row piles, etc.

The theory and measured result show that the settlement of the short pile with large diameter is mainly the elastic deformation and the compression deformation of bedrock is very small.

9.1 Settlement Calculation of Deep Foundation with End-Bearing Pile of Super High-Rise Buildings

When considering the effect of bedrock, the settlement of the end-bearing pile is the sum of the elastic compressive deformation of the body and the compressive deformation of the bedrock at pile toes. That is

$$S = \frac{NL}{EA} + \frac{N}{C_0 A} \tag{9-1}$$

where: S—the settlement of the pile tip;

N—the axial pressure of the pile tip;

L—Length of pile;

E—The elastic module of pile body;

A—The area of the pile body;

C_0—the vertical reaction coefficient of pile toe when the single axial limit compression strength of the rock sample is 1000KPa, C_0=300,000 kPa/m. If single axial compressive deformation of the pile body is considered only, just the first part of the above formula need to be calculated.

9.2 Foundation Settlement Analysis of Shenzhen Saige Plaza

Completely inverse process is used for the construction of Shenzhen Saige Plaza. For the inner cylinder, dense-disposing steel pipe columns are used. The temporary retaining structure of the inner cylinder is composed of steel pipe columns, temporary column of podium and the diaphragm wall. The inner cylinder was dug to the bottom at one time after the construction of the first floor, which can be called natural construction process. For the construction between the inner cylinder and the outside cylinder, inverse process was used; aboveground and underground engineering were progressing at the same time. When the superstructure was constructed to 22 floors, earthwork was just finished and then the foundation slab can be constructed using inverse process. According to this construction method, the uneven settlement is very sensitive. In order to analyse the settlement of the large diameter pile, now the geological condition and inverse construction process are to be introduced briefly.

The superstructure of Shenzhen Saige Plaza has 72 floors, including 10 floors of podium. The elevation of the parking apron on the top of the building is 291.60m. The total height of the building is 353.80m. Underground structure has 4 levels, the depth is 19.50m, the floor area is 169,459 m^2. Round steel pipe column-steel structure system is employed. It is the tallest building of the same structural system worldwide.

9.2.1 The Engineering Situation

Saige Plaza project is at the intersection of Middle Shenzhen Road and North Huaqiang Road of Shenzhen city. It is a modern, multi-functional, intelligentized super high-rise building. The aboveground part has 72 floors and the height is 291.6m; the underground part has 4 floors and the depth is 19.50m, the total floor area is 169,469 m^2. Saige Plaza engineering is designed by Huayi Design Consultant Ltd. of Hongkong, and general contract constructed by No.2 branch of China Construction. It is the highest building in the world with concrete filled steel tube.

Saige Plaza engineering adopts special structure of concrete filled steel tube. The tower is frame-tube structure, the frame is composed of concrete filled steel tube columns and steel beams. The inner tube is composed of concrete filled steel tube, densely disposed columns and vertical profile steel and horizontal beams.

In the tube, along the two major axial directions, there are four stiff concrete shear walls. The podium and the basement are of structure of frame-shear wall which is composed of concrete filled steel tube column with net spacing of 12m and section steel concrete beams.

Fig. 9-1 Shenzhen Saige Plaza Engineering

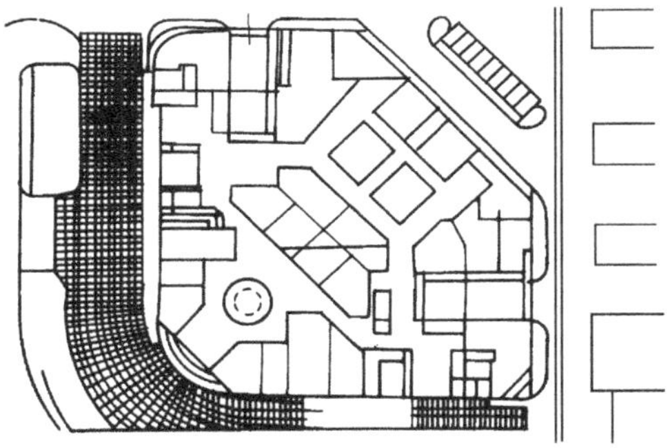

Fig. 9-2 Plan graph of Saige Site

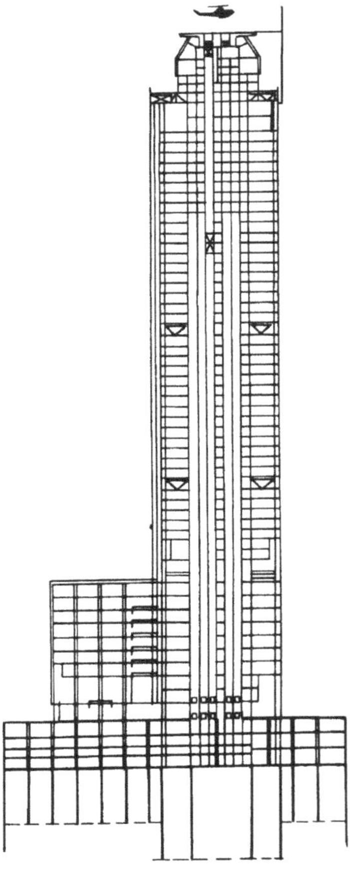

Fig. 9-3 Structural profile of Saige Plaza

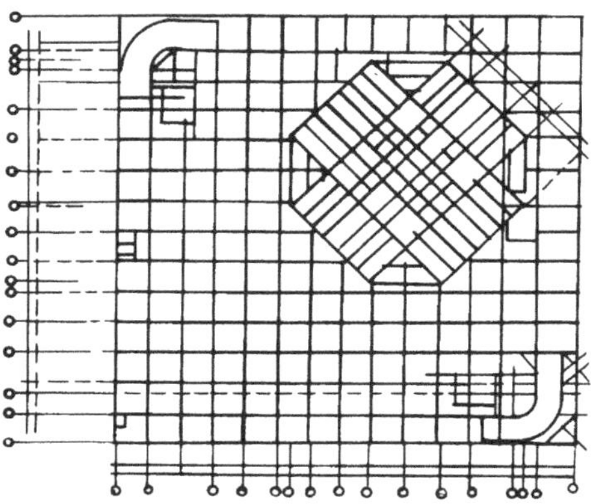

Fig. 9-4 Plan graph of basement

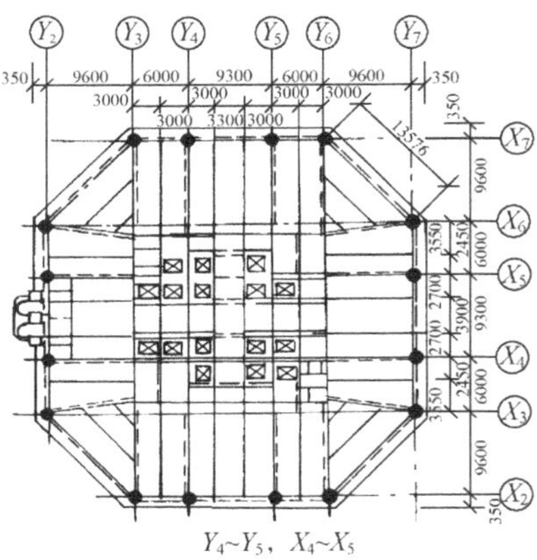

Fig. 9-5 Plan schematic diagram of main tower

9.2.2 The Engineering Geological Condition

According to the drill data, the geology of the subgrade layer from top to bottom of the field is as follows:

1. The friable accumulation horizon of quaternary

The artificial filled stratum is mainly composed of silt clay. The thickness of the upper part is 0.20—0.40m, the thickness of the lower part of sand-grant cushion is 0.30—3.10m.

The talus accumulation clay, containing 15%—30% quartz gravel in 2—3mm, it's in hard plastic-hard state, the layer thickness is 1.00—12.90m.

The eluvium's gravel silt clay is composed of weathered exuviating of coarse grain granite, containing 20%—40% quartz, it's in plastic-hard plastic state, the layer thickness is 9.60—25.30m.

Silt clay: it is composed of weathered exuviating of fine-grained granite, it's in plastic-hard plastic state. The layer thickness is 2.10—6.60m.

2. YanShan Stage granite

The underlying bedrock in the site is intrusive rock of YanShan Stage, the lithology is coarse grain granite, fine-grained granite and siliceous dike. The fine-granite Ned granite is intrusive entity of latter stage, lying under the coarse grain granite, being buried shallowly in the south of the site and buried deeply in the north of the site. The quartz dike is the latest intrusive entity. According to the weathering rank, it is divided into four zones as of all weathered, strong weathered, intermediary weathered and slightly weathered, which are to be illustrated as follows:

The all weathered coarse grain granite is completly weathered into clay, retaining the original rock structure, the core being in soil state. The SPT blow count is 30-50 counts. The thickness is 0.80—7.80m.

The strong weathered coarse grain granite is weathered into clay, potash feldspar is at granular, retaining the original crystalline, turning to be sandy by hand pinch. The original rock structure is clear; the weathering fissure is well developed. The core is in sandy state or chunky state. The rock can be broken by hand. The SPT blow count is more than 50 counts, and the thickness is 2.50—12.20m.

The intermediary coarse grain granite is a bit weathered. The fissure is developed, and the face of fissure is eroded by iron-manganese. The core is crushed, in short prismatic or shiver.

The mineral of the slightly weathered coarse grain granite is unweathered, only the joint surface had shallow rust. The core is complete, in long column. The rock is hard, the thickness is 0.30—19.70m, and is no exposed.

9.2.3 The Combined Retaining Structure of Deep Foundation Pit

In inverse construction technology, retaining of the deep foundation is very important, it could even be the key of the whole inverse process. Saige Plaza is in the center downtown area, being surround by buildings already completed. Saige Electric Accessory Market on the south is an 8-storey building, and it is with common shallow foundation. Its exterior wall is only 1.5m away from the south diaphragm wall of the basement of Saige Plaza. Therefore the reliability of the retaining structure of the deep foundation pit is extremely important for the completely inverse construction process of Saige Plaza. In the inverse construction programme of the basement of Saige Plaza, the retaining structure of the deep foundation pit is of combined structure, which is jointly composed of diaphragm continuous wall (0.8m in thickness) and boundary frame along the wall together with its floors, the combined structure is for bearing horizontal force of the foundation pit. The method of "*inner common, outer inverse*" is used for construction, that is, common process is applied to the construction of the inner tube, while inverse method is applied to the construction of between the inner tube and outer tube.

9.2.4 Processes of the Completely Inverse Construction Method

For buildings with boundary composite structure, the construction method of "*inner common, outer inverse*" has certain advantage. It can make fully use of the effect of retaining structure and post effect of inner tube. The process of this method is as follows:

1) When constructing the first floor, except the core tube and the two entrances to the basement, the rest floor structures are all linked with the top beams of diaphragm continuous wall, forming an integrity. And it has horizontal supporting effect on the top of the diaphragm continuous wall.

2) After finihing the construction of the first floor, it could be deemed that a fixed fulcrum has been laid on the top of the diaphragm continuous wall. Firstly, the safe depth of the first time digging of the diaphragm continuous wall is checked, and checking computations shows the digging depth could be −7.0m, then the structure of underground level one can be constructed, as is shown in Fig. 9-6.

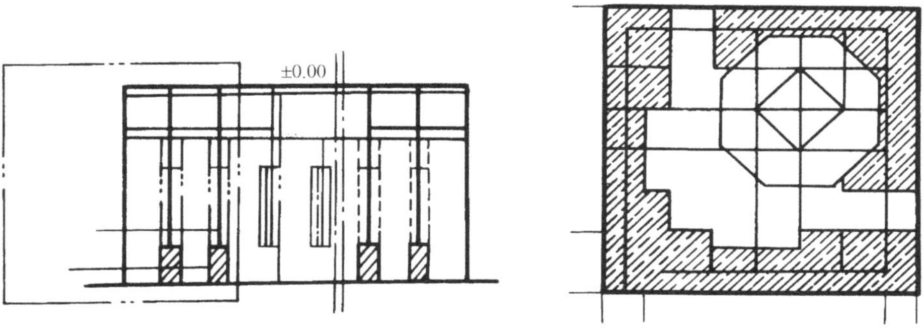

Fig. 9-6 Retaining condition between the first time digging and the second time digging

3) After the construction of the boundary structure of the underground level one, the second time digging of earthwork goes to −11.00m. The boundary structure is checked as Fig. 9-7. and checking computations shows the digging depth could be the elevation of −11.00m, then the structure of underground level two can be constructed.

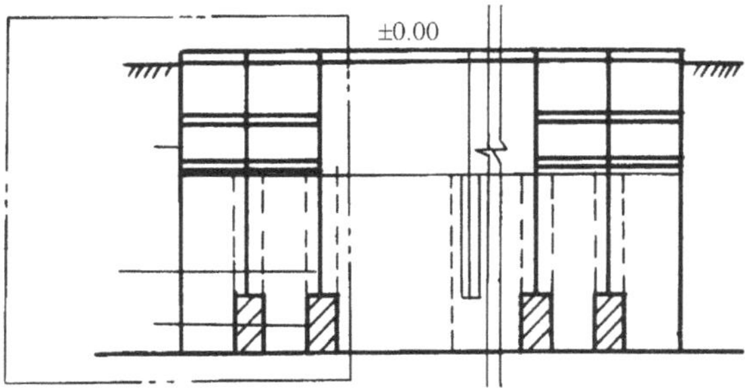

Fig. 9-7 Retaining condition between the second time digging and the third time digging

4) After the construction of the boundary structure of the underground level two, checking computations shows the third time digging of earthwork can go to −14.00m, then the structure of underground level three can be constructed, as shown in Fig. 9-8.

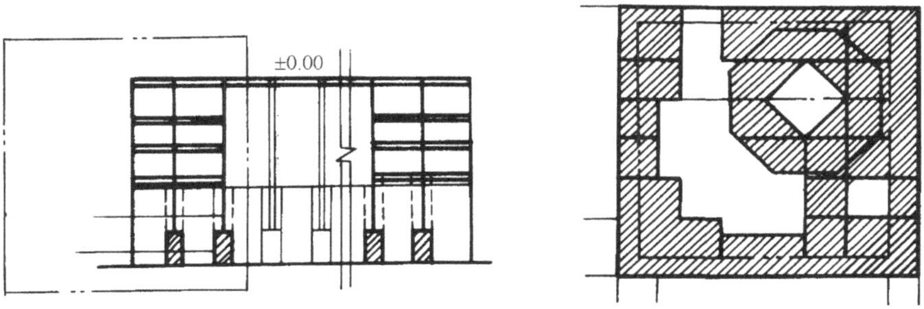

Fig. 9-8 Retaining condition between the third time digging and the fourth time digging

5) Before the fourth time digging of earthwork, firstly, the structure of underground level one is expanded wherever the condition can be satisfied, so that for the boundary structure, there is almost a fixed fulcrum at the elevation of the underground level one, then the boundary structure is checked, presuming digging goes to −18.25m. Through checking calculation, deformation of the boundary structure is within acceptable range, so the earthwork digging goes to −18.25m. Thus, the boundary structure has fully met the requirements of the deep foundation pit retaining associated with inverse construction method of Saige Plaza.

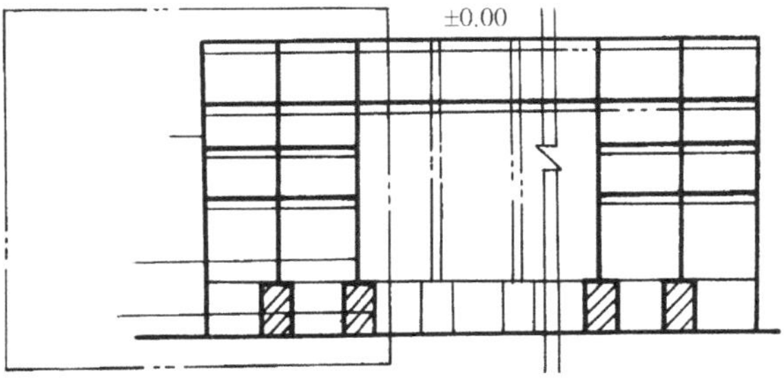

Fig. 9-9 Retaining condition after the fourth time digging

9.2.5 Real Measured Settlement Data of Foundation of Saige Plaza

The foundation of Saige Plaza is pile-raft foundation. manual hole digging pile are adopted for the main building, the diameters are between ϕ 3200 to ϕ 4800, the length is about 22m, designed as one pile under one column, the bearing stratum of the pile end is slightly weathered granite. (The outer tube has 4 columns-4 piles for each side, the inner tube has 8 columns-8 piles for each side.) The thickness of the foundation slab is 1.3m. The pile diameter of the annex building is between ϕ 1600 to ϕ 2600, L=16m. The settlement of foundation is stable, the measured value is small, the maximum value being only 15.88mm. The distribution of measured points is shown as Fig. 9-10. The major data of settlement is showed in Table 9-1 and Table 9-2. The foundation settlement is already stable one year after tructure capping. The last settlement measured result was of June 21, 1999, being the 16th settlement measure, also the measured result one year after completion.

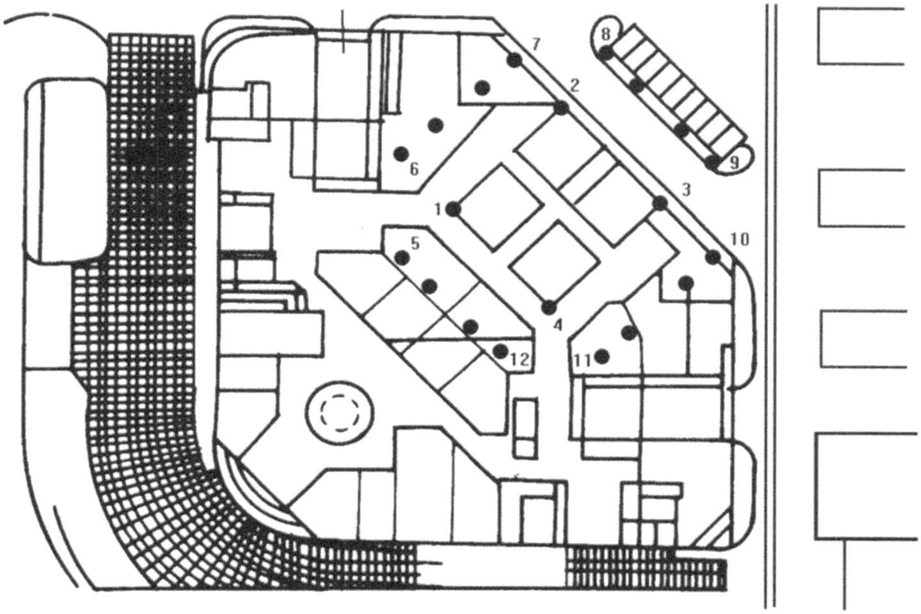

Fig. 9-10 Distribution of settlement points of Saige Plaza

Table 9-1 Observed data of settlement points of Saige Plaza

order	The 13 th times		The 14th times		The 15th times		The 16th times	
elevation	October 29th,1998		Janaury 9th,1999		March 27th ,1999		June 21th, 1999	
dot mark	settlement(mm)		settlement(mm)		settlement(mm)		settlement(mm)	
	this time	accumulation	this time	accumulation	this time	accumulation	this time	accumulation
B	-3.24	-9.10	-5.08	-14.18	+0.05	-14.13	-0.16	-14.29
C			-3.91	-8.54	-0.90	-9.44	-0.03	-9.47
D			-4.54	-6.32	-0.92	-7.24	-0.65	-7.89
E						-9.35	-0.37	-9.72
F	-1.53	-4.64	-4.30	-8.94	+0.26	-8.68	-0.45	-9.13
G						-8.11	-0.32	-8.43
H								
I			-2.95	-5.35				

Table 9-2 Observed data of settlement points of Saige Plaza

order	The 13 th times		The 14th times		The 15th times		The 16th times	
elevation	October 29th,1998		Janaury 9th,1999		March 27th ,1999		June 21th, 1999	
dot mark	settlement/mm		settlement/mm		Settlement/mm		settlement/mm	
	this time	accumulation	this time	accumulation	this time	accumulation	this time	accumulation
1	-2.14	-9.04	-5.53	-14.57	-0.01	-14.58	-0.63	-15.21
2	-3.05	-8.83	-3.99	-12.82	-0.53	-13.35	-0.34	-13.69
3	-2.87	-7.87	-4.33	-12.20	-0.35	-12.55	-1.38	-13.93
4	-3.57	-10.54	-4.36	-14.90	-0.18	-15.08	-0.80	-15.88
5	-3.18	-5.46	-3.57	-9.03	+0.55	-8.48	-0.47	-8.95
6	-2.99	-5.39	-4.38	-9.77	-0.60	-10.37		
7	-3.69	-6.32	-3.09	-9.41	-0.58	-9.99	+0.53	-9.46
8			-3.15	-2.32	-0.99	-3.31	+0.48	-2.83
9	-2.76	-2.50	Fail to allocate point of staff due to staging					
10	-3.15	-8.83	-2.92	-11.75	-0.59	-12.34	0	-12.34
11	-2.13	-4.07	Blocked		-3.69	-7.76	-0.33	-8.09
12	-2.94	-5.48	-3.36	-8.84	+0.12	-8.72	-0.76	-9.48

9.2.6 Analysis and Conclusion of Foundation Settlement Data of Saige Plaza

For foundation settlement of Saige plaza, the theoretical calculation value is very close to the measured value. Settlements of the four corners of the inner tube are -15.21mm, 13.69mm, 13.93mm and 15.88mm, with the maximum settlement difference being 2.19mm, thus the settlement of these four corners of the inner tube is quite even. The average settlement of the four corners of the outer tube (two points for each corner, taking the average value) are -8.95mm, -6.145mm, -12.34mm, 8.785mm, with the maximum settlement difference being -6.195mm. The settlement of the four corners of the outer tube is also quite even. Thus the following conclusions could be drawn:

(1) For deep foundation of super high-rise building with end-bearing manual hole digging pile with large diameter, if pile toe bearing stratum is of slightly weathered granite, the settlement of foundation needn't be calculated.

(2) For super high-rise building with end-bearing manual hole digging pile with large diameter, if pile toe bearing stratum is of slightly weathered granite, foundation settlement is mainly from elastic deformation of the pile body, whileas there is little deformation for bedrock.

(3) When mechanical hole-digging is applied to large diameter pile, the deformation of sediment has great impact, sediment should be cleared away as much as possible, or post grouting technology should be used.

(4) When mechanical hole-digging is applied to large diameter pile, condition of the bottom of each pile should be check so as to make sure that the bearing stratum reach slightly weathered granite, and guarantee the settlement of pile foundation is even.

9.3 Chapter Summary

In this chapter, the settlement calculation method of end-bearing short pile with large diameter is presented, and the settlement data of Saige Plaza is analyzed. It's of special instruction for settlement calculation of the same type of deep foundations.

References

Chen X.F. 2004. Methods and Research Progress of Deep Foundation Settlement Calculation. Journal of Civil Engineering.

Poulos H.G., et al. 1997. Comparison of Some Method for Analysis of Piled Rafts Proc. 14th Int. Conf. SMFE.

Lu X.Q., et al. 1987. Theory and Practice of Diaphragm Wall, Beijing: China Railway Industry Press.

Tang M.X. 1996. Research of the Interaction of High-rise Building and Load-bearing Diaphragm Walls and Pile-box(raft) Foundation. Doctoral Dissertation of Tongji University.

Tang Y.J., Hou X.Y. 1998. Test Analysis of Reverse Method for High-rise Building Construction, Supplement of Engineering Mechanics.

Wang W.D., 1999. Calculation Research of the Interaction of Load-bearing Diaphragm Walls and Pile- raft Foundation. Memoir of the Eighth Mechanics and Geotechnical Engineering Academic Conference of China Civil Engineering Institution, Beijing: Wanguo Academic Press.

Chapter 10 Forecast and Suggestion of Research on Settlement Calculation

Settlement calculation of deep foundation of super high-rise building is a critical topic for construction engineering. Due to the complexity of geology and geological soil (tri-phase object), the difference with theories, calculated settlement results hardly comply with measured data, and there has't been any satisfactory formula for settlement calculation, especially for deep foundation, such as box-raft foundation, single pile and pile group foundation. In China, the difference between calculated value and measured data is modify by applying a unified empirical coefficient. This method is admittedly to have the minimum variance of all the settlement calculation methods at present. However, there is so tremendous differentce with the geological condition of each region of China and so great differentce with regional soil characteristics, that calculation result is basically unsatisfactory. Is might be more close to the real condition to apply the regional empirical settlement formula.

The reason for these issues is that all methods are based on the liner elastic theory except numerical method, while the constitutive relation of subgrade hardly complies with this theory. Occasionally, some scholars are kown to adopt the nonlinear elastic theory, rheological theory to calculate settlement foundation, but without presenting any good results. For all the methods widely adopted now, it is presumed that the stiffneses of superstructure and foundation are both zero, and then settlements of the center point and corner point are calculated. Obviously, it dose not comply with actuality. In Chapter 3, the author promotes adoption of finite element method, which takes the "*superstructure, foundation and subgrade*" as "*integrated structure*" and as a problem of "*time and space*", for the study on settlement of the whole structure. Althrough there are much difficulties using numerical method at present, it can be realized gradually. In addition, the physical & mechanical characteristics of subgrade is too complex to have calculation parameters of settlement be set precisely, and mechanics of deep soil is sometimes involved (for example, compression modules is uncertain and hard to be set precisely), therefore up till now no perfect formula for settlement calculation has been found. At present, reliable, regional, simple and economical formula for settlement calculation should be explored, so as to minimize the variance of calculation results as much as possible.

1. Innovative achievements and conclusion of the book

The approach of combining theory with practice is adopted in this book, on the basis of theoretical research, study, analysis and conclusion are conducted with referrence to the measured settlement data of five engineering cases, thus the following important innovative achievements are obtained:

1) It is put forward that the influence of retaining structure of deep foundation pit should be considered when calculating the settlement of box foundation of super high-rise building. And the relationship between retaining structure and basement exterior wall should be classified into two conditions (two kinds of walls are combined, or separated), settlement calculation method is presented respectively. Compared with analysis result of finite element method and measured data, there is litter variance when using these methods.

2) For the research on layer-wise summation method, the step-layer-wise summation method of inclined formation is put forward, so as to solve the settlement calculation of horizontally uneven subgrade.

3) For the research on stress-strain regularity, mechanical law of single pile, pile group effect, characteristic of short pile and super-long pile, a new design method is put forward, which is *pile group with space-varying rigidity and equal settlement.* The method makes full use of prominent advantages of long pile or super-long pile in controlling settlement, and advantages of short pile or mid-long pile in bearing loads, and combines both in an optimized way to form pile group with space varying rigidity. Research result shows that effect of group pile mainly depends on piles geometric features, such as pile arrangement plan, length of pile, pile spacing and pile diameter, besides subgrade characteristics and pile formation technology, which presents theoretical basis and necessary condition for the optimized combination of the above both. This method is not only technologically advanced, but also cost-economical.

4) Since there is no good method to calculate foundation settlement in sandy subgrade, an empirical formula is put forward for explorating strong weathered granite foundation, which is called comprehensive coefficient method. By taking into account various impacting factors, and comparing with measured settlement result, the coefficient is getting more and more accurate with the increase of measured data.

In addition, based on the research on the measured settlement data of five super high-rise buildings, which are Qingdao Zhongyin Building, Shanghai Senmao Building and Shenzhen Saige Building, Guangdong International Building and Shanghai Jinmao Building, and associated with constitutive relation of subgrade, foundation stress calculation and foundation deformation is analysed, thus two empirical coefficients and several useful conclusions are got, which are of important instructive effect on engineering design and theoretical research.

In summary, the conclusions of this book are as follows:

1) In strong weathered granite area of Qingdao, when using the new code for foundation and subgrade to calculate settlement of box foundation, the regional empirical coefficient ψ_s =0.2 (got fitting of a large number of tests).

2) According to *Code for Box Foundation*(JGJ 6-99), when using the deformation modules of subgrade to calculate the final settlement, the adjustment coefficient β=0.4 of settlement calculation depth in the strong weathered granite area of Qingdao.

3) At present, there are misunderstandings are in the study on constitutive model of subgrade, for the research on foundation settlement, analytical solution, semi-theory and semi-empirical formula and empirical formula are all based on elastic mechanics. It should be presumed that subgrade is in elastic, continuous and liner condition. On the contrary, for the numerical analysis which is represented by finite element method and boundary element method, several elastic-plastic, nonlinear, viscoelastic plasticity and viscoelasticity model can be applied, even cnstructure model can be applied, such as composite, block and granular media etc. Both the calculation method and software programme have been gradually mature, and the key issue is choice and determination of calculation parameters. Through this, the direction and the technology routing of settlement research can be obtained. Therefore, to set up measured database of engineering settlement and build expert system of settlement, and to fix regional formula for settlement calculation are important subjects for the whole research on settlement and deep foundation settlement of super high-rise building.

4) Calculation of foundation induced stress is very important for regional settlement calculation, it is suitable to adopt Boussinesq and Mindlin solution of semi-spacing question.

5) Settlement of clay subgrade can be divided into initial settlement, consolidation settlement and secondary consolidation settlement. While, for settlement of sandy subgrade, it is difficult to differentiate initial settlement from consolidation settlement, and its settlement calculation hasn't been solved up till now. The ratio of initial settlement of Qingdao Zhongyin Tower is no less than 90%. Although there is a lot of formula for settlement calculation, only the modified layer-wise summation method is reletively close to the reality.

6) The difference of settlement calculation of deep foundation of super high-rise building with multi-story building is that retaining structure effect of deep foundation pit should be considered for the former (lateral confined effect). According to the relation between basement exterior wall and retaining structure (two walls combined or separated), whatever kind of condition, the effect of retaining structure cannot be neglected, especially for box foundation. In

the book, calculation model and calculation method with consideration of the effect of retaining structure are introduced, and these methods are used to calculate Qingdao Zhongyin Tower, the result is close to measured data. The result of finite element method is very close to that of simplified method, both being a little more than 90mm.

7) The settlement data of Qingdao Zhongyin Tower is very complete. Some useful conclusions have been drawn after analysis and research (refer to Chapter 5 for detail).

8) Settlement calculation research of single pile and pile group shows that the data of compressive test of single pile (*Q-S* Curve) must be fully utilized, not only as the basis for bearing capacity, but also as the basis of settlement calculation of pile group. Thus the relation of settlement between single pile and pile group should be researched.

9) The research result of pile group effect shows that the pile group effect is depended on geometric characteristic of pile such as pile length, pile diameter and pile arrangement design, besides subgrade condition, pile formation technology and pile type determination.

10) The outstanding advantage of super-long pile is controlling settlement deformation, and the advantage of short pile and medium-long pile is bearing load. For super-long bored pile, it is suitable to apply post grouting technology, in order to solve the problem of pile end sedimentary and relaxation of hole wall.

11) The calculation value and real value of deep foundation settlement of Jinmao Tower in Shanghai are both a little more than 80mm, the maximum settlement of Sanmao Tower in Shanghai is 55mm. For more than ten high-rise buildings in Shanghai with pile length of 75.0m, the measured settlement values fall between 30mm to 90mm. Thus an important conclusion can be drawn: for high-rise building or super high-rise building in Shanghai with super-long pile ($l>50$m) whose pile foundations are designed according to the code, the real settlement values are usually 60mm~100mm, which confirms the advantage mentioned above of super-long pile in controlling settlement deformation.

12) It is of distinctive advantage to use spline function to analyse the interaction effect of superstructure, subgrade and foundation.

13) Settlement calculation of space-varying rigidity pile group can be simplified by applying comprehensive modules of pile-subgrade.

14) For super high-rise building with box foundation whose subgrade is rock, the settlement is compressive deformation of rock subgrade.

15) For super high-rise building with limited compressive layer subgrade on the rock, the settlement is the elastic compression of large diameter dip-hole pile and rock compression under the pile toe, but mainly the former. The conclusion has been proved by measured

settlement of Saige Tower and Empiror Tower in Shenzhen.

2. Subjects of deep foundation settlement of super high-rise building requiring further research

According to the theory and engineering application research of deep foundation settlement of super high-rise building, the author puts forward the following subjects which require further study:

1) Set up the relation between single pile settlement and pile group settlement, research the "*time & space*" issue of deep foundation settlement.

2) Build measured database and expert system of deep foundation settlement of super high-rise building in China.

3) Develop finite element optimization software and CAD system for settlement calculation.

4) Research the precise selection of calculation parameters.

5) Develop the exploration and research on properties of super-deep geotechnical mechanics.

6) Determine the relative coefficient for test data of single pile and pile group.

3. Suggestion on research of deep foundation settlement of super high-rise building

The research on the deep foundation settlement of super high-rise building needs large amount of and long-term observed data of settlement, and requirs full cooperation of relative branches and experts in specific disciplines, so that achievements and development can be gradually obtained. When searching and arranging the observation data of deep foundation of five super high-rise buildings, the author deeply feels that the data is so valuable and difficult to be collected. It really needs support from the government, even laws need to be made to regulate settlement observation. So the following suggestions are raised:

1) The nation should make law to require long-term observation of deep foundation settlement of super high-rise building, so as to build China's database and expert system of deep foundation settlement of super high-rise building.

2) Promote the applying of design method of *pile group with space-varying rigidity and equal settlement.*

The author's innovative achievement and research conclusion above XFC method have been evaluated by experts as great breakthrough achievement of theory of settlement calculation of deep foundation. Combining theory with practice, calculation with engineering, research with measured data, thus the achievement has important guiding significance for design and construction of super high-rise building's structure and deep foundation.

References

Chen X.F., Chen Wei. 2002. Deep Foundation Engineering in the 21st Century in China, Proceedings of International Conference on Engineering and Technological Science 2000, Session 5, Beijing: Science Press, Oct.11, 2000.

Chen X.F. 2001. Chinese Deep Foundation Engineering In the 21st Century, Beijing: Construction Technology Development Magazine.

Chen X.F. 2004. Technology and Management Development of China Construction, Beijing: China Building Industry Press.

He G.Q., Chen X.F., Xu Z.J. 1994. Design and Construction of High-rise Building, Beijing: Science Press.

Sun Jun, Hou X.Y. 1987. Underground Structure (Volumes), Beijing: Science Press.

Zienkiewicz O.C. 1971. The Finite Element Method in Engineering Science, New York: MeGraw-Hill.

Acknowlegments

Author wishes the gratification to Dr. Zhengmao Zhou for constent support and encouragement in the effort of the translation, and very thanks to professor X.Q.Yang, associate professor X.L.Li, Mr. Xun Meng and associate professor Shaoming Liao of Tongji University for checking and helping with the manuscript of this book, and also very thanks to Dr. Jie Gao, Dr. Jing Jia, Dr. Sipeng Xu, Dr. Yuntao Wu, Mr. Jiming He, Mr. Yingchao Li for helping and translating the manuscript of Charper 1 to 10 and Contents, to senior engineer Wei Chen of China Academy of Building Research Institue for helping and translating the manuscript of References, to Mr. Jun Zhao of China Academy of Comunecation Research Institue for helping and translating the manuscript of its Preface, to Dr. Wei Shau, Dr. M.L Shen, senior engineer Birong Yang, Mr. Chong Chen and Mr. Xin Tang for the effort of the translation.

Name Index

W

X

Y

Z

Subject Index

F

G

H

I

J

L

M

Q

R

S

T

U

V

W

Y

Z

The manufacturer's authorised representative in the EU is Springer
Nature Customer Service Centre GmbH, Europaplatz 3, 69115 Heidelberg,
Germany. If you have any concerns regarding our products, please
contact ProductSafety@springernature.com

Printed and bound by CPI Group (UK) Ltd, Croydon, CR0 4YY
05/10/2026
02228131-0010

Xiangfu Chen

Settlement Calculation on High-Rise Buildings

Theory and Application